PEARSON

Math
Makes Sense

Lorraine Baron

Garry Davis

Susan Ludwig

Kanwal Neel

Shannon Sookochoff

David Van Bergeyk

Trevor Brown

Sharon Jeroski

Sandra Glanville Maurer

Robert Sidley

David Sufrin

Jerrold Wiebe

PEARSON

Publisher
Mike Czukar

Research and Communications Manager
Barbara Vogt

Publishing Team

Enid Haley   Claire Burnett
Lesley Haynes   Marina Djokic
Ioana Gagea   Ellen Davidson
Lynne Gulliver   Jane Schell
Bronwyn Enright   Karen Alley
Alison Dale   David Liu
Judy Wilson

Photo Research
Lisa Brant

Design and Art Direction
Word & Image Design Studio Inc.

Composition
Lapiz Digital Services, India

ISBN-13 978-0-321-49558-7
ISBN-10   0-321-49558-6

Printed and bound in the United States.

2 3 4 5 CC5 13 12 11 10 09

The information and activities presented in this
book have been carefully edited and reviewed.
However, the publisher shall not be liable for any
damages resulting, in whole or in part, from the
reader's use of this material.

Brand names that appear in photographs of
products in this textbook are intended to provide
students with a sense of the real-world
applications of mathematics and are in no way
intended to endorse specific products.

The publisher wishes to thank the staff and
students of St. John's High School, Winnipeg and
Anderson Collegiate and Vocational Institute,
Whitby, for their assistance with photography.

Statistics Canada information is used with the
permission of Statistics Canada. Users are
forbidden to copy the data and redisseminate
them in an original or modified form, for
commercial purposes, without permission from
Statistics Canada. Information on the availability of
the wide range of data from Statistics Canada can
be obtained from Statistics Canada's Regional
Offices or the Statistics Canada Web site.

PEARSON

Consultants, Advisers, and Reviewers

Series Consultants
Trevor Brown
Maggie Martin Connell
Mignonne Wood
Craig Featherstone
John A. Van de Walle

Assessment Consultant
Sharon Jeroski

Aboriginal Content Consultant
Sonya Ellison, Frontier School Division, MB

Advisers and Reviewers
Pearson Education thanks its advisers and reviewers, who helped shape the vision for *Pearson Math Makes Sense* through discussions and reviews of prototype materials and manuscript.

Thanks to all our Previewers and the Test and Try schools, acknowledged on our *Math Makes Sense* Web site. A special thank you to the staff and grade 9 students at Holy Cross High School in Saskatoon and St. Michaels University School in Victoria for their recommendations for improvements to this resource prior to publication.

Alberta

Bob Berglind
Calgary Board of Education

Jacquie Bouck
Lloydminster Public School Division 99

Theresa S. Chalifoux
Edmonton Catholic Schools

Carolyne Chipiuk
Edmonton Public School Board

Lissa D'Amour
Medicine Hat School District 76

Margo Fosti
Calgary Board of Education

Florence Glanfield
University of Alberta

Lauri Goudreault
Holy Family Catholic Regional District #37

Kyle Honish
Calgary Board of Education

Mary-Elizabeth Kaiser
Calgary Board of Education

Ted McInnis
Rocky View Schools

Leslie McRae
Calgary Board of Education

Ken Pistotnik
Edmonton Catholic Schools

Delcy Rolheiser
Edmonton Public School Board

Table of Contents

UNIT 3 Rational Numbers

UNIT 4 Linear Relations

UNIT 9 Probability and Statistics

Welcome to
Pearson Math Makes Sense 9

Math helps you understand your world.

This book will help you improve your problem-solving skills and show you how you can use your math now, and in your future career.

The opening pages of **each unit** are designed to help you prepare for success.

UNIT 1
Square Roots and Surface Area

Which geometric objects can you name?

How could you determine their surface areas?

What You'll Learn

- Determine the square roots of fractions and decimals that are perfect squares.
- Approximate the square roots of fractions and decimals that are non-perfect squares.
- Determine the surface areas of composite 3-D objects to solve problems.

Why It's Important

Real-world measures are often expressed as fractions or decimals. We use the square roots of these measures when we work with formulas such as the Pythagorean Theorem.
An understanding of surface area allows us to solve practical problems such as calculating: the amount of paper needed to wrap a gift; the number of cans of paint needed to paint a room; and the amount of siding needed to cover a building

Key Words
- perfect square
- non-perfect square
- composite object

4

5

Find out **What You'll Learn** and **Why It's Important**. Check the list of **Key Words**.

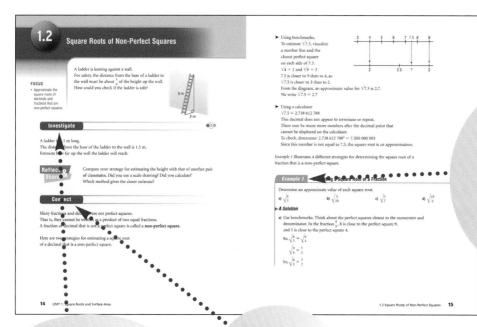

Examples show you how to use the ideas and that there may be different ways to approach the question.

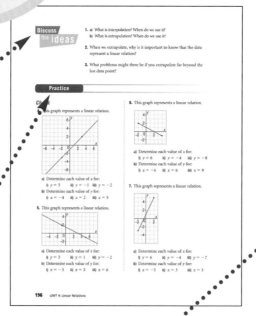

Investigate an idea or problem, usually with a partner, and often using materials.

Connect summarizes the math.

Discuss the Ideas invites you to talk about the math.

Practice questions reinforce the math.

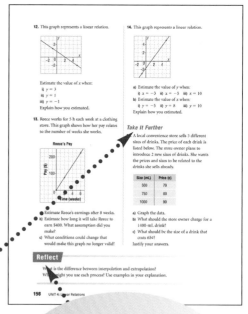

Take It Further questions offer enrichment and extension.

Reflect on the big ideas of the lesson. Think about your learning style and strategies.

Use the **Mid-Unit Review** to refresh
your memory of key concepts.

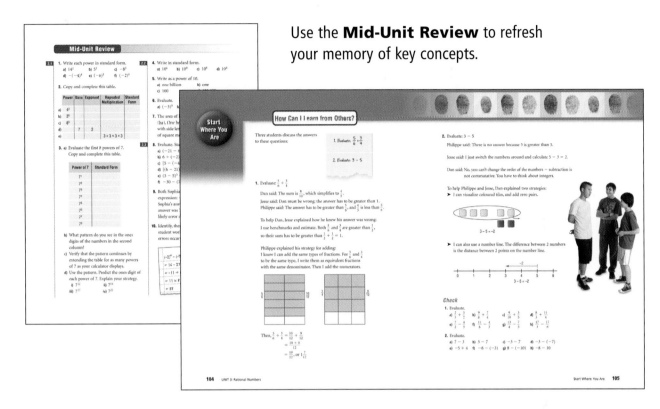

Start Where You Are illustrates strategies you may
use to show your best performance.

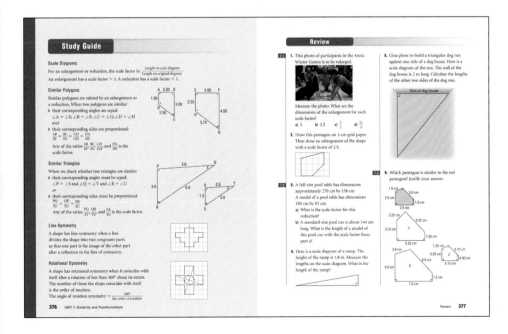

Study Guide
summarizes key ideas
from the unit.

Review questions
allow you to find out
if you are ready to
move on.

The *Practice and
Homework Book*
provides additional
support.

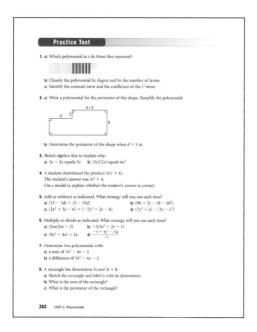

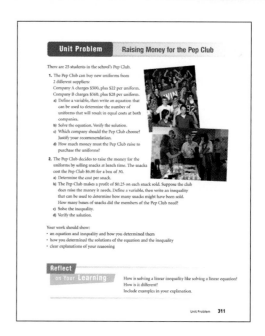

The **Practice Test** models the kind of test your teacher might give.

The **Unit Problem** presents problems to solve, or a project to do, using the math of the unit.

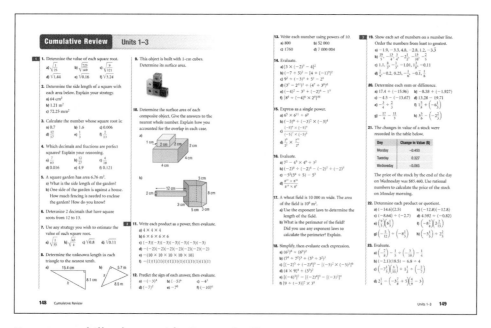

Keep your skills sharp with **Cumulative Review**.

Explore some interesting math when you do the **Projects**.

Play a **Game** with your classmates or at home to reinforce your skills.

Icons remind you to use **technology**. Follow the instructions for using a computer or calculator to do math.

The **Illustrated Glossary** is a dictionary of important math words.

Project

Making Squares into Cubes

Part 1

➤ Copy the squares below onto 1-cm grid paper.

Materials
- 1-cm grid paper
- wooden or plastic cubes
- ruler
- 1-cm grid card stock
- scissors
- tape

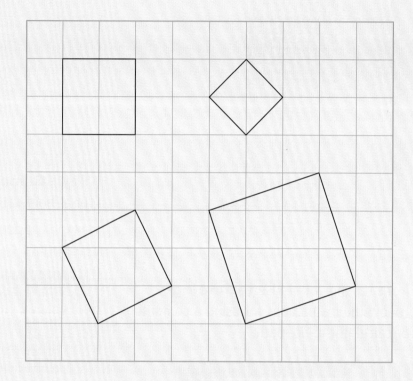

➤ Determine the area of each square and its side length.
➤ Describe your method and why you know it works.
➤ Compare methods with your classmates.
  Write a description of a method that is different from your method.

Part 2

➤ Choose one of these areas:
  32 cm², 40 cm², 45 cm²
  Draw a square with the area you chose.
➤ Label the area of your square.
  Determine its side length.

➤ How could you fill your square with copies of one of the squares in Part 1? Use as many copies of one square in Part 1 as you like. Sketch what you find.

➤ How is the smaller square related to the larger square?

Part 3

➤ Sketch a cube. Explain how you would determine the surface area of the cube. Share your strategy for determining the surface area with a classmate. Did both of you come up with the same strategy? If not, will both strategies work?

➤ Build a cube from 1-cm grid card stock. Each face of your cube should be the square you drew in Part 2. Use tape to assemble your cube.

➤ Draw a net of your cube.

➤ Calculate the surface area of your cube. Show your calculations.

➤ Describe how you would calculate the volume of your cube.

➤ Is the volume of your cube less than or greater than the volume of a cube with edge length 6 cm? Explain.

Take It Further

➤ Draw squares with these areas: 5 cm^2, 20 cm^2, 45 cm^2, 80 cm^2, and 125 cm^2 How are these squares related? What makes these squares a "family"?

➤ What other families of squares could you draw? Draw 3 squares from that family. Describe the family of squares. Determine the side length of each square.

Square Roots and Surface Area

Which geometric objects
can you name?

How could you determine
their surface areas?

What You'll Learn

- Determine the square roots of
  fractions and decimals that are
  perfect squares.
- Approximate the square roots of
  fractions and decimals that are
  non-perfect squares.
- Determine the surface areas of composite
  3-D objects to solve problems.

Why It's Important

Real-world measures are often
expressed as fractions or decimals.
We use the square roots of these measures
when we work with formulas such as the
Pythagorean Theorem.
An understanding of surface area allows us
to solve practical problems such as calculating:
the amount of paper needed to wrap a gift;
the number of cans of paint needed to paint a room;
and the amount of siding needed to cover a building

Key Words

- perfect square
- non-perfect square
- composite object

Square Roots of Perfect Squares

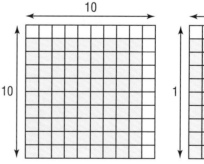

FOCUS

• Determine the square roots of decimals and fractions that are perfect squares.

A children's playground is a square with area 400 m².
What is the side length of the square?
How much fencing is needed to go around the playground?

Investigate ②

Each square below has been divided into 100 equal parts.
In each diagram, what is the area of one small square?

For the shaded square on the left:
➤ What is its area?
➤ Write this area as a product.
➤ How can you use a square root to relate the side length and area?

For the shaded square on the right:
➤ What is its area?
➤ Write this area as a product of fractions.
➤ How can you use a square root to relate the side length and area?

For the area of each square in the table:
➤ Write the area as a product.
➤ Write the side length as a square root.

Area as a Product	Side Length as a Square Root
$49 =$	
$\frac{49}{100} =$	
$64 =$	
$\frac{64}{100} =$	
$121 =$	
$\frac{121}{100} =$	
$144 =$	
$\frac{144}{100} =$	

Reflect & Share

Compare your results with those of your classmates.
How can you use the square roots of whole numbers to determine the square roots of fractions?
Suppose each fraction in the table is written as a decimal.
How can you use the square roots of whole numbers to determine the square roots of decimals?

Connect

To determine the area of a square, we multiply the side length by itself.
That is, we *square* the side length.

$$\text{Area} = \left(\frac{15}{10}\right)^2$$
$$= \frac{15}{10} \times \frac{15}{10}$$
$$= \frac{225}{100}$$

The area is $\frac{225}{100}$ square units.

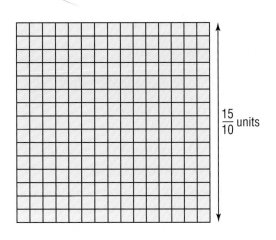

$\frac{15}{10}$ units

To determine the side length of a square, we calculate the square root of its area.

$$\text{Side length} = \sqrt{\frac{169}{100}}$$

$$= \sqrt{\frac{13}{10} \times \frac{13}{10}}$$

$$= \frac{13}{10}$$

The side length is $\frac{13}{10}$ units.

Area: $\frac{169}{100}$ square units

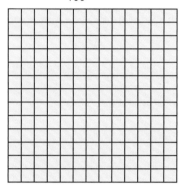

Squaring and taking the square root are opposite, or inverse, operations.

The side length of a square is the square root of its area.

That is, $\sqrt{\frac{225}{100}} = \frac{15}{10}$ and $\sqrt{\frac{169}{100}} = \frac{13}{10}$

We can rewrite these equations using decimals:

$$\sqrt{2.25} = 1.5 \text{ and } \sqrt{1.69} = 1.3$$

1.5 and 1.3 are terminating decimals.

The square roots of some fractions are repeating decimals.

To determine the side length of the shaded square, take the square root of $\frac{1}{9}$:

$$\sqrt{\frac{1}{9}} = \sqrt{\frac{1}{3} \times \frac{1}{3}}$$

$$= \frac{1}{3}$$

$$= 0.333\,333\,333\,\ldots$$

$$= 0.\overline{3}$$

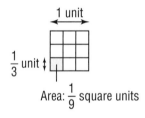

1 unit

$\frac{1}{3}$ unit

Area: $\frac{1}{9}$ square units

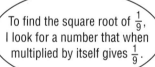

To find the square root of $\frac{1}{9}$, I look for a number that when multiplied by itself gives $\frac{1}{9}$.

When the area of a square is $\frac{1}{9}$ square units, its side length is $\frac{1}{3}$, or $0.\overline{3}$ of a unit.

A fraction in simplest form is a **perfect square** if it can be written as a product of two equal fractions.

When a decimal can be written as a fraction that is a perfect square, then the decimal is also a perfect square. The square root is a terminating or repeating decimal.

Example 1   **Determining a Perfect Square Given its Square Root**

Calculate the number whose square root is:

a) $\frac{3}{8}$ b) 1.8

► **A Solution**

a) Visualize $\frac{3}{8}$ as the side length of a square.

The area of the square is: $\left(\frac{3}{8}\right)^2 = \frac{3}{8} \times \frac{3}{8}$

$$= \frac{9}{64}$$

So, $\frac{3}{8}$ is a square root of $\frac{9}{64}$.

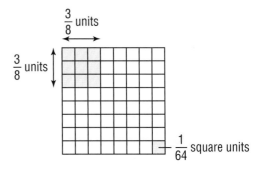

b) Visualize 1.8 as the side length of a square.

The area of the square is: $1.8^2 = 1.8 \times 1.8$

$$= 3.24$$

So, 1.8 is a square root of 3.24.

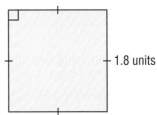

Example 2   **Identifying Fractions that Are Perfect Squares**

Is each fraction a perfect square? Explain your reasoning.

a) $\frac{8}{18}$ b) $\frac{16}{5}$ c) $\frac{2}{9}$

► **A Solution**

a) $\frac{8}{18}$

Simplify the fraction first. Divide the numerator and denominator by 2.

$$\frac{8}{18} = \frac{4}{9}$$

Since $4 = 2 \times 2$ and $9 = 3 \times 3$, we can write:

$$\frac{4}{9} = \frac{2}{3} \times \frac{2}{3}$$

Since $\frac{4}{9}$ can be written as a product of two equal fractions,
it is a perfect square.

So, $\frac{8}{18}$ is also a perfect square.

b) $\frac{16}{5}$

The fraction is in simplest form.

So, look for a fraction that when multiplied by itself gives $\frac{16}{5}$.

The numerator can be written as $16 = 4 \times 4$, but the denominator cannot be written as a product of equal factors.

So, $\frac{16}{5}$ is not a perfect square.

c) $\frac{2}{9}$

The fraction is in simplest form.

So, look for a fraction that when multiplied by itself gives $\frac{2}{9}$.

The denominator can be written as $9 = 3 \times 3$, but the numerator cannot be written as a product of equal factors.

So, $\frac{2}{9}$ is not a perfect square.

Example 3   **Identifying Decimals that Are Perfect Squares**

Is each decimal a perfect square? Explain your reasoning.

a) 6.25   **b)** 0.627

▶ *Solutions*

Method 1	*Method 2*
a) Write 6.25 as a fraction. $$6.25 = \frac{625}{100}$$ Simplify the fraction. Divide the numerator and denominator by 25. $$6.25 = \frac{25}{4}$$ $\frac{25}{4}$ can be written as $\frac{5}{2} \times \frac{5}{2}$. So, $\frac{25}{4}$, or 6.25 is a perfect square.	Use a calculator. Use the square root function. **a)** $\sqrt{6.25} = 2.5$ The square root is a terminating decimal, so 6.25 is a perfect square.
b) Write 0.627 as a fraction. $$0.627 = \frac{627}{1000}$$ This fraction is in simplest form. Neither 627 nor 1000 can be written as a product of equal factors, so 0.627 is not a perfect square.	**b)** $\sqrt{0.627} \doteq 0.791\,833\,316$ The square root appears to be a decimal that neither terminates nor repeats, so 0.627 is not a perfect square. To be sure, write the decimal as a fraction, then determine if the fraction is a perfect square, as shown in *Method 1*.

1. How can you tell if a decimal is a perfect square?

2. How can you tell if a fraction is a perfect square?

Practice

Check

3. Use each diagram to determine the value of the square root.

a) $\sqrt{0.25}$ 1 unit

b) $\sqrt{\dfrac{9}{16}}$ 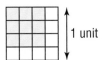 1 unit

c) $\sqrt{\dfrac{16}{25}}$ 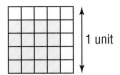 1 unit

4. a) List all the whole numbers from 1 to 100 that are perfect squares.

b) Write a square root of each number you listed in part a.

5. Use your answers to question 4. Determine the value of each square root.

a) $\sqrt{0.36}$ b) $\sqrt{0.49}$

c) $\sqrt{0.81}$ d) $\sqrt{0.16}$

e) $\sqrt{\dfrac{1}{36}}$ f) $\sqrt{\dfrac{25}{9}}$

g) $\sqrt{\dfrac{64}{100}}$ h) $\sqrt{\dfrac{36}{16}}$

6. a) List all the whole numbers from 101 to 400 that are perfect squares.

b) Write a square root of each number you listed in part a.

7. Use your answers to questions 4 and 6. Determine the value of each square root.

a) $\sqrt{\dfrac{169}{16}}$ b) $\sqrt{\dfrac{400}{196}}$

c) $\sqrt{\dfrac{256}{361}}$ d) $\sqrt{\dfrac{225}{289}}$

e) $\sqrt{144}$ f) $\sqrt{0.0225}$

g) $\sqrt{0.0121}$ h) $\sqrt{3.24}$

i) $\sqrt{0.0324}$ j) $\sqrt{0.0169}$

Apply

8. Which decimals and fractions are perfect squares? Explain your reasoning.

a) 0.12   b) 0.81   c) 0.25

d) 1.69   e) $\dfrac{9}{12}$ f) $\dfrac{36}{81}$

g) $\dfrac{81}{49}$ h) $\dfrac{75}{27}$ i) 0.081

j) $\dfrac{25}{10}$ k) 2.5   l) $\dfrac{8}{50}$

9. Calculate the number whose square root is:

a) 0.3   b) 0.12

c) 1.9   d) 3.1

e) $\dfrac{2}{3}$ f) $\dfrac{5}{6}$

g) $\dfrac{1}{7}$ h) $\dfrac{2}{5}$

10. Determine the value of each square root.

a) $\sqrt{12.25}$ b) $\sqrt{30.25}$

c) $\sqrt{20.25}$ d) $\sqrt{56.25}$

11. a) Write each decimal as a fraction.
Which fractions are perfect squares?

    i) 36.0   **ii)** 3.6   **iii)** 0.36

    iv) 0.036   **v)** 0.0036   **vi)** 0.000 36

b) To check your answers to part a, use a calculator to determine a square root of each decimal.

c) What patterns do you see in your answers to parts a and b?

d) When can you use the square roots of perfect squares to determine the square roots of decimals?

12. a) Use the fact that $\sqrt{9} = 3$ to write the value of each square root.

    i) $\sqrt{90\,000}$ **ii)** $\sqrt{900}$

    iii) $\sqrt{0.09}$ **iv)** $\sqrt{0.0009}$

b) Use the fact that $\sqrt{25} = 5$ to write the value of each square root.

    i) $\sqrt{0.0025}$ **ii)** $\sqrt{0.25}$

    iii) $\sqrt{2500}$ **iv)** $\sqrt{250\,000}$

c) Use the patterns in parts a and b. Choose a whole number whose square root you know. Use that number and its square root to write 3 decimals and their square roots. How do you know the square roots are correct?

13. Assessment Focus

a) Which letter on the number line below corresponds to each square root? Justify your answers.

    i) $\sqrt{12.25}$ **ii)** $\sqrt{\frac{121}{25}}$ **iii)** $\sqrt{16.81}$

    iv) $\sqrt{\frac{81}{100}}$ **v)** $\sqrt{0.09}$ **vi)** $\sqrt{\frac{841}{25}}$

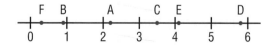

b) Sketch the number line in part a. Write 3 different decimals, then use the letters G, H, and J to represent their square roots. Place each letter on the number line. Justify its placement.

14. A square has area 5.76 cm².

a) What is the side length of the square?

b) What is the perimeter of the square? How do you know?

15. A square piece of land has an area not less than 6.25 km² and not greater than 10.24 km².

a) What is the least possible side length of the square?

b) What is the greatest possible side length of the square?

c) A surveyor determined that the side length is 2.8 km. What is the area of the square?

16. A student said that $\sqrt{0.04} = 0.02$.
Is the student correct?
If your answer is yes, how could you check that the square root is correct?
If your answer is no, what is the correct square root? Justify your answer.

17. Look at the perfect squares you wrote for questions 4 and 6.

The numbers 36, 64, and 100 are related:

$36 + 64 = 100$, or $6^2 + 8^2 = 10^2$

These numbers form a
Pythagorean triple.

a) Why do you think this name is appropriate?

b) How many other Pythagorean triples can you find? List each triple.

Take It Further

18. Are there any perfect squares between 0.64 and 0.81? Justify your answer.

19. A student has a rectangular piece of paper 7.2 cm by 1.8 cm. She cuts the paper into parts that can be rearranged and taped to form a square.

a) What is the side length of the square?

b) What are the fewest cuts the student could have made? Justify your answer.

Reflect

Explain the term *perfect square*. List some whole numbers, fractions, and decimals that are perfect squares. Determine a square root of each number.

Math Link

History

The Pythagorean Theorem is named for the Greek philosopher, Pythagoras, because he was the first person to record a proof for the theorem, around 540 BCE. However, clay tablets from around 1700 BCE show that the Babylonians knew how to calculate the length of the diagonal of a square. And, around 2000 BCE, it is believed that the Egyptians may have used a knotted rope that formed a triangle with side lengths 3, 4, and 5 to help design the pyramids.

FOCUS

• Approximate the square roots of decimals and fractions that are non-perfect squares.

A ladder is leaning against a wall.
For safety, the distance from the base of a ladder to the wall must be about $\frac{1}{4}$ of the height up the wall. How could you check if the ladder is safe?

9 m

2 m

Investigate

2

A ladder is 6.1 m long.
The distance from the base of the ladder to the wall is 1.5 m.
Estimate how far up the wall the ladder will reach.

Compare your strategy for estimating the height with that of another pair of classmates. Did you use a scale drawing? Did you calculate?
Which method gives the closer estimate?

Connect

Many fractions and decimals are not perfect squares.
That is, they cannot be written as a product of two equal fractions.
A fraction or decimal that is not a perfect square is called a **non-perfect square**.

Here are two strategies for estimating a square root
of a decimal that is a non-perfect square.

➤ Using benchmarks,
To estimate $\sqrt{7.5}$, visualize
a number line and the
closest perfect square
on each side of 7.5.
$\sqrt{4} = 2$ and $\sqrt{9} = 3$
7.5 is closer to 9 than to 4, so
$\sqrt{7.5}$ is closer to 3 than to 2.
From the diagram, an approximate value for $\sqrt{7.5}$ is 2.7.
We write $\sqrt{7.5} \doteq 2.7$

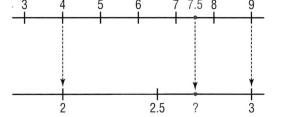

➤ Using a calculator
$\sqrt{7.5} \doteq 2.738\ 612\ 788$
This decimal does not appear to terminate or repeat.
There may be many more numbers after the decimal point that
cannot be displayed on the calculator.
To check, determine: $2.738\ 612\ 788^2 = 7.500\ 000\ 003$
Since this number is not equal to 7.5, the square root is an approximation.

Example 1 illustrates 4 different strategies for determining the square root of a
fraction that is a non-perfect square.

Example 1   Estimating a Square Root of a Fraction

Determine an approximate value of each square root.

a) $\sqrt{\dfrac{8}{5}}$ b) $\sqrt{\dfrac{3}{10}}$ c) $\sqrt{\dfrac{3}{7}}$ d) $\sqrt{\dfrac{19}{6}}$

▶ A Solution

a) Use benchmarks. Think about the perfect squares closest to the numerator and
denominator. In the fraction $\dfrac{8}{5}$, 8 is close to the perfect square 9,
and 5 is close to the perfect square 4.

So, $\sqrt{\dfrac{8}{5}} \doteq \sqrt{\dfrac{9}{4}}$

$\sqrt{\dfrac{9}{4}} = \dfrac{3}{2}$

So, $\sqrt{\dfrac{8}{5}} \doteq \dfrac{3}{2}$

b) Write the fraction as a decimal, then think about benchmarks.

Write $\frac{3}{10}$ as a decimal: 0.3

Think of the closest perfect squares on either side of 0.3.

$\sqrt{0.25} = 0.5$ and $\sqrt{0.36} = 0.6$

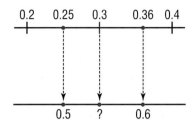

0.3 is approximately halfway between 0.25 and 0.36, so choose 0.55 as a possible estimate for a square root.

To check, evaluate:

$0.55^2 = 0.3025$

0.3025 is close to 0.3, so 0.55 is a reasonable estimate.

So, $\sqrt{\frac{3}{10}} \doteq 0.55$

c) Choose a fraction close to $\frac{3}{7}$ that is easier to work with.

$\frac{3}{7}$ is a little less than $\frac{1}{2}$.

$\frac{1}{2} = 0.5$

$\sqrt{0.5} \doteq \sqrt{0.49}$

And, $\sqrt{0.49} = 0.7$

So, $\sqrt{\frac{3}{7}} \doteq 0.7$

d) Use the square root function on a calculator.

$\sqrt{\frac{19}{6}} \doteq 1.779\ 513\ 042$

To the nearest hundredth, $\sqrt{\frac{19}{6}} \doteq 1.78$

Identify a decimal that has a square root between 10 and 11. Check the answer.

▶ *Solutions*

Method 1	Method 2
The number with a square root of 10 is: $10^2 = 100$ The number with a square root of 11 is: $11^2 = 121$ So, any number between 100 and 121 has a square root between 10 and 11. A decimal between 100 and 121 is 105.6. So, $\sqrt{105.6}$ is between 10 and 11. Use a calculator to check. $\sqrt{105.6} \doteq 10.276\ 186\ 06$ So, the decimal 105.6 is one correct answer.	One decimal between 10 and 11 is 10.4. To determine the number whose square root is 10.4, evaluate: $10.4^2 = 108.16$ So, $\sqrt{108.16}$ is between 10 and 11. Use a calculator to check. $\sqrt{108.16} = 10.4$ So, the decimal 108.16 is one correct answer.

Example 3   **Applying the Pythagorean Theorem**

The sloping face of this ramp is to be covered in carpet.
a) Estimate the length of the ramp to the nearest tenth of a metre.
b) Use a calculator to check the answer.
c) Calculate the area of carpet needed.

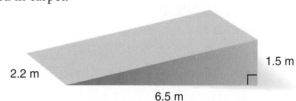

2.2 m   6.5 m   1.5 m

▶ *A Solution*

a) The ramp is a right triangular prism with a base that is a right triangle.
   The base of the prism is its side view.
   To calculate the length of the ramp, *r*, use the Pythagorean Theorem.

$$r^2 = 6.5^2 + 1.5^2$$
$$= 42.25 + 2.25$$
$$= 44.5$$
$$r = \sqrt{44.5}$$

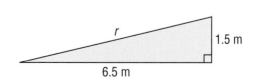

r   1.5 m   6.5 m

44.5 is between the perfect squares 36 and 49, and closer to 49.

So, $\sqrt{44.5}$ is between 6 and 7, and closer to 7.

Estimate $\sqrt{44.5}$ as 6.7.

To check, evaluate: $6.7^2 = 44.89$

This is very close to 44.5, so $r \doteq 6.7$

The ramp is about 6.7 m long.

> Since the dimensions of the ramp were given to the nearest tenth, the answer is also written in this form.

b) Use a calculator to check: $\sqrt{44.5} \doteq 6.670\ 832\ 032$

This number is 6.7 to the nearest tenth, so the answer is correct.

c) The sloping face of the ramp is a rectangle with dimensions 6.7 m by 2.2 m.

The area of the rectangle is about: $6.7 \times 2.2 = 14.74$

Round the answer up to the nearest square metre to ensure there is enough carpet.

So, about 15 m^2 of carpet are needed.

Discuss the ideas

1. Explain the term *non-perfect square*.

2. Name 3 perfect squares and 3 non-perfect squares between the numbers 0 and 10. Justify your answers.

3. Why might the square root shown on a calculator be an approximation?

Practice

Check

4. For each square root, name the two closest perfect squares and their square roots.

   a) $\sqrt{3.5}$ b) $\sqrt{13.5}$

   c) $\sqrt{53.5}$ d) $\sqrt{73.5}$

   e) $\sqrt{93.5}$ f) $\sqrt{113.5}$

5. For each square root, name the two closest perfect squares and their square roots.

   a) $\sqrt{\dfrac{5}{10}}$ b) $\sqrt{\dfrac{55}{10}}$

   c) $\sqrt{\dfrac{95}{10}}$ d) $\sqrt{\dfrac{595}{10}}$

   e) $\sqrt{\dfrac{795}{10}}$ f) $\sqrt{\dfrac{1095}{10}}$

Apply

6. Use benchmarks to estimate a fraction for each square root. State the benchmarks you used.

   a) $\sqrt{\dfrac{8}{10}}$ b) $\sqrt{\dfrac{17}{5}}$

   c) $\sqrt{\dfrac{7}{13}}$ d) $\sqrt{\dfrac{29}{6}}$

7. Use benchmarks to approximate each square root to the nearest tenth. State the benchmarks you used.

   a) $\sqrt{4.5}$ b) $\sqrt{14.5}$

   c) $\sqrt{84.5}$ d) $\sqrt{145.5}$

   e) $\sqrt{284.5}$ f) $\sqrt{304.5}$

8. Use each pair of squares to approximate each square root.
Explain your strategy.

a) $\sqrt{29.5}$

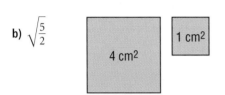

25 cm²   36 cm²

b) $\sqrt{\dfrac{5}{2}}$

4 cm²   1 cm²

9. Which of the following square roots are correct to the nearest tenth? How do you know? Correct the square roots that are incorrect.

a) $\sqrt{4.4} \doteq 2.2$ **b)** $\sqrt{0.6} \doteq 0.3$
c) $\sqrt{6.6} \doteq 2.6$ **d)** $\sqrt{0.4} \doteq 0.2$

10. Find 2 decimals that have square roots between each pair of numbers.
Justify your answers.

a) 3 and 4
b) 7 and 8
c) 12 and 13
d) 1.5 and 2.5
e) 4.5 and 5.5

11. Use any strategy you wish to estimate the value of each square root. Explain why you used the strategy you did.

a) $\sqrt{4.5}$ **b)** $\sqrt{\dfrac{17}{2}}$ **c)** $\sqrt{0.15}$ **d)** $\sqrt{\dfrac{10}{41}}$

e) $\sqrt{0.7}$ **f)** $\sqrt{\dfrac{8}{45}}$ **g)** $\sqrt{0.05}$ **h)** $\sqrt{\dfrac{90}{19}}$

12. Approximate each square root to the nearest tenth. Explain your strategy.

a) $\sqrt{\dfrac{3}{8}}$ **b)** $\sqrt{\dfrac{5}{12}}$ **c)** $\sqrt{\dfrac{13}{4}}$ **d)** $\sqrt{\dfrac{25}{3}}$

13. In each triangle, determine the unknown length.

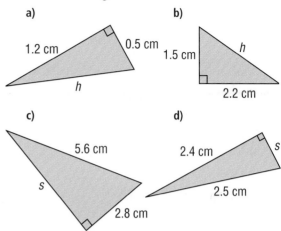

a)
1.2 cm   0.5 cm
h

b)
1.5 cm h
2.2 cm

c)
5.6 cm
s
2.8 cm

d)
2.4 cm s
2.5 cm

14. Assessment Focus How many decimals and fractions can you find with square roots between 0.5 and 0.6?
List the decimals and fractions.
Justify your answers. Show your work.

15. Sketch a number line from 0 to 10. Place each square root on the number line to show its approximate value.

a) $\sqrt{0.1}$ **b)** $\sqrt{56.3}$
c) $\sqrt{0.6}$ **d)** $\sqrt{0.03}$

16. a) Which square roots are correctly placed on the number line below?
How do you know?

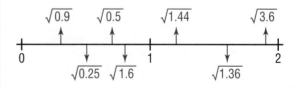

$\sqrt{0.9}$ $\sqrt{0.5}$ $\sqrt{1.44}$ $\sqrt{3.6}$

0   1   2

$\sqrt{0.25}$ $\sqrt{1.6}$ $\sqrt{1.36}$

b) Sketch a number line from 0 to 2. On the number line, correctly place the square roots that were incorrectly placed in part a.

17. Use a calculator to determine each square root. Which square roots are approximate? How do you know?
   a) $\sqrt{52.9}$ b) $\sqrt{5.29}$ c) $\sqrt{2.25}$ d) $\sqrt{22.5}$

18. Look at the numbers and their square roots you have determined in this lesson. How would you describe the numbers whose square roots are:
   a) less than the number?
   b) equal to the number?
   c) greater than the number?
   Justify your answer.

19. Determine a decimal or a fraction whose square root is between each pair of numbers.
   a) 0 and 1   b) 1.5 and 2
   c) $\frac{1}{2}$ and $\frac{3}{4}$ d) $3\frac{3}{4}$ and 4

20. On each grid below, the side length of each square represents 0.25 km.
   Determine the length of AB to the nearest hundredth of a kilometre.
   a)   b)

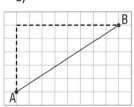

21. a) Use a calculator to approximate each square root.
   i) $\sqrt{0.005}$ ii) $\sqrt{0.5}$ iii) $\sqrt{50}$
   iv) $\sqrt{5000}$ v) $\sqrt{500\ 000}$

b) What patterns do you see in the square roots in part a? Use the patterns to write the previous two square roots less than $\sqrt{0.005}$ and the next two square roots greater than $\sqrt{500\ 000}$.

Take It Further

22. Are there any square numbers between 0.6 and 0.61? How do you know?

23. The grid below shows point A(1.1, 0.7) that is one vertex of a square with area 0.25 square units. What are the coordinates of the other three vertices of the square? Justify your answer.

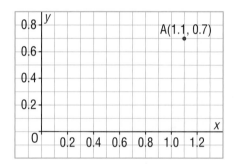

24. The side length of a square photograph is 5.5 cm. An enlargement of the photograph is a square with an area that is twice the area of the smaller photograph.
   a) Estimate the side length of the larger photograph. Justify your answer.
   b) Why is the side length of the larger photograph not twice the side length of the smaller photograph?

Reflect

Explain why the square root of a non-perfect square displayed on a calculator is only an approximation. Include examples in your explanation.

1.1

1. Explain how you can use each diagram to determine the square root.

a) $\sqrt{\dfrac{25}{36}}$

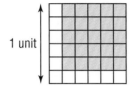

1 unit

b) $\sqrt{0.36}$

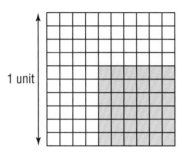

1 unit

2. Calculate the number whose square root is:

a) 1.4   b) $\dfrac{3}{8}$ c) $\dfrac{7}{4}$ d) 0.5

3. Determine the value of each square root.

a) $\sqrt{0.04}$ b) $\sqrt{\dfrac{1}{16}}$ c) $\sqrt{1.96}$ d) $\sqrt{\dfrac{4}{81}}$

e) $\sqrt{1.69}$ f) $\sqrt{\dfrac{121}{49}}$ g) $\sqrt{0.09}$ h) $\sqrt{\dfrac{289}{100}}$

4. Determine the value of each square root.

a) $\sqrt{3.24}$ b) $\sqrt{90.25}$ c) $\sqrt{2.56}$

5. A square has area 148.84 cm².
a) What is the side length of the square?
b) What is the perimeter of the square?

6. A student said that $\sqrt{0.16} = 0.04$.
Is the student correct?
If your answer is yes, how could you check that the square root is correct?
If your answer is no, explain how to get the correct square root.

7. Which decimals and fractions are perfect squares? Explain your reasoning.

a) $\dfrac{9}{64}$ b) 3.6   c) $\dfrac{6}{9}$ d) 5.76

1.2

8. Use benchmarks to estimate each square root.

a) $\sqrt{5.6}$ b) $\sqrt{\dfrac{9}{10}}$ c) $\sqrt{42.8}$

d) $\sqrt{\dfrac{356}{10}}$ e) $\sqrt{0.056}$ f) $\sqrt{\dfrac{9}{100}}$

9. In each triangle, determine the unknown length.

a)

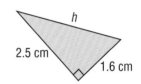

2.5 cm   h   1.6 cm

b)

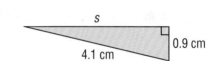

s   0.9 cm
4.1 cm

10. Which of the following square roots are correct to the nearest tenth?
How do you know? Correct the square roots that are incorrect.

a) $\sqrt{0.09} \doteq 0.3$ b) $\sqrt{1.7} \doteq 0.4$
c) $\sqrt{8.5} \doteq 2.9$ d) $\sqrt{27.5} \doteq 5.2$

11. Find 2 decimals that have square roots between each pair of numbers. Justify your answers.

a) 4 and 8   b) 0.7 and 0.9
c) 1.25 and 1.35   d) 0.25 and 0.35
e) 4.5 and 5.5   f) 0.05 and 0.1

How Can I Begin?

Suppose I have to solve this problem:

A right triangular prism is 20 cm long.

Each base is an isosceles triangle with side lengths
10 cm, 10 cm, and 8 cm.

What is the surface area of the prism?

➤ What is my first step?
- I could use a model.
- I could sketch a diagram.
- I could visualize the prism in my mind.

If I use a model, I can place stickers on the prism to label its dimensions.

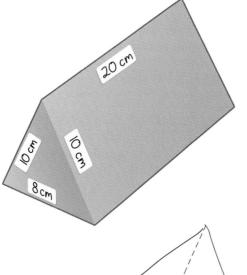

The model should have the shape of a triangular prism, but the dimensions of the prism do not have to match the given dimensions.

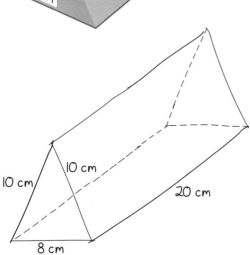

If I sketch a diagram, I label it with the given dimensions.

The diagram does not have to be drawn to scale.

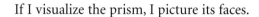

If I visualize the prism, I picture its faces.

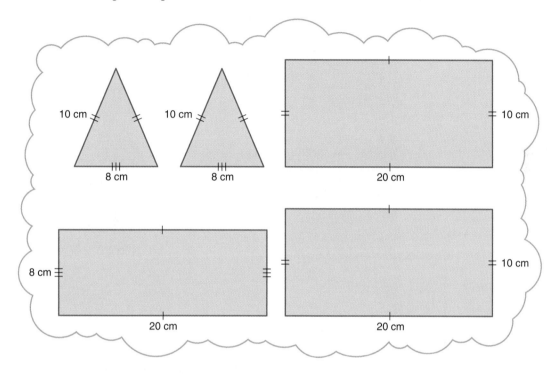

➤ What do I already know?
  • a strategy to find the area of a rectangle
  • a strategy to find the height of an isosceles triangle when the lengths of its sides are known
  • a strategy to find the area of an isosceles triangle

Use strategies *you* know to find the surface area of the right triangular prism.

Check

1. A right triangular prism is 35 cm high. Its bases are equilateral triangles, with side lengths 12 cm. What is the surface area of the prism?

2. A right cylinder is 35 cm long. Its diameter is 12 cm. What is the surface area of the cylinder?

Making a Larger Square from Two Smaller Squares

You will need
- 2 congruent square pieces of paper
- scissors
- square dot paper

Number of Players
- 2

Goal of the Game
- To cut two congruent squares and rearrange the pieces to form one larger square

Before you cut the squares, sketch them on square dot paper.
Draw possible cuts you could make.
Imagine joining all the pieces with no overlap.
Do the pieces form a larger square?

Check your prediction by cutting the squares and arranging the pieces to form a larger square. If your prediction did not work, try again using another two congruent squares.

Share your method with another pair of students.
Are there other possible ways of forming the larger square?
How could you do this by making the fewest cuts possible?

Suppose the area of each congruent square is 1 square unit.
- What is the area of the larger square?
- What is the side length of the larger square, to the nearest tenth?

Suppose the area of each congruent square is 2 square units.
Determine the area and side length of the larger square.

1.3 Surface Areas of Objects Made from Right Rectangular Prisms

These cube houses were built in Rotterdam, Netherlands.
Suppose you wanted to determine the surface area of one of these houses.
What would you need to know?

FOCUS

- Determine the surface areas of composite objects made from cubes and other right rectangular prisms.

Investigate ②

Each of you needs 5 linking cubes.
Assume each face of a linking cube has area 1 unit².

➤ What is the surface area of 1 cube?
  Put 2 cubes together to make a "train."
  What is the surface area of the train?
  Place another cube at one end of your train.
  What is its surface area now?
  Continue to place cubes at one end of the train, and determine its surface area.
  Copy and complete this table.
  What patterns do you see in the table?
  What happens to the surface area each time you place another cube on the train?
  Explain why the surface area changes this way.

Number of Cubes	Surface Area (square units)
1	
2	
3	
4	
5	

➤ With the 5 cubes, build an object that is different from the train and different from your partner's object.
  Determine its surface area.
  Compare the surface area of your object with that of your partner's object.

Compare your objects with those of another pair of students who made different objects. Are any of the surface areas different?
If your answer is yes, explain how they can be different when all the objects are made with 5 cubes.

Connect

Here is an object made from 4 unit cubes.
Each face of a cube is a square with area 1 unit^2.

Here are 2 strategies for determining the surface area of the object.

➤ Count the square faces of all the cubes,
then subtract 2 faces for each surface
where the cubes are joined.
We say the faces *overlap*.

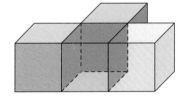

The object has 4 cubes. Each cube has 6 faces.
So, the number of faces is: $6 \times 4 = 24$
There are 3 places where the faces overlap,
so subtract: 3×2, or 6 faces
The surface area, in square units, is: $24 - 6 = 18$

➤ Count the squares on each of the 6 views.
There are:
4 squares on the top,
4 squares on the bottom,
3 squares on the front,
3 squares on the back,
2 squares at the right,
and 2 squares at the left.
The surface area, in square units, is:
$4 + 4 + 3 + 3 + 2 + 2 = 18$

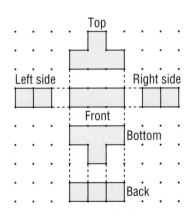

An object like that on page 26 is called a **composite object** because it is made up, or *composed*, of other objects.

(refers to page 26)

Example 1   **Determining the Surface Area of a Composite Object Made from Cubes**

Determine the surface area of this composite object.
Each cube has edge length 2 cm.

▶ *Solutions*

Method 1	**Method 2**
Count the squares on each of the 6 views:	The composite object has 5 cubes.
	Each cube has 6 square faces.
	So, the total number of squares is: $5 \times 6 = 30$

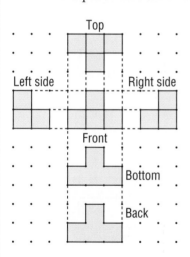

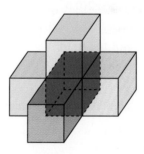

Method 1 (continued)

Each of the front, back, top, and bottom views has 4 squares.
Each of the right and left views has 3 squares.
The surface area, in squares, is:
$(4 \times 4) + (3 \times 2) = 22$
Each square has area: $2 \text{ cm} \times 2 \text{ cm} = 4 \text{ cm}^2$
So, the surface area is: $22 \times 4 \text{ cm}^2 = 88 \text{ cm}^2$

Method 2 (continued)

The cubes overlap at 4 places,
so there are 4×2, or 8 squares
that are not part of the surface area.
The surface area, in squares, is: $30 - 8 = 22$
Each square has area: $2 \text{ cm} \times 2 \text{ cm} = 4 \text{ cm}^2$
So, the surface area is: $22 \times 4 \text{ cm}^2 = 88 \text{ cm}^2$

We can use the surface area of composite objects to solve problems outside the classroom.

Example 2 **Determining the Surface Area of a Composite Object Made from Right Rectangular Prisms**

Renee uses 3 pieces of foam to make this chair.
Each piece of foam is a right rectangular prism with
dimensions 60 cm by 20 cm by 20 cm.
Can Renee cover the chair with 2 m² of fabric?
Explain.

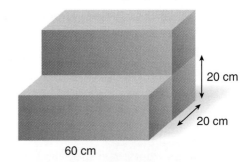

▶ *A Solution*

Convert each measurement to metres, then the
surface area is measured in square metres.
60 cm = 0.6 m   20 cm = 0.2 m

Determine the surface area of the rectangular prism
that is the base of the chair.

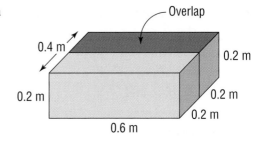

Area of top and bottom faces: 2(0.6 × 0.4) = 0.48
Area of front and back faces: 2(0.6 × 0.2) = 0.24
Area of left and right faces: 2(0.2 × 0.4) = 0.16
Surface area of the base of the chair:
0.48 + 0.24 + 0.16 = 0.88

Determine the surface area of the rectangular prism
that is the back rest.

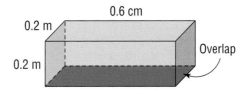

Area of top, bottom, front, and back:
4(0.6 × 0.2) = 0.48
Area of left and right faces: 2(0.2 × 0.2) = 0.08
Surface area of back rest: 0.48 + 0.08 = 0.56

Add the two surface areas, then subtract twice the area of the overlap
because neither of these areas is part of the surface area of the chair:
0.88 + 0.56 − 2(0.6 × 0.2) = 1.44 − 0.24
                                             = 1.2
The surface area that is to be covered in fabric is 1.2 m².
Since 2 m² > 1.2 m², Renee can cover the chair with 2 m² of fabric.

Example 3 | **Solving Problems Involving the Surface Area of a Composite Object**

A warehouse measures 60 m by 30 m by 20 m.
An office attached to one wall of the warehouse
measures 20 m by 20 m by 10 m.
a) Determine the surface area of the building.
b) A contractor quotes to paint the exterior of the
building at a rate of $2.50/m².
These parts of the building are not to be painted:
the 2 roofs; the office door with area 2 m²;
3 loading doors, each measuring 10 m by 15 m;
and 4 windows on the office, each with area 1 m².
How much would it cost to paint the building?

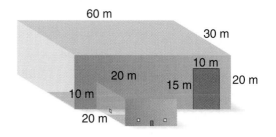

A Solution

The surface area is measured in square metres.

a) The 4 walls and roof of the warehouse form its surface area.
   Area of roof: 60 × 30 = 1800
   Area of left and right side walls: 2(30 × 20) = 1200
   Area of the front and back walls: 2(60 × 20) = 2400
   So, the surface area of the warehouse is: 1800 + 1200 + 2400 = 5400

   The 3 walls and roof of the office form its surface area.
   Area of roof: 20 × 20 = 400
   Area of front, left, and right side walls: 3(20 × 10) = 600
   So, the surface area of the office is: 400 + 600 = 1000

   For the surface area of the building, add the surface areas of the warehouse
   and the office, then subtract the area of the overlap.
   The area of the overlap, which is the back of the office, is: 20 × 10 = 200
   So, the surface area of the building is: 5400 m² + 1000 m² − 200 m² = 6200 m²

b) To calculate the area to be painted, subtract the areas of the roofs, doors,
   and windows from the surface area of the building.
   Area of roofs: 1800 + 400 = 2200
   Area of loading doors: 3(10 × 15) = 450
   Area of office door and windows: 2 + 4(1) = 6
   So, the area to be painted is: 6200 m² − 2200 m² − 450 m² − 6 m² = 3544 m²
   The cost to paint the building is: 3544 × $2.50 = $8860.00

1. When a composite object is made from right rectangular prisms, why is the surface area of the object not the sum of the surface areas of the individual prisms?

2. The surface area of an object is the area of a net of the object. How would drawing a net help you determine the surface area of a composite object?

3. In *Example 3*, why are the bases of the warehouse and office not included in the surface area?

Practice

Check

4. Make each composite object with cubes. Assume each face of a cube has area 1 unit². Determine the surface area of each composite object.

a)

b)

c)

d)

e)

f)

Apply

5. These are 1-cm cubes.

a) Determine the surface area of the composite object formed by placing cube 4 on top of each indicated cube.
   i) cube 1   ii) cube 2   iii) cube 3
b) Why are the surface areas in part a equal?

6. These are 1-cm cubes.

a) Determine the surface area of the composite object formed by placing cube 5 on top of each indicated cube.
   i) cube 1   ii) cube 2   iii) cube 3
b) Why are all the surface areas in part a not equal?

7. Why could you not use 6 views to determine the surface area of this composite object?

8. Determine the surface area of each composite object.
What effect does the overlap have on the calculation of the surface area?

a)

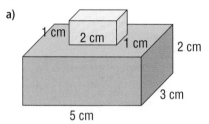

b)

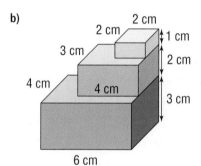

c)

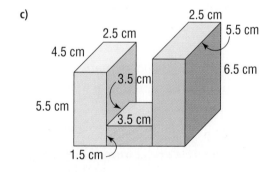

9. Work with a partner. Tape a tissue box on a shoebox to form a composite object.
   a) What is the area of the overlap?
   How did you calculate it?
   b) Determine the surface area of the object.
   How did you use the area of the overlap in your calculation?

10. Assessment Focus A garage has the dimensions shown. The attached shed has the same height as the garage, but is one-half as long and one-half as wide.

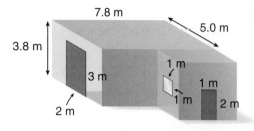

   a) What is the surface area of the building?
   b) Vinyl siding costs $15/m². The doors, windows, and roof will not be covered with siding. How much will it cost to cover this building with siding?

11. This is a floor plan of a building that is 8 m tall. It has a flat roof. What is the surface area of the building, including its roof?

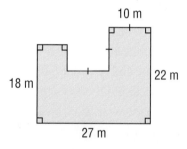

12. Use 27 small cubes to build a large cube.
   a) Determine and record its surface area.
   b) How many ways can you remove one cube without changing the surface area? Explain your work.
   c) Suppose you painted the large cube. How many small cubes would have paint on:
   i) exactly 1 face? **ii)** exactly 2 faces?
   iii) exactly 3 faces? **iv)** 0 faces?
   v) more than 3 faces?
   How could you check your answers?

Argyll Centre
6859 - 100 Avenue
Edmonton, AB T6A 0G3

13. Every January, the Ice Magic Festival is held at Chateau Lake Louise in Banff National Park. An ice castle is constructed from huge blocks of ice.

a) Suppose you have 30 blocks of ice measuring 25 cm by 50 cm by 100 cm. Sketch a castle with no roof that could be built with some or all of these blocks.

b) Determine the surface area of your castle, inside and out.

Take It Further

14. Use 6 centimetre cubes.
a) Build a composite object. Sketch the object, then determine and record its surface area.
b) Use the cubes to build other objects with different surface areas. Sketch each object and record its surface area.
c) Determine all the different surface areas for a composite object of 6 cubes.
d) Describe the object with the greatest surface area. Describe the object with the least surface area.

15. Use centimetre cubes. Build, then sketch all possible composite objects that have a surface area of 16 cm^2.

16. A pyramid-like structure is made with 1-m^3 wooden cubes. The bottom layer of the structure is a rectangular prism with a square base and a volume of 25 m^3. The next layer has a volume of 16 m^3. The pattern of layers continues until the top layer, which has a volume of 1 m^3. Determine the surface area of the structure. Describe any patterns you find.

17. The SOMA Puzzle was invented by a Danish poet and scientist named Piet Hein in 1936. The object of the puzzle is to arrange these 7 pieces to form one large cube:

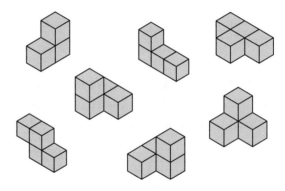

a) Determine the surface area of each piece.
b) Use linking cubes to make your own pieces and arrange them to form a large cube.
c) Suppose you painted the large cube. How many faces of the original 7 pieces would not be painted? How do you know?

Reflect

Why is it important to consider the areas of overlap when determining the surface area of a composite object? Include an example in your explanation.

1.4 Surface Areas of Other Composite Objects

FOCUS

- Determine the surface areas of composite objects made from right prisms and right cylinders.

A student designed this stand for a table lamp. How could the student determine the surface area of this stand? What would he need to know?

Investigate ● 2 ●

To meet safety regulations, a wheelchair ramp must be followed by a landing. This wheelchair ramp and landing lead into an office building. Calculate the surface area of the ramp and landing.

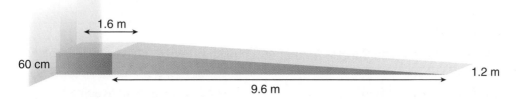

1.6 m

60 cm

9.6 m

1.2 m

Reflect & Share

What strategies did you use to determine the surface area?
What assumptions did you make?
Compare your strategy and calculations with those of another pair of students.
How many different ways can you determine the surface area? Explain.

Connect

We use the strategies from Lesson 1.3 to determine the surface area of a composite object made from right cylinders and right triangular prisms. That is, consider each prism or cylinder separately, add their surface areas, then account for the overlap.

For composite objects involving right prisms, we can use word formulas to determine the surface areas of the prisms.

➤ A right rectangular prism has 3 pairs of congruent faces:
- the top and bottom faces
- the front and back faces
- the left side and right side faces

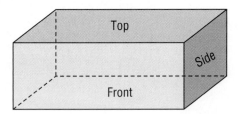

The surface area is the sum of the areas of the faces:
Surface area = 2 × area of top face + 2 × area of front face + 2 × area of side face

➤ A right triangular prism has 5 faces:
- 2 congruent triangular bases
- 3 rectangular faces

The surface area is the sum of the areas of the triangular bases and the rectangular faces:
Surface area = 2 × area of base + areas of 3 rectangular faces

Determining the Surface Area of a Composite Object Made from Two Prisms

Determine the surface area of this object.

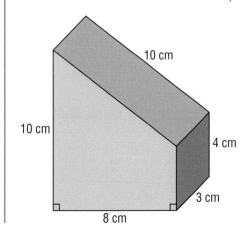

▶ *A Solution*

The object is composed of a right triangular prism on top of a right rectangular prism. The surface area is measured in square centimetres.

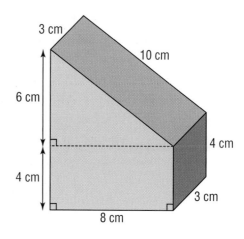

For the surface area of the rectangular prism:

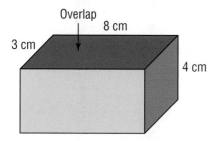

Surface area = 2 × area of top face + 2 × area of front face + 2 × area of side face
$\qquad$ = (2 × 8 × 3) + (2 × 8 × 4) + (2 × 3 × 4) $\quad$ Use the order of operations.
$\qquad$ = 48 + 64 + 24
$\qquad$ = 136

The surface area of the right rectangular prism is 136 cm².

For the surface area of the triangular prism:
Each base of the prism is a right triangle,
with base 8 cm and height 6 cm.

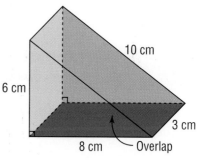

Surface area = 2 × area of base + areas of 3 rectangular faces
$\qquad$ = $(2 \times \frac{1}{2} \times 8 \times 6) + (3 \times 6) + (3 \times 8) + (3 \times 10)$ $\quad$ Use the fact that $2 \times \frac{1}{2} = 1$.
$\qquad$ = (1 × 8 × 6) + (3 × 6) + (3 × 8) + (3 × 10) $\quad$ Use the order of operations.
$\qquad$ = 48 + 18 + 24 + 30
$\qquad$ = 120

The surface area of the right triangular prism is 120 cm².

Add the two surface areas, then subtract twice the area of the overlap.
Surface area = 136 + 120 − (2 × 8 × 3)
$\qquad$ = 136 + 120 − 48
$\qquad$ = 208

The surface area of the object is 208 cm².

When a composite object includes a right cylinder,
we can use a formula to determine its surface area.
A cylinder has 2 congruent bases and a curved surface.
Each base is a circle, with radius r and area πr^2.
The curved surface is formed from a rectangle with:
- one side equal to the circumference of the circular base, and
- one side equal to the height of the cylinder

The circumference of the circular base is $2\pi r$.

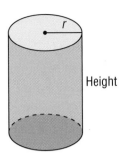

Height

Surface area = area of two circular bases + curved surface area
$\qquad$ = 2 × area of one circular base + circumference of base × height of cylinder
$\qquad$ = 2 × πr^2 + $2\pi r$ × height

Sometimes, one base of the cylinder is not included in the surface area calculation
because the cylinder is sitting on its base. Then,

Surface area = area of one base + circumference of base × height of cylinder
$\qquad$ = πr^2 + $2\pi r$ × height

Example 2	**Determining the Surface Area of a Composite Object Made from Two Cylinders**

Two round cakes have diameters of 14 cm and 26 cm, and are 5 cm tall.
They are arranged as shown. The cakes are covered in frosting. What is the area of frosting?

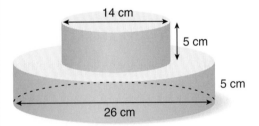

14 cm

5 cm

5 cm

26 cm

▶ **Solutions**

Method 1

Calculate the surface area of each cake.
Do not include the base it sits on because this will not be frosted.
The surface area is measured in square centimetres.

For the smaller cake:

The diameter is 14 cm, so the radius, r, is 7 cm. The height is 5 cm.

Surface area = area of one base + circumference of base × height of cylinder

$\qquad$ = $\pi r^2 + 2\pi r \times$ height

$\qquad$ = $(\pi \times 7^2) + (2 \times \pi \times 7 \times 5)$ $\qquad$ Use a calculator and the order of operations.

$\qquad$ $\doteq$ 373.85

For the larger cake:

The diameter is 26 cm, so the radius, r, is 13 cm. The height is 5 cm.

Surface area = area of one base + circumference of base × height of cylinder

$\qquad$ = $\pi r^2 + 2\pi r \times$ height

$\qquad$ = $(\pi \times 13^2) + (2 \times \pi \times 13 \times 5)$ $\quad$ Use a calculator.

$\qquad$ $\doteq$ 939.34

To calculate the area of frosting, add the two surface areas, then subtract
the area of the overlap; that is, the area of the base of the smaller cake: $\pi \times 7^2$

Area of frosting $\doteq$ 373.85 + 939.34 − $(\pi \times 7^2)$ $\;$ Use a calculator.

$\qquad$ $\doteq$ 1159.25

The area of frosting is about 1159 cm^2.

Since the dimensions were given to the nearest centimetre, the surface area
is given to the nearest square centimetre.

Method 2

Calculate the surface area directly.

The overlap is the area of the base of the smaller cake.
So, instead of calculating the area of the top of the
smaller cake, then subtracting that area as the overlap,
we calculate only the curved surface area of the
smaller cake.

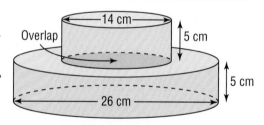

Area of frosting = curved surface area of smaller cake

$\qquad$ + surface area of larger cake, without one base

$\qquad$ = $(2 \times \pi \times 7 \times 5) + [(\pi \times 13^2) + (2 \times \pi \times 13 \times 5)]$ $\qquad$ Use a calculator.

$\qquad$ $\doteq$ 1159.25

The area of frosting is about 1159 cm^2.

When some of the lengths on a right triangular prism are not given, we may need to
use the Pythagorean Theorem to calculate them.

Example 3   **Using the Pythagorean Theorem in Surface Area Calculations**

The roof, columns, and base of this porch are to be painted.
The radius of each column is 20 cm.
What is the area to be painted, to the nearest square metre?

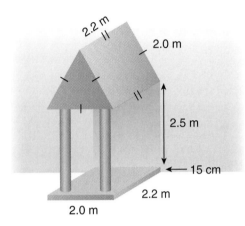

▶ *A Solution*

The roof is a triangular prism with its base an equilateral triangle.
To determine the area of the triangular base, we need to know the height of the triangle.
Let the height of the triangle be h.

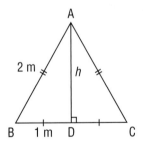

The height, AD, bisects the base, BC.
Use the Pythagorean Theorem in $\triangle$ABD.

$h^2 + 1^2 = 2^2$

$h^2 + 1 = 4$ Solve for h^2.

$\quad h^2 = 4 - 1$

$\quad\quad = 3$

$\quad h = \sqrt{3}$ Determine the square root.

$\quad\quad \doteq 1.732$

The height of the equilateral triangle is about 1.7 m.

Since one base of the triangular prism is against the house, it will not be painted.
The rectangular faces are congruent because they have the same length and width.

So, for the roof:

Surface area = area of one triangular base + areas of 3 congruent rectangular faces

$$\doteq \left(\frac{1}{2} \times 2.0 \times 1.732\right) + [3 \times (2.0 \times 2.2)]$$
$$= 1.732 + 13.2$$
$$= 14.932$$

The base of the porch is a right rectangular prism with only the front, top, and 2 side faces to be painted. The units must match, so convert 15 cm to 0.15 m.

Surface area = area of front face + area of top face + 2 × area of side face

$$= (2.0 \times 0.15) + (2.0 \times 2.2) + [2 \times (2.2 \times 0.15)]$$
$$= 0.3 + 4.4 + 0.66$$
$$= 5.36$$

The two columns are cylinders. Only the curved surfaces need to be painted. The radius is 20 cm, which is 0.2 m.

Surface area = 2 × (circumference of base × height of cylinder)

$$= 2 \times (2\pi r \times \text{height})$$
$$= 2 \times (2 \times \pi \times 0.2 \times 2.5)$$
$$\doteq 6.283$$

To calculate the area to be painted, add the surface areas of the roof, base, and columns, then subtract the area of overlap at the top and bottom of the columns. The area of overlap is 4 times the area of the base of one column.

The area of each circular base is:

$$\pi r^2 = \pi \times 0.2^2$$
$$\doteq 0.126$$

Surface area = area of roof + area of base + area of cylinders

$$- 4 \times \text{area of circular base of column}$$
$$\doteq 14.932 + 5.36 + 6.283 - (4 \times 0.126)$$
$$= 26.071$$

The area to be painted is about 26 m².

Discuss the ideas

1. What can you use to calculate an unknown length when the base of a right prism is a right triangle? Explain why.

2. When do you think it is not helpful to draw a net to calculate the surface area of a composite object?

Practice

Check

3. Determine the surface area of each composite object. Give the answers to the nearest whole number.

a) cylinder on a cube

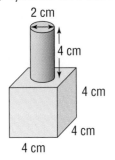

2 cm

4 cm

4 cm

4 cm

4 cm

b) cylinder on a rectangular prism

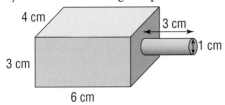

4 cm

3 cm

3 cm

1 cm

6 cm

c) cylinder on a cylinder

10 cm

2 cm

10 cm

2 cm

d) cube on a triangular prism

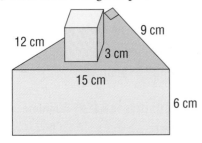

12 cm

9 cm

3 cm

15 cm

6 cm

e) cube on a triangular prism

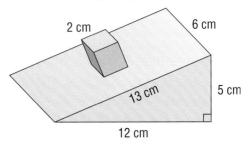

2 cm

6 cm

13 cm

5 cm

12 cm

4. Determine the surface area of each composite object. Give the answers to the nearest tenth.

a)

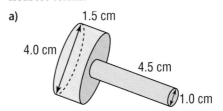

1.5 cm

4.0 cm

4.5 cm

1.0 cm

b) The cylinder is 3.5 m long with diameter 0.5 m.

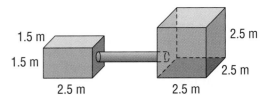

1.5 m

1.5 m

2.5 m

2.5 m

2.5 m

2.5 m

2.5 m

5. Determine the surface area of each composite object.

a) The cylinder is 2.5 m long with radius 0.5 m.

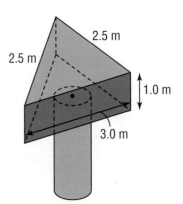

2.5 m

2.5 m

1.0 m

3.0 m

b) The base of the triangular prism is an equilateral triangle with side length 2.8 cm.

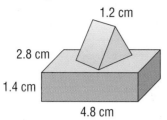

Apply

6. Here is the lamp stand from the top of page 33. The base of the lamp is a triangular prism with an equilateral triangle base. The surface of the stand is to be painted. What is the area that will be painted? Give the answer to the nearest whole number.

7. Assessment Focus

a) A playhouse has the shape of a rectangular prism with a triangular prism roof. Determine the surface area of the playhouse.

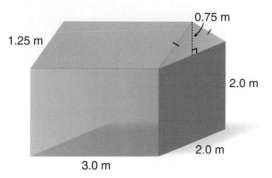

b) What are possible dimensions for a door and 2 windows? Explain how including these features will affect the surface area of the playhouse.

c) Determine the surface area of the playhouse not including its doors and windows.

8. Jemma has built this doghouse. The roof is a triangular prism with an isosceles triangle base. There is an overhang of 0.1 m. There is an opening for the doorway.

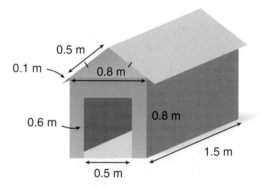

a) Determine the surface area of the doghouse.

b) The doghouse is to be covered with 2 coats of wood stain. Wood stain can be bought in 1-L or 4-L cans. One litre of stain covers 6 m². How many cans of either size are needed? Explain your thinking.

9. Each layer of a three-layer cake is a cylinder with height 7.5 cm.
The bottom layer has diameter 25 cm.
The middle layer has diameter 22.5 cm.
The top layer has diameter 20 cm.
The surface of the cake is frosted.
a) Sketch the cake.
b) What area of the cake is frosted?

10. In question 9, you determined the surface area of a three-layer cake.

   a) Suppose a fourth layer, with diameter 27.5 cm, is added to the bottom of the cake. What is the surface area of cake that will be frosted now?

   b) Suppose a fifth layer, with diameter 30 cm, is added to the bottom of the cake. What is the surface area of cake that will be frosted now?

   c) How does the surface area change when each new layer is added?

   Give all the answers to the nearest tenth.

11. Rory will paint this birdhouse he built for his backyard. The perch is a cylinder with length 7 cm and diameter 1 cm. The diameter of the entrance is 3 cm. What is the area that needs to be painted? Give the answer to the nearest whole number.

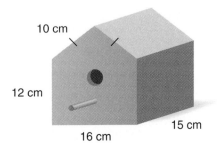

10 cm

12 cm

16 cm

15 cm

12. Shael and Keely are camping with their parents at Waskesiu Lake in Prince Albert National Park. Their tent trailer is 5 m long and 2.5 m wide. When the trailer is set up, the canvas expands to a height of 2.5 m. At each end, there is a fold out bed that is 1.7 m wide, in a space that is shaped like a triangular prism. The diagram shows a side view of the trailer.

1.7 m

   a) Determine the surface area of the canvas on the trailer.

   b) Two parallel bars, 1.3 m high, are placed vertically at each end to support the canvas and provide more space in the beds. Does the surface area of the canvas change when the bars are inserted? Explain how you know.

1.3 m

1.7 m

13. a) What is the surface area of a cube with edge length 24 cm?

   b) The cube is cut along a diagonal of one face to form two triangular prisms. These prisms are glued together to form a longer triangular prism. What is the surface area of this prism? Give the answer to the nearest whole number.

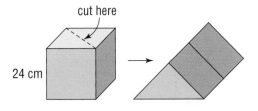

cut here

24 cm

   c) Why do the cube and the triangular prism have different surface areas?

14. A birdbath and stand are made from 3 cylinders. The top and bottom cylinders have radius 22 cm and height 13 cm. The middle cylinder has radius 15 cm and height 40 cm. The "bath" has radius 15 cm and depth 2 cm. The birdbath and stand are to be tiled. Calculate the area to be tiled.

Take It Further

15. a) What is the surface area of a cylinder that is 50 cm long and has diameter 18 cm?
b) The cylinder is cut in half along its length and the two pieces are glued together end to end.
   i) Sketch the composite object.
   ii) What is its surface area?
Give the answers to the nearest whole number.

16. Grise Fiord, Nunavut, is Canada's northernmost Inuit community and it is home to 150 residents. In Inuktitut, this hamlet is called Aujuittuq, which means "the place that never thaws." Although the ground is frozen most of the year, it softens in the summer. The freezing and thawing of the ground would ruin a house foundation. The houses are made of wood, and are built on platforms. The homes are compact and have few windows.

a) Design and sketch the exterior of a home that could fit on a platform that is 10 m wide and 20 m long.
b) Determine the surface area of this home.
c) Every outside face needs to be insulated. Insulation costs $4.25/m^2$.
How much will it cost to insulate this home?

Reflect

Sketch a building or structure in your community that is made up of two or more prisms or cylinders. Explain how you would determine its surface area.

Perfect Squares

When a fraction can be written as a product of two equal fractions,
the fraction is a perfect square.

For example, $\frac{144}{25}$ is a perfect square because $\frac{144}{25} = \frac{12}{5} \times \frac{12}{5}$; and $\sqrt{\frac{144}{25}} = \frac{12}{5}$

When a decimal can be written as a fraction that is a perfect square,
then the decimal is also a perfect square.

The square root is a terminating or repeating decimal.

For example, 12.25 is a perfect square because $12.25 = \frac{1225}{100}$, and $\sqrt{\frac{1225}{100}} = \frac{35}{10}$, or 3.5

Non-Perfect Squares

A fraction or decimal that is not a perfect square is a non-perfect square.
To estimate the square roots of a non-perfect square,
use perfect squares as benchmarks or use a calculator.

For example, $\sqrt{\frac{143}{25}} \doteq \sqrt{\frac{144}{25}}$, which is $\frac{12}{5}$, or 2.4

And, $\sqrt{6.4} \doteq 2.5$ to the nearest tenth

Surface Area of a Composite Object

This is the sum of the surface areas of the objects that make up the
composite object, minus the overlap.

The objects that make up the composite object can be:

▶ A right rectangular prism with
   Surface area = 2 × area of top face + 2 × area of front face
   + 2 × area of side face

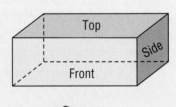

▶ A right triangular prism with
   Surface area = 2 × area of base + areas of 3 rectangular faces

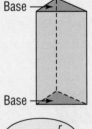

▶ A right cylinder, radius r, with
   Surface area = 2 × area of one circular base
   + circumference of base × height of cylinder
   $= 2\pi r^2 + 2\pi r \times \text{height}$

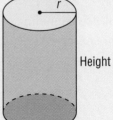

1.1 **1.** Use grid paper to illustrate each square root as the side length of a square, then determine the value of the square root.

a) $\sqrt{1.21}$ b) $\sqrt{\dfrac{9}{25}}$ c) $\sqrt{0.64}$

d) $\sqrt{\dfrac{81}{16}}$ e) $\sqrt{2.56}$ f) $\sqrt{\dfrac{1}{36}}$

g) $\sqrt{0.25}$ h) $\sqrt{\dfrac{100}{64}}$ i) $\sqrt{3.61}$

j) $\sqrt{\dfrac{4}{121}}$ k) $\sqrt{2.89}$ l) $\sqrt{\dfrac{36}{49}}$

2. Determine each square root.

a) $\sqrt{\dfrac{144}{25}}$ b) $\sqrt{\dfrac{225}{64}}$

c) $\sqrt{\dfrac{196}{81}}$ d) $\sqrt{\dfrac{324}{121}}$

e) $\sqrt{0.0196}$ f) $\sqrt{0.0289}$

g) $\sqrt{1.69}$ h) $\sqrt{4.41}$

3. Which fractions and decimals are perfect squares? Explain your reasoning.

a) $\dfrac{48}{120}$ b) 1.6   c) $\dfrac{49}{100}$

d) 0.04   e) $\dfrac{144}{24}$ f) 2.5

g) $\dfrac{50}{225}$ h) 1.96   i) $\dfrac{63}{28}$

4. Calculate the number whose square root is:

a) $\dfrac{3}{5}$ b) 1.6   c) $\dfrac{9}{7}$ d) 0.8

5. Determine the side length of a square with each area below. Explain your strategy.

a) 0.81 m²   b) 0.01 m²
c) 4.84 cm²   d) 6.25 cm²
e) 0.16 km²   f) 1.44 km²

1.2 **6.** Use benchmarks to approximate each square root to the nearest tenth. State the benchmarks you used.

a) $\sqrt{3.8}$ b) $\sqrt{33.8}$

c) $\sqrt{133.8}$ d) $\sqrt{233.8}$

7. Use benchmarks to estimate a fraction for each square root. State the benchmarks you used.

a) $\sqrt{\dfrac{77}{10}}$ b) $\sqrt{\dfrac{18}{11}}$ c) $\sqrt{\dfrac{15}{39}}$

d) $\sqrt{\dfrac{83}{19}}$ e) $\sqrt{\dfrac{28}{103}}$ f) $\sqrt{\dfrac{50}{63}}$

8. Use any strategy you wish to estimate the value of each square root. Explain why you used the strategy you did.

a) $\sqrt{5.9}$ b) $\sqrt{\dfrac{7}{20}}$ c) $\sqrt{0.65}$

d) $\sqrt{\dfrac{21}{51}}$ e) $\sqrt{23.2}$ f) $\sqrt{\dfrac{88}{10}}$

9. Which of the following square roots are correct to the nearest tenth? How do you know? Correct the square roots that are incorrect.

a) $\sqrt{2.4} \doteq 1.5$ b) $\sqrt{1.6} \doteq 0.4$
c) $\sqrt{156.8} \doteq 15.6$ d) $\sqrt{47.8} \doteq 6.9$
e) $\sqrt{0.5} \doteq 0.7$ f) $\sqrt{0.7} \doteq 0.5$

10. Which square roots are correctly placed on the number line below? How do you know?

$\sqrt{27.4}$ $\sqrt{37.2}$ $\sqrt{82.8}$

5   6   7   8   9   10
$\sqrt{25.3}$ $\sqrt{60.8}$ $\sqrt{98.1}$

11. Use the square roots listed below. Which square roots are between each pair of numbers? Justify your answers.

  a) 1 and 2   **b)** 11 and 12
  c) 3.5 and 4.5   **d)** 1.5 and 2.5
  e) 4.5 and 5.5   **f)** 14.5 and 15.5

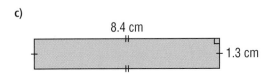

$\sqrt{12.9}$ $\sqrt{4.8}$ $\sqrt{134.5}$ $\sqrt{1.2}$

$\sqrt{21.2}$ $\sqrt{15.2}$ $\sqrt{222.1}$ $\sqrt{9.6}$

$\sqrt{3.2}$ $\sqrt{237.1}$ $\sqrt{2.3}$ $\sqrt{213.1}$

$\sqrt{125.4}$ $\sqrt{23.1}$ $\sqrt{129.9}$ $\sqrt{2.8}$

$\sqrt{5.7}$ $\sqrt{29.1}$

12. Determine the length of a diagonal of each rectangle.

  a)

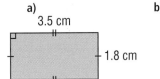

3.5 cm
1.8 cm

  b)

2.5 cm

  c)

8.4 cm
1.3 cm

13. Determine a decimal or a fraction whose square root is between each pair of numbers.

  a) $\frac{1}{3}$ and 1   **b)** 0.2 and 0.3

  c) 1.4 and 1.41   **d)** $\frac{1}{10}$ and $\frac{3}{10}$

14. a) Use a calculator to approximate each square root.

    i) $\sqrt{0.0015}$ **ii)** $\sqrt{0.15}$ **iii)** $\sqrt{15}$

    iv) $\sqrt{1500}$ **v)** $\sqrt{150\,000}$

  b) What patterns do you see in the square roots in part a? Use the patterns to write the previous two square roots less than $\sqrt{0.0015}$ and the next two square roots greater than $\sqrt{150\,000}$.

1.3

15. Each object is built with 1-cm cubes. Determine its surface area.

  a)

  b)

  c)

16. Determine the surface area of each composite object. What effect does the overlap have on the surface area?

  a) rectangular prism and cube

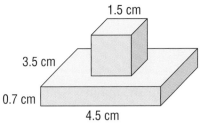

1.5 cm
3.5 cm
0.7 cm
4.5 cm

  b) two rectangular prisms

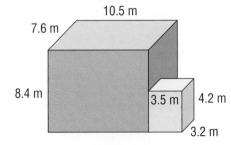

10.5 m
7.6 m
8.4 m
3.5 m
4.2 m
3.2 m

c) triangular prism, rectangular prism, and cube

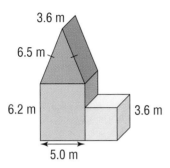

3.6 m

6.5 m

6.2 m   3.6 m

5.0 m

17. A desk top is a rectangular prism with dimensions 106 cm by 50 cm by 2 cm. Each of 4 legs of the desk is a rectangular prism with dimensions 75 cm by 3 cm by 3 cm.
a) Sketch the desk.
b) Determine the surface area of the desk.

18. An Inukshuk is a human-like object constructed from stone by Canada's Inuit People. Traditionally, Inukshuks were used as markers during the Caribou hunt. The Inukshuk is now a symbol of leadership, cooperation, and human spirit. Each stone is separate; the stones are balanced to make the Inukshuk. This giant Inukshuk in Igloolik, Nunavut was built to commemorate the new millenium.

Construct an Inukshuk of cardboard boxes or other materials. Determine its surface area.

1.4 **19.** Determine the surface area of each composite object. Give the answers to the nearest tenth.
a) The rectangular prism has dimensions 2.5 cm by 2.5 cm by 15.0 cm. The cylinder is 3.5 cm high with radius 9.6 cm.

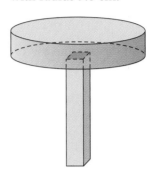

b) Each of the two congruent cylinders is 2.8 cm long, with radius 7.8 cm. The middle cylinder is 10.4 cm long, with radius 3.6 cm.

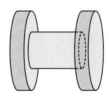

20. There are 2 wooden ramps, each of which is a triangular prism with a right triangle base; and a platform that is a rectangular prism. The ramps are joined to the platform to make one larger ramp for a BMX bike. This ramp will be painted completely.

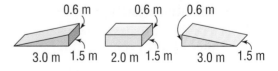

0.6 m   0.6 m   0.6 m

3.0 m   1.5 m   2.0 m   1.5 m   3.0 m   1.5 m

a) Calculate the surface area to be painted.
b) The paint costs $19.95 for one 3.78-L container. This will cover 35 m². The surface area needs 2 coats of paint. How much paint is needed and how much will it cost?

1. Sketch this number line.

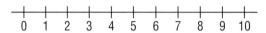

   a) Do *not* use a calculator. Determine or estimate each square root. Where necessary, write the square root to the nearest tenth. Place each square root on the number line.

   i) $\sqrt{\dfrac{49}{4}}$ ii) $\sqrt{6.25}$ iii) $\sqrt{\dfrac{64}{9}}$ iv) $\sqrt{98.5}$ v) $\sqrt{\dfrac{9}{100}}$ vi) $\sqrt{\dfrac{9}{10}}$

   b) How can you use benchmarks to determine or estimate square roots?

2. a) Use a calculator to determine or estimate each square root. Where necessary, write the square root to the nearest hundredth.

   i) $\sqrt{\dfrac{3}{7}}$ ii) $\sqrt{52.5625}$ iii) $\sqrt{\dfrac{576}{25}}$ iv) $\sqrt{213.16}$ v) $\sqrt{135.4}$

   b) Which square roots in part a are exact? Which are approximate?

   c) Explain why a square root shown on a calculator display may be approximate.

3. a) Identify a perfect square between 0 and 0.5.
      How do you know the number is a perfect square?

   b) Identify a number whose square root is between 0 and 0.5.
      How can you check your answer?

4. One canoe is 2.56 km due south of a small island, S. Another canoe is 8.28 km due east of the island. How far apart are the canoes? How do you know?

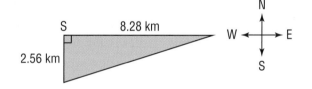

5. A garden shed is built against one wall of a garage. The shed has a sloping roof.
   a) What is the surface area of the shed, not including its door and window?
   b) The shed is to be painted with 2 coats of paint. Paint costs $3.56/L. One litre covers 10 m². What will it cost to paint the shed?

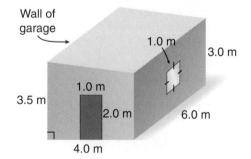

6. Each of two congruent cubes has volume 64 cm³. The cubes are joined at their faces to a cylinder that is 5 cm long and has radius 2 cm.
   a) Sketch the object.   b) What is the surface area of this object?

Unit Problem
Design a Play Structure

You will design a play structure for young children, constructed of light-weight nylon fabric and fibreglass poles.

Your budget for this project is $800. A student has offered to sew the fabric for a donation of $125 toward upgrading the school sewing machines.

The design can only include cylinders, rectangular prisms, and triangular prisms.
There should be between 6 and 8 objects, with at least one of each type.
The objects can be connected face to face.
Keep in mind that cylinders and openings need to allow enough movement space to safely accommodate a small child.

The fabric is available in three different colours:
Red costs $10/m^2.   Yellow costs $11/m^2.   Blue costs $12/m^2.

The skeleton of the structure is made from fibreglass poles that cost $3/m.
A fabric cylinder needs flexible circular supports every 1 m for reinforcement.
These cost $4/m.
Joiners are included at no cost.

Your work should show:
- models or sketches of your design
- the surface area of each object
- the cost of each object
- how you calculated the total surface area and the cost of the project
- an explanation of any unique features of your structure and why you included them

Reflect
on Your Learning

What have you learned about perfect squares, non-perfect squares, and square roots?
How are square roots used when you calculate surface area?

Powers and Exponent Laws

Imagine folding a piece of paper in half to form 2 layers.

Imagine folding it in half again to form 4 layers.

Try this with a sheet of paper. How many times can you fold the paper before it is impossible to make another fold?

What You'll Learn

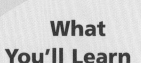

- Use powers to represent repeated multiplication.
- Use patterns to understand a power with exponent 0.
- Solve problems involving powers.
- Perform operations with powers.
- Explain and apply the order of operations with exponents.

Why It's Important

Powers provide an efficient way to record our work. The properties of powers lead to even more efficient ways to perform some calculations. Powers are used in many formulas with applications in science, construction, and design.

Key Words

- power
- base
- exponent
- square number
- cube number
- power of a power
- power of a product
- power of a quotient

FOCUS
- Use powers to represent repeated multiplication.

What is the area of this square?
Write the area as a product.

1 unit

What is the volume of this cube?
Write the volume as a product.

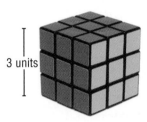

3 units

Investigate ②

You will need congruent square tiles and congruent cubes.

➤ Use the tiles to make as many different-sized larger squares as you can.
Write the area of each square as a product. Record your results in a table.

Number of Tiles	Area (square units)	Side Length (units)	Area as a Product
1	1	1	1 × 1

➤ Use the cubes to make as many different-sized larger cubes as you can.
Write the volume of each cube as a product. Record your results in a table.

Number of Cubes	Volume (cubic units)	Edge Length (units)	Volume as a Product
1	1	1	1 × 1 × 1

Reflect & Share

What patterns do you see in the tables?
Use the patterns to predict the areas of the next 3 squares and the volumes of the next 3 cubes.
How are these areas and volumes the same? How are they different?

Connect

When an integer, other than 0, can be written as a product of equal factors, we can write the integer as a **power**.

For example, $5 \times 5 \times 5$ is 5^3.

5 is the **base**.

3 is the **exponent**.

5^3 is the *power*.

5^3 is a power of 5.

We say: 5 to the 3rd, or 5 cubed

➤ A power with an integer base and exponent 2 is a **square number**.
   When the base is a positive integer, we can illustrate a square number.

Here are 3 ways to write 25.
   Standard form: 25
   As repeated multiplication: 5×5
   As a power: 5^2

$5 \times 5 = 5^2$
$= 25$
25 is a square number.

➤ A power with an integer base and exponent 3 is a **cube number**.
   When the base is a positive integer, we can illustrate a cube number.

Here are 3 ways to write 125.
   Standard form: 125
   As repeated multiplication: $5 \times 5 \times 5$
   As a power: 5^3

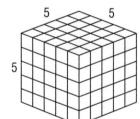

$5 \times 5 \times 5 = 5^3$
$= 125$
125 is a cube number.

Example 1 Writing Powers

Write as a power.
a) $3 \times 3 \times 3 \times 3 \times 3 \times 3$ b) 7

▶ A Solution

a) $3 \times 3 \times 3 \times 3 \times 3 \times 3$
   The base is 3. There are 6 equal factors, so the exponent is 6.
   So, $3 \times 3 \times 3 \times 3 \times 3 \times 3 = 3^6$
b) 7
   The base is 7. There is only 1 factor, so the exponent is 1.
   So, $7 = 7^1$

Example 2 Evaluating Powers

Write as repeated multiplication and in standard form.

a) 3^5 **b)** 7^4

▶ A Solution

a) $3^5 = 3 \times 3 \times 3 \times 3 \times 3$ As repeated multiplication

     $= 243$ Standard form

b) $7^4 = 7 \times 7 \times 7 \times 7$ As repeated multiplication

     $= 2401$ Standard form

Examples 1 and *2* showed powers with positive integer bases.
A power can also be negative or have a base that is a negative integer.

Example 3 Evaluating Expressions Involving Negative Signs

Identify the base of each power, then evaluate the power.

a) $(-3)^4$ **b)** -3^4 **c)** $-(-3^4)$

▶ A Solution

a) The base of the power is -3.

    $(-3)^4 = (-3) \times (-3) \times (-3) \times (-3)$ As repeated multiplication

    Apply the rules for multiplying integers:
    The sign of a product with an even
    number of negative factors is positive.

    So, $(-3)^4 = 81$ Standard form

b) The base of the power is 3.
    The exponent applies only to the base 3,
    and not to the negative sign.

    $-3^4 = -(3^4)$

       $= -(3 \times 3 \times 3 \times 3)$

       $= -81$

c) From part b, we know that $-3^4 = -81$.

    So, $-(-3^4) = -(-81)$ $-(-81)$ is the opposite of -81, which is 81.

        $= 81$

We may write the product of integer factors without the multiplication sign. In *Example 3a*, we may write $(-3) \times (-3) \times (-3) \times (-3)$ as $(-3)(-3)(-3)(-3)$.

A calculator can be used to evaluate a power such as $(-7)^5$ in standard form.

$$(-7)\,\hat{}\,5 =$$
$$-16807.$$

1. Can every integer, other than 0, be written as a power? Explain.

2. Why is -3^4 negative but $(-3)^4$ positive? Give another example like this.

3. Two students compared the calculator key sequences they used to evaluate a power. Why might the sequences be different?

Practice

Check

4. Write the number of unit squares in each large square as a power.

a)   b)   c) [grid square image]

5. Write the number of unit cubes in each large cube as a power.

a) [cube] b) [cube] c)

6. Use grid paper. Draw a picture to represent each square number.

a) 4^2 b) 6×6 c) 49

d) 10^2 e) 81   f) 12×12

7. Write the base of each power.

a) 2^7 b) 4^3

c) 8^2 d) $(-10)^5$

e) $(-6)^7$ f) -8^3

8. Write the exponent of each power.

a) 2^5 b) 6^4

c) 9^1 d) -3^2

e) $(-2)^9$ f) $(-8)^3$

9. Write each power as repeated multiplication.

a) 3^2 b) 10^4

c) 8^5 d) $(-6)^5$

e) -6^5 f) -4^2

10. a) Explain how to build models to show the difference between 3^2 and 2^3.

b) Why is one number called a square number and the other number called a cube number?

2.1 What Is a Power?   **55**

11. Use repeated multiplication to show why 6^4 is not the same as 4^6.

12. Write as a power.
  a) $4 \times 4 \times 4 \times 4$
  b) $2 \times 2 \times 2$
  c) $5 \times 5 \times 5 \times 5 \times 5 \times 5$
  d) $10 \times 10 \times 10$
  e) $(-79)(-79)$
  f) $-(-2)(-2)(-2)(-2)(-2)(-2)(-2)(-2)$

Apply

13. Write each product as a power, then evaluate.
  a) 5×5
  b) $3 \times 3 \times 3 \times 3$
  c) $10 \times 10 \times 10 \times 10 \times 10$
  d) $-(9 \times 9 \times 9)$
  e) $(-2)(-2)(-2)$
  f) $-(-4)(-4)(-4)$
  g) $(-5)(-5)(-5)(-5)$
  h) $-(5)(5)(5)(5)$
  i) $-(-5)(-5)(-5)(-5)$

14. Predict whether each answer is positive or negative, then evaluate.
  a) 2^3 b) 10^6 c) 3^1 d) -7^3
  e) $(-7)^3$ f) $(-2)^8$ g) -2^8 h) -6^4
  i) $(-6)^4$ j) $-(-6)^4$ k) $(-5)^3$ l) -4^4

15. Canada Post often creates special postage stamps to celebrate important events and honour famous people.

a) Captain George Vancouver was a Dutch explorer who named almost 400 Canadian places. To commemorate his 250th birthday in 2007, Canada Post created a $1.55 stamp.
  i) How many stamps are in a 3 by 3 block? Write the number of stamps as a power.
  ii) What is the value of these stamps?

b) In July 2007, Canada hosted the FIFA U-20 World Cup Soccer Championships. Canada Post issued a 52¢ stamp to honour all the players and fans.
  i) How many stamps are in a 4 by 4 block? Write the number of stamps as a power.
  ii) What is the value of these stamps?

16. Evaluate.
  a) 3^{12} b) -7^7
  c) 5^{11} d) $-(-4)^{10}$
  e) $(-9)^8$ f) 2^{23}

17. Assessment Focus
  a) Write as repeated multiplication and in standard form.
     i) 4^3 ii) -4^3 iii) $-(-4^3)$ iv) (-4^3)
  b) Which products in part a are positive? Why? Which products are negative? Why?
  c) Write as repeated multiplication and in standard form.
     i) 4^2 ii) -4^2 iii) $-(-4^2)$ iv) (-4^2)
  d) Which products in part c are positive? Why? Which products are negative? Why?
  e) Write other sets of powers like those in parts a and c. Explain how you know if each product is positive or negative before you write the power in standard form.

18. a) Is the value of -3^5 different from the value of $(-3)^5$ or (-3^5)? What purpose do the brackets serve?

b) Is the value of -4^6 different from the value of $(-4)^6$ or (-4^6)? What purpose do the brackets serve?

19. a) When does a negative base in a power produce a negative product? Give 3 examples.

b) When does a negative base in a power produce a positive product? Give 3 examples.

Take It Further

20. Write each number as a power with base 2. Explain your method.

a) 4   **b)** 16   **c)** 64

d) 256   **e)** 32   **f)** 128

21. a) Write each number as a power in as many ways as possible.

i) 16   **ii)** 81   **iii)** 256

b) Find other numbers that can be written as a power in more than one way. Show your work.

22. a) How are the powers in each pair the same? How are they different?

i) 2^3 or 3^2 **ii)** 2^5 or 5^2

iii) 3^4 or 4^3 **iv)** 5^4 or 4^5

b) In part a, which is the greater power in each pair? Explain how you know.

23. Without evaluating all the powers, write them in order from greatest to least: $3^5, 5^2, 3^4, 6^3$ Explain your strategy.

24.

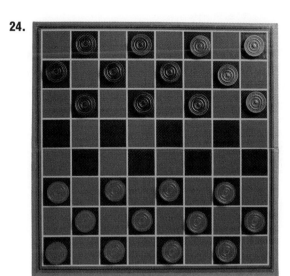

How many squares of each side length are there on a checkerboard? Write each number as a power.

a) 1 unit   **b)** 2 units

c) 3 units   **d)** 4 units

e) 5 units   **f)** 6 units

g) 7 units   **h)** 8 units

What patterns do you see in the answers?

25. Explain how to tell if a number is a square number, or a cube number, or neither. Give examples.

Reflect

What is a power?

Why are brackets used when a power has a negative base?

Powers of Ten and the Zero Exponent

FOCUS

• Explore patterns and powers of 10 to develop a meaning for the exponent 0.

Nuclear reactions in the core of the sun create solar energy. For these reactions to take place, extreme temperature and pressure are needed. The temperature of the sun's core is about 10^7 °C. What is this temperature in millions of degrees Celsius?

Investigate

Choose a number between 1 and 10 as the base of a power.
Use the exponents 5, 4, 3, 2, and 1.
Use your base and each exponent to write a power.
Then write the power as repeated multiplication and in standard form.
Record your results in a table.

Exponent	Power	Repeated Multiplication	Standard Form
5			
4			
3			
2			
1			

Describe any patterns in your table.
Continue the patterns to complete the entries in the last row.

Compare your tables and patterns with those of other pairs of students.
What do you think is the value of a power with exponent 0?
Use a calculator to check your answer for different integer bases.

This table shows decreasing powers of 10.

Number in Words	Standard Form	Power
One billion	1 000 000 000	10^9
One hundred million	100 000 000	10^8
Ten million	10 000 000	10^7
One million	1 000 000	10^6
One hundred thousand	100 000	10^5
Ten thousand	10 000	10^4
One thousand	1 000	10^3
One hundred	100	10^2
Ten	10	10^1
One	1	10^0

⟵ We use the pattern in the exponents to write 1 as 10^0.

We could make a similar table for the powers of any integer base except 0.
So, 1 can be written as any power with exponent 0.
For example, $1 = 2^0$
$$1 = 13^0$$
$$1 = (-5)^0$$

▶ **Zero Exponent Law**
A power with an integer base, other than 0, and an exponent 0 is equal to 1.
$n^0 = 1, \qquad n \neq 0$

Example 1   **Evaluating Powers with Exponent Zero**

Evaluate each expression.
a) 4^0 　　　　 b) -4^0 　　　　 c) $(-4)^0$

▶ **A Solution**

A power with exponent 0 is equal to 1.
a) $4^0 = 1$ 　　　　 b) $-4^0 = -1$ 　　　　 c) $(-4)^0 = 1$

We can use the zero exponent and powers of 10 to write a number.

Example 2   Writing Numbers Using Powers of Ten

Write 3452 using powers of 10.

▶A Solution

Use a place-value chart.

Thousands	Hundreds	Tens	Ones
3	4	5	2

$3452 = 3000 + 400 + 50 + 2$
$= (3 \times 1000) + (4 \times 100) + (5 \times 10) + (2 \times 1)$ We use brackets for clarity.
$= (3 \times 10^3) + (4 \times 10^2) + (5 \times 10^1) + (2 \times 10^0)$

Example 3   Interpreting Numbers in the Media

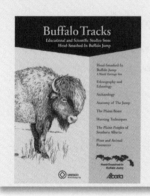

Buffalo Tracks
Educational and Scientific Studies from
Head-Smashed-In Buffalo Jump

Head-Smashed-In Buffalo Jump is a UNESCO World Heritage Site in Southern Alberta. This site covers 600 hectares and contains cultural remains used in the communal hunting of buffalo. Head-Smashed-In was first used for hunting bison at least 5700 years ago and perhaps as early as 10 000 years ago. It is estimated that close to sixty million Plains Bison roamed the prairies prior to the Europeans' arrival in Western Canada. Less than one hundred years later, fewer than 1000 animals remained.

Use powers of 10 to write each number in the above paragraph.

▶A Solution

$600 = 6 \times 100$
$\quad = 6 \times 10^2$
$5700 = 5000 + 700$
$\qquad = (5 \times 1000) + (7 \times 100)$
$\qquad = (5 \times 10^3) + (7 \times 10^2)$
$10\ 000 = 1 \times 10^4$
$60\ 000\ 000 = 6 \times 10\ 000\ 000$
$\qquad\qquad = 6 \times 10^7$
$100 = 1 \times 10^2$
$1000 = 1 \times 10^3$

1. In *Example 1*, why are 4^0 and $(-4)^0$ equal to 1, while -4^0 is equal to -1?

2. What is meant by "a power of 10"? Name 6 numbers that are powers of 10.

3. How would you use patterns to explain that $10^0 = 1$?

Practice

Check

4. Evaluate each power.
   a) 50^0 b) 9^0 c) 1^0 d) 17^0

5. Evaluate each power.
   a) $(-6)^0$ b) -11^0 c) -8^0 d) $(-24)^0$

6. Write each number as a power of 10.
   a) 1000   b) 100 000   c) 1 000 000 000
   d) ten thousand   e) one hundred billion

Apply

7. Write 1 as a power in three different ways.

8. Evaluate each power of 10.
   a) 10^7 b) 10^2 c) 10^0
   d) 10^{10} e) 10^1 f) 10^6

9. Use powers of 10 to write each number.
   a) 6 000 000 000   b) 200   c) 51 415
   d) 60 702 008   e) 302 411   f) 2 000 008

10. Write each number in standard form.
   a) 7×10^7
   b) $(3 \times 10^4) + (9 \times 10^3) + (5 \times 10^1) + (7 \times 10^0)$
   c) $(8 \times 10^8) + (5 \times 10^5) + (2 \times 10^2)$
   d) $(9 \times 10^{10}) + (8 \times 10^9) + (1 \times 10^0)$
   e) 1×10^{15}
   f) $(4 \times 10^3) + (1 \times 10^0) + (9 \times 10^5) + (3 \times 10^1)$

11. The data below refer to trees in Vancouver. Use powers of 10 to write each number.
   - Street trees have an estimated value of over $500 million.
   - In the past decade, the Park Board has planted almost 40 000 new street trees.
   - Nearly 3 million ladybugs are released every year to help control aphids on street trees.
   - The most common street tree is the Japanese flowering cherry, with over 17 000 growing on city streets.
   - There are 130 000 trees lining the streets of Vancouver.
   - There are nearly 600 different types of trees.

12. Assessment Focus   Choose a negative integer as the base of a power. Copy and complete the table below. Use patterns to explain why the power with exponent 0 is equal to 1.

Exponent	Power	Standard Form
5		
4		
3		
2		
1		
0		

13. In each pair, which number is greater?
How do you know?
a) $(4 \times 10^3) + (6 \times 10^2) + (6 \times 10^1)$
$+ (7 \times 10^0)$ or 4327
b) $(2 \times 10^4) + (4 \times 10^3) + (2 \times 10^2)$
$+ (4 \times 10^1)$ or 2432
c) $(7 \times 10^7) + (7 \times 10^3)$ or 777 777

14.

- Worldwide, about one billion people lack access to safe drinking water.
- Glacier ice over 100 000 years old can be found at the base of many Canadian Arctic ice caps.
- Approximately 1000 kg of water is required to grow 1 kg of potatoes.

- Henderson Lake, British Columbia, has the greatest average annual precipitation in Canada of 6655 mm. That is more than 100 times as much as Eureka, in Nunavut, which has the least average annual precipitation of 64 mm.
- In November 2007, at the request of local First Nations, over 10 million hectares of the Mackenzie River Basin were protected from industrial development.

Using this information:
a) Identify the powers of 10 and write them using exponents.
b) Arrange the numbers in order from least to greatest.
c) Explain how writing powers of 10 using exponents can help you to order and compare numbers.

Take It Further

15. What are the meanings of the words trillion, quadrillion, and quintillion?
Write these numbers as powers.
What strategies did you use?

Reflect

Why is a power with exponent 0 equal to 1?

Math Link

Your World

The amount of data that an MP3 player can store is measured in gigabytes. For example, one MP3 player can store 2 GB (gigabytes) of songs. One song uses about 7000 KB (kilobytes) of space, where 1 GB $= 2^{20}$ KB. About how many songs can the MP3 player hold?

Order of Operations with Powers

FOCUS

• Explain and apply the order of operations with exponents.

This was a skill-testing question in a competition:

$6 \times (3 + 2) - 10 \div 2$

Which answer is correct: 5, 10, 15, or 25?

How do you know?

Investigate

Use each of the digits 2, 3, 4, and 5 once to write an expression.

➤ The expression must have at least one power.

The base of the power can be a positive or negative integer.

➤ The expression can use any of:

addition, subtraction, multiplication, division, and brackets

Evaluate the expression.

Write and evaluate as many different expressions as you can.

Reflect & Share

Share your expressions with another pair of students.

Where does evaluating a power fit in the order of operations?

Why do you think this is?

To avoid getting different answers when we evaluate an expression, we use this order of operations:
- Evaluate the expression in brackets first.
- Evaluate the powers.
- Multiply and divide, in order, from left to right.
- Add and subtract, in order, from left to right.

Example 1   **Adding and Subtracting with Powers**

Evaluate.

a) $3^3 + 2^3$　　　　　　**b)** $3 - 2^3$　　　　　　**c)** $(3 + 2)^3$

▶ **A Solution**

a) Evaluate the powers before adding.
$$3^3 + 2^3 = (3)(3)(3) + (2)(2)(2)$$
$$= 27 + 8$$
$$= 35$$

b) Evaluate the power, then subtract.
$$3 - 2^3 = 3 - (2)(2)(2)$$
$$= 3 - 8$$
$$= -5$$

c) Add first, since this operation is within the brackets. Then evaluate the power.
$$(3 + 2)^3 = 5^3$$
$$= (5)(5)(5)$$
$$= 125$$

When we need curved brackets for integers, we use square brackets to show the order of operations. When the numbers are too large to use mental math, we use a calculator.

Example 2   **Multiplying and Dividing with Powers**

Evaluate.

a) $[2 \times (-3)^3 - 6]^2$　　　　**b)** $(18^2 + 5^0)^2 \div (-5)^3$

▶ **A Solution**

a) Follow the order of operations.
Do the operations in brackets first: evaluate the power $(-3)^3$
$$[2 \times (-3)^3 - 6]^2 = [2 \times (-27) - 6]^2 \qquad \text{Then multiply: } 2 \times (-27)$$
$$= [-54 - 6]^2 \qquad\qquad \text{Then subtract: } -54 - 6$$
$$= (-60)^2 \qquad\qquad\quad \text{Then evaluate the power: } (-60)^2$$
$$= 3600$$

b) Use a calculator to evaluate $(18^2 + 5^0)^2 \div (-5)^3$.

For the first bracket:

Use mental math when you can: $5^0 = 1$

Evaluate $18^2 + 1$ to display 325.

Evaluate 325^2 to display 105 625.

For the second bracket:

$(-5)^3$ is negative, so simply evaluate 5^3 to display 125.

To evaluate $105\,625 \div (-125)$, the integers have opposite signs, so the quotient is negative.

Evaluate $105\,625 \div 125$ to display 845.

So, $(18^2 + 5^0)^2 \div (-5)^3 = -845$

```
18² + 1
                  325.

325²
              105625.

5^3
                  125.

105625/125
                  845.
```

Example 3 — Solving Problems Using Powers

Lyn has a square swimming pool, 2 m deep with side length 4 m. The swimming pool is joined to a circular hot tub, 1 m deep with diameter 2 m. Lyn adds 690 g of chlorine to the pool and hot tub each week. This expression represents how much chlorine is present per 1 m³ of water:

$$\frac{690}{2 \times 4^2 + \pi \times 1^3}$$

The suggested concentration of chlorine is 20 g/m³ of water.

What is the concentration of chlorine in Lyn's pool and hot tub?

Is it close to the suggested concentration?

▶ A Solution

Use a calculator. Since the denominator has a sum, draw brackets around it.

This ensures the entire denominator is divided into the numerator.

Key in the expression as it now appears: $\dfrac{690}{(2 \times 4^2 + \pi \times 1^3)} \doteq 19.634\,85$

The concentration is about 19.6 g/m³. This is very close to the suggested concentration.

Discuss the ideas

1. Explain why the answers to $3^3 + 2^3$ and $(3 + 2)^3$ are different.

2. Use the meaning of a power to explain why powers are evaluated before multiplication and division.

Check

3. Evaluate.

a) $3^2 + 1$ b) $3^2 - 1$

c) $(3 + 1)^2$ d) $(3 - 1)^2$

e) $2^2 + 4$ f) $2^2 - 4$

g) $(2 + 4)^2$ h) $(2 - 4)^2$

i) $2 - 4^2$ j) $2^2 - 4^2$

4. Evaluate. Check using a calculator.

a) $2^3 \times 5$ b) 2×5^2

c) $(2 \times 5)^3$ d) $(2 \times 5)^2$

e) $(-10)^3 \div 5$ f) $(-10) \div 5^0$

g) $[(-10) \div 5]^3$ h) $[(-10) \div 5]^0$

5. Evaluate.

a) $2^3 + (-2)^3$ b) $(2 - 3)^3$

c) $2^3 - (-3)^3$ d) $(2 + 3)^3$

e) $2^3 \div (-1)^3$ f) $(2 \div 2)^3$

g) $2^3 \times (-2)^3$ h) $(2 \times 1)^3$

Apply

6. a) Evaluate. Record your work.

     i) $4^2 + 4^3$ ii) $5^3 + 5^6$

b) Evaluate. Record your work.

     i) $6^3 - 6^2$ ii) $6^3 - 6^5$

7. Identify, then correct, any errors in the student work below. Explain how you think the errors occurred.

$$3^2 + 2^2 \times 2^4 + (-6)^2$$
$$= 9 + 4 \times 16 - 36$$
$$= 13 \times 16 - 36$$
$$= 172$$

8. State which operation you will do first, then evaluate.

a) $(7)(4) - (5)^2$ b) $6(2 - 5)^2$

c) $(-3)^2 + (4)(7)$ d) $(-6) + 4^0 \times (-2)$

e) $10^2 \div [10 \div (-2)]^2$ f) $[18 \div (-6)]^3 \times 2$

9. Sometimes it is helpful to use an acronym as a memory trick. Create an acronym to help you remember the order of operations. Share it with your classmates.

> An acronym_ a word for from the fi letters of c words.

10. Evaluate.

a) $(3 + 4)^2 \times (4 - 6)^3$

b) $(8 \div 2^2 + 1)^3 - 3^5$

c) $4^3 \div [8(6^0 - 2^1)]$

d) $9^2 \div [9 \div (-3)]^2$

e) $(2^2 \times 1^3)^2$

f) $(11^3 + 5^2)^0 + (4^2 - 2^4)$

11. Explain why the brackets are not necessary to evaluate this expression.
$(-4^3 \times 10) - (6 \div 2)$
Evaluate the expression, showing each step.

12. Winona is tiling her 3-m by 3-m kitchen floor. She bought stone tiles at \$70/m². It costs \$60/m² to install the tiles. Winona has a coupon for a 25% discount off the installation cost. This expression represents the cost, in dollars, to tile the floor:
$70 \times 3^2 + 60 \times 3^2 \times 0.75$
How much does it cost to tile the floor?

13. Evaluate this expression:
$2^3 + (3 \times 4)^2 - 6$
Change the position of the brackets. Evaluate the new expression. How many different answers can you get by changing only the position of the brackets?

14. Evaluate each pair of expressions. Why are some answers the same? Why are other answers different?
   a) $3 + 5 \times 8$ and $5 \times 8 + 3$
   b) $3^2 + 2^2$ and $(3 + 2)^2$
   c) $3^3 \times 2^3 - 5^2$ and $(3 \times 2)^3 - 5 \times 5$
   d) $2^3 \times 3^2$ and $(2 \times 3)^5$
   e) $5 \times 3 - 3^2 \times 4 + 20 \times 7$ and $5 \times (3 - 3^2) \times 4 + 20 \times 7$

15. This student got the correct answer, but she did not earn full marks. Find the mistake this student made. Explain how it is possible she got the correct answer. Write a more efficient solution for this problem.

$$-(24 - 3 \times 4^2)^0 \div (-2)^3$$
$$= -(24 - 12^2)^0 \div (-8)$$
$$= -(24 - 144)^0 \div (-8)$$
$$= -(-120)^0 \div (-8)$$
$$= -1 \div (-8)$$
$$= \frac{1}{8}$$

16. Use a calculator to evaluate. Write the key strokes you used.
   a) $(14 + 10)^2 \times (21 - 28)^3$
   b) $(36 \div 2^2 + 11)^3 - 10^5$
   c) $\dfrac{12^3}{36(12^0 - 13^1)}$
   d) $\dfrac{81^2}{9^2 + (-9)^2}$
   e) $(14^2 + 6^3)^2$
   f) $(11^3 + 25^2)^0 + (27^2 - 33^4)$

17. **Assessment Focus** Predict which expression has a value closest to 0. Explain your strategy for predicting, then verify your prediction.
$$(30 + 9 \times 11 \div 3)^0$$
$$(-3 \times 6) + 4^2$$
$$1 + (1 \div 1)^2 + 1^0$$

18. Robbie, Marcia, and Nick got different answers when they evaluated this expression: $(-6)^2 - 2[(-8) \div 2]^2$ Robbie's answer was 68, Marcia's answer was 4, and Nick's answer was -68.
   a) Who had the correct answer?
   b) Show and explain how the other two students might have got their answers. Where did they go wrong?

19. A timber supplier manufactures and delivers wood chips. The chips are packaged in boxes that are cubes with edge length 25 cm. The cost of the chips is $14/m^3$, and delivery costs $10 per 25 km. One customer orders 150 boxes of wood chips and she lives 130 km from the supplier. This expression represents the cost, in dollars:
$$\frac{10 \times 130}{25} + 25^3 \div 10^6 \times 14 \times 150$$
How much does the customer pay?

20. Copy each statement. Insert brackets to make each statement true.
   a) $10 + 2 \times 3^2 - 2 = 106$
   b) $10 + 2 \times 3^2 - 2 = 24$
   c) $10 + 2 \times 3^2 - 2 = 84$
   d) $10 + 2 \times 3^2 - 2 = 254$

21. Copy each statement. Insert brackets to make each statement true.
   a) $20 \div 2 + 2 \times 2^2 + 6 = 26$
   b) $20 \div 2 + 2 \times 2^2 + 6 = 30$
   c) $20 \div 2 + 2 \times 2^2 + 6 = 8$
   d) $20 \div 2 + 2 \times 2^2 + 6 = 120$

22. Blake answered the following skill-testing question to try to win a prize:
$5 \times 4^2 - (2^3 + 3^3) \div 5$
Blake's answer was 11.
Did Blake win the prize? Show your work.

23. Write an expression that includes integers, powers, brackets, and all four operations. Evaluate the expression. Ask a classmate to evaluate the expression. Did both of you follow the same order of operations? Is it possible to get the same answer if you follow a different order of operations? Explain.

Take It Further

24. Copy and complete each set of equations. Describe any patterns you see. Extend each pattern by 2 more rows.
   a) $1^3 = 1^2$
   $1^3 + 2^3 = 3^2$
   $1^3 + 2^3 + 3^3 = 6^2$
   $1^3 + 2^3 + 3^3 + 4^3 =$
   $1^3 + 2^3 + 3^3 + 4^3 + 5^3 =$

   b) $3^2 - 1^2 = \square^3$
   $6^2 - 3^2 = \square^3$
   $10^2 - 6^2 = \square^3$
   $15^2 - 10^2 = \square^3$
   $21^2 - 15^2 = \square^3$

25. Choose two numbers between -5 and $+5$.
   a) Square the numbers, then add the squares. Write this as an expression.
   b) Add the numbers, then square the sum. Write this as an expression.
   c) Compare the answers to parts a and b. What do you notice?
   d) A student said, "The sum of the squares of two numbers is equal to the square of the sum of the numbers." Do you agree with this statement? Justify your answer.

26. Use four 4s and any operations, brackets, or powers to write an expression for each whole number from 1 to 9.

27. a) Write each product as a power of 2 and in standard form.
   i) $2 \times 2 \times 2 \times 2$
   ii) 2×2
   iii) $2 \times 2 \times 2 \times 2 \times 2$
   iv) $2 \times 2 \times 2$
   b) Write each number as a sum, using only powers of 2.
   For example: $27 = 16 + 8 + 2 + 1$
   $= 2^4 + 2^3 + 2^1 + 2^0$
   i) 28 **ii)** 12
   iii) 25 **iv)** 31
   v) 50 **vi)** 75
   c) Repeat part b with a different base. Share your results with a classmate.

Reflect

Why is the order of operations important? Include examples in your explanation.

2.1

1. Write each power in standard form.

a) 14^2 b) 5^1 c) -8^3

d) $-(-4)^4$ e) $(-6)^3$ f) $(-2)^8$

2. Copy and complete this table.

	Power	Base	Exponent	Repeated Multiplication	Standard Form
a)	4^3				
b)	2^5				
c)	8^6				
d)		7	2		
e)				$3 \times 3 \times 3 \times 3$	

3. a) Evaluate the first 8 powers of 7. Copy and complete this table.

Power of 7	Standard Form
7^1	
7^2	
7^3	
7^4	
7^5	
7^6	
7^7	
7^8	

b) What pattern do you see in the ones digits of the numbers in the second column?

c) Verify that the pattern continues by extending the table for as many powers of 7 as your calculator displays.

d) Use the pattern. Predict the ones digit of each power of 7. Explain your strategy.

    i) 7^{12} ii) 7^{14}

    iii) 7^{17} iv) 7^{22}

2.2

4. Write in standard form.

a) 10^6 b) 10^0 c) 10^8 d) 10^4

5. Write as a power of 10.

a) one billion   b) one

c) 100   d) 100 000

6. Evaluate.

a) $(-5)^0$ b) 25^0 c) -6^0 d) 9^0

7. The area of land is measured in hectares (ha). One hectare is the area of a square with side length 100 m. Write the number of square metres in 1 ha as a power.

2.3

8. Evaluate. State which operation you do first.

a) $(-21 - 6)^2 + 14$

b) $6 \div (-2) + (2 \times 3)^2$

c) $[5 - (-4)]^3 - (21 \div 7)^4$

d) $[(6 - 21)^3 \times (2 + 2)^6]^0$

e) $(3 - 5)^5 \div (-4)$

f) $-30 - (7 - 4)^3$

9. Both Sophia and Victor evaluated this expression: $-2^4 \times 5 + 16 \div (-2)^3$ Sophia's answer was -82 and Victor's answer was 78. Who is correct? Find the likely error made by the other student.

10. Identify, then correct, any errors in the student work below. How do you think the errors occurred?

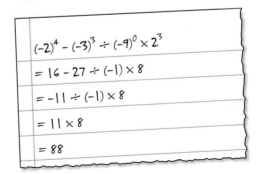

$(-2)^4 - (-3)^3 \div (-9)^0 \times 2^3$

$= 16 - 27 \div (-1) \times 8$

$= -11 \div (-1) \times 8$

$= 11 \times 8$

$= 88$

What Strategy Could I Try?

Suppose I have to evaluate this expression:

$$\frac{3^2(5^0 + 2 + 2^2)}{2(5 + 4^2)}$$

➤ What math tools could I use?

- mental math
- mental math, and paper and pencil
- a calculator

If I use only mental math, I might forget the numbers, so I write down the values of the numerator and denominator.

If I use mental math, and paper and pencil,

- I must use the order of operations.
- The fraction bar acts like a bracket, so I work on the numerator and denominator separately.
- I write down the values of the numerator and the denominator.
- I look for friendly numbers to help with the division.

In the numerator, $5^0 = 1$, and $2^2 = 4$, so $(5^0 + 2 + 2^2) = 7$, so the numerator is $3 \times 3 \times 7$.

In the denominator, $4^2 = 16$, so $(5 + 4^2) = 21$, so the denominator is $2(5 + 4^2) = 2 \times 21 = 2 \times 3 \times 7$.

So, $\dfrac{3^2(5^0 + 2 + 2^2)}{2(5 + 4^2)} = \dfrac{3 \times 3 \times 7}{2 \times 3 \times 7} = \dfrac{3}{2}$

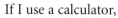

If I use a calculator,

- The fraction bar means divide the numerator by the denominator.
- My calculator uses the order of operations.
- Can I enter the expression as it is written?
- Do I need to add extra brackets, or change any operations?

My calculator uses the order of operations, so I don't need any extra brackets in the numerator. The denominator is the product of 2 factors, so I do need to place brackets around these factors.

I didn't use extra brackets. I realized that the numerator must be divided by both factors of the denominator. I divided by 2, then I divided by $(5 + 4^2)$.

Check

Use any strategies *you* know to evaluate these expressions.

1. a) $\dfrac{3^2 \times 6^2}{2^2 + 1}$ **b)** $\dfrac{3^2 \times 6^2}{2^3 \div 2^2}$ **c)** $\dfrac{3^2 + 6^2}{2^2 - 1}$

   d) $\dfrac{3^2 - 6^2}{2^2 - 1}$ **e)** $\dfrac{6^2 \div 3^2}{2^2 \div 2}$

2. a) $\dfrac{3^4 - 2^2}{4^3 + 4^2 - 3^1}$ **b)** $\dfrac{4^2(3^4 \div 2^0)}{2^4(3^4 - 2^0)}$ **c)** $\dfrac{2^4(4^3 \div 2^2) - 4^0}{3(3^4 + 2^2)}$

GAME

Operation Target Practice

You will need

- two different-coloured number cubes labelled 1 to 6

Number of Players

- 3 or more

Goal of the Game

- To use the order of operations to write an expression for the target number

How to Play

1. Decide which number cube will represent the tens and which will represent the ones of a 2-digit number.

2. One player rolls the cubes and states the 2-digit target number formed.

3. Use three, four, or five operations.
   Each player writes an expression equal to the target number.
   A power counts as an operation; brackets do not.

4. Score 1 point if you were able to write an expression that equals the target number.
   Score another point if you wrote a correct expression that no one else wrote.

5. The next player repeats Step 2, then all of you repeat Steps 3 and 4.

6. The first player to get 10 points wins.

2.4 Exponent Laws I

FOCUS
• Understand and apply the exponent laws for products and quotients of powers.

When we multiply numbers, the order in which we multiply does not matter.
For example, $(2 \times 2) \times 2 = 2 \times (2 \times 2)$
So, we usually write the product without brackets:
$2 \times 2 \times 2$

Investigate

You will need 3 number cubes: 2 of one colour, the other a different colour

Two of you investigate multiplying powers. Make a table like this:

Product of Powers	Product as Repeated Multiplication	Product as a Power
$5^4 \times 5^2$	$(5 \times 5 \times 5 \times 5) \times (5 \times 5)$	$5^?$

Two of you investigate dividing powers. Make a table like this:

Quotient of Powers	Quotient as Repeated Multiplication	Quotient as a Power
$5^4 \div 5^2 = \dfrac{5^4}{5^2}$	$\dfrac{5 \times 5 \times 5 \times 5}{5 \times 5}$	$5^?$

Roll the cubes.
Use the numbers to create powers, as shown.

Record each quotient of powers with the greater exponent in the dividend (the numerator).

Express each power as repeated multiplication, and then as a single power.
Repeat the activity at least five times.

Use this number as the base

Use these numbers as the exponents

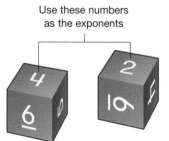

Reflect & Share

Describe the patterns in your table.
Share your patterns with the other pair in your group.
How are your patterns the same? How are they different?
Check your patterns with those of another group.
Use your patterns to describe a way to multiply two powers with the same base, and a way to divide two powers with the same base.

Connect

Patterns arise when we multiply and divide powers with the same base.

➤ To multiply $(-7)^3 \times (-7)^5$:

$$
\begin{aligned}
(-7)^3 \times (-7)^5 &= (-7)(-7)(-7) \times (-7)(-7)(-7)(-7)(-7) \\
&= (-7)(-7)(-7)(-7)(-7)(-7)(-7)(-7) \\
&= (-7)^8
\end{aligned}
$$

The base of the product is -7. The exponent is 8.
The sum of the exponents of the powers that were multiplied is $3 + 5 = 8$.
This relationship is true for the product of any two powers with the same base.
We use variables to represent the powers in the relationship:

> ▌ **Exponent Law for a Product of Powers**
> To multiply powers with the same base, add the exponents.
> $a^m \times a^n = a^{m + n}$
> The variable a is any integer, except 0.
> The variables m and n are any whole numbers.

➤ To divide $8^7 \div 8^4$:

$$8^7 \div 8^4 = \frac{8^7}{8^4}$$

$$= \frac{8 \times 8 \times 8 \times 8 \times 8 \times 8 \times 8}{8 \times 8 \times 8 \times 8}$$

$$= \frac{\overset{1}{\cancel{8}} \times \overset{1}{\cancel{8}} \times \overset{1}{\cancel{8}} \times \overset{1}{\cancel{8}} \times 8 \times 8 \times 8}{\underset{1}{\cancel{8}} \times \underset{1}{\cancel{8}} \times \underset{1}{\cancel{8}} \times \underset{1}{\cancel{8}}}$$

> Divide the numerator and denominator of the fraction by their common factors:
> $8 \times 8 \times 8 \times 8$

$$= \frac{8 \times 8 \times 8}{1}$$

$$= 8 \times 8 \times 8$$

$$= 8^3$$

So, $8^7 \div 8^4 = 8^3$
The base of the quotient is 8. The exponent is 3.
The difference of the exponents of the powers that were divided is $7 - 4 = 3$.
This relationship is true for the quotient of any two powers with the same base.

▶ **Exponent Law for a Quotient of Powers**

To divide powers with the same base, subtract the exponents.

$$a^m \div a^n = a^{m-n} \qquad m \geq n$$

a is any integer, except 0; m and n are any whole numbers.

Example 1   **Simplifying Products and Quotients with the Same Base**

Write each expression as a power.

a) $6^5 \times 6^4$

b) $(-9)^{10} \div (-9)^6$

▶ **A Solution**

a) The powers have the same base.

Use the exponent law for products: add the exponents.
$$6^5 \times 6^4 = 6^{(5+4)}$$
$$= 6^9$$

b) The powers have the same base.

Use the exponent law for quotients: subtract the exponents.
$$(-9)^{10} \div (-9)^6 = (-9)^{(10-6)}$$
$$= (-9)^4$$

Example 2   **Evaluating Expressions Using Exponent Laws**

Evaluate.

a) $(-2)^4 \times (-2)^7$

b) $3^2 \times 3^4 \div 3^3$

▶ **Solutions**

Method 1	**Method 2**
Simplify first using the exponent laws.	Use the order of operations.
a) The bases are the same. Add exponents. $$(-2)^4 \times (-2)^7 = (-2)^{(4+7)}$$ $$= (-2)^{11}$$ $$= -2048$$	a) Evaluate each power first. Then use a calculator. $$(-2)^4 \times (-2)^7 = 16 \times (-128)$$ $$= -2048$$
b) All the bases are the same so add the exponents of the two powers that are multiplied. Then, subtract the exponent of the power that is divided. $$3^2 \times 3^4 \div 3^3 = 3^{(2+4)} \div 3^3$$ $$= 3^6 \div 3^3$$ $$= 3^{(6-3)}$$ $$= 3^3$$ $$= 27$$	b) Evaluate each power first. Then use a calculator. $$3^2 \times 3^4 \div 3^3 = 9 \times 81 \div 27$$ Multiply and divide in order from left to right. $$3^2 \times 3^4 \div 3^3 = 27$$

Example 3 **Using Exponent Laws and the Order of Operations**

Evaluate.

a) $6^2 + 6^3 \times 6^2$

b) $(-10)^4[(-10)^6 \div (-10)^4] - 10^7$

▶ *A Solution*

a) Multiply first. Add the exponents.

$$6^2 + 6^3 \times 6^2 = 6^2 + 6^{(3+2)}$$
$$= 6^2 + 6^5 \qquad \text{Evaluate each power.}$$
$$= 36 + 7776 \qquad \text{Then add.}$$
$$= 7812$$

b) Evaluate the expression in the square brackets first.

Divide by subtracting the exponents.

$$(-10)^4[(-10)^6 \div (-10)^4] - 10^7 = (-10)^4[(-10)^{(6-4)}] - 10^7$$
$$= (-10)^4(-10)^2 - 10^7 \qquad \text{Multiply: add the exponents}$$
$$= (-10)^{(4+2)} - 10^7$$
$$= (-10)^6 - 10^7 \qquad \text{Evaluate each power.}$$
$$= 1\,000\,000 - 10\,000\,000 \quad \text{Then subtract.}$$
$$= -9\,000\,000$$

Discuss the ideas

1. Use your own words to explain how to:
   a) multiply two powers with the same base
   b) divide two powers with the same base

2. Do you think it makes sense to simplify an expression as much as possible before using a calculator? Explain.

3. When can you not add or subtract exponents to multiply or divide powers?

Practice

Check

4. Write each product as a single power.
   a) $5^5 \times 5^4$
   b) $10^2 \times 10^{11}$
   c) $(-3)^3 \times (-3)^3$
   d) $21^6 \times 21^4$
   e) $(-4)^1 \times (-4)^3$
   f) $6^{12} \times 6^3$
   g) $2^0 \times 2^4$
   h) $(-7)^3 \times (-7)^0$

5. Write each quotient as a power.
   a) $4^5 \div 4^3$
   b) $8^9 \div 8^6$
   c) $15^{10} \div 15^0$
   d) $(-6)^8 \div (-6)^3$
   e) $\dfrac{2^{12}}{2^{10}}$
   f) $\dfrac{(-10)^{12}}{(-10)^6}$
   g) $\dfrac{6^5}{6^1}$
   h) $\dfrac{(-1)^5}{(-1)^4}$

Apply

6. a) Evaluate.

   i) $3^4 \div 3^4$ **ii)** $(-4)^6 \div (-4)^6$

   iii) $\dfrac{5^8}{5^8}$ **iv)** $\dfrac{(-6)^3}{(-6)^3}$

b) Use the results of part a. Explain how the exponent law for the quotient of powers can be used to verify that a power with exponent 0 is 1.

7. a) Compare these products.

   i) $3^4 \times 3^9$ **ii)** $3^9 \times 3^4$

b) Explain the results in part a.

8. Express as a single power.

   a) $3^4 \times 3^9 \div 3^{11}$

   b) $(-4)^3 \div (-4)^2 \times (-4)^{10}$

   c) $6^0 \times 6^3 \div 6^2$

   d) $\dfrac{4^3 \times 4^5}{4^2 \times 4^6}$ **e)** $\dfrac{(-3)^4 \times (-3)^4}{(-3)^4}$

9. a) Express as a single power, then evaluate.

   i) $(-6)^1 \times (-6)^7 \div (-6)^7$

   ii) $(-6)^7 \div (-6)^7 \times (-6)^1$

b) Explain why changing the order of the terms in the expressions in part a does not affect the answer.

10. Simplify, then evaluate.

   a) $10^2 \times 10^2 + 10^4$ **b)** $10^3 \times 10^3 - 10^3$

   c) $10^{11} - 10^3 \times 10^6$ **d)** $10^1 + 10^5 \times 10^2$

   e) $10^6 \div 10^2 \times 10^2$ **f)** $10^9 \div 10^9$

   g) $\dfrac{10^{12}}{10^6}$ **h)** $\dfrac{10^4 \times 10^3}{10^2}$

   i) $\dfrac{10^{11}}{10^4 \times 10^2}$ **j)** $\dfrac{10^5}{10^3} + 10^2$

11. a) Evaluate: $2^6 - 2^2 \times 2^3$

   Describe the steps you used.

   b) Evaluate: $2^6 \times 2^2 - 2^3$

   Describe the steps you used.

   c) Were the steps for parts a and b different? Explain.

12. Assessment Focus An alfalfa field is a rectangle 10^4 m long and 10^3 m wide.

a) Write an expression for the area of the field, then evaluate the expression.

b) Write an expression for the perimeter of the field, then evaluate the expression.

c) i) Use the area in part a. Find all possible dimensions for a rectangular field with side lengths that are powers of 10.

   ii) Find the perimeter of each field in part i.

d) Explain why the exponent laws are helpful for solving area problems, but not for perimeter problems.

13. Evaluate.

   a) $2^3 \times 2^2 - 2^5 \times 2$

   b) $3^2 \times 3 + 2^2 \times 2^4$

   c) $4^2 - 3^0 \times 3 + 2^3$

   d) $(-3)^6 \div (-3)^5 - (-3)^5 \div (-3)^3$

   e) $(-2)^4[(-2)^5 \div (-2)^3] + (-2)^4$

   f) $-2^4(2^6 \div 2^2) - 2^4$

   g) $(-5)^3 \div (-5)^2 \times (-5)^0 + (-5)^2 \div (-5)$

14. Provide examples to show why the exponent laws for products and quotients cannot be applied when the powers have different bases.

15. Identify, then correct any errors in the student work below. Explain how you think the errors occurred.

a) $4^3 \times 4^4 = 4^{12}$ b) $\dfrac{(-7^6)}{(-7^3)} = (-7)^2$

c) $3^2 \times 2^3 = 6^5$ d) $\dfrac{5^8}{5^4 \times 5^2} = 1$

e) $1^2 + 1^3 \times 1^2 = 1^7$

16. Muguet uses a microscope to view bacteria. The bacteria are first magnified 10^2 times. This image is then magnified 10^1 times.
  a) Use powers to write an expression for the total magnification.
  b) How many times as large as the actual bacteria does the image appear?

17. a) Evaluate.
    i) $5^2 + 5^3$ ii) $5^2 \times 5^3$
  b) In part a, explain why you could use an exponent law to simplify one expression, but not the other.

18. a) Evaluate.
    i) $4^3 - 4^2$ ii) $4^3 \div 4^2$
  b) In part a, explain why you could use an exponent law to simplify one expression, but not the other.

19. Simplify, then evaluate only the expressions with a positive value. Explain how you know the sign of each answer without evaluating.
  a) $(-2)^2 \times (-2)^3$
  b) $(-2)^0 \times (-2)^5$
  c) $(-2)^5 \div (-2)^3$
  d) $(-2)^6 \div (-2)^6$
  e) $\dfrac{(-2)^3 \times (-2)^4}{(-2)^3 \times (-2)^2}$
  f) $\dfrac{(-2)^6}{(-2)^3 \times (-2)^2}$

Take It Further

20. Find two powers that have a product of 64. How many different pairs of powers can you find?

21. Write a product or quotient, then use the exponent laws to find the number of:
  a) centimetres in 1 km
  b) millimetres in 1 km
  c) kilometres in 10^5 m
  d) metres in 10^9 mm

1 km = 1000 m
1 m = 100 cm
1 cm = 10 mm

22. Write a product or quotient, then use the exponent laws to find the number of:
  a) square metres in 10^2 km^2
  b) square metres in 10^6 cm^2
  c) square millimetres in 10^6 cm^2
  d) square centimetres in 1 km^2

23. Explain how the exponent laws help you to convert among units of measure.

Reflect

When can you use the exponent laws to evaluate an expression with powers?
When can you *not* use these laws? Include examples in your explanation.

2.5 Exponent Laws II

A power indicates repeated multiplication.

What is the standard form of $(2^3)^2$? How did you find out?

$(2^3)^2$ is a **power of a power**.

The base of a power may be a product; for example, $(2 \times 3)^4$.

$(2 \times 3)^4$ is a **power of a product**.

FOCUS

• Understand and apply exponent laws for powers of: products; quotients; and powers.

Investigate

Copy and complete this table.

Choose your own power of a power to complete the 5th and 6th rows.

Choose your own power of a product to complete the 11th and 12th rows.

Power	As Repeated Multiplication	As a Product of Factors	As a Power	As a Product of Powers
$(2^4)^3$	$2^4 \times 2^4 \times 2^4$	$(2)(2)(2)(2) \times (2)(2)(2)(2) \times$ $(2)(2)(2)(2)$	$2^?$	
$(3^2)^4$				
$[(-4)^3]^2$				
$[(-5)^3]^5$				
$(2 \times 5)^3$	$(2 \times 5) \times (2 \times 5)$ $\times (2 \times 5)$	$2 \times 2 \times 2 \times 5 \times 5 \times 5$		$2^? \times 5^?$
$(3 \times 4)^2$				
$(4 \times 2)^5$				
$(5 \times 3)^4$				

What patterns do you see in the rows of the table?
Compare your patterns with those of another pair of classmates.
Use these patterns to record a rule for:
  • writing the power of a power as a single power
  • writing the power of a product as a product of two powers
How can you check your rules?

Connect

We can use the exponent laws from Lesson 2.4 to simplify powers written in other forms.

➤ **Power of a power**
We can raise a power to a power.
For example, 3^2 raised to the power 4 is written as $(3^2)^4$.
$(3^2)^4$ is a *power of a power*.
$(3^2)^4$ means $3^2 \times 3^2 \times 3^2 \times 3^2$.
So, $3^2 \times 3^2 \times 3^2 \times 3^2 = 3^{2+2+2+2}$ Using the exponent law for the product of powers
$= 3^8$
The exponent of 3^8 is the product of the exponents in $(3^2)^4$.
That is, $(3^2)^4 = 3^{2 \times 4}$
$= 3^8$
We can use this result to write an exponent law for the power of a power.

> **Exponent Law for a Power of a Power**
> To raise a power to a power, multiply the exponents.
> $(a^m)^n = a^{mn}$
> a is any integer, except 0.
> m and n are any whole numbers.

mn means $m \times n$

➤ **Power of a product**
The base of a power may be a product; for example, $(3 \times 4)^5$.
$(3 \times 4)^5$ is a *power of a product*.
$(3 \times 4)^5$ means $(3 \times 4) \times (3 \times 4) \times (3 \times 4) \times (3 \times 4) \times (3 \times 4)$
So, $(3 \times 4) \times (3 \times 4) \times (3 \times 4) \times (3 \times 4) \times (3 \times 4)$
$= 3 \times 4 \times 3 \times 4 \times 3 \times 4 \times 3 \times 4 \times 3 \times 4$ Removing the brackets
$= (3 \times 3 \times 3 \times 3 \times 3) \times (4 \times 4 \times 4 \times 4 \times 4)$ Grouping equal factors
$= 3^5 \times 4^5$ Writing repeated multiplications as powers

We can use this result to write an exponent law for the power of a product.

> **Exponent Law for a Power of a Product**
> $(ab)^m = a^m b^m$
> a and b are any integers, except 0.
> m is any whole number.

➤ Power of a quotient

The base of a power may be a quotient; for example, $\left(\frac{5}{6}\right)^3$.

$\left(\frac{5}{6}\right)^3$ is a **power of a quotient**.

$\left(\frac{5}{6}\right)^3$ means $\left(\frac{5}{6}\right) \times \left(\frac{5}{6}\right) \times \left(\frac{5}{6}\right)$

So, $\left(\frac{5}{6}\right) \times \left(\frac{5}{6}\right) \times \left(\frac{5}{6}\right) = \frac{5}{6} \times \frac{5}{6} \times \frac{5}{6}$

$\qquad\qquad\qquad = \frac{5 \times 5 \times 5}{6 \times 6 \times 6}$ Multiplying the fractions

$\qquad\qquad\qquad = \frac{5^3}{6^3}$ Writing repeated multiplications as powers

We can use this result to write an exponent law for the power of a quotient.

> **Exponent Law for a Power of a Quotient**
> $\left(\frac{a}{b}\right)^n = \frac{a^n}{b^n}$ $b \neq 0$
> a and b are any integers, except 0.
> n is any whole number.

We can use these exponent laws to simplify or evaluate an expression.

Example 1   Simplifying a Power of a Power

Write as a power.
a) $[(-7)^3]^2$ b) $-(2^4)^5$ c) $(6^2)^7$

➤ **A Solution**

Use the exponent law for a power of a power.
a) $[(-7)^3]^2 = (-7)^{3 \times 2}$ b) $-(2^4)^5 = -(2^{4 \times 5})$ c) $(6^2)^7 = 6^{2 \times 7}$
$\qquad\quad\;\; = (-7)^6$ $\qquad\quad = -2^{20}$ $\qquad\quad = 6^{14}$

Example 2   **Evaluating Powers of Products and Quotients**

Evaluate.

a) $[(-7) \times 5]^2$ 　　　 b) $[24 \div (-6)]^4$ 　　　 c) $-(3 \times 2)^2$ 　　　 d) $\left(\dfrac{78}{13}\right)^3$

▶ *Solutions*

Method 1	**Method 2**
a) Use the exponent law for a power of a product. $[(-7) \times 5]^2 = (-7)^2 \times 5^2$ $\qquad\qquad = 49 \times 25$ $\qquad\qquad = 1225$	Use the order of operations. a) $[(-7) \times 5]^2 = (-35)^2$ $\qquad\qquad\qquad = 1225$
b) Use the exponent law for a power of a quotient. Write the quotient in fraction form. $[24 \div (-6)]^4 = \left(\dfrac{24}{-6}\right)^4$ $\qquad\qquad = \dfrac{24^4}{(-6)^4}$ $\qquad\qquad = \dfrac{331\,776}{1296}$ $\qquad\qquad = 256$	b) $[24 \div (-6)]^4 = (-4)^4$ $\qquad\qquad\qquad = 256$
c) Use the exponent law for a power of a product. $-(3 \times 2)^2 = -(3^2 \times 2^2)$ $\qquad\qquad = -(9 \times 4)$ $\qquad\qquad = -36$	c) $-(3 \times 2)^2 = -(6)^2$ $\qquad\qquad = -6^2$ $\qquad\qquad = -36$
d) Use the exponent law for a power of a quotient. $\left(\dfrac{78}{13}\right)^3 = \dfrac{78^3}{13^3}$ $\qquad = \dfrac{474\,552}{2197}$ $\qquad = 216$	d) $\left(\dfrac{78}{13}\right)^3 = 6^3$ $\qquad\qquad = 216$

We can use the order of operations with the exponent laws when an expression involves the sum or difference of powers.

Simplify, then evaluate each expression.

a) $(3^2 \times 3^3)^3 - (4^3 \times 4^2)^2$ **b)** $(6 \times 7)^2 + (3^8 \div 3^6)^3$ **c)** $[(-5)^3 + (-5)^4]^0$

▶ *A Solution*

Use the exponent laws to simplify first, where appropriate.

a) In each set of brackets, the bases are the same, so use the exponent law for products.

$(3^2 \times 3^3)^3 - (4^3 \times 4^2)^2$

$= (3^{2+3})^3 - (4^{3+2})^2$ Add the exponents in each set of brackets.

$= (3^5)^3 - (4^5)^2$ Use the power of a power law.

$= 3^{5 \times 3} - 4^{5 \times 2}$ Multiply the exponents.

$= 3^{15} - 4^{10}$ Use a calculator.

$= 14\ 348\ 907 - 1\ 048\ 576$

$= 13\ 300\ 331$

b) Multiply in the first set of brackets. Use the exponent law for the quotient of powers in the second set of brackets.

$(6 \times 7)^2 + (3^8 \div 3^6)^3$

$= (42)^2 + (3^{8-6})^3$

$= 42^2 + (3^2)^3$ Use the power of a power law.

$= 42^2 + 3^6$ Use a calculator.

$= 1764 + 729$

$= 2493$

c) The expression is a power with exponent 0, so its value is 1.

$[(-5)^3 + (-5)^4]^0 = 1$

Discuss the ideas

1. Why do you add the exponents to simplify $3^2 \times 3^4$, but multiply the exponents to simplify the expression $(3^2)^4$?

2. a) What is the difference between a quotient of powers and a power of a quotient?

   b) What is the difference between a product of powers and a power of a product?

3. In *Example 3*, is it easier to key the original expressions in a calculator or use the exponent laws to simplify first? Justify your answer.

Check

4. Write each expression as a product of powers.

a) $(6 \times 4)^3$ b) $(2 \times 5)^4$ c) $[(-2) \times 3]^5$

d) $(25 \times 4)^2$ e) $(11 \times 3)^1$ f) $[(-3) \times (-2)]^3$

5. Write each expression as a quotient of powers.

a) $(8 \div 5)^3$ b) $(21 \div 5)^4$ c) $[(-12) \div (-7)]^5$

d) $\left(\frac{10}{3}\right)^3$ e) $\left(\frac{1}{3}\right)^2$ f) $\left(\frac{27}{100}\right)^4$

6. Write as a power.

a) $(3^2)^4$ b) $(6^3)^3$ c) $(5^3)^1$

d) $(7^0)^6$ e) $-(8^2)^2$ f) $[(-3)^4]^2$

7. Simplify $(2^4)^2$ and $(2^2)^4$. What do you notice? Explain the results.

8. Write each expression as a product or quotient of powers.

a) $[3 \times (-5)]^3$ b) $-(2 \times 4)^5$

c) $\left(\frac{2}{3}\right)^4$ d) $\left(\frac{-7}{-2}\right)^2$

e) $-[(-10) \times 3]^3$ f) $(16 \div 9)^2$

Apply

9. Why is the value of $(-5^2)^3$ negative?

10. Simplify each expression, then evaluate it. For each expression, state the strategy you used and why.

a) $(3 \times 2)^3$ b) $[(-2) \times 4]^2$ c) $\left(\frac{9}{-3}\right)^3$

d) $\left(\frac{8}{2}\right)^2$ e) $(12^8)^0$ f) $[(-4)^2]^2$

11. Why is the value of $[(-2)^3]^4$ positive but the value of $[(-2)^3]^5$ is negative?

12. Compare the values of $-(4^2)^3$, $(-4^2)^3$, and $[(-4)^2]^3$.
What do you notice? Explain the results.

13. **Assessment Focus** For each expression below:

i) Evaluate it in two different ways:
   - do the operation in brackets first
   - use the exponent laws

ii) Compare the results.
   Which method do you prefer?
   Was it always the same method each time? Explain.

a) $(4 \times 3)^3$ b) $[(-2) \times (-5)]^2$ c) $\left(\frac{6}{2}\right)^4$

d) $\left(\frac{14}{2}\right)^0$ e) $[(-5)^2]^2$ f) $(2^5)^3$

14. Simplify, then evaluate. Show your work.

a) $(3^2 \times 3^1)^2$ b) $(4^6 \div 4^4)^2$

c) $[(-2)^0 \times (-2)^3]^2$ d) $(10^6 \div 10^4)^3$

e) $(10^3)^2 \times (10^2)^3$ f) $(12^2)^4 \div (12^3)^2$

g) $(5^2)^6 \div (5^3)^4$ h) $[(-2)^2]^3 \times (-2)^3$

15. Find any errors in this student's work. Copy the solution and correct the errors.

a) $(3^2 \times 2^2)^3 = (6^4)^3$

$= 6^{12}$

$= 2\ 176\ 782\ 336$

b) $[(-3)^2]^3 = (-3)^5$

$= -243$

c) $\left(\frac{6^2}{6^1}\right)^2 = 6^4$

$= 1296$

d) $(2^6 \times 2^2 \div 2^4)^3 = (2^3)^3$

$= 2^9$

$= 512$

e) $(10^2 + 10^3)^2 = (10^5)^2$

$= 10^{10}$

$= 10\ 000\ 000\ 000$

16. Simplify, then evaluate each expression.
  a) $(4^2 \times 4^3)^2 - (5^4 \div 5^2)^2$
  b) $(3^3 \div 3^2)^3 + (8^4 \times 8^3)^0$
  c) $(2^3)^4 + (2^4 \div 2^3)^2$
  d) $(6^2 \times 6^0)^3 + (2^6 \div 2^4)^3$
  e) $(5^3 \times 5^3)^0 - (4^2)^2$
  f) $(10^5 \div 10^2)^2 + (3^3 \div 3^1)^4$

17. Simplify, then evaluate each expression.
  a) $[(-2)^3 \times (-2)^2]^2 - [(-3)^3 \div (-3)^2]^2$
  b) $[(-2)^3 \div (-2)^2]^2 - [(-3)^3 \times (-3)^2]^2$
  c) $[(-2)^3 \times (-2)^2]^2 + [(-3)^3 \div (-3)^2]^2$
  d) $[(-2)^3 \div (-2)^2]^2 + [(-3)^3 \times (-3)^2]^2$
  e) $[(-2)^3 \div (-2)^2]^2 - [(-3)^3 \div (-3)^2]^2$
  f) $[(-2)^3 \times (-2)^2]^2 + [(-3)^3 \times (-3)^2]^2$

18. Use grid paper. For each expression below:
  i) Draw a rectangle to represent the expression.
  ii) Use the exponent laws to write the expression as a product of squares.
  iii) Draw a rectangle to represent the new form of the expression.
  iv) Compare the two rectangles for each expression.
    How are the rectangles the same?
    How are they different?
    Use these rectangles to explain how the square of a product and the product of squares are related.
  a) $(2 \times 3)^2$ **b)** $(2 \times 4)^2$
  c) $(3 \times 4)^2$ **d)** $(1 \times 4)^2$

19. Simplify, then evaluate each expression.
  a) $(2^3 \times 2^6)^2 - (3^7 \div 3^5)^4$
  b) $(6 \times 8)^5 + (5^3)^2$
  c) $[(-4)^3 \times (-4)^2]^2 + (4^3 \times 4^2)^2$
  d) $[(-2)^4]^3 + [(-4)^3]^2 - [(-3)^2]^4$
  e) $[(-3)^4]^2 \times [(-4)^0]^2 - [(-3)^3]^0$
  f) $[(-5) \times (-4)]^3 + [(-6)^3]^2$
    $- [(-3)^9 \div (-3)^8]^5$

Take It Further

20. a) Write 81:
    i) as a power of 9
    ii) as a power of a product
    iii) as a power of 3
  b) Write 64:
    i) as a power of 8
    ii) as a power of a product
    iii) as a power of 2
  c) Find other numbers for which you can follow steps similar to those in parts a and b.

21. a) List the powers of 2 from 2^0 to 2^{12} in standard form.
  b) Use your list from part a to write each number in the expressions below as a power of 2. Evaluate each expression using the exponent laws and the list in part a.
    i) 32×64 **ii)** $16 \times 8 \times 32$
    iii) $1024 \div 128$ **iv)** $\frac{16 \times 256}{1024}$
    v) $(8 \times 4)^3$ **vi)** $\left(\frac{256}{64}\right)^4$

Reflect

Design and create a poster that summarizes all the exponent laws you have learned. Provide an example of each law.

▶ A power represents repeated multiplication.

$2^5 = 2 \times 2 \times 2 \times 2 \times 2$

$\quad = 32$

$(-3)^4 = (-3)(-3)(-3)(-3)$

$\qquad = 81$

$-3^4 = -(3)(3)(3)(3)$

$\qquad = -81$

▶ A power with an integer base, other than 0, and an exponent 0 is equal to 1.

$2^0 = 1$

$(-4)^0 = 1$

$-4^0 = -1$

▶ To evaluate an expression, follow this order of operations:

Evaluate inside brackets.

Evaluate powers.

Multiply and divide, in order, from left to right.

Add and subtract, in order, from left to right.

Exponent Laws

m and n are whole numbers.

a and b are any integers, except 0.

▶ Product of Powers

$a^m \times a^n = a^{m+n}$

▶ Quotient of Powers

$a^m \div a^n = a^{m-n} \quad m \geq n$

▶ Power of a Power

$(a^m)^n = a^{mn}$

▶ Power of a Product

$(ab)^m = a^m b^m$

▶ Power of a Quotient

$\left(\dfrac{a}{b}\right)^n = \dfrac{a^n}{b^n} \quad b \neq 0$

Review

2.1

1. Write as repeated multiplication, then in standard form.
  a) 4^3 b) 7^2 c) $-(-2)^5$
  d) -3^4 e) -1^8 f) $(-1)^8$

2. Use tiles and cubes to explain the difference between 2^2 and 2^3.

3. Write as a power, then in standard form.
  a) $3 \times 3 \times 3 \times 3 \times 3 \times 3$
  b) $(-8)(-8)(-8)$
  c) $-(2 \times 2 \times 2 \times 2 \times 2 \times 2 \times 2)$
  d) 12×12
  e) $4 \times 4 \times 4 \times 4 \times 4$
  f) $(-5)(-5)(-5)(-5)$

4. Explain the difference between 5^8 and 8^5.

5. A telephone tree is used to send messages.
  The person at the top calls 2 people.
  Each person calls 2 more people.
  Suppose it takes 1 min to call someone.
  A message is relayed until the bottom row of the tree has 256 people.
  How long does this take?
  How do you know?

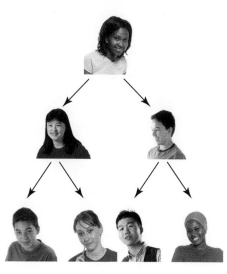

6. a) Is the value of -4^2 different from the value of $(-4)^2$? What purpose do the brackets serve?
  b) Is the value of -2^3 different from the value of $(-2)^3$? What purpose do the brackets serve?

7. a) Evaluate each expression.
    i) -3^2 **ii)** $-(3)^2$ **iii)** $-(-3)^2$ **iv)** $(-3)^2$
  b) For each expression in part a that includes brackets, explain what the brackets show.

2.2

8. Write as a power of 10.
  a) one hundred million
  b) $10 \times 10 \times 10 \times 10$
  c) 1
  d) 1 000 000 000
  e) one thousand

9. Use powers of 10 to write each number.
  a) 700 000 000
  b) 345
  c) 80 027

10. a) Copy and complete this table.

Power	Repeated Multiplication	Standard Form
3^5	$3 \times 3 \times 3 \times 3 \times 3$	243
3^4		
	$3 \times 3 \times 3$	
3^2		
		3

  b) Describe the patterns in the table.
  c) Extend the pattern to show why any number with an exponent of 0 is equal to 1.

11. a) The tallest tree in the world, Hyperion in California, is about 10^2 m tall. The highest mountain, Mount Everest, is about 10^4 m high. About how many times as high as the tree is the mountain?

b) Earth's diameter is about 10^7 m. The largest known star has a diameter of about 10^{12} m. About how many times as great as the diameter of Earth is the diameter of the largest known star?

12. Write each number in standard form.
   a) $(4 \times 10^3) + (7 \times 10^2) + (2 \times 10^1) + (9 \times 10^0)$
   b) $(3 \times 10^5) + (2 \times 10^2) + (8 \times 10^0)$

2.3 **13.** Evaluate.
   a) $3^4 + 3^2$ **b)** $(-4)^2 + (-4)^3$
   c) $10^3 - 10^2$ **d)** $(-5)^4 - (-5)^2$

14. Evaluate.
   a) $2^3 + (5 - 2)^4$
   b) $100 \div 2 + (4 + 1)^3$
   c) $(6^2 + 7^2)^0 - (8^4 + 2^4)^0$
   d) $3 \times 2^3 + 8 \div 4$
   e) $(21 \div 7)^4 - 2^3$
   f) $[(-4)^0 \times 10]^6 \div (15 - 10)^2$

15. Scientists grow bacteria. This table shows how the number of bacteria doubles every hour.

Time	Elapsed Time After Noon (h)	Number of Bacteria
noon	0	1000×2^0
1:00 P.M.	1	1000×2^1
2:00 P.M.	2	1000×2^2
3:00 P.M.	3	1000×2^3

   a) Evaluate the expressions in the table to find the number of bacteria at each time.
      i) noon   **ii)** 1:00 P.M.
      iii) 2:00 P.M. **iv)** 3:00 P.M.
   b) The pattern continues. Write an expression, then evaluate it, to find the number of bacteria at each time.
      i) 4:00 P.M. **ii)** 6:00 P.M.
      iii) 9:00 P.M. **iv)** midnight

16. Use a calculator to evaluate this expression:
   $4^3 - (2 \times 3)^4 + 11$
   Change the position of the brackets. Evaluate the new expression. How many different answers can you get by changing only the position of the brackets?

17. Identify, then correct, any errors in the student work below. Explain how you think the errors occurred.

$$(-2)^2 \times 2^3 - 3^2 \div (-3) + (-4)^2$$
$$= (-2)^5 - 9 \div (-3) + 16$$
$$= -32 - 3 + 16$$
$$= -35 + 16$$
$$= -19$$

2.4

18. Write each product as a power, then evaluate the power.
a) $5^3 \times 5^4$ b) $(-2)^3 \times (-2)^2$
c) $3^2 \times 3^3 \times 3^1$ d) $-10^4 \times 10^0$

19. There are about 10^{11} galaxies in the universe. Each galaxy contains about 10^{11} stars. About how many stars are in the universe?

20. Write each quotient as a power, then evaluate the power.
a) $7^5 \div 7^3$ b) $(-10)^9 \div (-10)^3$
c) $\dfrac{8^4}{8^2}$ d) $-\dfrac{6^7}{6^4}$

21. a) Can you use the laws of exponents to simplify $6^3 \times 5^5$? Explain.
b) Can you use the laws of exponents to simplify $27^2 \div 9^2$? Explain.

22. Find and correct any errors in the student work below.
Explain how you think the errors occurred.

a) $(-3)^6 \div (-3)^2 = (-3)^3$
$= -27$

b) $(-4)^2 + (-4)^2 = (-4)^4$
$= -256$

c) $\dfrac{(-5)^2 \times (-5)^4}{(-5)^3 \times (-5)^0} = \dfrac{(-5)^6}{(-5)^3}$
$= 5^2$
$= 25$

2.5

23. Write each expression as a product or quotient of powers, then evaluate it.
a) $(3 \times 5)^3$ b) $(12 \div 3)^5$
c) $[(-4) \times 2]^4$ d) $(63 \times 44)^0$
e) $\left(\dfrac{3}{2}\right)^5$ f) $\left(\dfrac{15}{2}\right)^2$

24. Write each expression as a power.
a) $(3^2)^3$ b) $(4^0)^6$
c) $[(-2)^3]^3$ d) $(5^5)^2$

25. For each expression below:
Evaluate it in two different ways:
   i) do the operation in brackets first
   ii) use the exponent laws
In each case, which method is more efficient? Explain why.
a) $(5 \times 3)^3$
b) $(3 \times 3)^4$
c) $(8 \div 2)^5$
d) $\left(\dfrac{9}{3}\right)^2$
e) $(2^3)^4$
f) $(6^2)^0$

26. Write each expression as a power, then evaluate.
a) $6^4 \times 6^3$
b) $(-11)^7 \div (-11)^5$
c) $\dfrac{3^4 \times 3^5}{3^3}$
d) $\dfrac{5^5}{5^3 \times 5^2}$
e) $\dfrac{(-4)^3 \times (-4)^6}{(-4)^2 \times (-4)^4}$
f) $\dfrac{10^6 \times 10^0}{10^3 \times 10^2}$

27. Simplify, then evaluate each expression.
a) $2^3 \times 2^2 - 2^0 + 2^4 \div 2^3$
b) $\dfrac{(-2)^3 \times (-2)^2}{(-2)^3 - (-2)^2}$
c) $12^2 \times 12^4 \div (-2)^4 - 12^0$
d) $\dfrac{(-12)^2 \times (-12)^4}{(-2)^4 - 12^0}$

1. Write as a product or quotient of powers.

   a) $(3 \times 4)^3$
   b) $[(-5) \times 2]^4$
   c) $\left(\dfrac{1}{4}\right)^4$
   d) $-\left(\dfrac{9}{3}\right)^3$

2. Simplify.

   a) $-(2^3)^3$
   b) $(6^2)^0$
   c) $[(-5)^2]^3$
   d) $-[(-3)^2]^4$

3. Simplify each expression, then evaluate it.

   a) $[(-3) \times (-2)]^4$
   b) $\left(\dfrac{1}{2}\right)^5$
   c) $(6^0)^4$
   d) $[(-3)^2]^3$

4. Is the value of a power with a negative base always negative?
   Or, is it always positive? Or, is it sometimes negative and sometimes positive?
   Illustrate your answer with some examples.

5. A baseball diamond is a square
   with side length about 27 m.
   Is the area of the baseball diamond
   greater or less than 10^3 m²?
   How do you know?

6. Explain why the brackets are not necessary in this expression:
   $(-3^5 \times 10) - (9 \div 3)$
   Evaluate the expression, showing each step.

7. Identify the correct answer for $(2^3 + 4)^2 \times (-10)^3 \div (5 + 5)^2$.

   a) -240
   b) -1440
   c) 1440
   d) $-28\ 825$

   Explain how each of the other incorrect answers could have been determined.

8. Evaluate only the expressions with a positive value. Explain how you know the
   sign of each expression before you evaluate it.

   a) $(-5)^3 \times (-5)^2 \div (-5)^1$
   b) $[(-9)^6 - (-9)^3]^0$

   c) $\dfrac{(-1)^2 \times (-1)^4}{(-1)^3 \times (-1)^2}$
   d) $(-4)^6 + (-4)^4 \times (-4)^0$

Unit Problem   How Thick Is a Pile of Paper?

You will need a sheet of paper and a ruler.

➤ Fold the paper in half to form 2 layers. Fold it in half again.
  Keep folding until you cannot make the next fold.

➤ Create a table to show how many layers of paper there are after each fold.

Number of Folds	Number of Layers
0	1
1	2

Complete the table for the number of folds you were able to make.

➤ Look for a pattern in the numbers of layers.
  How can you express the pattern using powers?
  Draw another column on your table to show the *Number of Layers as Powers*.
  Suppose you could make 25 folds.
  Use patterns in the table to predict a power for the number of layers after
  25 folds. Evaluate the power.

➤ Measure the thickness of 100 sheets (200 pages) in your math textbook.
  Use this measure to calculate the thickness of 1 sheet of paper in millimetres.
  How high would the layers be if you could make 25 folds? Give your answer
  in as many different units as you can.
  What do you know that is approximately this height or length?

Your work should show:
  • a completed table showing the numbers of layers
  • the calculations of the thickness of 1 layer and the height after 25 folds
  • an example of something with the same height

Reflect
on Your Learning

What have you learned about powers and
their exponent laws?
What ways can you think of to remember
the laws and how to use them?

Rational Numbers

Suppose you are ice fishing on Blachford Lake, NWT. The temperature at midnight is −12°C. At 6 A.M. the next day, the temperature is −11°C. What must the temperature have been at some time during the night?

What You'll Learn

- Compare and order rational numbers.
- Solve problems by adding, subtracting, multiplying, and dividing rational numbers.
- Explain and apply the order of operations with rational numbers, with and without technology.

Why It's Important

You have learned ways to use positive fractions and decimals. In some applications, such as temperature, finances, and graphing on a grid, negative fractions and negative decimals are required.

Key Words

- rational number
- irrational number

What Is a Rational Number?

FOCUS
• Compare and order rational numbers.

The label on a package of frozen cranberries says that it must be stored at a temperature between $-18°C$ and $-22°C$. Name some possible temperatures. How could these temperatures be shown on a number line?

Investigate

➤ Determine each quotient.
$$\frac{12}{2} \quad \frac{-12}{2} \quad \frac{12}{-2}$$

➤ Use what you know about integer division to determine each quotient.
$$\frac{11}{2} \quad \frac{-11}{2} \quad \frac{11}{-2}$$
$$\frac{3}{5} \quad \frac{-3}{5} \quad \frac{3}{-5}$$

➤ On a number line, mark a point for each quotient.
   How can you name the point another way?

Reflect & Share

Compare your strategies and answers with those of another pair of classmates.
Use integer division to explain what each fraction means.
How could you write each answer as a decimal?

Connect

We extend a number line to the left of 0 to show negative integers.
We can also represent negative fractions on a number line.
$-\frac{3}{4}$ is the same distance to the left of 0 as $\frac{3}{4}$ is to the right of 0.

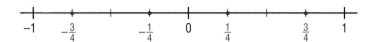

We use the same symbol to represent a negative number as we use for subtraction.

For every positive fraction, there is a corresponding negative fraction.
$-\frac{3}{4}$ and $\frac{3}{4}$ are opposites.
Any fraction can be written as a decimal; so, for every positive decimal there is a corresponding negative decimal.

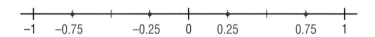

0.25 and -0.25 are opposites.

Any number that can be written as a fraction with an integer numerator and a non-zero integer denominator is a **rational number**; for example, $\frac{3}{4}, \frac{-3}{4}, \frac{3}{-4}$
To visualize $\frac{-3}{4}$, use a number line and think of $(-3) \div 4$.

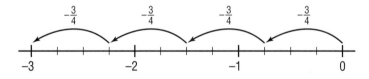

Each part is $-\frac{3}{4}$.
So, $\frac{-3}{4}$ is the same as $-\frac{3}{4}$.
The value of a fraction remains the same if its numerator and denominator are multiplied by the same non-zero number.
$\frac{3}{-4}$ can be written as $\frac{3}{-4} \times \frac{-1}{-1} = \frac{-3}{4}$
Since $\frac{3}{-4} = \frac{-3}{4}$ and $\frac{-3}{4} = -\frac{3}{4}$, then $\frac{3}{-4} = \frac{-3}{4} = -\frac{3}{4}$

A fraction can be written as a terminating or repeating decimal:

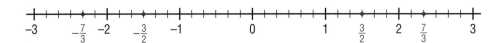

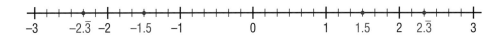

Any mixed number can be written as an improper fraction:
$$3\frac{1}{4} = \frac{13}{4} \quad \text{and} \quad -3\frac{1}{4} = -\frac{13}{4}$$

So, mixed numbers are rational numbers.

Any integer can be written as a fraction with denominator 1;
for example, $-12 = \frac{-12}{1}$, so integers are rational numbers.

All these numbers are rational numbers:
$$-\frac{3}{4}, 0.5, -1.8, 0, -5, \frac{7}{3}, 2, -3.\overline{3}, 1\frac{3}{4}$$

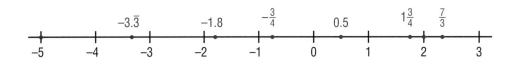

▶ **Definition of a Rational Number**
A rational number is any number that can be written in the form $\frac{m}{n}$,
where m and n are integers and $n \neq 0$.

Not all numbers can be written as fractions. For example, π and $\sqrt{2}$ are numbers
that you have used in calculations but they cannot be written as fractions.
These are **irrational numbers**.

Write 3 rational numbers between each pair of numbers.

a) 1.25 and -3.26 b) -0.25 and -0.26 c) $-\frac{1}{2}$ and $\frac{1}{4}$ d) $-\frac{1}{2}$ and $-\frac{1}{4}$

▶ *A Solution*

There are many rational numbers between any two given numbers.
Sketch or visualize a number line in each case.

a) 1.25 and -3.26

Label a number line with integers from -4 to 2.

From the number line, 3 possible rational numbers are:
-2.5, -1, and 0.3

b) -0.25 and -0.26

Label a number line with these rational numbers.
Divide the line into 10 equal parts.

From the number line, 3 possible rational numbers are:
-0.252, -0.255, and -0.259

c) $-\frac{1}{2}$ and $\frac{1}{4}$

Label a number line from -1 to 1.
Divide the line into quarters.

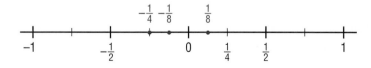

From the number line, 3 possible rational numbers are:
$-\frac{1}{4}$, $-\frac{1}{8}$, and $\frac{1}{8}$

d) $-\frac{1}{2}$ and $-\frac{1}{4}$

Label a number line from -1 to 0. Divide the line into quarters.

Write equivalent fractions for $-\frac{1}{2}$ and $-\frac{1}{4}$ with denominators of 8 to identify fractions between the two numbers.

$$-\frac{1}{2} = -\frac{2}{4} = -\frac{4}{8} \qquad\qquad -\frac{1}{4} = -\frac{2}{8}$$

Between $-\frac{4}{8}$ and $-\frac{2}{8}$, there is only one fraction, $-\frac{3}{8}$, with denominator 8.
So, write equivalent fractions with denominator 16:

$$-\frac{1}{2} = -\frac{2}{4} = -\frac{4}{8} = -\frac{8}{16} \qquad\qquad -\frac{1}{4} = -\frac{2}{8} = -\frac{4}{16}$$

Divide the number line into sixteenths.

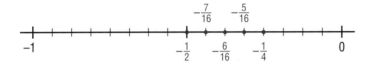

From the number line, 3 possible rational numbers are: $-\frac{5}{16}$, $-\frac{6}{16}$, and $-\frac{7}{16}$

Example 2   **Ordering Rational Numbers in Decimal or Fraction Form**

a) Use a number line. Order these numbers from least to greatest.

$0.35,\ 2.5,\ -0.6,\ 1.7,\ -3.2,\ -0.\overline{6}$

b) Order these numbers from greatest to least. Record the numbers on a number line.

$-\frac{3}{8},\ \frac{5}{9},\ -\frac{10}{4},\ -1\frac{1}{4},\ \frac{7}{10},\ \frac{8}{3}$

▶ **Solutions**

a) $0.35,\ 2.5,\ -0.6,\ 1.7,\ -3.2,\ -0.\overline{6}$

Mark each number on a number line.
$-0.\overline{6} = -0.666\ 666...$; so, $-0.\overline{6} < -0.6$

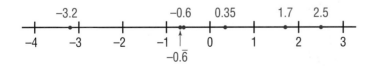

For least to greatest, read the numbers from left to right: $-3.2,\ -0.\overline{6},\ -0.6,\ 0.35,\ 1.7,\ 2.5$

b) $-\frac{3}{8}, \frac{5}{9}, -\frac{10}{4}, -1\frac{1}{4}, \frac{7}{10}, \frac{8}{3}$

Visualize a number line.

Consider the positive numbers: $\frac{5}{9}, \frac{7}{10}, \frac{8}{3}$

Only $\frac{8}{3}$ is greater than 1.

Both $\frac{5}{9}$ and $\frac{7}{10}$ are between 0 and 1.

To order $\frac{5}{9}$ and $\frac{7}{10}$, write them with a common denominator:

$9 \times 10 = 90$

$\frac{5}{9} = \frac{50}{90} \qquad \frac{7}{10} = \frac{63}{90}$

Since $\frac{63}{90} > \frac{50}{90}$, then $\frac{7}{10} > \frac{5}{9}$

Consider the negative numbers: $-\frac{3}{8}, -\frac{10}{4}, -1\frac{1}{4}$

$-1\frac{1}{4}$ is the improper fraction $-\frac{5}{4}$, which is greater than $-\frac{10}{4}$.

$-\frac{3}{8}$ is greater than $-1\frac{1}{4}$.

From greatest to least, the numbers are:

$\frac{8}{3}, \frac{7}{10}, \frac{5}{9}, -\frac{3}{8}, -1\frac{1}{4}, -\frac{10}{4}$

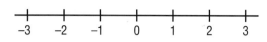

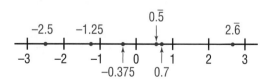

$-\frac{3}{8}, \frac{5}{9}, -\frac{10}{4}, -1\frac{1}{4}, \frac{7}{10}, \frac{8}{3}$

Write each number as a decimal.

Use a calculator when necessary.

$-\frac{3}{8} = -0.375 \qquad \frac{5}{9} = 0.\overline{5}$

$-\frac{10}{4} = -2.5 \qquad -1\frac{1}{4} = -1.25$

$\frac{7}{10} = 0.7 \qquad \frac{8}{3} = 2.\overline{6}$

Mark each decimal on a number line.
Use the order of the decimals to
order the fractions.

From greatest to least, the
numbers are:

$\frac{8}{3}, \frac{7}{10}, \frac{5}{9}, -\frac{3}{8}, -1\frac{1}{4}, -\frac{10}{4}$

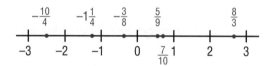

Example 3 **Ordering Rational Numbers in Fraction and Decimal Form**

Order these rational numbers from least to greatest.

$1.13, -\dfrac{10}{3}, -3.4, 2.\overline{7}, \dfrac{3}{7}, -2\dfrac{2}{5}$

Record the numbers on a number line.

▶ *A Solution*

$1.13, -\dfrac{10}{3}, -3.4, 2.\overline{7}, \dfrac{3}{7}, -2\dfrac{2}{5}$

Write the fractions and mixed number as decimals.

$-\dfrac{10}{3} = -3.\overline{3}$

$\dfrac{3}{7} = 0.\overline{428\ 571}$

$-2\dfrac{2}{5} = -2.4$

Mark each decimal on a number line.

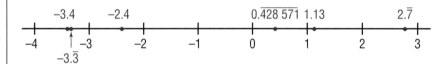

For least to greatest, read the decimals from left to right.

The order is:

$-3.4, -\dfrac{10}{3}, -2\dfrac{2}{5}, \dfrac{3}{7}, 1.13, 2.\overline{7}$

Discuss the ideas

1. How can you use what you know about fractions and integers to explain what a rational number is?

2. How are positive fractions and their opposites related on a number line?

3. In the definition of a rational number as $\dfrac{m}{n}$, where m and n are integers, why is it important that $n \neq 0$?

4. Describe the numbers that are rational, but are not positive fractions or integers.

Check

5. Identify equal rational numbers in the list that follows.

$\frac{2}{3}$ $\frac{-3}{2}$ $\frac{-2}{3}$ $-\frac{2}{3}$

$-\frac{3}{2}$ $\frac{2}{-3}$ $\frac{3}{-2}$ $\frac{3}{2}$

6. For each rational number, write two fractions that represent the same number.

a) $\frac{7}{-9}$ b) $\frac{-5}{3}$ c) $-\frac{6}{11}$

7. Write each rational number as a decimal.

a) $\frac{6}{5}$ b) $-\frac{6}{5}$

c) $\frac{9}{4}$ d) $-\frac{11}{6}$

8. Write the rational number represented by each letter on the number line, as a decimal.

a)

b)

c)

d)

9. For each pair of rational numbers in question 8, identify the greater number.

10. Write the rational number represented by each letter on the number line, as a fraction.

a)
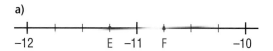

b)

c)

d)
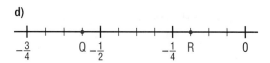

11. For each pair of rational numbers in question 10, identify the lesser number.

Apply

12. Write 3 rational numbers between each pair of numbers.
Sketch a number line to show all the rational numbers.

a) $3.7, 4.2$

b) $-1.5, 0$

c) $-4.5, -4$

d) $-5.6, -4.5$

e) $-5.6, 5.7$

f) $5.6, -5.7$

g) $-5.6, -5.7$

h) $-2.98, -2.99$

13. The thermostat on a freezer is set at $-18°C$. The compressor on the freezer turns on and cools down the freezer when the temperature rises to $-15.5°C$. The compressor turns off when the temperature drops to $-19.5°C$.

  a) Sketch a thermometer and mark the 3 freezer temperatures.

  b) A package of meat must remain below $-18°C$. Should this freezer be used? Explain.

14. Write 3 rational numbers between each pair of numbers. Sketch a number line to show all the rational numbers.

  a) $\frac{5}{8}, \frac{13}{8}$

  b) $\frac{17}{10}, -\frac{11}{5}$

  c) $-\frac{15}{4}, -\frac{11}{3}$

  d) $-\frac{1}{2}, -\frac{1}{8}$

  e) $\frac{1}{6}, 0.5$

  f) $-0.25, -\frac{1}{3}$

  g) $-\frac{14}{5}, -3$

  h) $5\frac{3}{5}, 5\frac{4}{5}$

15. Sketch a number line and mark each rational number on it:
  $\frac{3}{5}, -\frac{5}{7}, -\frac{8}{3}, -\frac{19}{5}$

16. Which rational number is greater? Which strategies did you use to find out?

  a) $2.34, 2.3$

  b) $-2.34, -2.3$

  c) $-1.4, 1.4$

  d) $3.96, -4.12$

  e) $-5.\overline{6}, -5.6$

  f) $2.8\overline{6}, 2.866$

17. Which rational number is less? Explain how you know.

  a) $\frac{3}{4}, \frac{3}{5}$

  b) $2\frac{1}{2}, -1\frac{7}{8}$

  c) $-\frac{13}{10}, -\frac{13}{5}$

  d) $-\frac{11}{3}, -\frac{5}{6}$

18. Which rational number is greater? How do you know?

  a) $\frac{3}{4}, \frac{6}{7}$

  b) $-\frac{3}{4}, -\frac{6}{7}$

  c) $-\frac{6}{7}, -\frac{7}{6}$

  d) $-\frac{9}{5}, \frac{5}{9}$

19. A student said, "When I compare two numbers, I know that the lesser number is closer to 0." Is this statement always true? Sometimes true? Never true? Explain.

20. Assessment Focus

  a) Mark these rational numbers on a number line:
  $1.4, -\frac{11}{8}, -3.6, 4\frac{1}{3}, 0.8, -\frac{17}{3}$

  b) Which rational numbers in part a are less than -1? How do you know?

  c) Which rational numbers in part a are greater than -2? How do you know?

  d) Write one rational number between each pair of numbers on the number line.

21. Use $<, >$, or $=$ to make each expression true. Justify your answers.

  a) $-\frac{5}{7} \ \square \ -\frac{4}{7}$

  b) $-\frac{5}{6} \ \square \ -\frac{5}{7}$

  c) $-2.2 \ \square \ -\frac{11}{5}$

  d) $-4.\overline{46} \ \square \ -4.46$

22. Three hikers are returning to base camp after a mountain climbing expedition. Hiker A is 26.4 m above base camp, hiker B is 37.2 m below base camp, and hiker C is 15.7 m below base camp.

a) Represent each hiker's distance above or below base camp as a rational number.

b) Sketch and label a vertical number line to show the base camp and the positions of the hikers.

c) Which hiker is closest to base camp? Explain your reasoning.

d) Which hiker has the lowest altitude? How do you know?

23. Show each set of numbers on a number line. Order the numbers from least to greatest.

a) $1.5, -3.5, 4, 0, -2.5, 7.5$

b) $-1.7, 5.9, -3.2, -0.8, 1, 4.3$

c) $1.2, 2.1, -2.01, -1.2, 1.\overline{2}, -1.22$

d) $5.44, -5.4, -5.04, 5.\overline{4}, 5.04, -5.\overline{44}$

24. Show each set of numbers on a number line. Order the numbers from greatest to least.

a) $\dfrac{3}{8}, -\dfrac{3}{4}, -\dfrac{1}{2}, -\dfrac{5}{8}, \dfrac{1}{4}, 0$

b) $\dfrac{10}{9}, -\dfrac{5}{3}, \dfrac{7}{2}, -\dfrac{3}{2}, -\dfrac{7}{6}, \dfrac{17}{3}$

c) $-\dfrac{9}{5}, -\dfrac{17}{10}, -1\dfrac{1}{2}, \dfrac{16}{4}, -\dfrac{11}{4}, \dfrac{21}{5}$

d) $-\dfrac{11}{2}, \dfrac{10}{3}, 2\dfrac{1}{4}, -\dfrac{8}{6}, \dfrac{7}{12}, -\dfrac{6}{4}$

25. Show each set of numbers on a number line. Order the numbers from least to greatest.

a) $3.8, \dfrac{3}{8}, -1.5, \dfrac{5}{3}, -2.3, -\dfrac{3}{2}$

b) $0.3, -0.\overline{3}, \dfrac{1}{3}, -0.3, 0.33, -3$

Take It Further

26. Use the definition of a rational number to show that each of the following numbers is rational.

a) 3 b) -2 c) -0.5 d) -7.45

27. Which of the following numbers do you think are rational numbers? Explain why.

a) $4.\overline{21}$ b) $-3.121\ 121\ 112\ 111\ 12\ldots$

c) 2.78 d) $-2.122\ 222\ 22\ldots$

Reflect

What is a rational number? List 3 rational numbers in decimal form and 3 rational numbers in fraction form. Show the numbers on a number line.

How Can I Learn from Others?

Three students discuss the answers to these questions:

1. Evaluate: $\dfrac{5}{6} + \dfrac{3}{4}$

2. Evaluate: $3 - 5$

1. Evaluate: $\dfrac{5}{6} + \dfrac{3}{4}$

Dan said: The sum is $\dfrac{8}{10}$, which simplifies to $\dfrac{4}{5}$.

Jesse said: Dan must be wrong; the answer has to be greater than 1.

Philippe said: The answer has to be greater than $\dfrac{5}{6}$, and $\dfrac{4}{5}$ is less than $\dfrac{5}{6}$.

To help Dan, Jesse explained how he knew his answer was wrong:

I use benchmarks and estimate. Both $\dfrac{5}{6}$ and $\dfrac{3}{4}$ are greater than $\dfrac{1}{2}$, so their sum has to be greater than $\dfrac{1}{2} + \dfrac{1}{2} = 1$.

Philippe explained his strategy for adding:

I know I can add the same types of fractions. For $\dfrac{5}{6}$ and $\dfrac{3}{4}$ to be the same type, I write them as equivalent fractions with the same denominator. Then I add the numerators.

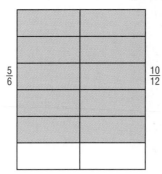
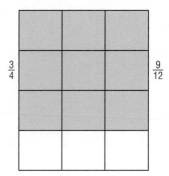

Then, $\dfrac{5}{6} + \dfrac{3}{4} = \dfrac{10}{12} + \dfrac{9}{12}$

$= \dfrac{10 + 9}{12}$

$= \dfrac{19}{12}$, or $1\dfrac{7}{12}$

2. Evaluate: $3 - 5$

Philippe said: There is no answer because 5 is greater than 3.

Jesse said: I just switch the numbers around and calculate $5 - 3 = 2$.

Dan said: No, you can't change the order of the numbers — subtraction is not commutative. You have to think about integers.

To help Philippe and Jesse, Dan explained two strategies:
➤ I can visualize coloured tiles, and add zero pairs.

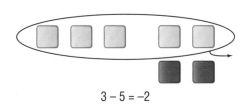

$3 - 5 = -2$

➤ I can also use a number line. The difference between 2 numbers is the distance between 2 points on the number line.

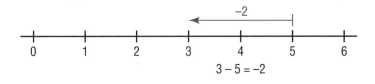

$3 - 5 = -2$

Check

1. Evaluate.

a) $\dfrac{2}{3} + \dfrac{5}{2}$ b) $\dfrac{9}{8} + \dfrac{7}{4}$ c) $\dfrac{9}{10} + \dfrac{3}{5}$ d) $\dfrac{8}{3} + \dfrac{11}{4}$

e) $\dfrac{7}{2} - \dfrac{4}{5}$ f) $\dfrac{11}{6} - \dfrac{4}{3}$ g) $\dfrac{13}{4} - \dfrac{7}{5}$ h) $\dfrac{17}{3} - \dfrac{17}{6}$

2. Evaluate.

a) $7 - 3$ b) $3 - 7$ c) $-3 - 7$ d) $-3 - (-7)$

e) $-5 + 4$ f) $-6 - (-3)$ g) $8 - (-10)$ h) $-8 - 10$

Adding Rational Numbers

At 6 A.M., the temperature was −3°C. By 10 A.M., the temperature had risen by 6°C. How can you use a number line to determine the temperature at 10 A.M.?

Investigate ②

Use what you know about adding integers and adding fractions to determine each sum. Draw a number line to illustrate each sum.

$3 + 7$	$\frac{3}{8} + \frac{7}{8}$	$1\frac{3}{8} + 2\frac{7}{8}$
$-3 + 7$	$-\frac{3}{8} + \frac{7}{8}$	$-1\frac{3}{8} + 2\frac{7}{8}$
$-3 + (-7)$	$-\frac{3}{8} + \left(-\frac{7}{8}\right)$	$-1\frac{3}{8} + \left(-2\frac{7}{8}\right)$
$3 + (-7)$	$\frac{3}{8} + \left(-\frac{7}{8}\right)$	$1\frac{3}{8} + \left(-2\frac{7}{8}\right)$

Compare your strategies with those of another pair of students.

How did the first sum in each line help you determine the other sums? How could you check your answers?

How are the strategies for adding rational numbers similar to those for adding integers and adding fractions?

Check your ideas by adding other rational numbers.

To add rational numbers in fraction form, recall how to add fractions and add integers.

➤ To add $\frac{2}{3} + \frac{1}{5}$, use a common denominator.

So, $\frac{2}{3} + \frac{1}{5} = \frac{10}{15} + \frac{3}{15}$ Write the numerators as a sum of integers.

$\phantom{So, \frac{2}{3} + \frac{1}{5}} = \frac{10 + 3}{15}$

$\phantom{So, \frac{2}{3} + \frac{1}{5}} = \frac{13}{15}$

➤ Here are 2 strategies to add $\frac{2}{3} + \left(-\frac{1}{5}\right)$:

• Visualize a number line.

To add $-\frac{1}{5}$, start at $\frac{2}{3}$ then move $\frac{1}{5}$ to the left.

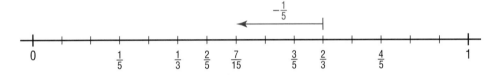

$\frac{2}{3} + \left(-\frac{1}{5}\right) = \frac{7}{15}$

• Use equivalent fractions.

$\frac{2}{3} + \left(-\frac{1}{5}\right) = \frac{2}{3} + \left(\frac{-1}{5}\right)$

$\phantom{\frac{2}{3} + \left(-\frac{1}{5}\right)} = \frac{10}{15} + \left(\frac{-3}{15}\right)$ Add the integers in the numerator.

$\phantom{\frac{2}{3} + \left(-\frac{1}{5}\right)} = \frac{10 - 3}{15}$

$\phantom{\frac{2}{3} + \left(-\frac{1}{5}\right)} = \frac{7}{15}$

A number line is useful when the denominators of the fractions are compatible or when we want to estimate a sum.

Example 1 **Adding Rational Numbers in Fraction and Mixed Number Form**

Evaluate.

a) $-\dfrac{5}{8} + \left(-\dfrac{7}{2}\right)$ **b)** $-\dfrac{1}{4} + 2\dfrac{1}{6}$

▶ *A Solution*

a) $-\dfrac{5}{8} + \left(-\dfrac{7}{2}\right)$

The denominators are compatible, so use a number line.

To add $-\dfrac{7}{2}$, start at $-\dfrac{5}{8}$ then move $\dfrac{7}{2}$ to the left.

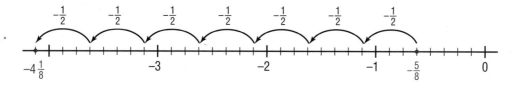

$-\dfrac{5}{8} + \left(-\dfrac{7}{2}\right) = -4\dfrac{1}{8}$

b) $-\dfrac{1}{4} + 2\dfrac{1}{6}$

Write the mixed number $2\dfrac{1}{6}$ as the improper fraction $\dfrac{13}{6}$,

then write the fractions with a common denominator of 12.

Then, $-\dfrac{1}{4} + 2\dfrac{1}{6} = \dfrac{-3}{12} + \dfrac{26}{12}$

$= \dfrac{-3 + 26}{12}$

$= \dfrac{23}{12}$, or $1\dfrac{11}{12}$

Example 2   **Adding Rational Numbers in Mixed Number Form**

Evaluate.

$-3\frac{1}{3} + 2\frac{5}{6}$

▶ **Solutions**

Method 1

$-3\frac{1}{3} + 2\frac{5}{6}$

Draw a number line.

Use a common denominator of 6, and divide the line into sixths.

Start at $-3\frac{1}{3}$ and move $2\frac{5}{6}$ to the right.

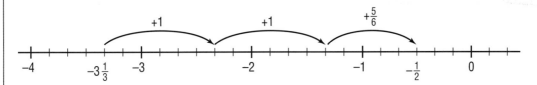

From the number line, $-3\frac{1}{3} + 2\frac{5}{6} = -\frac{1}{2}$

Method 2	**Method 3**
$-3\frac{1}{3} + 2\frac{5}{6}$	$-3\frac{1}{3} + 2\frac{5}{6}$
Use equivalent fractions with denominator 6.	Add the whole numbers and add the fractions.

Method 2

$-3\frac{1}{3} = -\frac{10}{3} = \frac{-20}{6}$

$-3\frac{1}{3} + 2\frac{5}{6} = \frac{-20}{6} + \frac{17}{6}$

$= \frac{-20 + 17}{6}$

$= \frac{-3}{6}$

$= -\frac{1}{2}$

Method 3

$-3\frac{1}{3} + 2\frac{5}{6} = -3 + \left(-\frac{1}{3}\right) + 2 + \frac{5}{6}$

$= [-3 + 2] + \left[\left(-\frac{1}{3}\right) + \frac{5}{6}\right]$

$= -1 + \left(\frac{-2}{6}\right) + \frac{5}{6}$

$= -1 + \frac{3}{6}$

$= -1 + \frac{1}{2}$

$= -\frac{1}{2}$

You can use what you know about adding integers and adding decimals to add rational numbers in decimal form.

Visualize a number line.

• $-3.1 + 1.2$

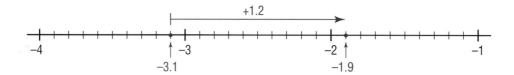

$-3.1 + 1.2 = -1.9$ This is an addition statement.

• $3.1 + (-1.2)$

Remember that when we add a negative number, we move to the left.

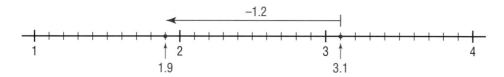

$3.1 + (-1.2) = 1.9$

Example 3   Solving a Problem by Adding Rational Numbers

At the beginning of June, the Frosty Snow Blower Company was $235.46 in debt.
By the end of August, the company had increased its debt by $156.71.
a) Use a rational number to represent each amount.
b) Calculate how much the company owed at the end of August.

▶ A Solution

a) A debt of $235.46 can be represented as -235.46.
    A debt of $156.71 can be represented as -156.71.
b) At the end of August, the company owed:
    $-235.46 + (-156.71)$
    Use a calculator.

$-235.46 + (-156.71) = -392.17$
At the end of August, the company owed $392.17.

Discuss the ideas

1. How can you use what you know about representing the sum of 2 integers on a number line to add 2 rational numbers?

2. How can you use what you know about adding integers and adding fractions to add 2 rational numbers in fraction form?

Practice

Check

3. Write the addition statement that each number line represents.

a)
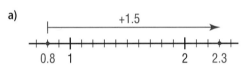

b)
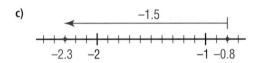

c)

d)
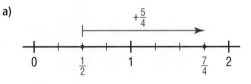

4. Write the addition statement that each number line represents.

a)
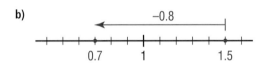

b)
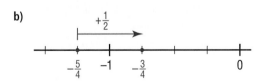

c)

d)
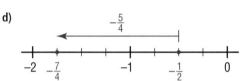

5. Determine each sum.

a) i) $3 + 2$ ii) $3.8 + 2.4$

b) i) $-3 + (-2)$ ii) $-3.8 + (-2.4)$

c) i) $-3 + 2$ ii) $-3.8 + 2.4$

d) i) $3 + (-2)$ ii) $3.8 + (-2.4)$

6. Which of the following expressions have the same sum as $-2.3 + (-1.9)$? Use a number line to explain how you know.

a) $2.3 + 1.9$

b) $(-2.3) + 1.9$

c) $-1.9 + (-2.3)$

d) $(-2.3) + (-1.9)$

7. Determine each sum.

a) i) $9 + 3$ ii) $\frac{9}{2} + \frac{3}{2}$

b) i) $-9 + (-3)$ ii) $-\frac{9}{2} + \left(-\frac{3}{2}\right)$

c) i) $-9 + 3$ ii) $-\frac{9}{2} + \frac{3}{2}$

d) i) $9 + (-3)$ ii) $\frac{9}{2} + \left(-\frac{3}{2}\right)$

8. Which of the following expressions have the same sum as $-\frac{3}{4} + \frac{7}{8}$? Use a number line to show how you know.

a) $-\frac{3}{4} + \left(-\frac{7}{8}\right)$ b) $-\frac{7}{8} + \frac{3}{4}$

c) $\frac{7}{8} + \left(-\frac{3}{4}\right)$ d) $\frac{7}{8} + \frac{3}{4}$

Apply

9. Use integers to estimate each sum. Then, determine each sum.

a) $-5.6 + 3.2$
b) $7.95 + (-4.51)$
c) $-0.325 + (-32.5)$
d) $-123.5 + 27.45$
e) $82.001 + 100.28$
f) $-17.84 + (-0.098)$

10. Is it possible to add 2 rational numbers and get a sum that is less than both the numbers you added? Explain your reasoning.

11. Determine each sum.

a) $-\frac{2}{3} + \frac{1}{2}$ b) $\frac{4}{5} + \left(-\frac{1}{3}\right)$

c) $-\frac{11}{4} + \left(-\frac{6}{5}\right)$ d) $\frac{13}{5} + \frac{9}{2}$

e) $-2\frac{1}{3} + \left(-1\frac{3}{4}\right)$ f) $\frac{9}{5} + \left(-\frac{17}{6}\right)$

g) $-3\frac{3}{4} + 4\frac{5}{8}$ h) $1\frac{5}{6} + \left(-5\frac{2}{3}\right)$

i) $-3\frac{1}{4} + \left(-2\frac{1}{6}\right)$ j) $2\frac{3}{5} + \left(-1\frac{7}{8}\right)$

12. Assessment Focus What can you say about the sign of the sum of 2 rational numbers in each case? Include examples and explain your reasoning.

a) Both rational numbers are positive.
b) Both rational numbers are negative.
c) One rational number is positive and one rational number is negative.

13. Zoe owes her mother $36.25, then Zoe borrows another $25.35.

a) Write each amount as a rational number.
b) Use the numbers in part a.
  i) Write an expression for the amount Zoe owes.
  ii) How much does Zoe owe?
c) Zoe pays back $14.75.
  i) Write an expression for the amount Zoe now owes.
  ii) How much does Zoe now owe?

14. Estimate whether each sum is greater than or less than 0. Explain how you know. Calculate to check your prediction.

a) $-0.61 + 0.23$ b) $12.94 + (-12.56)$

c) $-\frac{7}{3} + \left(\frac{17}{5}\right)$ d) $\frac{7}{4} + \left(-\frac{6}{5}\right)$

15. On Tuesday, December 23rd, the lowest temperature in Winnipeg was $-13.4°C$. By noon the next day, the temperature had increased by $5.7°C$.

a) What was the temperature at noon?
b) On Wednesday, December 24th, the lowest temperature was $3.7°C$ less than the lowest the previous day. What was the lowest temperature on Wednesday?
c) Sketch a thermometer to show these changes in temperature.

16. For each pair of expressions below, how can you tell which sum is greater without adding? Explain your reasoning. Determine each sum to check.
  a) i) $-9.23 + 3.46$ **ii)** $9.23 + (-3.46)$
  b) i) $-\frac{2}{3} + \left(-\frac{3}{4}\right)$ **ii)** $-\frac{2}{3} + \frac{3}{4}$

17. In January, Keith earned $45.50 babysitting and $22.25 shovelling snow. He spent $15.77 on a CD, and $33.10 on a computer game.
  a) Write each amount above as a rational number. Justify your choice of sign for each number.
  b) Write an addition statement that represents Keith's balance at the end of January.
  c) What is Keith's balance?

18. The table shows the money earned and spent by Lucille in the first six months of running her new business, Lucille's Café.

Item	Income	Expense
New tables and chairs		$545.50
New stove		$978.44
Profit on food	$2115.70	
Repair of roof		$888.00
Profit on coffee	$2570.40	
Salary of part-time cook		$2540.20

Did Lucille's business make a profit in the first six months? Use rational numbers in your explanation.

19. Use a calculator to help determine a rational number that makes each sentence true.
  a) $5.6 + \square \le 9.1$
  b) $11.8 + (-\square) \le 23.4$
  c) $-7.2 + \square \ge 7.2$
  d) $-7.2 + \square \le 7.2$

Take It Further

20. Determine the missing rational number in each addition statement. What strategies did you use?
  a) $-\frac{3}{4} + \square = \frac{7}{8}$
  b) $\square + \frac{4}{5} = -\frac{2}{3}$
  c) $\square + \left(-\frac{5}{2}\right) = 3\frac{1}{8}$
  d) $\frac{7}{3} + \square = -\frac{5}{4}$

21. Determine the range of numbers that makes this sentence true. Explain your reasoning.
  $7.9 + \square \le 11.2$

22. Use any four of the rational numbers: $-1, -2, -3, -4, 1, 2, 3, 4$ in the boxes below to make an expression with the greatest sum less than 0. Explain how you know you have determined the greatest sum less than 0.

$$\frac{\square}{\square} + \frac{\square}{\square}$$

Reflect

Before you add 2 rational numbers, how can you tell if their sum will be positive or negative? Include both fraction and decimal examples in your explanation.

3.3 Subtracting Rational Numbers

FOCUS

• Solve problems that require subtracting rational numbers.

Canada's national debt was $559 billion in 1999. By 2008, this debt had been reduced to $467 billion.
How would you write each amount as a rational number?
How could you use a number line to calculate the difference in debt?

Investigate

2

Here is part of a stock market report from February 5, 2008, for some Canadian companies.

Company	Stock price at the end of the day ($)	Stock price at the start of the day ($)
Bombardier	4.670	4.710
Canadian National Railway	50.630	51.330
Canadian Tire Corporation	64.840	65.970
Potash Corporation of Saskatchewan	144.580	144.15

For each stock:

➤ Determine: (price at the end of the day) − (price at the start of the day)
➤ What does it mean when this difference in prices is positive? Is negative?
➤ Sketch a number line to show each subtraction.
➤ Use rational numbers to write a subtraction statement.

Compare your strategies and answers with those of another pair of students.
How did you use what you know about subtracting integers to subtract rational numbers?
How could you check your answers?

Connect

To subtract 2 rational numbers, we use a strategy similar to that for subtracting integers.

- For $5 - (-3)$, add the opposite: $5 + (+3)$
  Start at 5 then move 3 to the right.

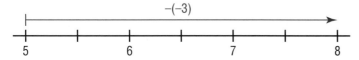

$5 - (-3) = 8$

- For $1\frac{1}{2} - \left(-\frac{1}{4}\right)$, add the opposite: $1\frac{1}{2} + \left(+\frac{1}{4}\right)$
  Start at $1\frac{1}{2}$ then move $\frac{1}{4}$ to the right.

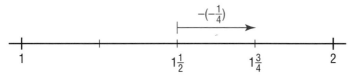

$1\frac{1}{2} - \left(-\frac{1}{4}\right) = 1\frac{3}{4}$

Example 1   **Subtracting Rational Numbers in Fraction and Mixed Number Form**

a) $\dfrac{5}{6} - \dfrac{4}{3}$ b) $-\dfrac{5}{4} - \left(-3\frac{1}{5}\right)$

A Solution

a) $\dfrac{5}{6} - \dfrac{4}{3}$

On a number line, start at $\dfrac{5}{6}$ then move $\dfrac{4}{3}$ to the left.

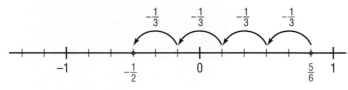

$\dfrac{5}{6} - \dfrac{4}{3} = -\dfrac{1}{2}$

b) $-\frac{5}{4} - \left(-3\frac{1}{5}\right)$

Visualize a number line to estimate the difference.

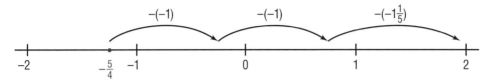

The difference is a little less than 2.

Use equivalent fractions to calculate the difference.

Write $-3\frac{1}{5}$ as the improper fraction $-\frac{16}{5}$.

So, $-\frac{5}{4} - \left(-3\frac{1}{5}\right) = -\frac{5}{4} - \left(-\frac{16}{5}\right)$

$\phantom{So, -\frac{5}{4} - \left(-3\frac{1}{5}\right)} = -\frac{25}{20} - \left(-\frac{64}{20}\right)$

$\phantom{So, -\frac{5}{4} - \left(-3\frac{1}{5}\right)} = \frac{-25 - (-64)}{20}$

$\phantom{So, -\frac{5}{4} - \left(-3\frac{1}{5}\right)} = \frac{-25 + 64}{20}$

$\phantom{So, -\frac{5}{4} - \left(-3\frac{1}{5}\right)} = \frac{39}{20}, \text{ or } 1\frac{19}{20}$

To subtract the integers in the numerator, add the opposite.

Example 2   **Subtracting Rational Numbers in Mixed Number Form**

Evaluate. $2\frac{1}{2} - 4\frac{7}{8}$

▶ **Solutions**

Method 1

$2\frac{1}{2} - 4\frac{7}{8}$

On a number line, start at $2\frac{1}{2}$ then move $4\frac{7}{8}$ to the left.

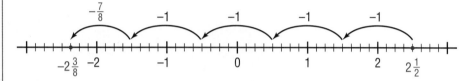

$2\frac{1}{2} - 4\frac{7}{8} = -2\frac{3}{8}$

Method 2

$2\frac{1}{2} - 4\frac{7}{8}$

Write each mixed number as an improper fraction.

$2\frac{1}{2} - 4\frac{7}{8} = \frac{5}{2} - \frac{39}{8}$ Use equivalent fractions.

$$= \frac{20}{8} - \frac{39}{8}$$

$$= \frac{20 - 39}{8}$$

$$= \frac{-19}{8}$$

$$= -\frac{19}{8}, \text{ or } -2\frac{3}{8}$$

We can use a number line to subtract rational numbers in decimal form.
To subtract $-2.3 - (-3.9)$, add the opposite: $-2.3 + (+3.9)$

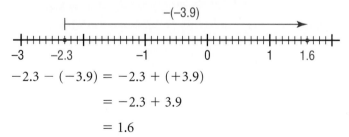

$-2.3 - (-3.9) = -2.3 + (+3.9)$

$$= -2.3 + 3.9$$

$$= 1.6$$

Example 3 **Solving a Problem by Subtracting Rational Numbers**

A diver jumps off a cliff that is 14.7 m above sea level. After hitting the water, he plunges 3.8 m below the surface of the water before returning to the surface.

a) Use rational numbers to represent the difference in heights from the top of the cliff to the bottom of his dive. Sketch a number line.

b) The water is 5.6 m deep. What is the distance from the ocean floor to the bottom of the dive?

▶ **A Solution**

a) A distance measured above the water can be considered as positive.
A distance measured below the water can be considered as negative.
The diver travels 14.7 m above the water and −3.8 m below the water.
The difference in heights is: $14.7 - (-3.8)$
From the number line:
$14.7 - (-3.8) = 14.7 + 3.8$ Adding the opposite decimal
$\qquad\qquad\quad = 18.5$
The diver travelled 18.5 m.

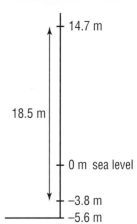

b) The diver travelled −3.8 m below the surface.
The ocean floor is −5.6 m below the surface.
The difference in heights is: $-5.6 - (-3.8)$
$-5.6 - (-3.8) = -5.6 + 3.8$
$\qquad\qquad\quad = -1.8$
The distance from the bottom of the ocean floor to the bottom of the dive is 1.8 m.

Discuss the ideas

1. When you use a number line to subtract 2 rational numbers, how do you know in which direction to move?

2. How can you use what you know about subtracting integers and subtracting fractions to subtract 2 rational numbers in fraction form?

Practice

Check

3. Determine each difference.
   a) i) $5 - 3$ ii) $5.1 - 3.3$
   b) i) $-5 - 3$ ii) $-5.1 - 3.3$
   c) i) $-3 - (-5)$ ii) $-3.3 - (-5.1)$
   d) i) $3 - 5$ ii) $3.3 - 5.1$

4. Which of the following expressions have the same answer as $-7.2 - 1.8$? How do you know?
   a) $7.2 - 1.8$ b) $-7.2 - (-1.8)$
   c) $1.8 - (-7.2)$ d) $-1.8 - 7.2$

5. Determine each difference.
   a) i) $11 - 2$ ii) $\dfrac{11}{5} - \dfrac{2}{5}$
   b) i) $-11 - 2$ ii) $-\dfrac{11}{5} - \dfrac{2}{5}$
   c) i) $11 - (-2)$ ii) $\dfrac{11}{5} - \left(-\dfrac{2}{5}\right)$
   d) i) $2 - (-11)$ ii) $\dfrac{2}{5} - \left(-\dfrac{11}{5}\right)$

Apply

6. Which of the following expressions have the same answer as $-\dfrac{3}{10} - \dfrac{9}{5}$? How do you know?
   a) $-\dfrac{3}{10} - \left(-\dfrac{9}{5}\right)$ b) $\dfrac{3}{10} - \dfrac{9}{5}$
   c) $-\dfrac{9}{5} - \dfrac{3}{10}$ d) $\dfrac{9}{5} - \dfrac{3}{10}$

7. Use integers to estimate each difference. Then, determine each difference.
   a) $10.8 - 3.5$ b) $-37.23 - 48.54$
   c) $50.06 - (-14.67)$ d) $64.19 - 95.76$
   e) $-28.31 - 9.72$ f) $70.59 - (-81.25)$

8. On January 25th, 2008, the lowest temperature in Iqaluit, Nunavut, was $-28.5°C$.
   On the same day, the lowest temperature in Inuvik, Northwest Territories, was $-33.1°C$.
   a) What is the difference in these temperatures?
   b) Why are there two possible answers to part a?

9. Determine each difference.
   a) $\dfrac{17}{3} - \dfrac{19}{2}$ b) $-\dfrac{13}{5} - \dfrac{7}{3}$ c) $1\dfrac{5}{6} - 6\dfrac{3}{4}$
   d) $-\dfrac{19}{6} - \dfrac{7}{8}$ e) $\dfrac{15}{4} - \dfrac{5}{12}$ f) $-2\dfrac{1}{8} - \left(-4\dfrac{1}{3}\right)$

10. Assessment Focus Is it possible to subtract 2 rational numbers and get a difference that is greater than both the numbers you subtracted? Explain your reasoning. Include examples of rational numbers in decimal form and in fraction form.

11. In Asia, the lowest point on land is the shore of the Dead Sea, which is 417.5 m below sea level. The highest point is the peak of Mount Everest, which 8844.43 m above sea level.

a) Write each measurement above as a rational number.

b) Write a subtraction statement that represents the distance between the highest point and the lowest point. What is this distance?

12. Predict whether each answer is positive or negative. Explain how you know. Calculate to check your prediction.

a) $-3.86 - 41.12$ b) $1.32 - (-5.79)$

c) $-\frac{5}{4} - \left(-\frac{7}{2}\right)$ d) $-\frac{23}{5} - \frac{5}{3}$

13. Evaluate each expression.

a) $\frac{3}{5} - \left(-\frac{1}{2}\right) + \frac{2}{3}$

b) $-2.34 + 8.6 + (-5.71)$

c) $-\frac{16}{5} - \left(-\frac{14}{3}\right) + \frac{13}{4}$

d) $23.5 + (-12.61) - 3.2$

14. Determine a rational number that makes each statement true. Use a calculator to check your answer.

a) $-1.2 - \square \le 3.7$

b) $4.3 - \square \ge 8.9$

c) $\square - 2.9 \ge 5.3$

d) $\square - 7.2 \le -10.9$

Take It Further

15. Determine the missing number in each subtraction statement.

a) $\square - 28.4 = 37.3$ b) $\frac{9}{10} - \square = \frac{3}{5}$

c) $\square - 0.05 = -2.08$ d) $\frac{11}{6} - \square = -\frac{7}{3}$

e) $-1.25 - \square = 3.75$ f) $-3\frac{1}{2} - \square = 5\frac{1}{4}$

16. Find two pairs of rational numbers that make each equation true.

a) $-7.4 + \square - \square = -10.9$

b) $\square - (-12.8) + \square = -1.1$

c) $-21.6 - \square - \square = -15.4$

17. Determine the range of numbers that makes each sentence true. Explain your thinking.

a) $-11.8 - \square \le 5.7$

b) $6.3 - \square \ge 9.4$

Reflect

How is subtracting 2 rational numbers similar to adding 2 rational numbers? How is it different? Include examples of rational numbers in your explanation.

3.1

1. a) Sketch a number line. On the line, place each rational number below.

$-1.3, 2\frac{3}{4}, 1.51, -\frac{8}{5}, -\frac{9}{3}$

b) Which numbers in part a are less than -1.5? Explain how you know.

2. Order the following rational numbers from least to greatest. Place each number on a number line to support your answer.

$-\frac{6}{5}, 1.2, -1.1, -\frac{1}{4}, 0.2, -1\frac{3}{8}$

3. Replace each $\square$ with $<$ or $>$. How could you check your answers?

a) $-\frac{2}{3} \square -\frac{3}{4}$ **b)** $-\frac{8}{3} \square -\frac{9}{4}$

c) $-2.5 \square 0.5$ **d)** $-\frac{4}{5} \square -0.9$

4. Identify a rational number between each pair of numbers. Sketch a number line to illustrate each answer.

a) $1.2, 1.4$ **b)** $-\frac{3}{4}, \frac{5}{8}$

c) $0.4, \frac{1}{3}$ **d)** $-1.05, -\frac{9}{10}$

3.2

5. a) How can you determine the sign of the sum of two numbers before you add them?

b) Determine the sign of each sum, then check by using a calculator.

i) $2.35 + 3.47$

ii) $-5.783 + (-0.247)$

iii) $-\frac{2}{3} + \left(-1\frac{1}{8}\right)$

iv) $-5.27 + 6.58$

v) $-\frac{17}{5} + \frac{4}{9}$

vi) $0.085 + (-0.125)$

6. Determine each sum.

a) $8.37 + 0.58$ **b)** $-21.25 + (-36.57)$

c) $-157.4 + 32.7$ **d)** $\frac{5}{8} + \left(-\frac{1}{9}\right)$

e) $-8\frac{1}{4} + 5\frac{1}{5}$ **f)** $-\frac{5}{3} + \left(-\frac{23}{7}\right)$

3.3

7. The temperature of a freezer changed from $-16.1°C$ to $-14.7°C$.

a) **i)** By how much did the temperature change?

ii) Is this an increase or a decrease in temperature? Explain how you know.

b) By how much does the temperature need to change again before it is at $-3.8°C$?

8. Determine each difference.

a) $40.25 - 63.10$ **b)** $-112.2 - (-14.8)$

c) $\frac{2}{5} - \frac{9}{10}$ **d)** $-4\frac{4}{9} - 3\frac{5}{6}$

e) $-1.8 - 4.3$ **f)** $\frac{23}{8} - \left(-\frac{7}{2}\right)$

9. The lowest point on land in North America is Death Valley at 86 m below sea level. The highest point is the peak of Mt. McKinley at 6193.7 m above sea level. How can you use rational numbers to calculate the distance between these two points?

10. a) How can you determine the sign of the difference of two numbers before you subtract them?

b) Determine the sign of each difference, then check by using a calculator.

i) $62.4 - 53.7$ **ii)** $-0.54 - 1.98$

iii) $\frac{1}{12} - \frac{9}{10}$ **iv)** $5\frac{2}{3} - \left(-7\frac{1}{2}\right)$

Closest to Zero

How to Play

An Ace is worth 1, a Jack is worth 11, a Queen is worth 12, and a King is worth 13.
All the red cards are negative and the black cards are positive.

1. For each round, each player is dealt 4 cards.
2. Each player organizes her 4 cards to create 2 proper fractions – two cards are the numerators and two are the denominators.
3. Each player chooses to add or subtract her 2 fractions. This is then the value of that player's hand.
4. The winner of the round is the person whose hand has a value closest to 0. The winner gets 1 point.
   If a player has a hand whose value *is* 0, then that person wins the round and gets 2 points.
   Players record their points.
5. The cards are shuffled and play continues with the next round.
   The first player to get 10 points is the winner.

Play the game a few times.
What strategies do you have for winning a round?

You will need
- a deck of 52 playing cards
- a calculator (optional)

Number of Players
- 2 to 4

Goal of the Game
- To add or subtract fractions to get an answer that is close to 0

3.4 Multiplying Rational Numbers

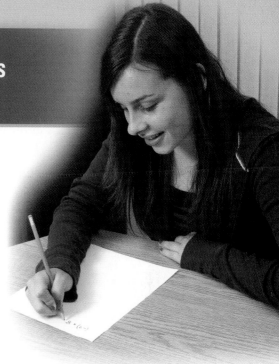

FOCUS

• Solve problems that require multiplying rational numbers.

What strategies do you use:
- to multiply two integers such as $(-9) \times 8$?
- to multiply two fractions such as $\frac{3}{4} \times \frac{5}{2}$?

Investigate

➤ Use what you know about multiplying integers and multiplying fractions to predict each product of rational numbers.

6×8	5×7	$\frac{6}{5} \times \frac{8}{7}$		
$(-7) \times 9$	4×2	$\left(-\frac{7}{4}\right) \times \frac{9}{2}$	$\left(\frac{-7}{4}\right) \times \frac{9}{2}$	$\left(\frac{7}{-4}\right) \times \frac{9}{2}$
$(-8) \times (-6)$	3×5	$\left(-\frac{8}{3}\right) \times \left(-\frac{6}{5}\right)$	$\left(\frac{-8}{3}\right) \times \left(\frac{-6}{5}\right)$	$\left(\frac{8}{-3}\right) \times \left(\frac{6}{-5}\right)$
$9 \times (-3)$	2×10	$\frac{9}{2} \times \left(-\frac{3}{10}\right)$	$\frac{9}{2} \times \left(\frac{-3}{10}\right)$	$\frac{9}{2} \times \left(\frac{3}{-10}\right)$

➤ Use a calculator to check your predictions.
➤ Choose 2 different rational numbers in fraction form. Determine their product. Check with a calculator.

Reflect & Share

Share your answers with another pair of students.
Explain to each other how you found the products.
How did the first 2 products in each line help you determine the next products?

To multiply 2 rational numbers, use the properties for determining the sign of the product of 2 integers to predict the sign of the product of the rational numbers. Then:

➤ If the rational numbers are in fraction form:
   Use the procedures for multiplying 2 fractions to determine the numerical value of the product.
➤ If the rational numbers are in decimal form:
   Use the procedures for multiplying 2 decimals to determine the numerical value of the product.

For example,

- When two rational numbers have the same sign, their product is positive.

$$\left(-\frac{3}{2}\right) \times \left(-\frac{1}{5}\right) = \frac{3}{10} \qquad \text{and} \qquad \frac{3}{2} \times \frac{1}{5} = \frac{3}{10}$$

$$(-1.5) \times (-1.8) = 2.7 \qquad \text{and} \qquad 1.5 \times 1.8 = 2.7$$

- When two rational numbers have opposite signs, their product is negative.

$$\frac{3}{2} \times \left(-\frac{1}{5}\right) = -\frac{3}{10} \qquad \text{and} \qquad \left(-\frac{3}{2}\right) \times \frac{1}{5} = -\frac{3}{10}$$

$$(-1.5) \times 1.8 = -2.7 \qquad \text{and} \qquad 1.5 \times (-1.8) = -2.7$$

When we use brackets to write a product statement, we do not need the multiplication sign. For the rational numbers above, we can write

$\frac{3}{2} \times \left(-\frac{1}{5}\right)$ as $\left(\frac{3}{2}\right)\left(-\frac{1}{5}\right)$, and $(-1.5) \times 1.8$ as $(-1.5)(1.8)$.

Example 1   Multiplying Rational Numbers in Fraction or Mixed Number Form

Determine each product.

a) $\left(-\frac{11}{7}\right)\left(-\frac{21}{44}\right)$

b) $\left(2\frac{2}{3}\right)\left(-1\frac{3}{4}\right)$

▶ **A Solution**

a) $\left(-\frac{11}{7}\right)\left(-\frac{21}{44}\right)$

Predict the sign of the product: since the fractions have the same sign, their product is positive.

Simplify the fractions before multiplying.

$$\left(-\frac{11}{7}\right)\left(-\frac{21}{44}\right) = \left(-\frac{\overset{1}{\cancel{11}}}{\underset{1}{\cancel{7}}}\right)\left(-\frac{\overset{3}{\cancel{21}}}{\underset{4}{\cancel{44}}}\right)$$

$$= \frac{1 \times 3}{1 \times 4}$$

$$= \frac{3}{4}$$

So, $\left(-\frac{11}{7}\right)\left(-\frac{21}{44}\right) = \frac{3}{4}$

> Look for common factors in the numerators and denominators:
> 11 and 44 have the common factor 11.
> 21 and 7 have the common factor 7.
> Divide numerator and denominator by their common factors.
> Then multiply the numerators and multiply the denominators.

b) $\left(2\frac{2}{3}\right)\left(-1\frac{3}{4}\right)$

Since the fractions have opposite signs, their product is negative.

Write the mixed numbers as fractions.

$$\left(\frac{8}{3}\right)\left(-\frac{7}{4}\right) = \left(\frac{\overset{2}{\cancel{8}}}{3}\right)\left(-\frac{7}{\underset{1}{\cancel{4}}}\right) \qquad \text{Dividing numerator and denominator by their common factor 4}$$

$$= \frac{(2)(-7)}{(3)(1)}$$

$$= -\frac{14}{3}$$

$$= -4\frac{2}{3}$$

So, $\left(2\frac{2}{3}\right)\left(-1\frac{3}{4}\right) = -4\frac{2}{3}$

Example 2   Multiplying Rational Numbers to Solve Problems

On February 5, 2008, the price of a share in CIBC changed by −$1.640.
A person owns 35 shares. By how much did those shares change in value that day?

▶ **Solutions**

Method 1	Method 2
Change in value: −$1.640 × 35 Since the rational numbers have opposite signs, their product is negative. To determine the product: $(-1.64)(35)$, multiply integers, then estimate to place the decimal point. $(-164)(35) = -5740$ Estimate to place the decimal point: Since −1.64 is close to −2, then $(-1.64)(35)$ is close to $(-2)(35) = -70$. So, place the decimal point after the 7 in −5740. −$1.640 × 35 = −$57.40 The shares lost $57.40 that day.	Change in value: −$1.640 × 35 Use a calculator. Key in 1.640 × 35 to display: 57.4 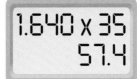 Since the rational numbers have opposite signs, their product is negative, so we do not need to enter the negative sign. −$1.640 × 35 = −$57.40 The shares lost $57.40 that day.

Example 3   Multiplying Rational Numbers in Decimal Form

Determine each product.

a) $(0.8)(-2.4)$ **b)** $(-1.25)(-2.84)$

▶ **A Solution**

a) $(0.8)(-2.4)$

Since the rational numbers have opposite signs, their product is negative.
Use mental math to determine the product:
$(8)(-24) = -192$
Estimate to place the decimal point:
Since 0.8 is close to 1 and −2.4 is close to −2, then
$(0.8)(-2.4)$ is close to $(1)(-2) = -2$.
So, place the decimal point after the 1 in −192.
Then, $(0.8)(-2.4) = -1.92$

b) $(-1.25)(-2.84)$

When there are more than 2 digits in both numbers being multiplied, use a calculator.
The rational numbers have the same sign, so their product is positive.
Key in 1.25×2.84 to display: 3.55

$(-1.25)(-2.84) = 3.55$

Discuss the ideas

1. Why does it help to predict the sign of a product before you multiply 2 rational numbers?

2. Why does it make sense that the rules for signs when you multiply integers must apply when you multiply rational numbers?

Practice

Check

3. Predict which products are greater than 0, then multiply to determine each product. Explain the strategy you used to predict.
a) $3 \times (-5.2)$
b) $2.6 \times (-4)$
c) $(-1.3) \times 5$
d) $(-0.9) \times (-7.1)$

4. Predict which products are less than 0, then multiply to determine each product. Explain the strategy you used to predict.
a) $(-3) \times \frac{2}{3}$
b) $\left(-\frac{1}{4}\right) \times (-5)$
c) $\left(\frac{4}{5}\right) \times (-2)$
d) $\left(-\frac{1}{2}\right) \times \frac{7}{8}$

5. Determine each product. Estimate to place the decimal point.
a) $(-0.64)(0.2)$
b) $(-0.5)(-5.71)$
c) $(-4.13)(-0.8)$
d) $(0.7)(8.5)$

6. Which of the following expressions have the same product as $\left(-\frac{3}{4}\right)\left(\frac{5}{2}\right)$?
Explain how you know.
a) $\left(\frac{5}{2}\right)\left(-\frac{3}{4}\right)$
b) $\left(\frac{3}{4}\right)\left(-\frac{5}{2}\right)$
c) $\left(-\frac{3}{2}\right)\left(\frac{5}{4}\right)$
d) $\left(\frac{3}{4}\right)\left(\frac{5}{2}\right)$
e) $\left(\frac{3}{2}\right)\left(-\frac{5}{4}\right)$
f) $\left(-\frac{3}{4}\right)\left(-\frac{5}{2}\right)$

7. Determine each product.
a) $\left(-\frac{1}{3}\right)\left(\frac{2}{5}\right)$
b) $\left(\frac{1}{4}\right)\left(-\frac{3}{5}\right)$
c) $\left(\frac{4}{5}\right)\left(\frac{1}{2}\right)$
d) $\left(-\frac{5}{6}\right)\left(-\frac{2}{3}\right)$

Apply

8. Suppose each rational number below is multiplied by -2.5.
Which products are greater than 10?
How can you find out by estimating?
Evaluate only those products that are greater than 10.

a) -5.1 b) 3.5 c) -4.4

d) -3.6 e) -5 f) 5

9. On February 5, 2008:

a) The price of a share in Petro-Canada changed by $-\$0.80$.
A person owns 120 shares. By how much did the shares change in value that day?

b) The price of a share in Research in Motion changed by $-\$2.10$.
A person owns 50 shares. By how much did the shares change in value that day?

c) The price of a share in Shoppers Drug Mart changed by $\$0.23$.
A person owns 65 shares. By how much did the shares change in value that day?

10. A diver descends at an average speed of 10.4 m/min. Use rational numbers to write her depth after 3.6 min.

11. Determine each product.

a) $(-1.23)(2.8)$ b) $(-23.7)(-1.2)$

c) $(15.2)(15.2)$ d) $(-20.1)(-5.2)$

12. Determine each product.

a) $\left(\dfrac{5}{4}\right)\left(-\dfrac{16}{5}\right)$ b) $\left(-\dfrac{2}{3}\right)\left(-\dfrac{5}{6}\right)$

c) $\left(-2\dfrac{8}{9}\right)\left(5\dfrac{1}{8}\right)$ d) $\left(-4\dfrac{2}{5}\right)\left(-\dfrac{5}{3}\right)$

13. **Assessment Focus**

a) Multiply: $(-26)(-4)$

b) Use your answer to part a to determine each product.

i) $(-2.6)(-0.4)$

ii) $(-0.26)(0.4)$

iii) $(260)(-0.04)$

iv) $(-0.026)(-4)$

c) Why did you not have to multiply to determine each product in part b?

d) Write 3 more products you could determine using your answer to part a.

14. A courier company has a bank account balance of $\$45\ 567.87$. The company must repaint all its 25 delivery trucks at an average cost of $\$3457.25$ per truck.

a) Write a multiplication statement with rational numbers to determine the cost of painting the trucks.

b) What is the bank account balance after the bill for painting has been paid? Explain your result.

15. Predict the sign of each product, then calculate the product.

a) $(-2.0)(-0.5)(3.1)$ b) $\left(\dfrac{5}{6}\right)\left(-\dfrac{4}{7}\right)\left(\dfrac{3}{2}\right)$

Take It Further

16. Determine the missing number in each product statement.
What strategies did you use?

a) $-3.25 \times \square = 15.275$ b) $-\dfrac{5}{4} \times \square = -\dfrac{35}{8}$

c) $\square \times 0.045 = -0.018$ d) $\square \times 3\dfrac{3}{4} = 5\dfrac{1}{4}$

17. A positive rational number is multiplied by a negative rational number. Is it possible that the product is closer to 0 than either of the numbers being multiplied? Explain.

18. Karen used her calculator to evaluate $-\dfrac{89}{91} \times \dfrac{31}{86}$. She reported the product as about $-0.352\ 542\ 806$.

a) How did Karen know that the value is approximate?

b) What is the exact answer?

Reflect

Rational numbers can be in fraction form or decimal form.
Which form do you prefer to multiply? Explain your choice.
Include examples in your explanation.

Math Link

History

When the New York Stock Exchange began in 1792, it modelled its system on the Spanish one. The Spanish dollar was divided into eight parts, so when a stock increased or decreased in value, the change was represented in eighths. A decrease was represented by a negative fraction, while an increase was represented by a positive fraction. In 2000, the New York Stock Exchange moved to the current system that shows the change in value of a stock as a decimal.
Here are the changes in values of 5 different stocks on a particular day:

$1\dfrac{5}{8}, \ -\dfrac{3}{16}, \ \dfrac{3}{4}, \ -1\dfrac{7}{16}, \ -1\dfrac{1}{2}$

Arrange the fractions from least to greatest. Write each fraction as a decimal to show the change in dollars.

Dividing Rational Numbers

Marcel has $2\frac{1}{4}$ cups of juice.

He pours $\frac{3}{4}$ of a cup of juice into each glass.
How many glasses can Marcel fill?
Write a division statement to describe
this situation.

FOCUS
* Solve problems that
  require dividing
  rational numbers.

Investigate 2

➤ The 3rd, 4th, and 5th terms of a number pattern are: $+27, -18, +12$
  * To get the next term, you divide the term before it by one of these rational
    numbers: $\frac{2}{3}, \frac{3}{2}, -\frac{2}{3}, -\frac{3}{2}$
    Which number is correct? How do you know?
  * Determine the 6th and 7th terms of the pattern.
    Describe your strategy and show your work.
  * Determine the 1st and 2nd terms of the pattern.
    Describe your strategy and show your work.

➤ Choose a different rational number and a different 1st term.
  Calculate the first 5 terms of your pattern.

Reflect & Share

Trade patterns with another pair of classmates.
Write the pattern rule and determine the next 3 terms
in your classmates' pattern.
How did you use what you know about rational numbers
to identify and extend the pattern?

To divide 2 rational numbers, use the properties for determining the sign of the quotient of 2 integers to predict the sign of the quotient of the rational numbers. Then:

➤ If the rational numbers are in fraction form:
  Use the procedures for dividing 2 fractions to determine the numerical value of the quotient.

➤ If the rational numbers are in decimal form:
  Use the procedures for dividing 2 decimals to determine the numerical value of the quotient.

For example,
- When two rational numbers have the same sign, their quotient is positive.

  $$\left(-\frac{3}{2}\right) \div \left(-\frac{1}{5}\right) = \frac{15}{2} \qquad \text{and} \qquad \frac{4}{5} \div \frac{3}{2} = \frac{8}{15}$$

  $$(-3.9) \div (-1.5) = 2.6 \qquad \text{and} \qquad 9.9 \div 4.5 = 2.2$$

- When two rational numbers have opposite signs, their quotient is negative.

  $$\frac{3}{2} \div \left(-\frac{1}{5}\right) = -\frac{15}{2} \qquad \text{and} \qquad \left(-\frac{4}{5}\right) \div \frac{3}{2} = -\frac{8}{15}$$

  $$(-3.9) \div 1.5 = -2.6 \qquad \text{and} \qquad 9.9 \div (-4.5) = -2.2$$

Example 1   **Dividing Rational Numbers in Fraction or Mixed Number Form**

Determine the sign of each quotient, then divide.

a) $\left(-\frac{5}{8}\right) \div \frac{3}{4}$ b) $\left(-4\frac{1}{5}\right) \div \left(-3\frac{1}{3}\right)$

➤ **A Solution**

a) $\left(-\frac{5}{8}\right) \div \frac{3}{4}$

  The fractions have opposite signs, so their quotient is negative.

  Use the strategy of dividing fractions with a common denominator.

  Write each fraction with a common denominator of 8.

  $$\left(-\frac{5}{8}\right) \div \frac{3}{4} = \left(-\frac{5}{8}\right) \div \frac{6}{8} \qquad \text{Since the denominators are the same,}$$
  $$= -\frac{5}{6} \qquad\qquad\qquad \text{divide the numerators.}$$

  So, $\left(-\frac{5}{8}\right) \div \frac{3}{4} = -\frac{5}{6}$

b) $\left(-4\frac{1}{5}\right) \div \left(-3\frac{1}{3}\right)$

The mixed numbers have the same sign, so their quotient is positive.

Write each mixed number as an improper fraction: $\left(-\frac{21}{5}\right) \div \left(-\frac{10}{3}\right)$

Use the strategy of multiplying the dividend by the reciprocal of the divisor.

$$\left(-4\frac{1}{5}\right) \div \left(-3\frac{1}{3}\right) = \left(-\frac{21}{5}\right) \div \left(-\frac{10}{3}\right)$$

$$= \left(-\frac{21}{5}\right) \div \left(-\frac{10}{3}\right)$$

$$= \frac{63}{50}$$

$$= 1\frac{13}{50}$$

> To get the reciprocal of a fraction, interchange the numerator and denominator. So, the reciprocal of $-\frac{10}{3}$ is $-\frac{3}{10}$.

So, $\left(-4\frac{1}{5}\right) \div \left(-3\frac{1}{3}\right) = 1\frac{13}{50}$

You could use a calculator to divide fractions and mixed numbers. You do not need to input the negative signs if you determine the sign of the quotient first.

When you divide decimals, the quotient may be a terminating or repeating decimal. If you divide using pencil and paper, and the quotient appears to be a repeating decimal, continue to divide until you can identify which digits repeat.

Example 2   Dividing Rational Numbers in Decimal Form

Divide.

a) $(-1.38) \div 0.6$ **b)** $(-0.25) \div (-0.3)$

▶ **A Solution**

a) $(-1.38) \div 0.6$

Since the dividend and divisor have opposite signs, their quotient is negative.
Estimate first; use compatible numbers.
-1.38 is close to -1, and 0.6 is close to 0.5.
$(-1) \div 0.5$ is -2.
So, $(-1.38) \div 0.6$ is about -2.

Divide integers:
$(-138) \div 6 = -23$
The estimate is -2, so place the decimal point in the quotient
between the 2 and the 3.
So, $(-1.38) \div 0.6 = -2.3$

b) $(-0.25) \div (-0.3)$

Since the dividend and divisor have the same sign, their quotient is positive.
Determine the numerical value of the quotient:
$0.25 \div 0.3 = 0.833\ 333...$
$\qquad\qquad = 0.8\overline{3}$
So, $(-0.25) \div (-0.3) = 0.8\overline{3}$

When the divisor is a decimal with more than 1 digit, we use a calculator to divide.

Example 3   Solving Problems Involving Rational Numbers

Determine the missing number in each division statement.

a) $\square \div (-2.6) = 9.62$ b) $\left(-\dfrac{5}{8}\right) \div \square = -\dfrac{15}{56}$

▶ *A Solution*

a) $\square \div (-2.6) = 9.62$

Division is the inverse of multiplication.
Any division statement can be written as an equivalent multiplication statement.
Estimate.
Think: $\square \div (-3) = 9$
We know that $(-27) \div (-3) = 9$, or as a multiplication statement: $(-27) = (-3) \times 9$
Rewrite the given statement the same way:
$\square \div (-2.6) = 9.62$ can be written as $\square = (-2.6) \times 9.62$
Use a calculator: $\square = -25.012$
The missing number is -25.012.

b) $\left(-\dfrac{5}{8}\right) \div \square = -\dfrac{15}{56}$

$\left(-\dfrac{5}{8}\right) \div \square = -\dfrac{15}{56}$ can be written as $\square = \left(-\dfrac{5}{8}\right) \div \left(-\dfrac{15}{56}\right)$

The quotient is positive.

Use the strategy of multiplying by the reciprocal
to determine the numerical value of the quotient.

$\square = \dfrac{5}{8} \div \dfrac{15}{56}$

$= \dfrac{5}{8} \times \dfrac{56}{15}$ Simplify by dividing by common factors in the numerator and denominator.

$= \dfrac{{}^{1}\cancel{5}}{{}_{1}\cancel{8}} \times \dfrac{\cancel{56}^{\,7}}{\cancel{15}_{\,3}}$

$= \dfrac{1}{1} \times \dfrac{7}{3}$

$= \dfrac{7}{3}$

The missing number is $\dfrac{7}{3}$.

> Solve a simpler problem.
> Think: $6 \div \square = 2$
> We know $6 \div 3 = 2$,
> so we write the related statement:
> $3 = 6 \div 2$

Discuss the ideas

1. How can you use what you know about dividing integers and dividing fractions to divide 2 rational numbers in fraction form?

2. How can you use what you know about dividing integers and dividing decimals to divide 2 rational numbers in decimal form?

Practice

Check

3. Predict the sign of each quotient, then calculate the quotient.

a) $(-1.5) \div 3$ b) $2.8 \div (-2)$

c) $(-8.4) \div (-4)$ d) $1.6 \div (-8)$

e) $(-14.4) \div (-6)$ f) $(-6.3) \div 7$

4. Predict the sign of each quotient, then calculate the quotient.

a) $\dfrac{1}{2} \div \left(-\dfrac{3}{4}\right)$ b) $\left(-\dfrac{2}{5}\right) \div \dfrac{3}{10}$

c) $\left(-\dfrac{7}{6}\right) \div \left(-\dfrac{8}{3}\right)$ d) $\dfrac{1}{4} \div \dfrac{11}{3}$

e) $\dfrac{5}{2} \div \left(-\dfrac{2}{3}\right)$ f) $\left(-\dfrac{9}{5}\right) \div \left(-\dfrac{11}{4}\right)$

5. Which of the following expressions have the same answer as $\left(-\dfrac{1}{3}\right) \div \left(-\dfrac{3}{4}\right)$?

a) $\left(-\dfrac{1}{3}\right) \times \left(-\dfrac{3}{4}\right)$ b) $\left(-\dfrac{3}{4}\right) \div \left(-\dfrac{1}{3}\right)$

c) $\left(-\dfrac{1}{3}\right) \times \left(-\dfrac{4}{3}\right)$ d) $\left(-\dfrac{4}{3}\right) \times \left(-\dfrac{1}{3}\right)$

e) $\dfrac{1}{3} \div \dfrac{3}{4}$ f) $\dfrac{4}{3} \times \dfrac{1}{3}$

Apply

6. At a sea port, the effect of the tide changed the water level by −5.6 m in 3.5 h. What was the mean change in water level per hour?

7. Determine each quotient without a calculator. Estimate to place the decimal point in the quotient.
   a) $0.32 \div 0.4$
   b) $(-1.17) \div 0.8$
   c) $0.25 \div (-0.6)$
   d) $(-1.02) \div (-0.2)$
   e) $3.76 \div (-0.3)$
   f) $3.15 \div 0.9$

8. On a winter's day, the temperature at 6 P.M. was 0°C. Suppose the temperature decreased by 2.5°C each hour until it was −12.5°C. How long did it take to reach this temperature? How do you know?

9. Use a calculator to determine each quotient.
   a) $20.736 \div (-1.8)$
   b) $(-27.94) \div 1.2$
   c) $(-84.41) \div (-2.3)$
   d) $23.04 \div 4.8$
   e) $76.63 \div (-7.5)$
   f) $(-0.1081) \div 0.45$

10. **Assessment Focus** Suppose each rational number below is divided by −0.5. Predict which quotients are greater than −10. Explain the strategies you used to predict. Then evaluate only those quotients that are greater than −10.
    a) −20.5 b) 18.8   c) 10.7   d) 0.6

11. To pay for a skiing holiday in Whistler, Paige borrowed $1450.50 from her parents. She pays back $30.75 each week.
    a) How many weeks will it be until Paige is no longer in debt? Justify your answer.
    b) How did you use rational numbers to calculate the answer in part a?

12. Determine each quotient.
    a) $\frac{5}{4} \div \left(-\frac{7}{6}\right)$
    b) $\frac{3}{10} \div \frac{12}{5}$
    c) $\left(-\frac{3}{4}\right) \div \left(-1\frac{1}{8}\right)$
    d) $\left(-4\frac{3}{5}\right) \div \frac{3}{4}$
    e) $3\frac{2}{3} \div \left(-2\frac{1}{4}\right)$
    f) $3\frac{4}{9} \div 6\frac{1}{3}$

13. A thermometer on a freezer is set at −5.5°C. Each time the freezer door is opened, the temperature increases by 0.3°C. Suppose there is a power outage. How many times can the door be opened before the temperature of the freezer increases to 5°C? Justify your solution.

14. On one day in January, the temperature changed by $-15.4°C$ in 5.5 h. What was the mean change in temperature per hour?

15. A person has 54 shares in WestJet Airlines. On February 6, 2008, these shares lost $17.28 in value. What was the change in value of 1 share? How do you know?

16. Suppose each rational number below was divided by $-\frac{2}{3}$. Predict which quotients would be less than $-\frac{1}{2}$. Explain the strategy you used to predict.

a) $-\frac{2}{3}$　　　　　b) $\frac{1}{3}$

c) $\frac{5}{6}$　　　　　d) $\frac{1}{4}$

17. Determine the missing number in each division statement.

a) $\square \div 1.25 = -3.6$

b) $\square \div \left(-\frac{3}{4}\right) = \frac{7}{8}$

c) $(-0.5875) \div \square = -0.25$

d) $\frac{68}{15} \div \square = -\frac{4}{5}$

18. Replace each $\square$ with a rational number to make each equation true. Explain the strategy you used.

a) $(-0.3) \times \square = 0.78$

b) $0.8 \times \square = -5.52$

c) $(-1.26) \div \square = 0.2$

d) $\square \div (-1.1) = 3.26$

Take It Further

19. Alex and Ellice run in opposite directions from school to their homes.
Ellice runs 1.3 km to her home in 7.8 min.
Alex runs 630 m to his home in 4.2 min.

a) Write division statements using positive and negative rational numbers to represent each student's average speed in metres per minute.
What do the positive and negative numbers represent?

b) Who runs at the greater average speed?

20. Write 6 division statements that have a quotient between $-\frac{3}{4}$ and $-\frac{1}{4}$.

21. Which expression below has the greatest value? How can you find out without calculating every answer?

a) $-\frac{1}{2} + \left(-\frac{2}{3}\right)$　　　　b) $-\frac{1}{2} - \left(-\frac{2}{3}\right)$

c) $\left(-\frac{1}{2}\right) \times \left(-\frac{2}{3}\right)$　　　　d) $\left(-\frac{1}{2}\right) \div \left(-\frac{2}{3}\right)$

Reflect

How is dividing rational numbers similar to multiplying them?
Include examples of fractions and decimals in your explanation.

Order of Operations with Rational Numbers

Two students were asked to evaluate: $(-8) - 2(24 \div (-8))^2$

Here are their calculations.

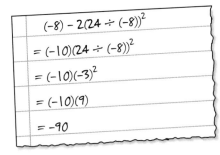

Why did both these students get incorrect answers?

What is the correct answer?

Investigate

2

Use a calculator when you need to.

Use any operations or brackets with these rational numbers: $-2.1, -0.5, 3.4, 0.9$

➤ Write an expression and determine its value.

➤ Try to find an expression with a greater value. What strategies did you use to do this?

➤ Repeat this activity several times. Which expression has the greatest value?

Compare your expression with the greatest value with that of another pair of students. Are the expressions the same? If not, whose expression has the greater value? Share your strategies.

Work together to find the expression with the least value.

Connect

In Lesson 3.1, you learned that integers and fractions are rational numbers. So, the order of operations for all rational numbers is the same as that for integers and fractions:

• Do the operations in brackets first.
• Do any work with exponents.
• Multiply and divide, in order, from left to right.
• Add and subtract, in order, from left to right.

Example 1   **Using the Order of Operations with Decimals**

Evaluate.

a) $(-0.8) + 1.2 \div (-0.3) \times 1.5$ b) $(-3.2) - 0.9 \div [0.7 - (-1.2)]^2$

▶ *A Solution*

a) $(-0.8) + 1.2 \div (-0.3) \times 1.5$ Divide first: $1.2 \div (-0.3) = -4$
$= (-0.8) + (-4) \times 1.5$ Then multiply: $(-4) \times 1.5 = -6$
$= (-0.8) + (-6)$ Then add.
$= -6.8$

b) $(-3.2) - 0.9 \div [0.7 - (-1.2)]^2$ Subtract in the brackets first: add the opposite.
$= (-3.2) - 0.9 \div [0.7 + 1.2]^2$ Add: $0.7 + 1.2 = 1.9$
$= (-3.2) - 0.9 \div [1.9]^2$ Use a calculator to evaluate the power: $[1.9]^2 = 3.61$
$= (-3.2) - 0.9 \div 3.61$ Then divide: $0.9 \div 3.61 \doteq 0.249\ 307\ 479$
$\doteq -3.2 - 0.249\ 307\ 479$
$\doteq -3.449\ 307\ 479$

Since the answer does not terminate or appear to repeat, round the answer to the nearest tenth because the numbers in the question are given in that form.
So, $(-3.2) - 0.9 \div [0.7 - (-1.2)]^2 \doteq -3.4$

After we substitute rational numbers for variables in a formula, we simplify the numerical expression using the order of operations.

When you evaluate with decimals, use a calculator when the divisor has more than 1 digit and when the number you multiply by has more than 2 digits.

Example 2   **Solving Problems Using the Order of Operations**

To convert a temperature in degrees Fahrenheit to degrees Celsius, we use the formula:

$C = \dfrac{F - 32}{1.8}$

In Fort Simpson, Northwest Territories, the mean temperature in December is $-9.4°F$. What is this temperature in degrees Celsius?

▶ A Solution

Substitute $F = -9.4$ into the formula:

$$C = \frac{F - 32}{1.8}$$

$$= \frac{-9.4 - 32}{1.8}$$

The fraction bar indicates division, but also acts like brackets.

That is, the expression means $C = (-9.4 - 32) \div 1.8$

So, simplify the numerator first, then divide.

$$C = \frac{-9.4 - 32}{1.8} \qquad \text{Subtract.}$$

$$= \frac{-41.4}{1.8} \qquad \text{Divide.}$$

$$= -23$$

The mean temperature in December is $-23°C$.

Example 3   Using the Order of Operations with Fractions

Evaluate.

$$\left(-\frac{1}{2}\right)\left(-\frac{1}{2}\right) - \left(-\frac{2}{3}\right) \div \left[\frac{1}{3} + \left(-\frac{3}{12}\right)\right]$$

▶ A Solution

$$\left(-\frac{1}{2}\right)\left(-\frac{1}{2}\right) - \left(-\frac{2}{3}\right) \div \left[\frac{1}{3} + \left(-\frac{3}{12}\right)\right] \qquad \text{Add in the square brackets first.}$$

$$= \left(-\frac{1}{2}\right)\left(-\frac{1}{2}\right) - \left(-\frac{2}{3}\right) \div \left[\frac{1}{3} - \frac{3}{12}\right] \qquad \text{Use a common denominator of 12.}$$

$$= \left(-\frac{1}{2}\right)\left(-\frac{1}{2}\right) - \left(-\frac{2}{3}\right) \div \left[\frac{4}{12} - \frac{3}{12}\right]$$

$$= \left(-\frac{1}{2}\right)\left(-\frac{1}{2}\right) - \left(-\frac{2}{3}\right) \div \left(\frac{1}{12}\right) \qquad \text{Multiply next.}$$

$$= \frac{1}{4} - \left(-\frac{2}{3}\right) \div \left(\frac{1}{12}\right) \qquad \text{Then divide: multiply by the reciprocal of the divisor.}$$

$$= \frac{1}{4} - \left(-\frac{2}{\cancel{3}_{1}}\right) \times \left(\frac{\cancel{12}^{4}}{1}\right)$$

$$= \frac{1}{4} - \left(-\frac{2}{1}\right) \times \left(\frac{4}{1}\right)$$

$$= \frac{1}{4} - (-8)$$

$$= \frac{1}{4} + 8$$

$$= 8\frac{1}{4}$$

1. What does a fraction bar indicate?

2. As the number of operations increases and the expressions become more complex, it is easy to make mistakes.
What can you do to prevent yourself making mistakes?

Practice

Check

3. Evaluate. Do not use a calculator.
   a) $2.3 - (-1.6) \times (0.8)$
   b) $(-14.8) \times 0.9 - 3.1$
   c) $(-12.8) \div (-0.2) + 4.5 \div 0.5$
   d) $(-4.8) \times (-0.4 + 0.6)^2$

4. Evaluate. Do not use a calculator.
   a) $\frac{1}{2} + \left(-\frac{3}{4}\right) \times \frac{1}{3}$
   b) $\left(-\frac{5}{4}\right) \div \left(-\frac{1}{4} + \frac{3}{2}\right)\left(-\frac{1}{4} + \frac{3}{2}\right)$
   c) $\left(-\frac{7}{10}\right) \div \left(-\frac{2}{5}\right) - \left(-\frac{1}{4}\right) \times \frac{1}{2}$
   d) $\frac{6}{5} \times \left(-\frac{2}{3} + \frac{8}{3}\right)^2 - \frac{5}{12}$

Apply

5. a) Use a calculator to evaluate the expression below. Key in the expression as it is written.
   $-2.8 - 1.4 \times 4.5$
   b) Does the calculator follow the order of operations or does it perform operations from left to right? How did you find out?

6. Estimate which expression has the greatest value. Then use a calculator to evaluate each expression to verify your prediction.
   a) $9.1 - 3.5 \times (4.2)^2$ b) $(9.1 - 3.5) \times (4.2)^2$
   c) $9.1 - (3.5 \times 4.2)^2$ d) $9.1[(-3.5) \times (4.2)^2]$

7. Evaluate.
   a) $\left(-\frac{2}{3}\right) \div \frac{1}{4} + \frac{1}{2} \times \frac{1}{2} \times \frac{1}{3}$
   b) $\left(-\frac{2}{3}\right) \div \left[\frac{1}{4} + \left(-\frac{1}{2}\right)\right] \times \frac{1}{3}$
   c) $\left(-\frac{2}{3}\right) \div \left[\frac{1}{4} - \left(-\frac{1}{2}\right)\right] \times \frac{1}{3}$
   d) $\left(-\frac{2}{3}\right) \div \left[\frac{1}{4} + \left(-\frac{1}{2}\right) \times \frac{1}{3}\right]$

8. Find the errors in each solution. Write the correct solution.

a) $(-3.7) \times (-2.8 + 1.5) - 4.8 \div (-1.2)$

$= (-3.7) \times (1.3) - 4.8 \div (-1.2)$

$= -4.81 - 4.8 \div (-1.2)$

$= -9.61 \div (-1.2)$

$= 8.008\overline{3}$

b) $-\frac{3}{8} - \frac{4}{5} \times \frac{3}{10} \div \left(-\frac{4}{5}\right)$

$= -\frac{15}{40} - \frac{32}{40} \times \frac{3}{10} \div \left(-\frac{4}{5}\right)$

$= -\frac{47}{40} \times \frac{3}{10} \div \left(-\frac{4}{5}\right)$

$= -\frac{141}{400} \div \left(-\frac{4}{5}\right)$

$= -\frac{141}{400} \times \left(-\frac{5}{4}\right)$

$= \frac{(-141) \times (-5)}{400 \times 4}$

$= \frac{705}{1600}$

9. A family moves from Chicago to Saskatoon. A company that rents moving trucks uses this formula, $C = 1.15[21.95d + 0.035(k - 120)]$, to determine the cost, including tax, of renting a truck for d days and k kilometres, when $k > 120$. The distance from Chicago to Saskatoon is 2400 km and the family travels for 4 days. What is the cost to rent the truck?

10. A can of soup is a cylinder with radius 3.5 cm and height 11.5 cm.

Use the formula:
Surface area = $2\pi r^2 + 2\pi r \times$ height,
where r is the radius of the can
a) Determine the area of tin needed to make the can, to the nearest square centimetre.
b) Explain how you used the order of operations in part a.

11. a) Use this formula to convert each Fahrenheit temperature below to Celsius:
$$C = \frac{F - 32}{1.8}$$
i) 0°F   **ii)** −40°F   **iii)** −53°F

b) Here is another way to write the formula in part a: $C = \frac{5}{9}(F - 32)$
Use this formula to convert each Fahrenheit temperature below to Celsius:
i) 50°F   **ii)** −13°F   **iii)** 32°F
c) Which formula in parts a and b was easier to use? Explain your choice.

12. Evaluate. State the order in which you carried out the operations.
a) $\left(-4\frac{1}{2}\right) + \left(-\frac{2}{3}\right) \times 2\frac{3}{4}$
b) $\left(-3\frac{2}{5}\right) \times \left(-1\frac{5}{6}\right) + \frac{3}{10}$
c) $(-3) \div \left(-\frac{4}{5}\right) + \left(-\frac{5}{12}\right) \times 1\frac{1}{2}$
d) $\left(1\frac{5}{8}\right) - \left(-2\frac{3}{4} + 2\right)\left(-2\frac{3}{4} + 2\right)$

13. Use a calculator to evaluate. Write the answers to the nearest hundredth where necessary.
a) $2.3 + (-11.2) \div (-0.2) - 3.7$
b) $(-3.4) \times 0.7 - (-1.8)(-1.8)$
c) $\dfrac{0.67 - 4.2 \div (-0.2)}{(-7.3 + 8.6)^2}$
d) $\dfrac{8.9 \times (-3.1 + 22.7)^2 + 4.7}{(-9.6) \div 0.04 - 0.4}$

14. On one day in Black Lake, Saskatchewan, the maximum temperature was −8.1°C and the minimum temperature was −16.7°C.
a) What was the mean temperature that day?
b) How did you use the order of operations in part a?

15. Assessment Focus Use these numbers to make 4 fractions: $2, -3, 4, -5, 6, -8, 10, -12$

a) Use the 4 fractions to write an expression using 3 different operations and brackets. Evaluate the expression.

b) Use the same 4 fractions a different way or use 4 different fractions. Write an expression whose value is as close to 0 as possible. Show your work.

16. The following maximum temperatures were recorded for one week in Abbotsford, BC: $-3.1°C, -4.5°C, -6.2°C, -1.2°C, 1.5°C,$ $2.3°C, 4.1°C$

a) Predict whether the mean maximum temperature for the week is above or below 0°C.

b) Calculate the mean maximum temperature for the week.

17. A student's solution to a problem, to the nearest hundredth, is shown below. The solution is incorrect. Identify the errors. Provide a correct solution.

$(-8.2)^2 \div (-0.3) - 2.9 \times (-5.7)$

$= 67.24 \div (-0.3) - 2.9 \times (-5.7)$

$= 67.24 \div (-0.3) - 16.53$

$= 67.24 \div (-16.83)$

$\doteq 4.00$

18. A student evaluated the following expression and the answer was 50.39 to the nearest hundredth. Another student evaluated the expression and the answer was 1.63 to the nearest hundredth.

$$\frac{23.7 - (-5.6) \div 0.7 + 6.8}{(-3) \times (-6.7) + 3.5}$$

a) Which answer is correct?

b) What mistake did one student likely make?

Take It Further

19. In question 11, you used these two versions of a formula to convert Fahrenheit temperatures to Celsius:

$$C = \frac{F - 32}{1.8} \quad \text{and} \quad C = \frac{5}{9}(F - 32)$$

Explain how to get one version of the formula from the other.

20. In Flin Flon, Manitoba, the mean of the maximum and minimum temperatures on one day was $-12.8°C$. The maximum temperature was $-11.5°C$. What was the minimum temperature?

21. Insert brackets in the expression below so the statement is correct. Is it possible to insert brackets and get a positive answer? Explain your thinking.
$$-3.8 + 9.1 \times -2.5 - 0.5 = -31.1$$

Reflect

When you use the order of operations with rational numbers, do you prefer to work with the numbers in decimal form or fraction form? Explain your choice.

Study Guide

A rational number is any number that can be written in the form $\frac{m}{n}$, where m and n are integers and $n \neq 0$.

This number line illustrates some different forms of rational numbers:

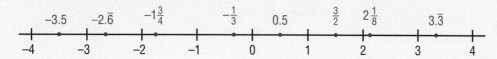

From least to greatest: $-3.5,\ -2.\overline{6},\ -1\frac{3}{4},\ -\frac{1}{3},\ 0.5,\ \frac{3}{2},\ 2\frac{1}{8},\ 3.\overline{3}$

To operate with rational numbers, apply what you know about operating with fractions, decimals, and integers.

- To add rational numbers, visualize a number line.

$$\frac{5}{8} + \left(-\frac{7}{2}\right) = -\frac{23}{8} \qquad\qquad (-5.6) + (-3.2) = -8.8$$

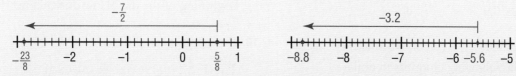

- To subtract rational numbers, visualize a number line.

$$-\frac{9}{8} - \frac{11}{4} = -\frac{31}{8} \qquad\qquad 0.89 - (-2.23) = 3.12$$

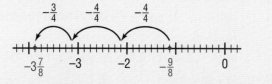
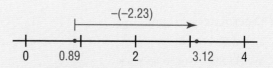

- To multiply rational numbers, determine the sign of the product first.

$$\left(\frac{3}{4}\right)\left(-\frac{5}{2}\right) = -\frac{15}{8} \qquad \text{and} \qquad (-4.13)(-0.8) = 3.304$$

- To divide rational numbers, determine the sign of the quotient first.

$$\left(-\frac{3}{10}\right) \div \left(-\frac{12}{5}\right) = \frac{1}{8} \qquad \text{and} \qquad 76.63 \div (-7.5) = -10.217\overline{3}$$

The order of operations with rational numbers is the same as the order for whole numbers, fractions, and integers:

- Do the operations in brackets first.
- Then evaluate the exponents.
- Then divide and multiply, in order, from left to right.
- Then add and subtract, in order, from left to right.

3.1 1. Which of the following rational numbers are between -2.5 and $-\frac{11}{3}$? How do you know?

   a) -3.4 b) $-\frac{9}{4}$ c) $-\frac{19}{6}$ d) -4.2

2. Order the following rational numbers from least to greatest. Show them on a number line.

   $3.12, -\frac{4}{3}, 0.9, -\frac{1}{2}, -0.4$

3. Write 3 rational numbers between each pair of numbers. Sketch number lines to show all the rational numbers.

   a) $-3.5, -3.1$ b) $\frac{1}{5}, \frac{7}{10}$

   c) $0.8, 0.9$ d) $-\frac{5}{2}, -\frac{3}{2}$

4. On one day, the prices of 5 stocks changed by the following amounts in dollars:

   $-0.09, -0.51, +0.95, +0.54, -2.00$

   Order the amounts from the greatest loss to the greatest gain.

3.2 5. Determine each sum.

   a) $-1.2 + (-0.3)$

   b) $134.89 + (-56.45)$

   c) $-23.6 - 4.57$

   d) $48.05 + 0.003$

6. A technician checked the temperature of a freezer and found that it was $-15.7°C$. She noted that the temperature had dropped $7.8°C$ from the day before.

   a) What was the temperature the day before?

   b) Show both temperatures on a vertical number line.

7. Determine each sum.

   a) $\frac{3}{4} + \frac{7}{8}$ b) $-1\frac{1}{2} + 3\frac{1}{3}$

   c) $-4\frac{5}{6} + \left(-1\frac{5}{12}\right)$ d) $\frac{11}{9} + \left(-\frac{17}{6}\right)$

3.3 8. Determine each difference.

   a) $-3.4 - (-4.8)$

   b) $-71.91 - 11.23$

   c) $90.74 - 100.38$

   d) $63.2 - 80.02$

9. At the end of a day, the price of a stock was $21.60. During the day, the price of the stock had changed by $-\$0.75$. What was the price of the stock at the beginning of the day? How do you know?

10. Determine each difference.

   a) $\frac{4}{3} - \frac{11}{6}$ b) $-\frac{5}{8} - \left(-\frac{7}{5}\right)$

   c) $3\frac{5}{7} - \left(-6\frac{9}{10}\right)$ d) $-\frac{23}{4} - \frac{23}{3}$

3.4 11. Predict which expressions have a value between -1 and 1. Calculate each product to check.

   a) $(-1.4) \times (-0.8)$ b) $25.6 \times (-0.05)$

   c) $\left(-\frac{3}{5}\right)\left(\frac{4}{3}\right)$ d) $\left(-\frac{5}{6}\right)\left(-\frac{2}{3}\right)$

12. The temperature in Richmond, BC, at 4:00 P.M. was $2°C$. The temperature drops $1.3°C$ each hour. What will the temperature be at 11:00 P.M.? Justify your answer.

13. Write 3 multiplication statements that have the same product as $\left(-\frac{4}{9}\right)\left(\frac{7}{5}\right)$. How can you check your answers?

14. Determine each product.
  a) $3.5 \times (-0.3)$ **b)** $(-4.1)(2.3)$
  c) $\left(-\dfrac{4}{7}\right)\left(-\dfrac{2}{3}\right)$ **d)** $1\dfrac{3}{5} \times \left(-2\dfrac{1}{2}\right)$

15. A mountain climber descends from base camp at an average speed of 5.9 m/h. How far below base camp will the climber be after 3.75 h? Use a vertical number line with the base camp at 0 to illustrate the climber's descent.

3.5 **16.** Predict which expressions have a value between -1 and 1. Calculate each quotient to check.
  a) $(-2.2) \div 0.4$ **b)** $10.6 \div (-9.2)$
  c) $\dfrac{9}{10} \div \left(-\dfrac{3}{2}\right)$ **d)** $\left(-\dfrac{5}{12}\right) \div \left(-\dfrac{5}{4}\right)$

17. Write 3 division statements that have the same quotient as $\dfrac{3}{8} \div \left(-\dfrac{5}{11}\right)$.

18. Replace each □ with a rational number to make each equation true. Explain the strategy you used.
  a) $(-0.2) \times □ = 0.75$
  b) $0.9 \times □ = -7.47$
  c) $(-0.624) \div □ = -0.4$

19. Determine each quotient.
  a) $8.4 \div (-1.2)$ **b)** $(-20.6) \div (-0.9)$
  c) $\left(-\dfrac{9}{11}\right) \div \left(\dfrac{7}{5}\right)$ **d)** $\left(-1\dfrac{2}{3}\right) \div 3\dfrac{1}{2}$

3.6 **20. a)** Evaluate each expression. Do not use a calculator.
  i) $-3.5 + 6.2 \times (-0.2)$
  ii) $(-3.5 + 6.2) \times (-0.2)$
  b) Are the answers in part a different? Explain.

21. Predict whether the value of each expression below is positive or negative. Explain how you predicted. Evaluate to check your prediction.
  a) $-\dfrac{3}{5} + \left[\dfrac{1}{3} \times \left(-\dfrac{3}{4}\right)\right]$
  b) $\left(-\dfrac{3}{5} + \dfrac{1}{3}\right) \times \left(-\dfrac{3}{4}\right)$
  c) $-\left(-\dfrac{3}{5} + \dfrac{1}{3}\right) \times \left(-\dfrac{3}{4}\right)$

22. A formula for the surface area of a right rectangular prism is:
2(length × width + length × height + width × height)

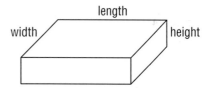

  a) Determine the surface area of a right rectangular prism with length 25.3 cm, width 15.2 cm, and height 9.7 cm.
  b) Explain how you used the order of operations in part a.

23. Evaluate each expression. Show your work to illustrate the order of operations.
  a) $-1.2 \div (0.6) - [6.3 + (-3.4)]$
  b) $-\dfrac{5}{12} + \left(\dfrac{4}{3}\right)\left(\dfrac{4}{3}\right)$
  c) $-\dfrac{4}{5} \div \left[\dfrac{1}{2} + \left(-\dfrac{1}{6}\right)\left(-\dfrac{1}{6}\right) \times \dfrac{1}{4}\right]$
  d) $\left(-\dfrac{2}{3}\right)\left(-\dfrac{2}{3}\right) \div \dfrac{2}{9} - \left(-\dfrac{4}{5}\right)$
  e) $-1\dfrac{3}{7} \times \dfrac{1}{2} + \left(-3\dfrac{1}{7}\right)$
  f) $0.2 - (-1.2) \times 0.5 \div (-0.1)$
  g) $(-0.2 + 0.9)^2 + 9.8 \div (-0.7)$

1. a) Identify a rational number between -0.5 and -0.6.

   b) How do you know the number you identified in part a is a rational number?

2. a) Write the following rational numbers on a copy of the number line below:
   $0.6, -0.\overline{3}, -2.5, 3.\overline{6}, 4\frac{1}{2}, -1\frac{3}{10}, -\frac{23}{5}, \frac{11}{3}$

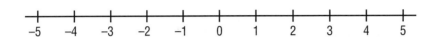

   b) List the numbers in part a from greatest to least.

3. Evaluate.

   a) $-7.4 - (-6.1)$ **b)** $\frac{4}{5} + \left(-\frac{3}{10}\right)$ **c)** $(-3.2)(-0.5)$ **d)** $\left(-\frac{3}{4}\right) \div \frac{1}{3}$

4. Sarah has a balance of $-\$2.34$ in her account.
   Each time she makes a withdrawal, she is charged $1.20.
   a) What does "a balance of $-\$2.34$" mean?
   b) Sarah makes three more withdrawals of $20.50 each.
   What is her balance now?
   How can you use rational numbers to calculate it?
   c) Sarah's overdraft limit is $500.00. How many more $20.50 withdrawals
   can she make? Justify your answer.

5. Evaluate. How could you check your answers?

   a) $(-56.8)(-14.5)$ **b)** $\left(-3\frac{1}{3}\right)\left(-2\frac{3}{10}\right)$

   c) $\left(-4\frac{2}{5}\right) \div \left(-1\frac{5}{7}\right)$ **d)** $45.8 \div (-12.2)$

6. a) A student evaluated the expression below and got the answer 1.
   What is the correct answer? How do you know?
   $$\frac{1}{2} + \left(-\frac{3}{4}\right) \div \left(-\frac{1}{4}\right)$$
   b) What might the student have done wrong to get the answer 1?

7. Evaluate. Use a calculator when you need to.
   a) $-3.1 + 4.5 \times (-2.9) - 7.2 \div (-3)$
   b) $(-9.7) \times (-1.2) + 5.4^2 \div (-3.6)$

Investigating Temperature Data

The table shows the monthly lowest temperature, in degrees Celsius, in Edmonton.

Jan.	Feb.	Mar.	Apr.	May	Jun.	Jul.	Aug.	Sep.	Oct.	Nov.	Dec.
−14.7	−12.8	−7.2	0.5	5.9	10.1	12.3	10.6	6.1	−0.8	−8.3	−13.4

1. Determine the mean monthly lowest temperature in Edmonton for that year.
   a) How did you use the order of operations in your calculation?
   b) Which months have temperatures below the mean? How do you know?

Here are the monthly highest temperatures in Edmonton for the same year.

Jan.	Feb.	Mar.	Apr.	May	Jun.	Jul.	Aug.	Sep.	Oct.	Nov.	Dec.
−5.8	−2.9	2.1	10.6	17.2	20.7	23.4	22.2	16.7	9.8	1.1	−4.3

2. Determine the mean monthly highest temperature in Edmonton for that year.

3. Choose three months. For each month, calculate the difference between:
   a) the mean monthly highest temperature and the monthly highest temperature
   b) the mean monthly lowest temperature and the monthly lowest temperature

4. Some climatologists predict that, by the end of the century, due to global warming, the mean temperature will increase by between 1.4°C and 11°C.
   a) How might the mean monthly highest temperature be affected? In what range could this temperature lie in 2100?
   b) Repeat part a for the mean monthly lowest temperature.

Your work should show:
• your calculations for the mean lowest and highest temperatures
• your calculations of the differences in temperatures
• the possible ranges for temperatures in the year 2100

Reflect
on Your Learning

What is the most important thing you have learned about rational numbers? Explain why it is important.

1 **1.** Determine the value of each square root.

a) $\sqrt{\dfrac{1}{25}}$ b) $\sqrt{\dfrac{225}{169}}$ c) $\sqrt{\dfrac{9}{121}}$

d) $\sqrt{1.44}$ e) $\sqrt{0.16}$ f) $\sqrt{3.24}$

2. Determine the side length of a square with each area below. Explain your strategy.

a) 64 cm^2

b) 1.21 m^2

c) 72.25 mm^2

3. Calculate the number whose square root is:

a) 0.7   b) 1.6   c) 0.006

d) $\dfrac{12}{17}$ e) $\dfrac{1}{3}$ f) $\dfrac{2}{13}$

4. Which decimals and fractions are perfect squares? Explain your reasoning.

a) $\dfrac{7}{63}$ b) $\dfrac{12}{27}$ c) $\dfrac{4}{18}$

d) 0.016   e) 4.9   f) 0.121

5. A square garden has area 6.76 m^2.

a) What is the side length of the garden?

b) One side of the garden is against a house. How much fencing is needed to enclose the garden? How do you know?

6. Determine 2 decimals that have square roots from 12 to 13.

7. Use any strategy you wish to estimate the value of each square root.

a) $\sqrt{\dfrac{1}{35}}$ b) $\sqrt{\dfrac{65}{4}}$ c) $\sqrt{0.8}$ d) $\sqrt{0.11}$

8. Determine the unknown length in each triangle to the nearest tenth.

a) 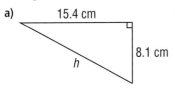   b)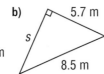

9. This object is built with 1-cm cubes. Determine its surface area.

10. Determine the surface area of each composite object. Give the answers to the nearest whole number. Explain how you accounted for the overlap in each case.

a)

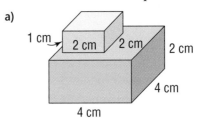

b)

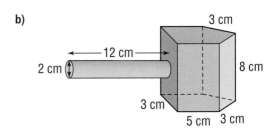

2 **11.** Write each product as a power, then evaluate.

a) $4 \times 4 \times 4$

b) $6 \times 6 \times 6 \times 6$

c) $(-3)(-3)(-3)(-3)(-3)(-3)(-3)$

d) $-(-2)(-2)(-2)(-2)(-2)(-2)(-2)$

e) $-(10 \times 10 \times 10 \times 10 \times 10)$

f) $-(1)(1)(1)(1)(1)(1)(1)(1)(1)(1)(1)(1)$

12. Predict the sign of each answer, then evaluate.

a) $-(-3)^4$ b) $(-5)^6$ c) -4^3

d) $(-7)^2$ e) -7^0 f) $(-10)^0$

13. Write each number using powers of 10.

    a) 800   **b)** 52 000

    c) 1760   **d)** 7 000 004

14. Evaluate.

    a) $[3 \times (-2)^3 - 4]^2$

    b) $(-7 + 5)^2 - [4 + (-1)^3]^2$

    c) $9^2 \div (-3)^3 + 5^2 - 2^5$

    d) $(3^7 - 2^{11})^1 \div (4^7 + 3^8)^0$

    e) $(-4)^2 - 3^3 + (-2)^4 - 1^5$

    f) $[8^4 \div (-4)^6 \times 2^0]^{10}$

15. Express as a single power.

    a) $6^5 \times 6^{11} \div 6^8$

    b) $(-3)^6 \div (-3)^2 \times (-3)^4$

    c) $\dfrac{(-5)^6 \times (-5)^9}{(-5)^7 \times (-5)^5}$

    d) $\dfrac{2^8}{2^2} \times \dfrac{2^{12}}{2^4}$

16. Evaluate.

    a) $7^2 - 4^3 \times 4^0 + 3^2$

    b) $(-2)^8 \div (-2)^4 - (-2)^7 \div (-2)^5$

    c) $-5^2(5^4 \div 5) - 5^3$

    d) $\dfrac{8^{13} \times 8^{14}}{8^{15} \times 8^9}$

17. A wheat field is 10 000 m wide. The area of the field is 10^8 m².

    a) Use the exponent laws to determine the length of the field.

    b) What is the perimeter of the field? Did you use any exponent laws to calculate the perimeter? Explain.

18. Simplify, then evaluate each expression.

    a) $(6^2)^8 \div (6^4)^2$

    b) $(7^4 \div 7^2)^3 + (3^5 \div 3^2)^3$

    c) $[(-2)^5 \div (-2)^4]^3 - [(-5)^2 \times (-5)^3]^0$

    d) $(4 \times 9)^4 + (3^5)^2$

    e) $[(-4)^3]^2 - [(-2)^4]^3 - [(-3)^2]^4$

    f) $[9 \div (-3)]^2 \times 3^4$

3 **19.** Show each set of numbers on a number line. Order the numbers from least to greatest.

    a) $-1.9, -3.3, 4.8, -2.8, 1.2, -3.\overline{3}$

    b) $\dfrac{19}{5}, -\dfrac{13}{4}, \dfrac{3}{4}, -2\dfrac{1}{2}, -\dfrac{13}{10}, -\dfrac{2}{5}$

    c) $1.1, \dfrac{4}{3}, -\dfrac{1}{3}, -1.01, 1\dfrac{3}{8}, -0.11$

    d) $\dfrac{2}{9}, -0.2, 0.25, -\dfrac{1}{6}, -0.\overline{1}, \dfrac{1}{8}$

20. Determine each sum or difference.

    a) $17.4 + (-15.96)$ **b)** $-8.38 + (-1.927)$

    c) $-4.5 - (-13.67)$ **d)** $13.28 - 19.71$

    e) $-\dfrac{3}{4} + \dfrac{2}{3}$ **f)** $1\dfrac{5}{8} + \left(-6\dfrac{1}{3}\right)$

    g) $-\dfrac{17}{4} - \dfrac{11}{3}$ **h)** $3\dfrac{5}{6} - \left(-2\dfrac{2}{3}\right)$

21. The changes in value of a stock were recorded in the table below.

Day	Change in Value ($)
Monday	−0.450
Tuesday	0.327
Wednesday	−0.065

The price of the stock by the end of the day on Wednesday was $85.460. Use rational numbers to calculate the price of the stock on Monday morning.

22. Determine each product or quotient.

    a) $(-14.6)(2.5)$ **b)** $(-12.8)(-12.8)$

    c) $(-8.64) \div (-2.7)$ **d)** $4.592 \div (-0.82)$

    e) $\left(\dfrac{9}{5}\right)\left(6\dfrac{1}{3}\right)$ **f)** $\left(-8\dfrac{3}{4}\right)\left(2\dfrac{2}{15}\right)$

    g) $\left(-\dfrac{5}{12}\right) \div \left(-8\dfrac{1}{3}\right)$ **h)** $\left(-3\dfrac{1}{5}\right) \div 2\dfrac{2}{3}$

23. Evaluate.

    a) $\left(-\dfrac{7}{8}\right) - \dfrac{1}{5} \div \left(-\dfrac{3}{10}\right) - \dfrac{1}{4}$

    b) $(-2.1)(18.5) - 6.8 \div 4$

    c) $\left(-7\dfrac{1}{3}\right)\left(\dfrac{6}{55}\right) + 1\dfrac{1}{2} \div \left(-\dfrac{2}{7}\right)$

    d) $2\dfrac{1}{4} - \left(-3\dfrac{7}{8} + 5\right)\left(\dfrac{4}{9} - 3\right)$

Linear Relations

How do you think music sales have changed over the past 10 years? 20 years?
In what format do you buy the music you listen to?
In what format did your parents buy the music they listened to as students?
Why might record companies be interested in keeping track of these data?

What You'll Learn

- Use expressions and equations to generalize patterns.
- Verify a pattern by using substitution.
- Graph and analyze linear relations.
- Interpolate and extrapolate to solve problems.

Why It's Important

Patterns and relationships are an important part of math. We can model many real-world situations with a linear relation, and use the relation to make predictions and solve problems. For example, the total cost of a pizza is a fixed cost for a particular size, plus a cost that depends on the number of toppings added.

Key Words

- dependent variable
- independent variable
- relation
- linear relation
- interpolation
- extrapolation

151

How Can I Explain My Thinking?

The pattern of figures below continues. Suppose I have to determine a rule for the number of squares in any figure n in this pattern.

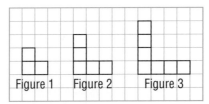

Figure 1   Figure 2   Figure 3

What tools can I use to explain my thinking?

- a diagram
- a table
- words

If I use a diagram, I can colour squares to show the structure of the pattern.

I might see the pattern this way.

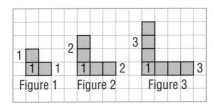

Figure 1   Figure 2   Figure 3

Figure 1: $1 + 1 + 1 = 1 + 2(1)$
Figure 2: $1 + 2 + 2 = 1 + 2(2)$
Figure 3: $1 + 3 + 3 = 1 + 2(3)$
Figure n: $1 + n + n = 1 + 2(n)$

I might also see the pattern this way.

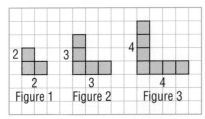

Figure 1   Figure 2   Figure 3

Figure 1: $2 + 2 - 1 = (1 + 1) + (1 + 1) - 1$
Figure 2: $3 + 3 - 1 = (2 + 1) + (2 + 1) - 1$
Figure 3: $4 + 4 - 1 = (3 + 1) + (3 + 1) - 1$
Figure n: $\quad\quad\quad\quad (n + 1) + (n + 1) - 1$

I am counting the yellow square twice, so I will have to subtract 1.

I might also see the pattern a third way.

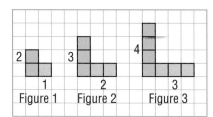

Figure 1: $2 + 1 = (1 + 1) + 1$
Figure 2: $3 + 2 = (2 + 1) + 2$
Figure 3: $4 + 3 = (3 + 1) + 3$
Figure n: $(n + 1) + n$

Figure Number	Number of Squares	Pattern
1	3	$2(1) + 1$
2	5	$2(2) + 1$
3	7	$2(3) + 1$
n		$2n + 1$

With each figure, I add 2 extra squares.
The numbers of squares are odd numbers.
Each number is 1 more than a multiple of 2.
So, figure n has $2n + 1$ squares.

If I use a table, I could record the number of squares in each figure and look for a pattern in the numbers. I could explain the pattern in words.

Check

Use the tools *you* find most helpful to determine a rule for the number of squares in figure n of each pattern.

1.

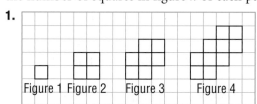

Figure 1   Figure 2   Figure 3   Figure 4

2.

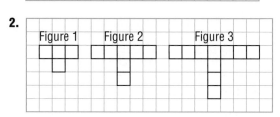

Figure 1   Figure 2   Figure 3

Writing Equations to Describe Patterns

FOCUS

• Use equations to describe and solve problems involving patterns.

Here is a pattern made from square tiles.

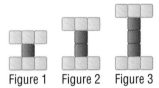

Figure 1   Figure 2   Figure 3

What stays the same in each figure? What changes?
How can we determine the number of square tiles in any figure in the pattern?

Investigate

A banquet hall has small square tables that seat 1 person on each side.
The tables can be pushed together to form longer tables.

1 table   2 tables   3 tables

The pattern continues.

➤ Sketch the next 2 table arrangements in the pattern.
  What stays the same in each arrangement? What changes?

➤ What different strategies can you use to determine the number of people at
  6 tables? At 10 tables? At 25 tables?

Compare your strategies and results with those of your classmates.
If you used different strategies, explain your strategies.
If you did not write an equation, work together to determine an equation
that relates the number of people to the number of tables.
Use the equation to determine:

• the number of people at 30 tables
• the number of tables needed to seat 30 people

A landscape designer uses wooden boards as edging for the plots in a herb garden.

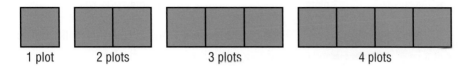

1 plot   2 plots   3 plots   4 plots

The number of boards, b, is *related* to the number of plots, p.
This relationship can be represented in different ways:

- using pictures
- using a table of values
- using an equation

Here are 2 ways to determine the equation.

➤ Determine a pattern in the number of boards.

Number of Plots, p	Number of Boards, b
1	4
2	7
3	10
4	13

+1 ⟩ +3
+1 ⟩ +3
+1 ⟩ +3

As the number of plots increases by 1,
the number of boards increases by 3.
Repeated addition of 3 is the same as multiplication by 3.
This suggests that the number of boards may be 3 times
the number of plots. So, the equation $b = 3p$ may represent
this relationship.

Check whether the equation $b = 3p$ is correct.
When $p = 1$,
$$b = 3(1)$$
$$= 3$$

This is 1 less than the number 4 in the table.
So, we add 1 to $3p$ to describe the number of
boards correctly.

The terms $3p + 1$ form an *expression* that represents
the number of boards for any number of plots p.
An equation is: $b = 3p + 1$

Number of Plots, p	Number of Boards, b
1	$3(1) + 1 = 4$
2	$3(2) + 1 = 7$
3	$3(3) + 1 = 10$
4	$3(4) + 1 = 13$

We verify the equation by substituting values of p and b
from the table.
For example, check by substituting $p = 4$ and $b = 13$ in $b = 3p + 1$.
Left side: $b = 13$ Right side: $3p + 1 = 3(4) + 1$
$$= 12 + 1$$
$$= 13$$
Since the left side equals the right side, the equation is verified.

➤ Determine a pattern in the figures that represent the garden.

| 1 plot | 2 plots | 3 plots | 4 plots |

Number of Plots, *p*	Pattern in the Number of Boards	Number of Boards, *b*
1	1 + 3	1 + 1(3)
2	1 + 3 + 3	1 + 2(3)
3	1 + 3 + 3 + 3	1 + 3(3)
4	1 + 3 + 3 + 3 + 3	1 + 4(3)
⋮		⋮
p		1 + *p*(3)

Each garden needs 1 board for the left border and 3 additional boards for each plot.
That is,
Number of boards = 1 + (Number of plots) × 3
As an equation:
$b = 1 + p(3)$
This can be rewritten as:
$b = 1 + 3p$

Addition is commutative, so $1 + 3p = 3p + 1$.
The equation gives a general pattern rule. We say the equation *generalizes* the pattern. We can use the equation to determine the value of any term.

| **Example 1** | **Writing an Equation to Represent a Written Pattern** |

An airplane is cruising at a height of 10 000 m. It descends to land. This table shows the height of the plane every minute after it began its descent. The height of the plane changes at a constant rate.

Time (*t* minutes)	Height (*h* metres)
0	10 000
1	9 700
2	9 400
3	9 100
4	8 800

a) Write an expression for the height in terms of the time since the plane began its descent.
b) Write an equation that relates the height of the plane to the time since it began its descent.
c) What is the height of the plane after 15 min?
d) How long after beginning its descent does the plane land?

▶ A Solution

a) When the time increases by 1 min, the height decreases by 300 m.
Add a third column to the table and write the height in terms of time.

Time (t minutes)	Height (h metres)	Height in Terms of Time
0	10 000	$10\,000 - 0 = 10\,000$
1	9 700	$10\,000 - 300(1) = 9700$
2	9 400	$10\,000 - 300(2) = 9400$
3	9 100	$10\,000 - 300(3) = 9100$
4	8 800	$10\,000 - 300(4) = 8800$
⋮		⋮
t		$10\,000 - 300(t)$

(Left side: +1 between each time row. Right side: −300 between each height expression.)

An expression for the height in terms of time is: $10\,000 - 300t$

b) For an equation that relates height to time, equate the expression in part a to the height, h.
An equation is: $h = 10\,000 - 300t$

c) To determine the height of the plane after 15 min, substitute $t = 15$ in the equation:

$$h = 10\,000 - 300t$$
$$= 10\,000 - 300(15)$$
$$= 10\,000 - 4500$$
$$= 5500$$

After 15 min, the plane is at a height of 5500 m.

d) When the plane lands, its height is 0.
Substitute $h = 0$ in the equation $h = 10\,000 - 300t$, then solve for t.

$$h = 10\,000 - 300t$$
$$0 = 10\,000 - 300t$$
$$300t + 0 = 10\,000 - 300t + 300t$$
$$300t = 10\,000$$
$$\frac{300t}{300} = \frac{10\,000}{300}$$
$$t = 33.\overline{3}$$

The plane lands about 33 min after beginning its descent.

I called Kelly's Cabs. The cost of a ride is shown on a poster in the cab.

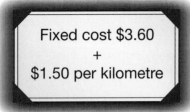

Fixed cost $3.60
+
$1.50 per kilometre

a) Write an expression for the fare in terms of the fixed cost and the cost per kilometre.
b) Write an equation that relates the fare to the distance travelled.
c) What is the fare for an 11-km ride?

▶ *A Solution*

a) The fare is $3.60, plus $1.50 per kilometre.
   That is, the fare is 3.60 + 1.50 × (distance in kilometres).
   Let d represent the distance in kilometres.
   So, an expression for the fare is: $3.60 + 1.50 × d$, or $3.60 + 1.50d$
b) Let F represent the fare in dollars.
   Then, an equation that relates F and d is: $F = 3.60 + 1.50d$
c) To determine the cost for an 11-km trip, use the equation: $F = 3.60 + 1.50d$
   Substitute: $d = 11$
   $F = 3.60 + 1.50(11)$
   $ = 3.60 + 16.50$
   $ = 20.10$
   The fare for an 11-km ride is $20.10.

Discuss the ideas

1. What different ways can you represent a relationship between two quantities?

2. What are the advantages and disadvantages of each way you described in question 1?

3. Suppose you have determined an equation that you think may describe a pattern.
   a) How could you check that your equation is correct?
   b) If you need to adjust the equation, how can you determine what needs to be changed?

Check

4. In each equation, determine the value of P when $n = 1$.

   a) $P = 2n$ b) $P = 3n$ c) $P = 4n$ d) $P = 5n$

5. In each equation, determine the value of A when $n = 2$.

   a) $A = 3n + 1$ b) $A = 3n + 2$
   c) $A = 3n + 3$ d) $A = 3n + 4$

6. In a table of values for a pattern, $P = 3$ when $n = 1$; which of the following equations might represent the pattern?

   a) $P = 3n$ b) $P = n + 3$
   c) $P = 2n + 1$ d) $P = 3 - n$

7. The pattern in this table continues. Which expression below represents the number of squares in terms of the figure number?

Figure, f	Number of Squares, s
1	6
2	7
3	8
4	9
5	10

   a) $5f$ b) $2f$ c) $f + 5$ d) $s + 5$

8. This pattern of squares continues. Which equation below relates the number of squares, n, in a picture to the size number, s?

Size 1   Size 2   Size 3

   a) $n = s + 4$ b) $n = 4s$
   c) $n = 4s + 1$ d) $s = 4n$

9. The pattern in this table continues. Which equation below relates the number of squares to the figure number?

Figure, f	Number of Squares, s
1	5
2	7
3	9
4	11
5	13

   a) $s = 4f + 1$ b) $s = 2f + 3$
   c) $s = f + 2$ d) $f = 2s + 3$

10. Here is a pattern made with toothpicks. The pattern continues.

1 house 2 houses   3 houses   4 houses

  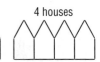

Here are the toothpicks rearranged to show what stays the same and what changes in each picture.

1 house 2 houses   3 houses   4 houses

  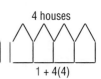

$1 + 1(4)$ $1 + 2(4)$ $1 + 3(4)$ $1 + 4(4)$

   a) Explain how the numbers in the expression below each picture describe the arrangement of toothpicks in the picture.
   b) Let n represent the number of houses in a picture. Write an expression for the number of toothpicks in n houses.
   c) Write an equation that relates the number of toothpicks, t, to n.
   d) Verify the equation by showing that it produces the correct number of toothpicks for the first four pictures in the pattern.

Apply

11. The pattern in each table below continues. For each table:

   i) Describe the pattern that relates v to t.

   ii) Write an expression for v in terms of t.

   iii) Write an equation that relates v to t.

   iv) Verify your equation by substituting values from the table.

a)

Term Number, t	Term Value, v
1	11
2	22
3	33
4	44

b)

Term Number, t	Term Value, v
1	5
2	8
3	11
4	14

c)

Term Number, t	Term Value, v
1	7
2	6
3	5
4	4

12. Here is a pattern of triangles made with congruent toothpicks. The pattern continues.

Figure 1   Figure 2   Figure 3   Figure 4

   a) Make a table of values for the figure number and the number of toothpicks in a figure. What patterns do you see?

   b) Write an expression for the number of toothpicks, t, in figure n.

   c) Determine the number of toothpicks in figure 45.

   d) Write an equation that relates t to n.

   e) Which figure has 17 toothpicks? How could you check your answer?

13. **Assessment Focus** Hexagonal tables are arranged as shown. The pattern continues. One person sits at each side of a table.

1 table   2 tables   3 tables   4 tables

   a) Determine the number of people who can be seated at each table arrangement. Record your results in a table.

   b) Describe the patterns in the table.

   c) What strategies can you use to determine the number of people who could be seated at any table arrangement in the pattern?

   d) Write an equation that relates the number of people, p, who can be seated at n tables. How can you check that your equation is correct?

   e) How many tables are needed to seat 41 people? How could you check your answer?

   Show your work.

14. The cost to print brochures is the sum of a fixed cost of $250, plus $1.25 per brochure.

   a) Write an equation that relates the total cost, C dollars, to the number of brochures, n.

   b) What is the cost of printing 2500 brochures?

   c) How many brochures can be printed for $625?

   Justify your answers.

15. A pizza with tomato sauce and cheese costs $9.00.

Each additional topping costs $0.75.

a) Create a table that shows the costs of a pizza for up to 5 toppings.

b) Write an equation that relates the cost, C dollars, to the number of toppings, n. Verify your equation by substituting values of n from the table.

c) Suppose a pizza costs $15.00. How many toppings were ordered? What strategy did you use? Try a different strategy to check your answer.

16. Clint has a window cleaning service. He charges a fixed cost of $12, plus $1.50 per window.

a) Write an equation that relates the total cost to the number of windows cleaned. How do you know that your equation is correct?

b) Clint charged $28.50 for a job. How many windows did he clean? How do you know?

17. A landscaper uses square patio stones as a border around a rectangular garden. The number of patio stones needed depends on the size of the garden. This pattern continues.

| Size 1 | Size 2 | Size 3 | Size 4 |

The landscaper uses 152 stones. What size of garden does she make? How can you check your answer?

18. Here is another way to rearrange the toothpicks in question 10.

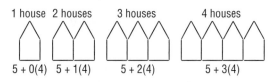

a) Explain how the expression below each picture describes the number of toothpicks in the picture.

b) Suppose n represents the number of houses. Write an equation that relates the number of toothpicks, t, to the number of houses, n.

c) Compare the equation in part b with the equation in question 10c. How can two different equations represent the same pattern? Explain.

19. Here is a pattern of squares. Each square has side length 1 cm. The pattern continues.

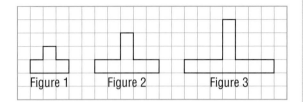

Figure 1   Figure 2   Figure 3

a) Make a table that shows each figure number, its perimeter, and its area.
b) Write an equation that can be used to determine the perimeter of any figure in the pattern. Verify the equation. How did you do this?
c) Write an equation that can be used to determine the area of any figure in the pattern. Verify the equation.
d) Determine the perimeter and area of figure 50.
e) Which figure has a perimeter of 100 cm?
f) Which figure has an area of 100 cm²?

20. The pattern in this table continues.

Term Number, *t*	Term Value, *v*
1	80
2	76
3	72
4	68

a) Write an equation that relates *v* to *t*.
b) Verify your equation by substituting values from the table.

21. Marcel has a sheet of paper. He cuts the paper in half to produce two pieces. Marcel places one piece on top of the other. He then cuts these pieces in half. The pattern continues. The table below shows some of Marcel's results.

Number of Cuts	1	2	3	4	5	6	7	8	9	10
Number of Pieces	2	4	8							

a) Copy and complete the table.
b) What patterns do you see in the numbers of pieces?
c) Determine the number of pieces after 15 cuts.
d) Write an equation that relates the number of pieces, *P*, to the number of cuts, *n*.
e) How many cuts have to be made to get more than 50 000 pieces? Explain how you found out.

Reflect

Describe some different ways to represent a pattern.
Which way do you prefer when you use a pattern to solve a problem?
Explain your choice.

Tables of Values and Graphing

A spreadsheet can be used to create a table of values or to graph a relation.

A taxi company charges a fixed cost of $2.70, plus $1.58 per kilometre travelled.

To create a table of values, first write an equation. Let d represent the distance travelled in kilometres and F represent the fare in dollars. Then the equation that relates d and F is: $F = 2.70 + 1.58d$

Generate a table of values.
Graph the data. If you need to, use the Help menu to show you how to do this with your software.

FOCUS

- Use a spreadsheet to create a table of values and a graph.

	A	B
1	d	F
2	0	2.7
3	1	4.28
4	2	5.86
5	3	7.44
6	4	9.02
7	5	10.6
8	6	12.18
9	7	13.76
10	8	15.34
11	9	16.92
12	10	18.5
13	11	20.08
14	12	21.66
15	13	23.24
16	14	24.82
17	15	26.4
18	16	27.98
19	17	29.56
20	18	31.14
21	19	32.72
22	20	34.3

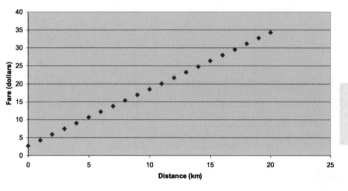

Your table and graph should look similar to these.

Check

1. A second taxi company charges a fixed cost of $4.20, plus $1.46 per kilometre.

a) Write an equation that relates the fare to the distance travelled.

b) Use a spreadsheet to generate a table of values.

c) Use the spreadsheet to graph the equation.

2. In Lesson 4.1, you solved problems involving equations. Choose two questions from *Practice*. For each question:

a) Use a spreadsheet to generate a table of values and solve the problem.

b) Use the spreadsheet to graph the equation.

4.2 Linear Relations

When a scuba diver goes under water, the weight of the water exerts pressure on the diver.

FOCUS

• Analyze the graph of a linear relation.

Diver's Depth (m)	Approximate Water Pressure (kiloPascals)
0	0
5	50
10	100
15	150
20	200

Pressure on a Diver

What patterns do you see in the table and in the graph?
What do these patterns tell you about the relationship between depth and water pressure?

Investigate

A local phone company offers a cell phone plan that has a fixed cost per month and a cost related to the number of text messages sent. The fixed cost is $20 and each message sent costs 10¢.

Represent the relation between the total cost and the number of text messages sent, as many different ways as you can.

Compare your representations with those of another pair of students. Did you use the same way to represent the pattern? If your patterns are different, explain your pattern to the other students.
If you represented the relation in a different way from your classmates, explain your way to them.

The first 4 rectangles in a pattern are shown below. The pattern continues.
Each small square has side length 1 cm.

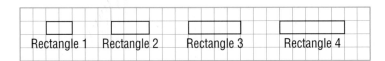

Rectangle 1   Rectangle 2   Rectangle 3   Rectangle 4

The perimeter of a rectangle is related to the rectangle number.
We can use words, a table, a graph, and an equation to represent this relationship.
Each representation tells us about the relationship between the rectangle number
and its perimeter.

In Words

Rectangle 1 has perimeter 6 cm; then, as the rectangle number increases by 1,
its perimeter increases by 2 cm.

In a Table

Rectangle Number, n	Perimeter, P (cm)
1	$6 = 2(1) + 4$
2	$8 = 2(2) + 4$
3	$10 = 2(3) + 4$
4	$12 = 2(4) + 4$

+1 +2

+1 +2

+1 +2

As the rectangle number
increases by 1, the perimeter
increases by 2 cm.

In a Graph

The graph also shows the pattern. After the first
point, each point on the graph is 1 unit right and
2 units up from the preceding point. If we place a
transparent ruler on the points, we see that they lie
on a straight line.

We do not join the points because the data are
discrete.

Graph of P against n

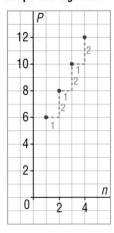

In an Equation

For rectangle n, the perimeter will be $2n + 4$.

The equation is: $P = 2n + 4$

The equation tells us that we can calculate the perimeter of any rectangle in the pattern by multiplying the rectangle number by 2, then adding 4.

The value of the variable P *depends* on the value of the variable n.

We say that P is the **dependent variable** and we plot it on the vertical axis.

The **independent variable** n is plotted on the horizontal axis.

When two variables are related, we have a **relation**.

> ▶ **Linear Relation**
>
> When the graph of the relation is a straight line, we have a **linear relation**. In a linear relation, a constant change in one quantity produces a constant change in the related quantity.

In the relation above, a constant change of 1 in n produced a constant change of 2 cm in P.

Here is the equation of a linear relation: $y = 3x - 5$

x is the independent variable and it is plotted on the horizontal axis.

y is the dependent variable and it is plotted on the vertical axis.

Here are the table and graph that represent this equation.

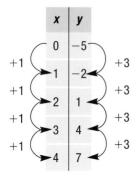

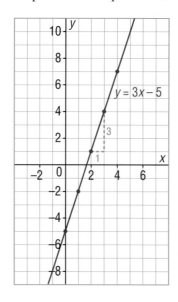

Write the equation on the grid.

When x increases by 1, y increases by 3. This is shown in the table and on the graph.

Since the points lie on a straight line, the equation $y = 3x - 5$ represents a linear relation.

Since we are not told that the data are discrete, we join the points with a line.

Example 1 **Graphing a Linear Relation from a Table of Values**

The table of values shows the cost of renting DVDs
at an online store.

a) Graph the data. Does it make sense to join
the points on the graph? Explain.

b) Is the relation linear? Justify your answer.

c) Use the table to describe the pattern in the rental costs.
How is this pattern shown in the graph?

Number of DVDs Rented, d	Cost, C ($)
1	3.50
2	7.00
3	10.50
4	14.00
5	17.50

▶ *A Solution*

a) Plot the points on a grid.

Cost to Rent DVDs

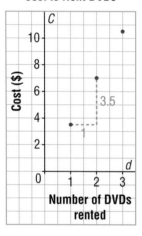

Since the cost depends
on the number of DVDs
rented, plot d horizontally
and C vertically.

The number of DVDs rented
is a whole number. We cannot
rent 1.5 DVDs or any other
fractional number of DVDs.
So, it does not make sense to
join the points.

b) The points on the graph lie on a straight line, so the relation is linear.

c) As the number of DVDs rented increases by 1, the rental cost increases by
$3.50. Each point on the graph is 1 unit right and 3.5 units up from the
previous point. The pattern of increases in the table produces a graph that
is a straight line.

Example 2 **Graphing a Linear Relation from an Equation**

A relation has the equation: $y = 6 - 3x$

a) Create a table of values for the relation for values of x from -3 to 3.

b) Graph the relation. Does it make sense to join the points on the graph? Explain.

c) What patterns are in the graph? How do these patterns relate to the table of values?

d) Is the relation linear? Justify your answer.

▶ Solutions

Method 1	Method 2

Method 1

a), b) To create a table of values, substitute the given values of x in the equation:

$$y = 6 - 3x$$

Substitute: $x = -3$	Substitute: $x = -2$
$y = 6 - 3(-3)$	$y = 6 - 3(-2)$
$\quad = 6 + 9$	$\quad = 6 + 6$
$\quad = 15$	$\quad = 12$
Substitute: $x = -1$	Substitute: $x = 0$
$y = 6 - 3(-1)$	$y = 6 - 3(0)$
$\quad = 6 + 3$	$\quad = 6 - 0$
$\quad = 9$	$\quad = 6$

Use mental math to repeat the above process for $x = 1$, $x = 2$, and $x = 3$. Write the values of x and y in a table.

x	y
−3	15
−2	12
−1	9
0	6
1	3
2	0
3	−3

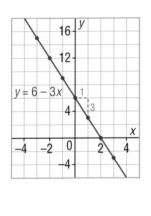

Since the data are not discrete, join the points to form a line.

Method 2

Use a spreadsheet.

a) Input the equation and make a table.

	A	B
1	x	y
2	-3	15
3	-2	12
4	-1	9
5	0	6
6	1	3
7	2	0
8	3	-3

b) Highlight the table. Graph the data.

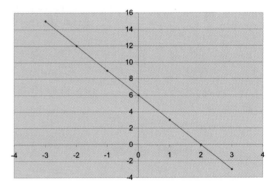

c) On the graph, to get from one point to the next, move 1 unit right and 3 units down.
In the table, when x increases by 1, y decreases by 3.

d) The relation is linear because its graph is a straight line.

Example 3   **Solving Problems Using a Linear Relation**

The student council is planning to hold a dance. The profit in dollars is 4 times the number of students who attend, minus $200 for the cost of the music.
a) Write an equation that relates the profit to the number of students who attend.
b) Create a table of values for this relation.
c) Graph the data in the table. Does it make sense to join the points? Explain.
d) How many students have to attend to make a profit?

▶ *A Solution*

a) Profit in dollars = 4 × number of students who attend − 200
   Choose variables to represent the numbers that change.
   Let n represent the number of students who attend.
   Let P represent the profit in dollars.
   An equation is: $P = 4n - 200$

b) Choose 3 values for n, then calculate the corresponding values of P.
   Use the equation: $P = 4n - 200$

n	P
0	−200
50	0
100	200

   Substitute: $n = 0$ Substitute: $n = 50$ Substitute: $n = 100$
   $P = 4(0) - 200$ $P = 4(50) - 200$ $P = 4(100) - 200$
   $\quad = 0 - 200$ $\quad = 200 - 200$ $\quad = 400 - 200$
   $\quad = -200$ $\quad = 0$ $\quad = 200$

c) Plot the points on a grid.

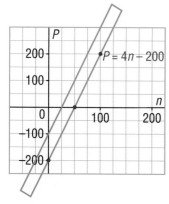

A straightedge verifies that the points lie on a straight line.
Some values between the plotted points are permitted, but not others.
For example, there could be 82 students attending the dance, but not 82.5.
So, the points are not joined.

d) When P is negative, a loss is made.
   When $P = 0$, $n = 50$, and the profit is 0.
   When $P > 0$, $n > 50$, and there is a profit.
   So, 51 or more students have to attend before a profit can be made.

Discuss the ideas

1. a) How do you know whether a graph represents a linear relation?
   b) How do you know whether a table of values represents a linear relation?

2. a) How many points do you need to graph a line?
   b) Why do we often use 3 points? Should we use more points? Explain.

3. How do you know when to connect the points on a graph?

Practice

Check

4. Which graphs represent a linear relation? How do you know?

a)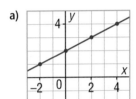

b)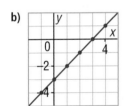

c)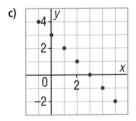

d)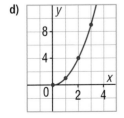

e)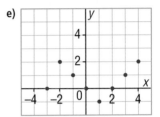

Apply

5. For each table of values below:
   i) Does it represent a linear relation?
   ii) If the relation is linear, describe it.
   iii) If the relation is not linear, explain how you know.

a)
x	y
1	4
2	13
3	22
4	31
5	40

b)
x	y
9	8
8	11
7	14
6	17
5	20

c)
x	y
0	0
1	2
2	6
3	12
4	20

d)
x	y
1	3
4	5
7	7
10	9
13	11

6. Graph the linear relations you identified in question 5. How does each graph verify your answers to question 5?

7. Copy and complete each table of values.

a) $y = 2x$

x	y
1	
2	
3	
4	

b) $y = x + 2$

x	y
1	
2	
3	
4	

c) $y = -2x$

x	y
2	
4	
6	
8	

d) $y = x - 2$

x	y
4	
5	
6	
7	

8. Here is a partially completed table of values for a linear relation.

x	2	3	4	5	6	7	8
y				15	18		

a) Determine the missing values of y. Explain how you found these values.

b) Describe the patterns in the table.

c) Write an equation that represents the linear relation. How do you know that your equation is correct?

d) Graph the data. How are the patterns you described in part b shown in the graph?

e) Suppose you want to determine the value of y when $x = -1$. How could you use the table and equation to do this? What is the value of y when $x = -1$?

9. Each table of values represents a linear relation. Copy and complete each table. Explain your reasoning.

a)

x	y
2	11
3	14
4	
5	
6	

b)

x	y
1	
3	8
5	9
7	
9	

c)

x	y
-4	
-2	7
0	3
2	
4	

d)

x	y
4	
6	-7
8	-4
10	
12	

10. Create a table of values for each linear relation, then graph the relation. Use values of x from -2 to 2.

a) $y = 3x$

b) $y = x + 3$

c) $y = x - 3$

d) $y = 5 - x$

e) $y = 1 - 4x$

f) $y = -2x - 3$

11. Jin is cycling at an average speed of 4 m/s. He travels a distance, d metres, in t seconds.

a) Write an equation that relates d and t.

b) Create a table of values for this relation.

c) Graph the data. Should you join the points? Explain your reasoning.

d) Is the relation between distance and time linear?

   i) How do you know from the table of values?

   ii) How you know from the graph?

e) How far does Jin travel in 3.5 h?

f) What time does it take Jin to travel 17 km?

12. In 2008, the Goods and Services Tax (GST) was 5%. To determine the tax, T dollars, charged on a given purchase price, p dollars, multiply the purchase price by 0.05.

a) Write an equation that relates T to p.

b) Copy and complete this table of values.

p	0	10	20	30	40
T					

c) What patterns do you see in the table?

d) Graph the data.
Which variable will you plot on the horizontal axis? Explain your reasoning.

e) Should you connect the points on the graph? Explain.

f) How are the patterns in the table shown in the graph?

13. An amusement park charges an admission fee of $10, plus $2 per ride.

a) Choose variables to represent the total cost in dollars and the number of rides that are taken. Write an equation that relates the total cost to the number of rides.

b) Graph the equation.

c) What is the total cost for 7 rides?

d) How many rides can be taken for a total cost of $38?

14. Assessment Focus Danica is having a party. She estimates that she will need 3 pieces of pizza for each guest invited, and 6 extra pieces in case someone shows up unexpectedly.

a) Explain why this situation can be represented by the equation $P = 3n + 6$. What do P and n represent in the equation?

b) Make a table of values for the relation.

c) Graph the data. Will you join the points on the graph? Explain.

d) Is the relation linear?
   i) How do you know from the table of values?
   ii) How do you know from the graph?

e) If the relation is linear, explain what this means in the context of this situation.

15. A small plane is at a height of 1800 m when it starts descending to land.
The plane's height changes at an average rate of 150 m per minute.

a) Choose variables to represent the height in metres and the time in minutes since the plane began its descent. Write an equation that relates the height to the time.

b) Graph the equation.

c) What is the height of the plane 6 min after it began its descent?

d) When is the plane 100 m above the ground?

16. Jada rollerblades from Regina to Saskatoon to raise funds for cancer research. The trip is 250 km. Jada estimates that she can rollerblade at an average speed of 8 km/h.

a) Choose variables to represent the time Jada has travelled in hours and the distance in kilometres that she has yet to travel. Write an equation that relates the distance to the time.

b) Graph the equation.

c) How far has Jada still to travel after 12 h?

d) How many hours will it take Jada to complete the trip?

17. Describe a situation that could be represented by each equation.

a) $M = 2n + 5$
b) $E = 3.50n$
c) $C = 12 + 5d$
d) $H = 100 - 5n$

Take It Further

18. This table of values represents a linear relation. Copy and complete the table. Explain your reasoning.

x	−3	−1	2	5	9	14	20
y	29		23				

Reflect

What does it mean when we say that the relation between two quantities is linear? What patterns are there in the table of values and in the graph of a linear relation? Include examples in your explanation.

Math Link

Science

When an object falls to the ground, it accelerates due to the force of gravity. The relation between the speed of the object and the time it falls is linear.

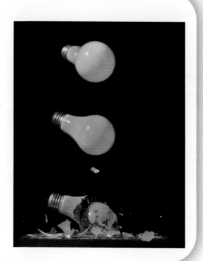

4.3 Another Form of the Equation for a Linear Relation

FOCUS

• Recognize the equations of horizontal, vertical, and oblique lines, and graph them.

Investigate

Suppose you have a piece of ribbon 20 cm long.

➤ How many different ways could you cut it into two pieces?
What are the possible lengths of the two pieces?

➤ How are the lengths of the two pieces related?
Show this relation:

• in words
• in a table
• in a graph
• as an equation

Reflect & Share

Share your different forms of the relation with another pair of students.
If any forms are different, is one of the forms incorrect?
How could you find out?
If you wrote your equation the same way, try to think of a different way to write it.

Two integers have a sum of 3.

Let x and y represent the two integers.

Here is a table of values and a graph to represent the relation.

First Integer, x	Second Integer, y
−6	9
−4	7
−2	5
0	3
2	1
4	−1
6	−3

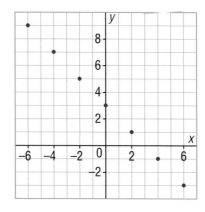

The points lie on a straight line, so the relation is linear.

We can write this linear relation as:

First integer + second integer = 3

Then, the linear relation is: $x + y = 3$

This equation has both variables on the left side of the equation.

It illustrates another way to write the equation of a linear relation.

Suppose one variable does not appear in the equation.

➤ Suppose x does not appear in $x + y = 3$.
  Then we have the equation $y = 3$.
  To graph this equation on a grid,
  plot points that have a y-coordinate of 3.
  All the points lie on a horizontal line
  that is 3 units above the x-axis.

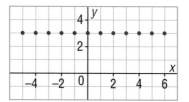

➤ Suppose y does not appear in $x + y = 3$.
  Then we have the equation $x = 3$.
  To graph this equation on a grid,
  plot points that have an x-coordinate of 3.
  All the points lie on a vertical line that is
  3 units to the right of the y-axis.

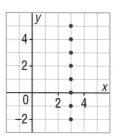

The graph of the equation $x = a$, where a is a constant, is a vertical line. Every point on the graph has an x-coordinate of a.

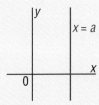

The graph of the equation $y = a$, where a is a constant, is a horizontal line. Every point on the graph has a y-coordinate of a.

Example 1   **Graphing and Describing Horizontal and Vertical Lines**

For each equation below:
i) Graph the equation.
ii) Describe the graph.

a) $x = -4$ b) $y + 2 = 0$ c) $2x = 5$

▶ *A Solution*

a) $x = -4$

i) The x-coordinate of every point on this line is -4.
ii) The graph is a vertical line that intersects the x-axis at -4.

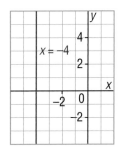

b) $y + 2 = 0$ Solve for y.
   $y + 2 - 2 = 0 - 2$ Subtract 2 from each side.
         $y = -2$

i) The y-coordinate of every point on this line is -2.
ii) The graph is a horizontal line that intersects the y-axis at -2.

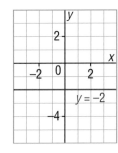

c) $2x = 5$ Solve for x.

$\dfrac{2x}{2} = \dfrac{5}{2}$ Divide both sides by 2.

$x = 2.5$

  i) The x-coordinate of every point
     on this line is 2.5.

  ii) The graph is a vertical line that
      intersects the x-axis at 2.5.

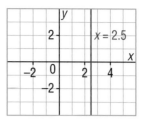

Example 2	Graphing an Equation in the Form $ax + by = c$

For the equation $3x - 2y = 6$:

a) Make a table of values for $x = -4$, 0, and 4.

b) Graph the equation.

▶ *A Solution*

a) $3x - 2y = 6$

  Substitute each value of x, then solve for y.

Substitute: $x = -4$	Substitute: $x = 0$	Substitute: $x = 4$
$3(-4) - 2y = 6$	$3(0) - 2y = 6$	$3(4) - 2y = 6$
$-12 - 2y = 6$	$0 - 2y = 6$	$12 - 2y = 6$
$-2y = 6 + 12$	$-2y = 6$	$-2y = 6 - 12$
$-2y = 18$	$y = -3$	$-2y = -6$
$y = -9$		$y = 3$

x	y
-4	-9
0	-3
4	3

b) Plot the points on a grid.
   Join the points.

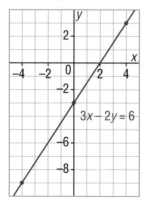

---

1. The graph of an equation such as $3x - 2y = 6$ is a slanted or an *oblique* line. How are the equations for oblique lines different from the equations for horizontal and vertical lines?

2. Students often mistakenly think that $x = 3$ is a horizontal line instead of a vertical line.
   Why might they make this mistake? How might the students reason to avoid making this mistake?

3. How do you recognize the equation of:
   a) a vertical line?   **b)** a horizontal line?

Practice

Check

4. Which equation describes each graph?
   i) $x = -2$ **ii)** $x = 2$
   iii) $y = -2$ **iv)** $y = 2$

   a)

   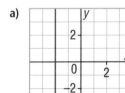

   b)

   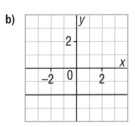

5. Does each equation describe a vertical line, a horizontal line, or an oblique line?
   Describe each horizontal and vertical line.
   a) $y = 7$ **b)** $x - y = 3$
   c) $x = -5$ **d)** $x + 9 = 0$
   e) $2y = 5$ **f)** $y = 6 - 2x$

Apply

6. Describe the graph of each line. Graph each line to check your description.
   a) $y = 5$ **b)** $x = -1$
   c) $x = -5$ **d)** $y = 7$

7. Write an equation to describe each line.

   a)

   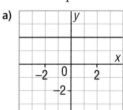

   b)

   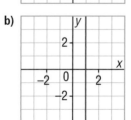

   c)

   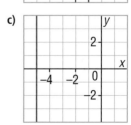

8. Which equation best describes the graph below? Explain your choice.

a) $x - 2 = 0$ b) $2x + 1 = 0$

c) $2y - 1 = 0$ d) $2x - 1 = 0$

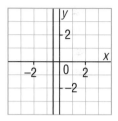

9. The sum of two numbers is 15. Let p and q represent the two numbers.

a) Complete a table for 6 different values of p.

b) Graph the data. Should you join the points? Explain.

c) Write an equation that relates p and q.

10. a) For each equation below:

- Make a table of values for $x = -2, 0,$ and 2.
- Graph the equation.

i) $x + y = 6$ ii) $x - y = 6$

iii) $x + y = -6$ iv) $x - y = -6$

b) How are the graphs in part a alike? How are they different?

11. Graph each line. Explain your work.

a) $y + 3 = -2$ b) $2x = 7$

c) $3x + 1 = -5$ d) $2y - 2 = 10$

12. Write the equations of the lines that intersect to form the shaded rectangle.

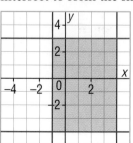

13. Assessment Focus

a) Graph the following lines on the same grid. What shape do they form?

i) $x = -3$ ii) $y = 2$

iii) $x - 1 = 0$ iv) $y + 2 = 0$

b) Construct a congruent shape on the grid with one of its vertices at the origin.

c) Write the equations of the lines that form the shape you drew.

d) Is there more than one shape you can draw in part b? If your answer is yes, draw any more possible shapes.

Show your work.

14. The distance between Edmonton and Calgary is about 300 km. Kate leaves Calgary to drive to Edmonton.

Let t kilometres represent the distance Kate has travelled. Let e kilometres represent the distance she has yet to travel to Edmonton.

a) Copy and complete this table for 6 different values of t.

Distance Travelled, t (km)	Distance to Edmonton, e (km)
0	300

b) What is the greatest value of t that could be in the table? Explain.

c) Graph the data. Should you join the points? Explain.

d) Write an equation that relates t and e.

15. For each equation below:
- Make a table for the given values of x.
- Graph the equation.

a) $2x + y = 6$; for $x = -3, 0, 3$

b) $3x - y = 2$; for $x = -2, 0, 2$

c) $x + 2y = -6$; for $x = -4, 0, 4$

d) $3x - 2y = -6$; for $x = -2, 0, 2$

16. a) On a grid, draw horizontal and vertical lines to construct a shape that satisfies the following conditions:
- The shape is a square with area 9 square units.
- One vertex is at the origin.

b) Write the equations of the lines that form the square.

c) Is it possible to draw another square that satisfies the conditions in part a? If your answer is yes, draw this square and write the equations of the lines that form it.

17. The difference of two numbers is 6. Let a represent the greater number and b the lesser number.

a) Complete a table for 6 different values of a.

b) Graph the data. Should you join the points? Explain.

c) Write an equation that relates b and a.

18. a) Graph these equations on the same grid:
$$x = 2 \quad y = 1 \quad x + y = 8$$

b) What shape is formed by the lines in part a? How do you know?

Take It Further

19. The sum of two rational numbers is $2\frac{1}{2}$.

a) Choose two variables to represent these rational numbers. Make a table to show 5 possible pairs of numbers that satisfy this relation.

b) Graph the data. Describe your graph.

c) Write an equation for the relation.

20. The difference of two rational numbers is -7.5.

a) Choose two variables to represent these rational numbers. Make a table to show 5 possible pairs of numbers that satisfy this relation.

b) Graph the data. Describe your graph.

c) Write an equation for the relation.

21. For each equation below:
- Make a table for 3 values of x.
- Graph the equation.

a) $\frac{1}{2}x + y = 4$

b) $\frac{1}{3}x - y = 2$

c) $\frac{1}{2}x + \frac{1}{3}y = 6$

d) $\frac{1}{3}x - \frac{1}{2}y = -1$

e) $\frac{1}{3}x + \frac{1}{2}y = -3$

f) $\frac{1}{4}x - \frac{1}{2}y = 1$

Reflect

How are the equations of horizontal and vertical lines alike? How are they different?

How can you recognize the equation of each line?

Mid-Unit Review

1. This pattern of squares continues.

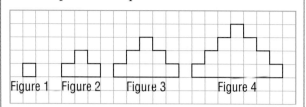

Figure 1   Figure 2   Figure 3   Figure 4

   a) Make a table that shows the figure
      number, n, and the perimeter of a
      figure, P. What patterns do you see?

   b) Write an expression for the perimeter of
      figure n.

   c) What is the perimeter of figure 40?

   d) Write an equation that relates P to n.

   e) Which figure has a perimeter of
      136 units? How do you know?

2. A phone company charges a fixed cost of
$10 per month, plus $0.25 per minute for
long distance calling.

   a) Write an equation that relates the monthly
      cost, C dollars, to t, the time in minutes.

   b) In one month, the time for the long
      distance calls was 55 minutes. What was
      the monthly cost?

   c) For one month, the cost was $22.50.
      How many minutes of long distance
      calls were made?

3. Create a table of values for each linear
relation, then graph the relation.
Use values of x from -3 to 3.

   a) $y = -3x$ b) $y = 2x$

   c) $y = 2 - 4x$ d) $y = -2x + 4$

   e) $y = -3 + x$ f) $y = -x + 3$

4. Alicia buys a $300-jacket on lay away. She
made a down payment of $30 and is paying
$15 per week. The total paid, P dollars, after
n weeks can be represented by the equation
$P = 15n + 30$.

   a) Create a table of values to show the total
      paid in each of the first 5 weeks.

   b) Graph the data. Should you join the
      points on the graph? Explain.

   c) How do the patterns in the graph relate
      to the patterns in the table?

5. Each table of values represents a linear
relation. Copy and complete each table.
Explain your reasoning.

a)

x	y
1	10
2	14
3	
4	
5	

b)

x	y
1	
3	-10
5	-14
7	
9	

c)

x	y
-2	
-1	
0	-3
1	3
2	

d)

x	y
2	
4	-2
6	-5
8	
10	

6. a) Graph each equation.

     i) $y = 1$ ii) $x = -4$

     iii) $x + y = 8$ iv) $2x - y = 12$

   b) For which equations in part a did you
      not need to make a table of values?
      Explain why.

7. The difference of two numbers is 1.
Let g represent the greater number and
n the lesser number.

   a) Complete a table for 4 different values
      of n.

   b) Graph the data. Should you join the
      points? Explain.

   c) Write an equation that relates n and g.

GAME

What's My Point?

How to Play

Write the equations of three different linear relations.
Graph each equation on a grid like this.
Plot all points that have integer coordinates.

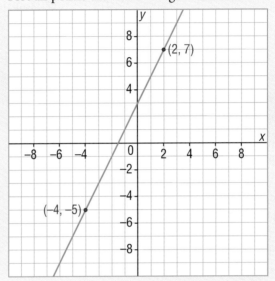

1. Player A chooses two points on one line.
   She keeps these points secret.
   Player A tells Player B the equation of the line.
   Player B tells the coordinates of a point on the line.
   Player A says whether Player B's point is:
   - one of the chosen points
   - on the line and above the chosen points
   - on the line and below the chosen points, or
   - between the chosen points
   Player B continues to name points on the line until he names both chosen points.
   Each guess counts as 1 point.

2. Player A and B switch roles, with Player A guessing the points selected by Player B.

3. Play continues until all three graphs have been used.
   The player with fewer points wins.

4. Suppose your opponent gave you the equation $y = 5x - 6$.
   Which two points might you guess? Explain.

5. Create a graph that might make it difficult for your opponent to guess your two points.
   Explain why it would be difficult.

4.4

Matching Equations and Graphs

FOCUS

• Match equations and graphs of linear relations.

Investigate

2

Bruce, Monica, and Sari participate in a 5-km walk for charity.
Each student has a different plan to raise money from her or his sponsors.
These graphs show how the amount of money a sponsor owes is related to
the distance walked.

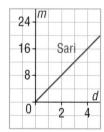

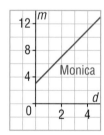

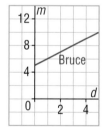

➤ Match each graph with its equation: $m = 2d + 3$ $m = 4d$ $m = d + 5$
  Explain your strategy.
➤ Describe each person's sponsorship plan.

Compare your strategies and descriptions with those of another
pair of students.
Did you use the same strategies to match each graph and its equation?
If not, explain your strategies to the other students.

The 3 graphs below have these equations, but the graphs are not in order:

$$y = 3x + 3 \qquad x + y = 3 \qquad y = 3x - 3$$

Graph A

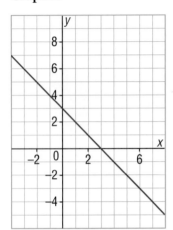

Graph B

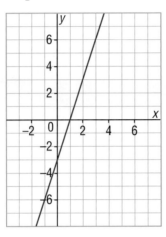

Graph C

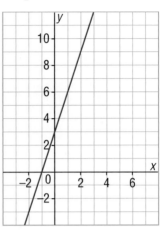

To match each equation with its graph,
use the equation to determine the coordinates of 3 points.
Then find which graph passes through those 3 points.

➤ For $y = 3x + 3$

Substitute: $x = 0$
$y = 3(0) + 3$
$y = 3$
One point is: $(0, 3)$

Substitute: $x = 1$
$y = 3(1) + 3$
$y = 6$
One point is: $(1, 6)$

Substitute: $x = 2$
$y = 3(2) + 3$
$y = 9$
One point is: $(2, 9)$

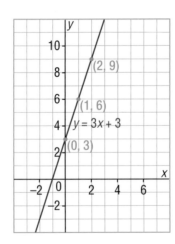

The graph that passes through these 3 points is Graph C.

➤ For $x + y = 3$

Substitute: $x = 0$
$0 + y = 3$
$\quad y = 3$
One point is: $(0, 3)$

Substitute: $x = 1$
$1 + y = 3$
$\quad y = 2$
One point is: $(1, 2)$

Substitute: $x = 2$
$2 + y = 3$
$\quad y = 1$
One point is: $(2, 1)$

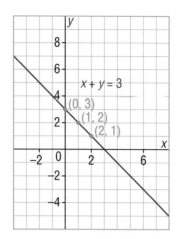

The graph that passes through these 3 points is Graph A.

So, the equation $y = 3x - 3$ must match Graph B. Substitute to check.

Substitute: $x = 0$
$y = 3(0) - 3$
$y = -3$
One point is: $(0, -3)$

Substitute: $x = 1$
$y = 3(1) - 3$
$y = 0$
One point is: $(1, 0)$

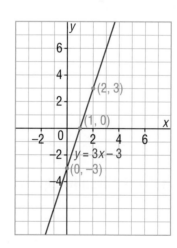

Substitute: $x = 2$
$y = 3(2) - 3$
$y = 3$
One point is: $(2, 3)$

The graph that passes through these 3 points is Graph B.

Example 1 **Matching Equations with Graphs that Pass through the Origin**

Match each graph on the grid with its equation below.

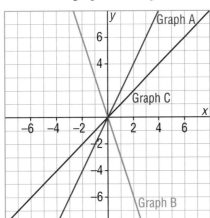

$y = x$

$y = 2x$

$y = -3x$

▶ *A Solution*

Rewrite $y = x$ as $y = 1x$. The coefficient of x represents the pattern of the points on the graph.

In the equation $y = 1x$, the 1 indicates that when x increases by 1 unit, y also increases 1 unit.
This matches Graph C.

In the equation $y = 2x$, the 2 indicates that when x increases by 1 unit, y increases by 2 units.
This matches Graph A.

In the equation $y = -3x$, the -3 tells us that when x increases by 1 unit, y decreases by 3 units.
This matches Graph B.

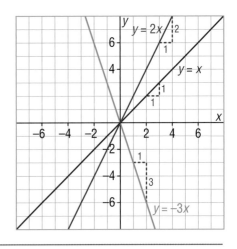

Example 2 **Identifying a Graph Given Its Equation**

Which graph on this grid has the equation $y = 3x - 4$?
Justify the answer.

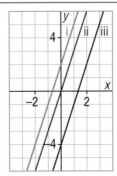

► *A Solution*

Pick 2 points on each graph and check to see if their coordinates satisfy the equation.

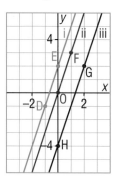

Two points on Graph i have coordinates
D($-1, -1$) and E($0, 2$).
Substitute $x = -1$ and $y = -1$ in $y = 3x - 4$.
Left side: $y = -1$ Right side: $3x - 4 = 3(-1) - 4$
$$= -7$$
The left side does not equal the right side.
So, these coordinates do not satisfy the equation and
Graph i does not have equation $y = 3x - 4$.

Two points on Graph ii have coordinates O($0, 0$) and F($1, 3$).
Substitute $x = 0$ and $y = 0$ in $y = 3x - 4$.
Left side: $y = 0$ Right side: $3x - 4 = 3(0) - 4$
$$= -4$$
The left side does not equal the right side.
So, these coordinates do not satisfy the equation and Graph ii does not have
equation $y = 3x - 4$.

Two points on Graph iii have coordinates G($2, 2$) and H($0, -4$).
Substitute $x = 2$ and $y = 2$ in $y = 3x - 4$.
Left side: $y = 2$ Right side: $3x - 4 = 3(2) - 4$
$$= 2$$
The left side does equal the right side, so the coordinates of G satisfy the equation.
Substitute $x = 0$ and $y = -4$ in $y = 3x - 4$.
Left side: $y = -4$ Right side: $3x - 4 = 3(0) - 4$
$$= -4$$
The left side does equal the right side, so the coordinates of H satisfy the equation.
Since both pairs of coordinates satisfy the equation, Graph iii has equation
$y = 3x - 4$.

Discuss the ideas

1. When we match an equation to a graph by determining coordinates of points on the graph, why is it helpful to check 3 points, even though 2 points are enough to identify a line?

2. When we choose points on a graph to substitute their coordinates in an equation, what is an advantage of choosing the points where the graph intersects the axes?

Practice

Check

3. Match each equation with a graph below.
   a) $y = 2x$ **b)** $y = 4x$ **c)** $y = -x$

   i)

   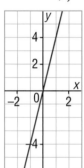

   ii)

   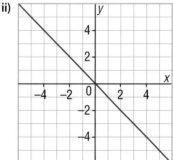

   iii)

   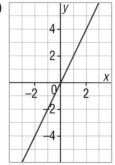

Apply

4. Match each equation with a graph on the grid below.
   a) $y = 3x$ **b)** $y = 5x$ **c)** $y = -2x$

   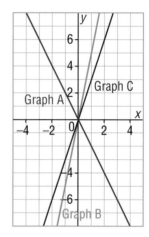

5. Match each equation with a graph below. Which strategy did you use?
   a) $y = 2x + 1$ **b)** $y = 2x + 3$ **c)** $y = 2x - 5$

   i)

   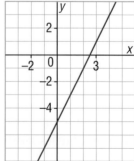

ii)

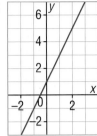

iii)

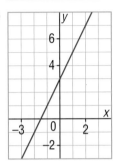

6. Match each equation with a graph below.
Justify your answers.

a) $x + y = 4$ **b)** $x - y = 4$ **c)** $x - y = -4$

i)

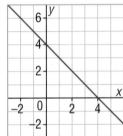

ii)

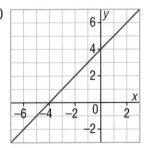

iii)

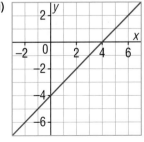

7. Match each equation with its graph below.
Explain your strategy.

a) $y = 2x$ **b)** $2y = 7$ **c)** $3y = 2$

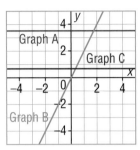

8. Which graph on this grid has equation
$y = 2x + 5$? Justify your answer.

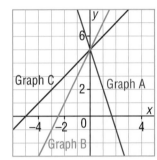

9. Which equation describes each graph?
Justify your answers.

a) **i)** $y = 2x + 1$ **ii)** $y = 2x + 3$
   iii) $y = x - 2$ **iv)** $y = -x + 2$

b) **i)** $x + 3y = 1$ **ii)** $3x - y = -3$
   iii) $3x + y = 1$ **iv)** $3x - y = 3$

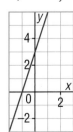

10. a) Write the equations of 3 different lines.

  b) Graph the lines on the same grid. Write the equations below the grid.

  c) Trade grids with a classmate. Match your classmates' graphs and equations.

11. Assessment Focus

  a) How are these 4 graphs alike?

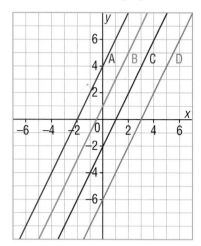

  b) How are the graphs different?

  c) Match each graph to its equation.

   i) $y = 2x - 2$

   ii) $y = 2x + 4$

   iii) $2x - y = 6$

   iv) $2x - y = -1$

  d) Did you use the same strategy each time?

  If your answer is yes, what strategy did you use and why?

  If your answer is no, explain why you used different strategies.

  Show your work.

12. The lines on the grid below intersect to form $\triangle PQR$. The equations of the lines are: $y = 1$, $2x + y = 8$, and $2y - x = 6$

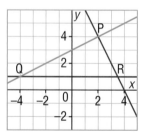

What is the equation of the line on which each side of the triangle lies?

a) PQ   **b)** QR   **c)** RP

Take It Further

13. The lines on the grid below intersect to form rectangle DEFG.

The equations of the lines are: $y = \frac{1}{2}x - \frac{1}{2}$; $y = -2x + 5$; $y = -2x - 8$; and $x - 2y = -8$

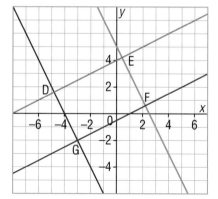

What is the equation of the line on which each side of the rectangle lies?

a) DE   **b)** DG   **c)** EF   **d)** FG

Reflect

What strategies have you learned to match an equation with its graph?
When might you use each strategy? Include examples in your explanation.

Using Graphs to Estimate Values

How do you think city planners can
predict the volume of water that will be
needed by its residents in the future?

FOCUS

• Use interpolation
and extrapolation to
estimate values on a
graph.

Investigate

A city has grown over the past few years. This table and graph show how the
volume of water used each month is related to the population.

Water Usage in One City

Population	Monthly Water Usage (ML)
100 000	750
130 000	975
180 000	1350
220 000	1650

1 ML is 1 000 000 L.

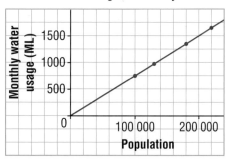

Use these data to:

• Estimate the monthly water usage for a population of 150 000 people.
• Estimate the population when the monthly water usage is 1400 ML.
• Predict the water usage for 250 000 people.

Share your answers and strategies for solving the problems with
another pair of students.
Did you use the table to estimate? Did you use the graph?
Are your estimates the same? Should they be? Explain.
Why do we call these numbers "estimates"?

This graph shows how the distance travelled by a car on the highway changes over a 4-h period.

To draw the graph, we plotted the distance travelled every hour, then drew a line through the points.

We can use **interpolation** to estimate values that lie *between* 2 data points on the graph.

Graph of a Car Journey

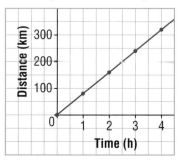

To estimate the distance travelled in 1.5 h:
- Begin at 1.5 on the *Time* axis.
- Draw a vertical line to the graph.
- Then draw a horizontal line from the graph to the *Distance* axis.
  This line intersects the axis at about 120 km.

So, the distance travelled in 1.5 h is about 120 km.

To estimate the time it takes to travel 300 km:
- Begin at 300 on the *Distance* axis.
- Draw a horizontal line to the graph.
- Then draw a vertical line from the graph to the *Time* axis.
  This line intersects the axis at about 3.75 h, which is 3 h 45 min.

So, it takes about 3 h 45 min to travel 300 km.

Graph of a Car Journey

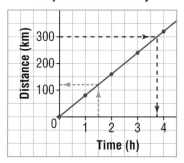

Suppose the car maintains the same average speed. We can extend the graph to predict how far the car will travel in a given time or to predict the time it takes to travel a given distance.

This is called **extrapolation**. When we use a graph to predict in this way, we assume that the relation is linear and will continue to be linear.
We use a ruler to extend the graph.

To estimate the time it takes to travel 450 km:

- Extend the grid so the *Distance* axis shows at least 450 km.
  Use a ruler to extend the graph.

- Repeat the process to estimate the time to travel 450 km.

It takes a little more than 5.5 h, or about 5 h 40 min to travel 450 km.

Graph of a Car Journey

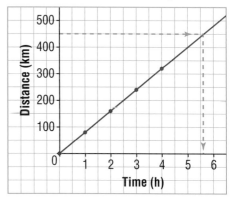

| Example 1 | **Using Interpolation to Solve Problems** |

Jenna borrows money from her parents for a school trip. She repays the loan by making regular weekly payments. The graph shows how the money is repaid over time. The data are discrete because payments are made every week.

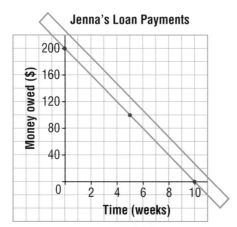

Jenna's Loan Payments

a) How much money did Jenna originally borrow?
b) How much money does she still owe after 3 weeks?
c) How many weeks will it take Jenna to repay one-half of the money she borrowed?

▶ **A Solution**

a) The money borrowed is the amount
   when the repayment time is 0.
   This is the point where the graph
   intersects the *Money owed* axis.
   Jenna originally borrowed $200.

b) Begin at 3 on the *Time* axis.
   Draw a vertical line to the graph,
   then a horizontal line to the
   Money owed axis.
   The amount owed is about
   halfway between 120 and 160.
   So, Jenna owes about $140 after 3 weeks.

c) Jenna borrowed $200.
   After she repays one-half of this amount, she still owes $100.
   Begin at 100 on the *Money owed* axis.
   Draw a horizontal line to the graph, then a vertical line to the *Time* axis.
   It will take Jenna about 5 weeks to repay one-half of the money.

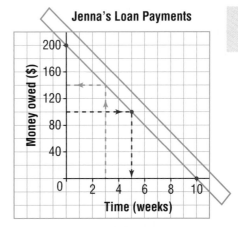

Use a straightedge to help.

Example 2	**Using Extrapolation to Solve Problems**

Maya jogs on a running track. This graph shows how far she jogs in 10 min.
Assume Maya continues to jog at the same average speed.

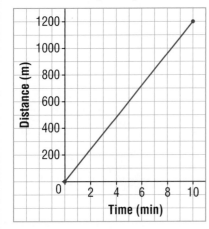

Use the graph.

a) Predict how long it will take Maya to jog 2000 m.

b) Predict how far Maya will jog in 14 min.

c) What assumption did you make?

A Solution

Extend the graph to include 2000 m vertically and 14 min horizontally.

a) Begin at 2000 on the *Distance* axis. Move across to the graph then down to the *Time* axis. It will take Maya between 16 and 17 min to jog 2000 m.

b) Begin at 14 on the *Time* axis. Move up to the graph then across to the *Distance* axis. The distance is about 1700 m. In 14 min, Maya will jog about 1700 m.

c) I assume that Maya will continue to jog at the same average speed as before.

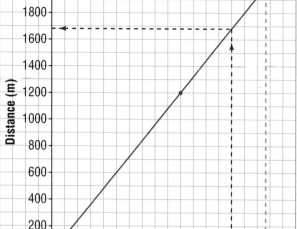

Maya's Jog

Example 3

Interpolating and Extrapolating to Determine Values of Variables from a Graph

Use this graph of a linear relation.
a) Determine the value of x when $y = 3$.
b) Determine the value of y when $x = 5$.

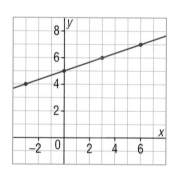

A Solution

Extend the graph to the left to be able to extrapolate for $y = 3$.
Label the extended x-axis.

a) Begin at 3 on the y-axis. Move across to the graph, then down to the x-axis. When $y = 3$, $x = -6$

b) Begin at 5 on the x-axis. Move up to the graph, then across to the y-axis. The value of y is between 6 and 7, but closer to 7. When $x = 5$, $y \doteq 6\frac{2}{3}$

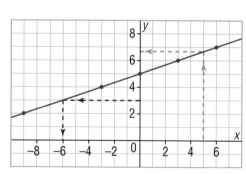

1. a) What is interpolation? When do we use it?
   b) What is extrapolation? When do we use it?

2. When we extrapolate, why is it important to know that the data represent a linear relation?

3. What problems might there be if you extrapolate far beyond the last data point?

Practice

Check

4. This graph represents a linear relation.

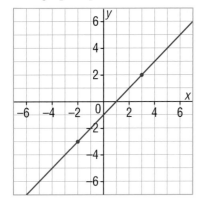

   a) Determine each value of x for:
      i) $y = 5$ ii) $y = -1$ iii) $y = -2$
   b) Determine each value of y for:
      i) $x = -4$ ii) $x = 2$ iii) $x = 5$

5. This graph represents a linear relation.

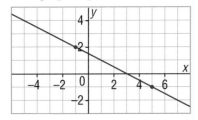

   a) Determine each value of x for:
      i) $y = 3$ ii) $y = 1$ iii) $y = -2$
   b) Determine each value of y for:
      i) $x = -3$ ii) $x = 3$ iii) $x = 6$

6. This graph represents a linear relation.

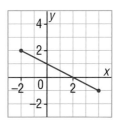

   a) Determine each value of x for:
      i) $y = 6$ ii) $y = -4$ iii) $y = -8$
   b) Determine each value of y for:
      i) $x = -6$ ii) $x = 6$ iii) $x = 9$

7. This graph represents a linear relation.

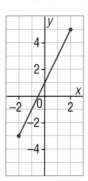

   a) Determine each value of x for:
      i) $y = 6$ ii) $y = -4$ iii) $y = -7$
   b) Determine each value of y for:
      i) $x = -5$ ii) $x = 3$ iii) $x = 5$

Apply

8. This graph shows how the price of a new game console changes with time.

Cost of a Game Console

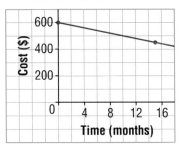

Use the graph.
- **a)** Estimate the cost of the game console 5 months after it is released.
- **b)** How many months is it until the console costs $500?
- **c)** Estimate the price of the console one year after it was released.

9. This graph shows the energy in Calories that Kendall burns when he works out on an elliptical machine.

Energy Burned on an Elliptical Machine

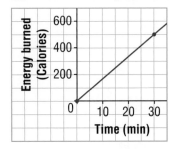

Use the graph.
- **a)** Estimate how many Calories Kendall burns in 20 min.
- **b)** Estimate for how long Kendall must exercise to burn 400 Calories.
- **c)** Estimate how many Calories Kendall burns in 6 min.

10. This graph represents a linear relation.

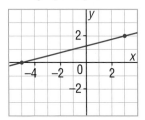

Estimate the value of y when:
- **a)** $x = -3$ **b)** $x = 0$ **c)** $x = 1$

Explain how you estimated.

11. **Assessment Focus** This graph shows how a speed in metres per second relates to a speed in kilometres per hour.

Graph for Converting Speeds

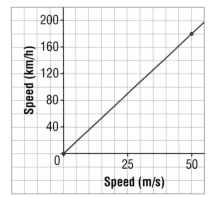

- **a)** Estimate the speed, in metres per second, of:
  - **i)** a car that is travelling at 70 km/h
  - **ii)** a train that is travelling at 110 km/h
- **b)** Estimate the speed, in kilometres per hour, of:
  - **i)** a racing car that is travelling at 60 m/s
  - **ii)** a bicycle that is travelling at 8 m/s
- **c)** For which of parts a and b did you use:
  - **i)** interpolation?
  - **ii)** extrapolation?

  Explain how you know.
- **d)** Explain why your answers are estimates and not exact.

12. This graph represents a linear relation.

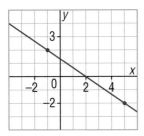

Estimate the value of *x* when:
   i) $y = 3$
   ii) $y = 1$
   iii) $y = -1$
Explain how you estimated.

13. Reece works for 5 h each week at a clothing store. This graph shows how her pay relates to the number of weeks she works.

Reece's Pay

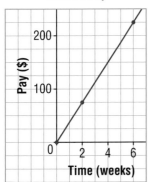

a) Estimate Reece's earnings after 8 weeks.
b) Estimate how long it will take Reece to earn $400. What assumption did you make?
c) What conditions could change that would make this graph no longer valid?

14. This graph represents a linear relation.

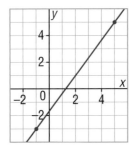

a) Estimate the value of *y* when:
   i) $x = -3$ ii) $x = -5$ iii) $x = 10$
b) Estimate the value of *x* when:
   i) $y = -5$ ii) $y = 8$ iii) $y = 10$
Explain how you estimated.

Take It Further

15. A local convenience store sells 3 different sizes of drinks. The price of each drink is listed below. The store owner plans to introduce 2 new sizes of drinks. She wants the prices and sizes to be related to the drinks she sells already.

Size (mL)	Price (¢)
500	79
750	89
1000	99

a) Graph the data.
b) What should the store owner charge for a 1400-mL drink?
c) What should be the size of a drink that costs 65¢?
Justify your answers.

Reflect

What is the difference between interpolation and extrapolation?
When might you use each process? Use examples in your explanation.

Interpolating and Extrapolating

Technology

FOCUS

• Use a graphing calculator to create a graph, then interpolate and extrapolate values.

We can use a graphing calculator to graph the data in a table of values. We can then interpolate and extrapolate from the graph to estimate or predict values that are not in the table.

The table at the right shows the costs of gas for 5 customers at a gas station.
What is the cost of 20 L of gas?
How much gas can be bought for $20.00?
What is the cost of 30 L of gas?

Volume of Gas (L)	Cost ($)
6	5.10
10	8.50
16	13.60
18	15.30
24	20.40

To graph the relation:
➤ Enter the data in a graphing calculator.
➤ Set up the calculator to plot the points.
➤ Display the graph.

To interpolate or extrapolate:
➤ To determine the cost of 20 L of gas, use the table feature or trace along the graph to interpolate.
The cost of 20 L of gas is $17.00.
➤ To determine how much gas can be bought for $20.00, find where the horizontal line $y = 20$ meets the graph. Input the equation $y = 20$, then use the trace or intersection feature to determine the coordinates of the point where the lines intersect.
About 23.5 L of gas can be bought for $20.00.
➤ To determine the cost of 30 L of gas, extend the table or trace along the graph to extrapolate. You may need to adjust the window before you trace along the graph.
The cost of 30 L of gas is $25.50.

Check

Follow the steps above to graph the data.

1. Use the graph to estimate each value.
  a) the cost of:
    i) 10 L of gas   **ii)** 50 L of gas
  b) the volume of gas that can be purchased for:
    i) $65.00   **ii)** $12.00
  Did you interpolate or extrapolate to determine these values? Explain.

Generalize a Pattern

Term Number, n	Term Value, v	Pattern
1	3	2(1) + 1
2	5	2(2) + 1
3	7	2(3) + 1
⋮	⋮	⋮
n		2(n) + 1

Each term value is 2 more than the preceding term value.
Start with the expression $2n$ and adjust it as necessary to produce the numbers in the table.
The expression is: $2n + 1$
The equation is: $v = 2n + 1$

Linear Relations

▶ The graph of a linear relation is a straight line.
To graph a linear relation, first create a table of values.
For example, to graph the linear relation: $y = -2x + 5$

x	y
0	5
1	3
2	1

Choose 3 values of x, then use the equation to calculate corresponding values of y.

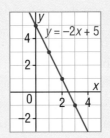

Each point on the graph is 1 unit right and 2 units down from the preceding point.

Another form of the equation of the graph above is $2x + y = 5$.

Horizontal and Vertical Lines

▶ The graph of the equation $x = a$, where a is a constant, is a vertical line.
The graph of the equation $y = a$, where a is a constant, is a horizontal line.

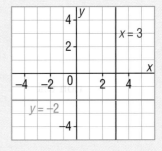

Interpolation and Extrapolation

▶ Interpolation is determining data points *between* given points on the graph of a linear relation.

Extrapolation is determining data points *beyond* given points on the graph of a linear relation.
When we extrapolate, we assume that the linear relation continues.

4.1 **1.** This pattern continues.

Figure 1   Figure 2   Figure 3   Figure 4

a) Determine the perimeter of each figure.

b) Draw the next 3 figures on grid paper.

c) Make a table to show the number of each figure and its perimeter.

d) Write an expression for the perimeter in terms of the figure number, n.

e) Write an equation that relates the perimeter P to n.

f) Determine the perimeter of figure 30.

g) Determine the figure number that has perimeter 90 units.

2. The pattern in this table continues.

Term Number, n	Term Value, v
1	−5
2	−2
3	1
4	4

a) Describe the patterns in the table.

b) Use n to write an expression for the term value.

c) Write an equation that relates v and n.

d) Verify the equation by substituting a pair of values from the table.

e) Determine the value of the 21st term.

f) Which term number has a value of 106? How do you know?

3. The first number in a pattern has the value 75. As the term number increases by 1, its value decreases by 4.

a) Create a table for this pattern.

b) Write an expression for the value of the term in terms of the term number n.

4.2 **4.** Norman has $140 in his savings account. Each month he deposits $20 into this account. Let t represent the time in months and A the account balance in dollars.

a) Create a table to show several values of t and A.

b) Graph the data. Will you join the points? Explain.

c) Is this relation linear? Justify your answer.

d) Describe the pattern in the table. How are these patterns shown in the graph?

e) Write an equation that relates A and t.

5. Copy and complete each table of values. Describe the patterns in the table.

a) $y = 4x$ b) $y = 10 - 2x$ c) $y = 3x + 4$

x	y
1	
2	
3	

x	y
0	
1	
2	

x	y
−3	
−2	
−1	

6. Graph the data from each table in question 5. For each graph, explain how the patterns in the graph match the patterns in the table.

4.3 **7.** A piece of string is 25-cm long. The string is cut into 2 pieces.

a) Make a table that shows 6 possible lengths for the two pieces of string.

b) Graph the data.

   i) Is the relation linear? How do you know?

   ii) Should you join the dots? Explain.

c) Choose 2 variables to represent the lengths of the longer and shorter pieces.

   i) Write an equation that relates the variables.

   ii) How could you check your equation?

8. Graph each equation. Do you need to make a table of values each time? Explain.

a) $x = -2$ b) $y = 3$

c) $x = 5$ d) $y = -1$

9. For each equation below:
- Make a table for the given values of x.
- Graph the equation.

a) $3x + y = 9$; for $x = -3, 0, 3$

b) $2x - y = 4$; for $x = -2, 0, 2$

c) $2x + y = -6$; for $x = -4, 0, 4$

d) $x - 2y = -6$; for $x = -2, 0, 2$

10. Does each equation represent a vertical line, a horizontal line, or an oblique line? How can you tell without graphing?

a) $x = 6$ b) $x - y = 3$

c) $y + 8 = 0$ d) $2x + 9 = 0$

4.4 **11.** Which equation describes the graph below? Justify your answer.

a) $y = -2x + 3$ b) $y = 2x - 3$

c) $y = 3x - 2$ d) $y = -3x - 2$

12. Which graph represents the equation $x - 2y = 4$? How do you know?

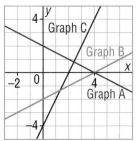

13. Match each equation with its graph below. Explain your strategy.

a) $x + 2y = 6$

b) $y = x - 3$

c) $y = 2x - 3$

d) $y = -4x + 5$

i)

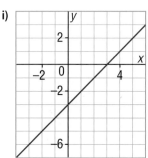

ii)

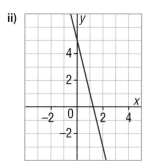

iii)

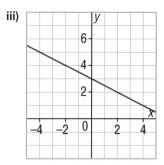

iv)

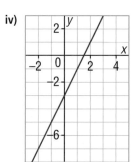

14. This graph shows how the mass of wheat changes with its volume.

Mass against Volume for Wheat

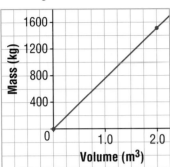

Use the graph.

a) Estimate the volume of 2000 kg of wheat.

b) Estimate the mass of 2.5 m³ of wheat.

15. Harold and Jenny are driving from Medicine Hat to Winnipeg. The graph shows the distance travelled and the distance yet to go.

Journey from Medicine Hat to Winnipeg

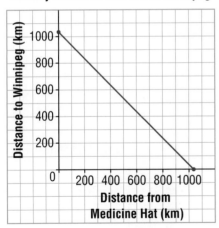

a) About how far is it from Medicine Hat to Winnipeg? How can you tell from the graph?

b) When Jenny and Harold have travelled 450 km, about how far do they still have to go?

16. The Dubois family lives in Regina. The family is planning a family holiday to the West Coast. This graph shows the gas consumption of the family's car.

Gas Consumption

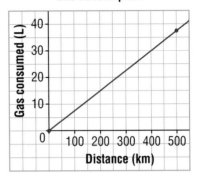

a) The distance from Regina to Vancouver is 1720 km. Estimate the volume of gasoline needed to travel from Regina to Vancouver. Explain how you did this.

b) To travel from Regina to Prince Albert, the car used about 30 L of gasoline. About how far is it between these two towns?

17. This graph represents a linear relation.

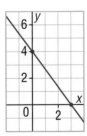

a) Estimate the value of y when:
   i) $x = -4$
   ii) $x = 2$
   iii) $x = 5$

b) Estimate the value of x when:
   i) $y = 7$
   ii) $y = 2$
   iii) $y = -3$

Explain how you estimated.

1. Here is a pattern made
from square tiles.

Figure 1   Figure 2   Figure 3   Figure 4

a) Make a table that shows how the
number of square tiles, *s*, in a figure
relates to the figure number, *f*.

b) Write an expression for the number
of square tiles in terms of *f*.

c) Write an equation that relates *s* and *f*.
Verify the equation by substituting the values from the table.

d) How are the expression and equation alike? How are they different?

e) Which figure has 225 tiles? Explain how you know.

2. a) Make a table of values for this equation: $y = -2x + 7$

b) Graph the relation.

c) Explain how the patterns in the graph match those in the table.

3. Does each equation describe a vertical, a horizontal, or an oblique line?
How do you know?

a) $x = 6$ b) $2y - 7 = 3$ c) $2x + 9 = 0$

4. Match each equation with its graph below. Explain your strategy.

a) $y = x + 3$ b) $y = 3$ c) $x + y = 3$ d) $x = -3$

i)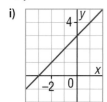

ii)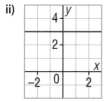

iii)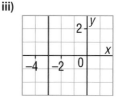

iv)

5. A family uses a cistern for drinking water at its cabin.
The graph shows how the volume of drinking water
in the cistern changes during a 10-day period.
Suppose the pattern in the water usage continues.

a) How many days did it take to use 200 L of water?

b) Estimate the volume of water in the cistern
after 22 days.

c) Estimate how much water is used in the
first 14 days.

d) What assumptions did you make?

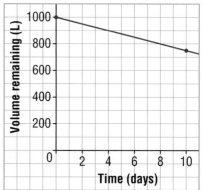

Water Consumption

The format in which music is produced and sold has changed over the past 30 years.

Part 1

The table shows the sales of cassette tapes in North America.

Year	Cassette Sales (billions)
1993	$2.9
1995	$2.3
1998	$1.4

a) Graph the data. Do the data represent a linear relation? How do you know?

b) Describe how the sales of cassettes changed over time.

c) Let t represent the number of years after 1993 and S the sales in billions of dollars. Write an equation that relates S and t.

d) Use the equation to determine the sales in 1997. Does the answer agree with the value in the graph? Explain.

e) Use the graph to predict the year in which the sales of cassettes were $0.

f) Cassettes were sold until 2004. Explain why this is different from the year predicted in the graph.

Part 2

As the sale of cassettes was decreasing, the sales of CDs were increasing. Assume the growth in CDs sales, from 1996 to 2000, was linear.

Year	CD Sales (millions)
1996	$9 935
2000	$13 215

a) Graph the data. Use the graph to estimate the CD sales for 1997, 1998, and 1999. Is this interpolation or extrapolation? Explain.

b) Estimate the total CD sales for this 5-year period.

c) Estimate the CD sales in 2001. Is this interpolation or extrapolation? Explain.

d) Use the graph to estimate the CD sales for 2005.

e) Which answer in parts c and d is more likely to be the closer estimate? Justify your answer.

Your work should show:
- accurate and labelled graphs
- how you wrote and used the equation
- clear explanations of your thinking

Reflect

on Your Learning

What is a linear relation? How may a linear relation be described? What can you determine when you know a relation is linear? Include examples.

Number Systems

Work with a partner.

Part 1

This is a Frayer model for **natural numbers**.

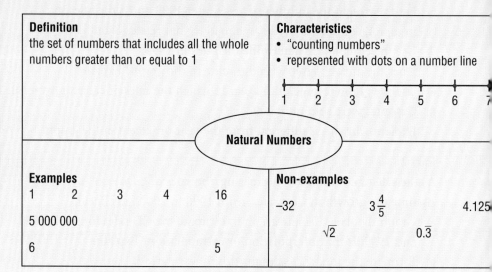

Definition	Characteristics
the set of numbers that includes all the whole numbers greater than or equal to 1	• "counting numbers" • represented with dots on a number line

Natural Numbers

Examples	Non-examples
1 2 3 4 16 5 000 000 6 5	-32 $3\frac{4}{5}$ 4.125 $\sqrt{2}$ $0.\overline{3}$

➤ Complete a Frayer model for each of these number systems:
- whole numbers
- integers
- rational numbers

Each of these number systems is part of a larger system of numbers called the **real numbers**.

Part 2

➤ Is it possible for a number to belong to more than one number system? Explain. Use examples to support your answer.

➤ Is it possible for an entire number system to belong to another number system? Explain.

➤ Draw a diagram to show how the number systems in Part 1 overlap.

Part 3

Choose a number system from Part 1; this is the name of your club.
Choose a number from your number system.

You are in charge of memberships for your club. It is your job to either accept or reject a number that wishes to join your club. Write a letter of acceptance or rejection for your partner's number. If the number belongs in your number system, it must be allowed membership.

Your letter should be written as a business letter.
It must address the following points:

➤ examples of other numbers in your club and what their characteristics are

➤ how your partner's number either fits or does not fit the characteristics of your club

➤ if you are accepting the number, why your club wants that number

➤ if you are rejecting the number, what other clubs the number could contact and why

Take It Further

➤ Numbers that are not rational numbers are called *irrational numbers*. Create a Frayer model for *irrational numbers*.

➤ Amend your diagram from Part 2 to include these numbers.

Polynomials

How could you solve this problem?

Denali and Mahala weed the borders on the north and south sides of their rectangular yard. Denali starts first and has weeded 1 m on the south side when Mahala says he should be weeding the north side. So, Denali moves to the north side. Mahala finishes weeding the south side. Then she moves to the north side where she weeds 2 m. Both students have then finished. Which student weeded more of the borders? How much more?

What You'll Learn

- Recognize, write, describe, and classify polynomials.
- Use algebra tiles, pictures, and algebraic expressions to represent polynomials.
- Strategies to add and subtract polynomials.
- Strategies to multiply and divide a polynomial by a monomial.

Why It's Important

Just as numbers are the building blocks of arithmetic, polynomials are the building blocks of algebra.
In later grades, you will use polynomials to model real-world situations in business, science, medicine, and engineering. The skills, understanding, and language that you develop in this unit will lay the foundation for this work.

Key Words

- polynomial
- term
- coefficient
- degree
- constant term
- monomial
- binomial
- trinomial
- like terms

FOCUS
• Model, write, and classify polynomials.

In arithmetic, we use Base Ten Blocks to model whole numbers. How would you model the number 234?

In algebra, we use algebra tiles to model integers and variables.

Yellow represents positive tiles. Red represents negative tiles.

How are Base Ten Blocks and algebra tiles alike?

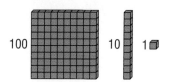

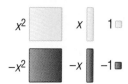

Investigate

Use algebra tiles.

➤ Model each expression. Sketch the tiles. How do you know which tiles to use? How do you know how many of each tile to use?

• $x^2 + x - 3$
• $-2x^2 - 3$
• $2x^2 + 3x$
• $-2x^2 - 3x + 1$
• $-3x + 3$

➤ Write your own expression. Have your partner model it with tiles. Model your partner's expression with tiles.

For the first activity, compare your sketches with those of another pair of students.
Did you use the same tiles each time? If not, is one of you wrong? Could both of you be correct? Explain.
Did the order in which you laid out the tiles matter? Explain.

We can use algebra tiles to model an expression such as $3x^2 - 2x + 5$.

To model $3x^2 - 2x + 5$, we use three x^2-tiles, two $-x$-tiles, and five 1-tiles.

A **polynomial** is one term or the sum of terms whose variables have whole-number exponents.

The expression $3x^2 - 2x + 5 = 3x^2 + (-2)x + 5$ is an example of a polynomial in the variable x. This polynomial has 3 terms: $3x^2$, $(-2)x$, and 5
Terms are numbers, variables, or the product of numbers and variables.
The **coefficients** of the variable are 3 and -2.

The term with the greatest exponent determines the **degree** of the polynomial. This polynomial has degree 2.

$\rightarrow\ 3x^2 - 2x + 5\ \leftarrow$

The term 5 is a **constant term**. Its value does not change when the value of x changes. A constant term has degree 0.

The term $-2x$ has degree 1 because $-2x = -2x^1$.

We can use any variable to write a polynomial and to describe the tiles that model it. For example, the tiles that model the polynomial $-5n^2 + 7n - 1$ also model the polynomial $-5p^2 + 7p - 1$.

We can also classify a polynomial by the number of terms it has.
Polynomials with 1, 2, or 3 terms have special names.
A **monomial** has 1 term; for example: $4a$, 6, $-2p^2$
A **binomial** has 2 terms; for example: $2c - 5$, $2m^2 + 3m$
A **trinomial** has 3 terms; for example: $2h^2 - 6h + 4$

A polynomial is usually written in descending order; that is, the exponents of the variable decrease from left to right; for example, the polynomial $2k - 4k^2 + 7$ is written as $-4k^2 + 2k + 7$.

An algebraic expression that contains a term with a variable in the denominator, such as $\frac{3}{n}$, or the square root of a variable, such as $\sqrt{n}$, is *not* a polynomial.

Which of these polynomials can be represented by the same algebra tiles?

a) $3x^2 - 5x + 6$ **b)** $-5 + 6r + 3r^2$ **c)** $-5m + 6 + 3m^2$

Justify the answer.

▶ *A Solution*

a) $3x^2 - 5x + 6$

Use three x^2-tiles, five $-x$-tiles, and six 1-tiles.

b) $-5 + 6r + 3r^2$

Use five -1-tiles, six r-tiles, and three r^2-tiles.

c) $-5m + 6 + 3m^2$

Use five $-m$-tiles, six 1-tiles, and three m^2-tiles.

In parts a and c, the same algebra tiles are used.

So, the polynomials $3x^2 - 5x + 6$ and $-5m + 6 + 3m^2$ can be represented by the same tiles.

Example 2   **Modelling Polynomials with Algebra Tiles**

Use algebra tiles to model each polynomial.

Is the polynomial a monomial, binomial, or trinomial? Explain.

a) $-2x^2$ **b)** $2b^2 - b + 4$ **c)** $5a - 3$

▶ *A Solution*

a) To represent $-2x^2$, use two $-x^2$-tiles. Since there is only one type of tile, $-2x^2$ is a monomial.

b) To represent $2b^2 - b + 4$, use two b^2-tiles, one $-b$-tile, and four 1-tiles. Since there are 3 types of tiles, $2b^2 - b + 4$ is a trinomial.

c) To represent $5a - 3$, use five a-tiles and three -1-tiles. Since there are 2 types of tiles, $5a - 3$ is a binomial.

Two polynomials are *equivalent* when they can be represented by identical algebra tiles.

Example 3   Recognizing Equivalent Polynomials

a) Which polynomial does each group of algebra tiles represent?

Model A   Model B   Model C

b) Which of the polynomials in part a are equivalent? How do you know?

▶ A Solution

a) Use a table.

Model	Description of Tiles	Polynomial
A	two x^2-tiles, eight $-x$-tiles, and two 1-tiles	$2x^2 - 8x + 2$
B	eight $-x$-tiles, two x^2-tiles, and two 1-tiles	$-8x + 2x^2 + 2$
C	four $-x$-tiles and six 1-tiles	$-4x + 6$

b) Both models A and B contain the same tiles. The polynomials represented by
these tiles have the same degree, and the same terms: $2x^2$, $-8x$, and 2
Both polynomials can be written as: $2x^2 - 8x + 2$
So, $2x^2 - 8x + 2$ and $-8x + 2x^2 + 2$ are equivalent polynomials.
Model C has no x^2-tiles, so its degree is different from that of
models A and B.

Discuss the ideas

1. In the polynomial $3 + 2p$, which term is the constant term?
How are constant terms modelled with algebra tiles?

2. Suppose you are given an algebra tile model of a polynomial.
How can you identify the terms, the coefficients, and the degree of
the polynomial? How can you identify the constant term?

3. What do we mean by "equivalent polynomials"? How can you
determine whether two polynomials are equivalent?

Check

4. Which of the following expressions are polynomials? Explain how you know.

a) $2 + 3n$

b) $3\sqrt{x}$

c) $-5m + 1 + 2m^2$

d) 7

e) $\dfrac{1}{x^2} + \dfrac{1}{x} + 1$

f) $\dfrac{1}{2}s$

5. Is each expression a monomial, binomial, or trinomial? Explain how you know.

a) $3t + 4t^2 - 2$

b) $5 - 3g$

c) $9k$

d) 11

6. Name the coefficient, variable, and degree of each monomial.

a) $-7x$

b) $14a^2$

c) m

d) 12

7. Identify the degree of each polynomial. Justify your answers.

a) $7j^2 + 4$

b) $9x$

c) $2 - 5p + p^2$

d) -10

Apply

8. Identify the polynomials that can be represented by the same set of algebra tiles.

a) $x^2 + 3x - 4$

b) $-3 + 4n - n^2$

c) $4m - 3 + m^2$

d) $-4 + r^2 + 3r$

e) $-3m^2 + 4m - 3$

f) $-h^2 - 3 + 4h$

9. Name the coefficients, variable, and degree of each polynomial. Identify the constant term if there is one.

a) $5x^2 - 6x + 2$

b) $7b - 8$

c) $12c^2 + 2$

d) $12m$

e) 18

f) $3 + 5x^2 - 8x$

10. One student says, "$4a$ is a monomial." Another student says, "$4a$ is a polynomial." Who is correct? Explain.

11. Use algebra tiles to model each polynomial. Sketch the tiles.

a) $4x - 3$

b) $-3n - 1$

c) $2m^2 + m + 2$

d) $-7y$

e) $-d^2 - 4$

f) 3

12. Match each polynomial with its corresponding algebra tile model.

a) $r^2 - r + 3$

b) $-t^2 - 3$

c) $-2v$

d) $2w + 2$

e) $2s^2 - 2s + 1$

Model A

Model B

Model C

Model D

Model E

13. Which polynomial does each collection of algebra tiles represent?

Is the polynomial a monomial, binomial, or trinomial? Explain.

a)

b)

c)

d)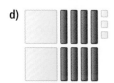

e)

f)

g)

h)

14. Write a polynomial with the given degree and number of terms. Use algebra tiles to model the polynomial. Sketch the tiles.

a) degree 1, with 2 terms

b) degree 0, with 1 term

c) degree 2, with 1 term

d) degree 2, with 3 terms and constant term 5

15. Identify which polynomials are equivalent. Explain how you know.

a)

b)

c)

d)

e)

f)

g)

h)

i)

16. Identify which polynomials are equivalent. Justify your answers.

a) $5 - v + 7v^2$

b) $7v + 5 - v^2$

c) $5v + v^2 - 7$

d) $-7 + 5v + v^2$

e) $5 - v^2 + 7v$

f) $7v^2 + v + 5$

17. Write an expression that is *not* a polynomial. Explain why it is not a polynomial.

18. Assessment Focus

   a) Use algebra tiles to model each polynomial. Sketch the tiles. Identify the variable, degree, number of terms, and coefficients.

     i) $-2x - 3x^2 + 4$

     ii) $m^2 + m$

   b) Write a polynomial that matches this description:

     a polynomial in variable c, degree 2, binomial, constant term -5

   c) Write another polynomial that is equivalent to the polynomial you wrote in part b. Explain how you know that the polynomials are equivalent.

19. a) Write as many polynomials as you can that are equivalent to $-8d^2 - 3d - 4$. How do you know you have written all possible polynomials?

   b) Which polynomial in part a is in descending order? Why is it useful to write a polynomial in this form?

Take It Further

20. The *stopping distance* of a car is the distance the car travels between the time the driver applies the brakes and the time the car stops. The polynomial $0.4s + 0.02s^2$ can be used to calculate the stopping distance in metres of a car travelling at s kilometres per hour on dry pavement.

   a) Determine the stopping distance for each speed:

     i) 25 km/h   ii) 50 km/h   iii) 100 km/h

   b) Does doubling the speed double the stopping distance? Explain.

Reflect

What is a polynomial?

How can you represent a polynomial with algebra tiles and with symbols?

Include examples in your explanation.

 **Math Link**

Your World

A polynomial can be used to model projectile motion. When a golf ball is hit with a golf club, the distance the ball travels in metres, in terms of the time t seconds that it is in the air, may be modelled by the polynomial $-4.9t^2 + 22.8t$.

When you work with integers,
a 1-tile and a −1-tile form a zero pair.  0

FOCUS

• Simplify
polynomials by
combining like
terms.

What do you think happens when you combine algebra tiles with opposite signs?
Which expression do these tiles represent?

Investigate

2

You will need algebra tiles and a paper bag.

➤ Put both colours of algebra tiles in a bag.
Take a handful of tiles and sketch them.
Construct a table to record your work.

Algebra Tile Model	Symbolic Record

Use symbols to write the polynomial modelled
by the tiles. Remove zero pairs.
Sketch the tiles that remain.
Use symbols to write the polynomial represented
by the smaller set of tiles.

➤ Return the algebra tiles to the bag.
Repeat the activity 4 more times.

Reflect & Share

Share your results with another pair of students.
How could you verify each other's results?
When can you remove zero pairs from a set of tiles?
How does removing zero pairs help you simplify the polynomial that
represents the set of tiles?

Here is a collection of red and yellow algebra tiles:

We organize the tiles by grouping like tiles:

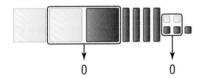

These tiles represent the polynomial: $2x^2 - x^2 - 4x + 2 - 3$

We simplify the tile model by removing zero pairs.

The remaining tiles represent the polynomial: $x^2 - 4x - 1$
We say that the polynomial $2x^2 - x^2 - 4x + 2 - 3$ *simplifies* to $x^2 - 4x - 1$.

A polynomial is in *simplified form* when:
- its algebra tile model uses the fewest tiles possible
- its symbolic form contains only one term of each degree and no terms with a zero coefficient

Terms that can be represented by algebra tiles with the same size and shape are called **like terms**.

$-x^2$ and $3x^2$ are like terms.
Each term is modelled with x^2-tiles.
Each term has the same variable, x,
raised to the same exponent, 2.

$-x^2$ and $3x$ are *unlike terms*.
Each term is modelled with a different
algebra tile.
Each term has the variable x,
but the exponents are different.

To simplify a polynomial, we group like terms and remove zero pairs.

$-x^2 + 3x^2$ simplifies to $2x^2$.

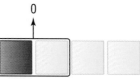

We can also simplify a polynomial by adding the coefficients of like terms. This is called *combining like terms*.

$-x^2 + 3x^2 = -1x^2 + 3x^2$ Add the integer coefficients: $-1 + 3 = 2$
$\qquad\qquad\; = 2x^2$

The polynomials $-x^2 + 3x^2$ and $2x^2$ are *equivalent*.

So, a polynomial in simplified form is also the equivalent polynomial in which all the like terms have been combined.

$-x^2 + 3x$ cannot be simplified.
We may not add coefficients when we have unlike terms.

Example 1   **Using Algebra Tiles to Simplify a Polynomial**

Use algebra tiles to simplify the polynomial $4n^2 - 1 - 3n - 3 + 5n - 2n^2$.
Record the process symbolically.

▶ *A Solution*

Tile Model

Display $4n^2 - 1 - 3n - 3 + 5n - 2n^2$.

Symbolic Record

$4n^2 - 1 - 3n - 3 + 5n - 2n^2$

Group like tiles.

Group like terms:

$4n^2 - 2n^2 + 5n - 3n - 1 - 3$

Remove zero pairs.

Combine like terms:

$2n^2 + 2n - 4$

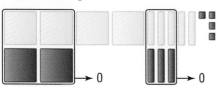

The remaining tiles represent $2n^2 + 2n - 4$.

Example 2 **Simplifying a Polynomial Symbolically**

Simplify: $14x^2 - 11 + 30x + 3 + 15x - 25x^2$

▶ **A Solution**

We need many tiles to model this polynomial.
So, we simplify it symbolically.

$14x^2 - 11 + 30x + 3 + 15x - 25x^2$ Group like terms.
$= 14x^2 - 25x^2 + 30x + 15x - 11 + 3$ Add the coefficients of like terms.
$= -11x^2 + 45x - 8$

In *Example 2*, the polynomials $14x^2 - 11 + 30x + 3 + 15x - 25x^2$ and
$-11x^2 + 45x - 8$ are equivalent.
Polynomials can be used to represent measures such as the side lengths of shapes.

Example 3 **Investigating Situations that Represent Polynomials**

a) Write a polynomial to represent the perimeter of each rectangle.

i)   X   X   X

X

ii)   X   X   X

b) Each polynomial represents the perimeter of a rectangle.
Use algebra tiles to make the rectangle.

i) $4a + 2$ ii) $10b$

▶ **A Solution**

a) i) The dimensions of the rectangle are
$3x$ and x. So, the perimeter of the
rectangle is:
$3x + x + 3x + x = 8x$

ii) The dimensions of the rectangle are
$3x$ and 2. So, the perimeter of the
rectangle is:
$3x + 2 + 3x + 2 = 6x + 4$

◀———— $3x$ ————▶

X

◀———— $3x$ ————▶

2

b) i) The perimeter is $4a + 2$.
Work backward.
Write the polynomial as the sum of equal pairs of terms.
$4a + 2 = 2a + 2a + 1 + 1$
The dimensions of the rectangle could be $2a$ and 1.

     a a

1

Another solution is:

$4a + 2 = a + (a + 1) + a + (a + 1)$

The dimensions of the rectangle could be a and $a + 1$.

ii) The perimeter is $10b$.

Write the polynomial as the sum of equal pairs of terms.

$10b = 4b + 4b + b + b$

The dimensions of the rectangle could be $4b$ and b.

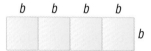

Another solution is:

$10b = 3b + 3b + 2b + 2b$

The dimensions of the rectangle could be $3b$ and $2b$.

A polynomial may contain more than one variable. Here is a polynomial in x and y:

$-2x^2 + 3xy + y^2 - 4x - 8y$

Example 4   Simplifying a Polynomial in Two Variables

Simplify: $4xy - y^2 - 3x^2 + 2xy - x - 3y^2$

▶ **A Solution**

$4xy - y^2 - 3x^2 + 2xy - x - 3y^2$	Group like terms.
$= 4xy + 2xy - y^2 - 3y^2 - 3x^2 - x$	Combine like terms.
$= 6xy - 4y^2 - 3x^2 - x$	

Discuss the ideas

1. Why can we combine like terms? Why can we not combine unlike terms?

2. How can you identify and combine like terms in an algebra tile model?

3. How can you identify and combine like terms symbolically?

Check

4. a) Use algebra tiles to model $3d$ and $-5d$. Sketch the tiles.

   b) Are $3d$ and $-5d$ like terms? How can you tell from the tiles? How can you tell from the monomials?

5. a) Use algebra tiles to model $4p$ and $2p^2$. Sketch the tiles.

   b) Are $4p$ and $2p^2$ like terms? How can you tell from the tiles? How can you tell from the monomials?

Apply

6. From the list, which terms are like $8x$?
   $-3x, 5x^2, 4, 3x, 9, -11x^2, 7x, -3$
   Explain how you know they are like terms.

7. From the list, which terms are like $-2n^2$?
   $3n, -n^2, -2, 4n, 2n^2, -2, 3, 5n^2$
   Explain how you know they are like terms.

8. For each part, combine tiles that represent like terms.
   Write the simplified polynomial.

   a)

   b)

   c)

   d)

e)

f)

9. Identify the equivalent polynomials in the diagrams below. Justify your answers.

   a)

   b)

   c)

   d)

   e)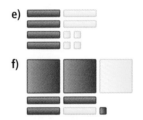

   f)

10. A student made these mistakes on a test.
   ➤ The student simplified
   $2x + 3x$ as $5x^2$.
   ➤ The student simplified
   $4 + 3x$ as $7x$.
   Use algebra tiles to explain what the student did wrong.
   What are the correct answers?

11. Use algebra tiles to model each polynomial, then combine like terms. Sketch the tiles.

a) $2c + 3 + 3c + 1$

b) $2x^2 + 3x - 5x$

c) $3f^2 + 3 - 6f^2 - 2$

d) $3b^2 - 2b + 5b + 4b^2 + 1$

e) $5t - 4 - 2t^2 + 3 + 6t^2$

f) $4a - a^2 + 3a - 4 + 2a^2$

12. Simplify each polynomial.

a) $2m + 4 - 3m - 8$

b) $4 - 5x + 6x - 2$

c) $3g - 6 - 2g + 9$

d) $-5 + 1 + h - 4h$

e) $-6n - 5n - 4 - 7$

f) $3s - 4s - 5 - 6$

13. Simplify each polynomial.

a) $6 - 3x + x^2 + 9 - x$

b) $5m - 2m^2 - m^2 + 5m$

c) $5x - x^2 + 3x + x^2 - 7$

d) $3p^2 - 2p + 4 + p^2 + 3$

e) $a^2 - 2a - 4 + 2a - a^2 + 4$

f) $-6x^2 + 17x - 4 - 3x^2 + 8 - 12x$

14. Simplify each polynomial.

a) $3x^2 + 5y - 2x^2 - 1 - y$

b) $pq - 1 - p^2 + 5p - 5pq - 2p$

c) $5x^2 + 3xy - 2y - x^2 - 7x + 4xy$

d) $3r^2 - rs + 5s + r^2 - 2rs - 4s$

e) $4gh + 7 - 2g^2 - 3gh - 11 + 6g$

f) $-5s + st - 4s^2 - 12st + 10s - 2s^2$

15. Identify the equivalent polynomials. Justify your answers.

a) $1 + 5x$

b) $6 - 2x + x^2 - 1 - x + x^2$

c) $4x^2 - 7x + 1 - 7x^2 + 2x + 3$

d) $4 - 5x - 3x^2$

e) $2x^2 - 3x + 5$

f) $3x + 2x^2 + 1 - 2x^2 + 2x$

16. Write 3 different polynomials that simplify to $-2a^2 + 4a - 8$.

17. Write a polynomial with degree 2 and 5 terms, which has only 2 terms when it is simplified.

18. **Assessment Focus**

a) A student is not sure whether $x + x$ simplifies to $2x$ or x^2.
Explain how the student can use algebra tiles to determine the correct answer. What is the correct answer?

b) Simplify each polynomial. How do you know that your answers are correct?

  i) $-2 + 4r - 2r + 3$

  ii) $2t^2 - 3t + 4t^2 - 6t$

  iii) $3c^2 + 4c + 2 + c^2 + 2c + 1$

  iv) $15x^2 - 12xy + 5y + 10xy - 8y - 9x^2$

c) Create a polynomial that cannot be simplified. Explain why it cannot be simplified.

19. Write a polynomial to represent the perimeter of each rectangle.

a)

b)
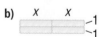

c)
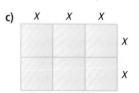

d)

20. Each polynomial below represents the perimeter of a rectangle. Use algebra tiles to make the rectangle. Sketch the tiles. How many different rectangles can you make each time?

a) $6c + 4$ b) $4d$ c) $8 + 2m$

d) $12r$ e) $6s$ f) $4a + 10$

Take It Further

21. Many algebra tile kits contain x-tiles and y-tiles.

 x

 $-x$

y

$-y$

What do you think an xy-tile looks like? Sketch your idea and justify your picture.

22. Write a polynomial for the perimeter of this shape. Simplify the polynomial.

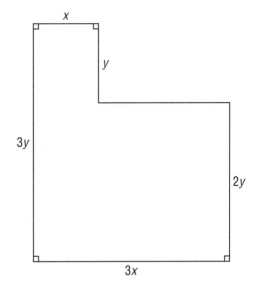

Reflect

Explain how like terms can be used to simplify a polynomial. Use diagrams and examples in your explanation.

Math Link

Your World

On a forward somersault dive, a diver's height above the water, in metres, in terms of the time t seconds after the diver leaves the board may be modelled by the polynomial $-4.9t^2 + 6t + 3$.

5.3 Adding Polynomials

FOCUS
- Use different strategies to add polynomials.

Investigate

You will need algebra tiles and a paper bag.
Conduct the activity 3 times.

Put both colours of algebra tiles in a paper bag.
Each person removes a handful of algebra tiles and
writes the simplified polynomial that the tiles model.
Add the two polynomials.
Record your work as an addition sentence.

Reflect & Share

Compare your strategies for adding two polynomials with those of
another pair of students.
If you used different strategies, explain your strategies.
If you used the same strategies, find a pair of students
who used a different strategy.
Which terms can be combined when you add polynomials?
Why can these terms be combined?

To add polynomials, we combine the algebra tiles that represent each polynomial and record the process symbolically. This develops a strategy to add polynomials without algebra tiles.

When we write the sum of two polynomials, we write each polynomial in brackets.
To determine the sum of $3x^2 + 2x + 4$ and $-5x^2 + 3x - 5$, we write:
$(3x^2 + 2x + 4) + (-5x^2 + 3x - 5)$

Tile Model

Display: $3x^2 + 2x + 4$

Display: $-5x^2 + 3x - 5$

Combine the displays.

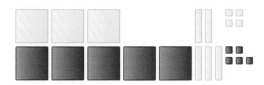

Group like tiles.

Remove zero pairs.

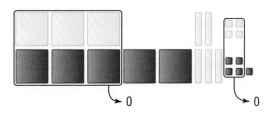

The remaining tiles represent
$-2x^2 + 5x - 1$.

Symbolic Record

The sum is:
$(3x^2 + 2x + 4) + (-5x^2 + 3x - 5)$

This is written as:
$3x^2 + 2x + 4 - 5x^2 + 3x - 5$

Group like terms:
$3x^2 - 5x^2 + 2x + 3x + 4 - 5$

Combine like terms:
$-2x^2 + 5x - 1$

Example 1   **Adding Polynomials Symbolically**

Add: $(7s + 14) + (-6s^2 + s - 6)$

► **Solutions**

Add the polynomials by adding the coefficients of like terms. In the second polynomial, the term s has coefficient 1, so write s as $1s$.

Method 1

Add horizontally.

$\quad (7s + 14) + (-6s^2 + 1s - 6)$ Remove the brackets.

$= 7s + 14 - 6s^2 + 1s - 6$ Group like terms.

$= -6s^2 + 7s + 1s + 14 - 6$ Combine like terms by adding their coefficients.

$= -6s^2 + 8s + 8$

Method 2

Add vertically. Align like terms, then add their coefficients.

$$\begin{array}{r} 7s + 14 \\ + \;\; -6s^2 + 1s - \;\; 6 \\ \hline -6s^2 + 8s + \;\; 8 \end{array}$$

So, $(7s + 14) + (-6s^2 + 1s - 6) = -6s^2 + 8s + 8$

Example 2   **Determining a Polynomial for the Perimeter of a Rectangle**

a) Write a polynomial for the perimeter of this rectangle.
   Simplify the polynomial.

b) Substitute to check the answer.

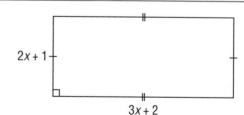

► **A Solution**

a) The perimeter is the sum of the measures of the four sides.

$$\begin{array}{r} 2x + 1 \\ + \;\; 2x + 1 \\ + \;\; 3x + 2 \\ + \;\; 3x + 2 \\ \hline 10x + 6 \end{array}$$

The perimeter is $10x + 6$.

b) Choose a value for x, such as $x = 1$.

Write the addition sentence:

$2x + 1 + 2x + 1 + 3x + 2 + 3x + 2 = 10x + 6$

Substitute $x = 1$.

Left side:

$2x + 1 + 2x + 1 + 3x + 2 + 3x + 2$

$= 2(1) + 1 + 2(1) + 1 + 3(1) + 2 + 3(1) + 2$

$= 2 + 1 + 2 + 1 + 3 + 2 + 3 + 2$

$= 16$

Right side:

$10x + 6 = 10(1) + 6$

$= 10 + 6$

$= 16$

Since the left side equals the right side, the polynomial for the perimeter is correct.

Example 3 Adding Polynomials in Two Variables

Add: $(2a^2 + a - 3b - 7ab + 3b^2) + (-4b^2 + 3ab + 6b - 5a + 5a^2)$

▶ **A Solution**

$(2a^2 + a - 3b - 7ab + 3b^2) + (-4b^2 + 3ab + 6b - 5a + 5a^2)$ Remove brackets.

$= 2a^2 + a - 3b - 7ab + 3b^2 - 4b^2 + 3ab + 6b - 5a + 5a^2$ Group like terms.

$= 2a^2 + 5a^2 + a - 5a - 3b + 6b - 7ab + 3ab + 3b^2 - 4b^2$ Combine like terms.

$= 7a^2 - 4a + 3b - 4ab - b^2$

Discuss the ideas

1. How can you use what you know about adding integers to add polynomials?

2. How is adding polynomials like simplifying a polynomial?

Practice

Check

3. Write the polynomial sum modelled by each set of tiles.

a)

b)
c)
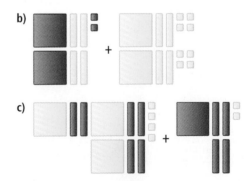

4. Explain how to use algebra tiles to determine $(3x^2 + 2) + (x^2 - 1)$. What is the sum?

5. Use algebra tiles to model each sum of binomials. Record your answer symbolically.
- **a)** $(5g + 3) + (2g + 4)$
- **b)** $(3 - 2j) + (-4 + 2j)$
- **c)** $(p + 1) + (5p - 6)$
- **d)** $(7 + 4m) + (-5m + 4)$

6. Add these polynomials. Visualize algebra tiles if it helps.

a) $\begin{array}{r} 2x + 4 \\ + \underline{3x - 5} \end{array}$

b) $\begin{array}{r} 3x^2 + 5x \\ + \underline{-2x^2 - 8x} \end{array}$

c) $\begin{array}{r} 3x^2 + 5x + 7 \\ + \underline{-8x^2 - 3x + 5} \end{array}$

7. Do you prefer to add vertically or horizontally? Give reasons for your choice.

Apply

8. Use a personal strategy to add.
- **a)** $(6x + 3) + (3x + 4)$
- **b)** $(5b - 4) + (2b + 9)$
- **c)** $(6 - 3y) + (-3 - 2y)$
- **d)** $(-n + 7) + (3n - 2)$
- **e)** $(-4s - 5) + (6 - 3s)$
- **f)** $(1 - 7h) + (-7h - 1)$
- **g)** $(8m + 4) + (-9 + 3m)$
- **h)** $(-8m - 4) + (9 - 3m)$

9. Add. Which strategy did you use each time?
- **a)** $(4m^2 + 4m - 5) + (2m^2 - 2m + 1)$
- **b)** $(3k^2 - 3k + 2) + (-3k^2 - 3k + 2)$
- **c)** $(-7p - 3) + (p^2 + 5)$
- **d)** $(9 - 3t) + (9t + 3t^2 - 6t)$
- **e)** $(3x^2 - 2x + 3) + (2x^2 + 4)$
- **f)** $(3x^2 - 7x + 5) + (6x - 6x^2 + 8)$
- **g)** $(6 - 7x + x^2) + (6x - 6x^2 + 10)$
- **h)** $(1 - 3r + r^2) + (4r + 5 - 3r^2)$

10. a) For each shape below, write the perimeter:
- as a sum of polynomials
- in simplest form

i)

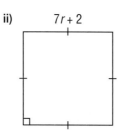

ii)

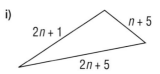

iii)

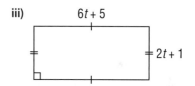

iv)

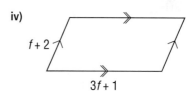

b) Use substitution to check each answer in part a.

11. Sketch 2 different shapes whose perimeter could be represented by each polynomial.
- **a)** $8 + 6r$
- **b)** $3s + 9$
- **c)** $4 + 12t$
- **d)** $20u$
- **e)** $7 + 5v$
- **f)** $4y + 6$
- **g)** $9 + 9c$
- **h)** $15m$

12. A student added $(4x^2 - 7x + 3)$ and $(-x^2 - 5x + 9)$ as follows.

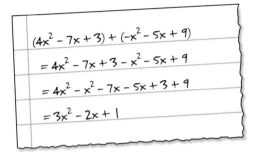

$$\underline{(4x^2 - 7x + 3) + (-x^2 - 5x + 9)}$$
$$= 4x^2 - 7x + 3 - x^2 - 5x + 9$$
$$= 4x^2 - x^2 - 7x - 5x + 3 + 9$$
$$= 3x^2 - 2x + 1$$

Is the student's work correct?
If not, explain where the student made any errors and write the correct answer.

13. **Assessment Focus**

These tiles represent the sum of two polynomials.

a) What might the two polynomials be? Explain how you found out.

b) How many different pairs of polynomials can you find? List all the pairs you found.

14. The sum of two polynomials is $12m^2 + 2m + 4$.
One polynomial is $4m^2 - 6m + 8$.
What is the other polynomial?
Explain how you found your answer.

15. Create a polynomial that is added to $3x^2 + 7x + 2$ to get each sum.
   a) $5x^2 + 10x + 1$ b) $2x^2 + 5x + 8$
   c) $4x^2 + 3x$ d) $-x^2 + x - 1$
   e) $2x + 3$ f) 4

16. a) What polynomial must be added to $5x^2 + 3x - 1$ to obtain a sum of 0? Justify your answer.

   b) How are the coefficients of the two polynomials related?
   Will this relationship be true for all polynomials with a sum of 0? Explain.

17. Add.
   a) $(3x^2 - 2y^2 + xy) + (-2xy - 2y^2 - 3x^2)$
   b) $(-5q^2 + 3p - 2q + p^2) + (4p + q + pq)$
   c) $(3mn + m^2 - 3n^2 + 5m) + (7n^2 - 8n + 10)$
   d) $(3 - 8f + 5g - f^2) + (2g^2 - 3f + 4g - 5)$

Take It Further

18. a) The polynomials $4x - 3y$ and $2x + y$ represent the lengths of two sides of a triangle. The perimeter of the triangle is $9x + 2$. Determine the length of the third side.

   b) Use substitution to check your solution in part a.

19. The polynomial $5y + 3x + 7$ represents the perimeter of an isosceles triangle. Write three polynomials that could represent the side lengths of the triangle. Find as many answers as you can.

Reflect

What strategies can you use for adding polynomials?
Which strategy do you prefer?
How can you check that your answers are correct?
Include examples in your explanation.

5.4 Subtracting Polynomials

What strategies do you know to subtract two integers, such as $-2 - 3$?
How could these strategies help you subtract two polynomials?

FOCUS

• Use different strategies to subtract polynomials.

Investigate

Use algebra tiles.

➤ Write two like monomials.
Subtract the monomials.
Write the subtraction sentence.
Subtract the monomials in the reverse order.
Write the new subtraction sentence.
Sketch the tiles you used.

➤ Repeat the process above for two binomials, then for two trinomials.

➤ Subtract. Use a strategy of your choice.
$(5x) - (3x)$
$(2x^2 + 3x) - (4x^2 - 6x)$
$(3x^2 - 6x + 4) - (x^2 + 3x - 2)$
Use a different strategy to verify your answer.

Compare your answers and strategies with those
of a pair of students who used a different strategy.
Explain your strategies to each other.
Work together to write an addition sentence that
corresponds to each subtraction sentence.

Here are two strategies to subtract polynomials.

➤ Using algebra tiles
To subtract: $(3x^2 - 4x) - (2x^2 - 6x)$
Use algebra tiles to model $3x^2 - 4x$.

To subtract $2x^2 - 6x$, we need to:
• Take away two x^2-tiles from three x^2-tiles.
• Take away six $-x$-tiles from four $-x$-tiles.
  To do this, we need 2 more $-x$-tiles.
  So, we add 2 zero pairs of x-tiles.

Now we can take away the tiles for $2x^2 - 6x$.

The remaining tiles represent $x^2 + 2x$.
So, $(3x^2 - 4x) - (2x^2 - 6x) = x^2 + 2x$

➤ Using the properties of integers
We know that -6 is the opposite of 6.
Subtracting -6 from an integer is the same as adding 6 to that integer.
The same process is true for like terms.

To subtract: $(3x^2 - 4x) - (2x^2 - 6x)$

$$
\begin{aligned}
(3x^2 - 4x) - (2x^2 - 6x) &= 3x^2 - 4x - (2x^2) - (-6x) && \text{Subtract each term.}\\
&= 3x^2 - 4x - 2x^2 - (-6x) && \text{Add the opposite term.}\\
&= 3x^2 - 4x - 2x^2 + 6x && \text{Collect like terms.}\\
&= 3x^2 - 2x^2 - 4x + 6x && \text{Combine like terms.}\\
&= x^2 + 2x
\end{aligned}
$$

Example 1 **Subtracting Two Trinomials**

Subtract: $(-2a^2 + a - 1) - (a^2 - 3a + 2)$

▶ **Solutions**

$(-2a^2 + a - 1) - (a^2 - 3a + 2)$

Method 1	Method 2
Use algebra tiles. Display: $-2a^2 + a - 1$  To subtract a^2, add a zero pair of a^2-tiles. To subtract $-3a$, add 3 zero pairs of a-tiles. To subtract 2, add 2 zero pairs of 1-tiles.  Now remove tiles for $a^2 - 3a + 2$. 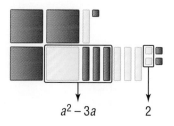 The remaining tiles represent $-3a^2 + 4a - 3$.	Use the properties of integers. $\quad (-2a^2 + a - 1) - (a^2 - 3a + 2)$ $= -2a^2 + a - 1 - (a^2) - (-3a) - (+2)$ $= -2a^2 + a - 1 - a^2 + 3a - 2$ $= -2a^2 - a^2 + a + 3a - 1 - 2$ $= -3a^2 + 4a - 3$

To check the difference when two numbers are subtracted,
we add the difference to the number that was subtracted;
for example, to check that $23 - 5 = 18$ is correct, we add: $5 + 18 = 23$

We can use the same process to check the difference of two polynomials.

Example 2   **Subtracting Trinomials in Two Variables**

Subtract: $(5x^2 - 3xy + 2y^2) - (8x^2 - 7xy - 4y^2)$

Check the answer.

▶ **A Solution**

$$(5x^2 - 3xy + 2y^2) - (8x^2 - 7xy - 4y^2) = 5x^2 - 3xy + 2y^2 - (8x^2) - (-7xy) - (-4y^2)$$
$$= 5x^2 - 3xy + 2y^2 - 8x^2 + 7xy + 4y^2$$
$$= 5x^2 - 8x^2 - 3xy + 7xy + 2y^2 + 4y^2$$
$$= -3x^2 + 4xy + 6y^2$$

To check, add the difference to the second polynomial:

$$(-3x^2 + 4xy + 6y^2) + (8x^2 - 7xy - 4y^2) = -3x^2 + 4xy + 6y^2 + 8x^2 - 7xy - 4y^2$$
$$= -3x^2 + 8x^2 + 4xy - 7xy + 6y^2 - 4y^2$$
$$= 5x^2 - 3xy + 2y^2$$

The sum is equal to the first polynomial.

So, the difference is correct.

Discuss the ideas

1. How is subtracting polynomials like subtracting integers?

2. How is subtracting polynomials like adding polynomials? How is it different?

3. When might using algebra tiles not be the best method to subtract polynomials?

Practice

Check

4. Write the subtraction sentence that these algebra tiles represent.

a)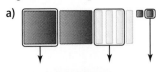

b)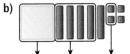

5. Use algebra tiles to subtract. Sketch the tiles you used.

a) $(5r) - (3r)$ b) $(5r) - (-3r)$

c) $(-5r) - (3r)$ d) $(-5r) - (-3r)$

e) $(3r) - (5r)$ f) $(-3r) - (5r)$

g) $(3r) - (-5r)$ h) $(-3r) - (-5r)$

Apply

6. Use algebra tiles to model each difference of binomials. Record your answer symbolically.

a) $(5x + 3) - (3x + 2)$

b) $(5x + 3) - (3x - 2)$

c) $(5x + 3) - (-3x + 2)$

d) $(5x + 3) - (-3x - 2)$

7. Use algebra tiles to model each difference of trinomials. Record your answer symbolically.
   a) $(3s^2 + 2s + 4) - (2s^2 + s + 1)$
   b) $(3s^2 - 2s + 4) - (2s^2 - s + 1)$
   c) $(3s^2 - 2s - 4) - (-2s^2 + s - 1)$
   d) $(-3s^2 + 2s - 4) - (2s^2 - s - 1)$

8. Use a personal strategy to subtract. Check your answers by adding.
   a) $(3x + 7) - (-2x - 2)$
   b) $(b^2 + 4b) - (-3b^2 + 7b)$
   c) $(-3x + 5) - (4x + 3)$
   d) $(4 - 5p) - (-7p + 3)$
   e) $(6x^2 + 7x + 9) - (4x^2 + 3x + 1)$
   f) $(12m^2 - 4m + 7) - (8m^2 + 3m - 3)$
   g) $(-4x^2 - 3x - 11) - (x^2 - 4x - 15)$
   h) $(1 - 3r + r^2) - (4r + 5 - 3r^2)$

9. The polynomial $4n + 2500$ represents the cost, in dollars, to produce n copies of a magazine in colour. The polynomial $2n + 2100$ represents the cost, in dollars, to produce n copies of the magazine in black-and-white.
   a) Write a polynomial for the difference in the costs of the two types of magazines.
   b) Suppose the company wants to print 3000 magazines. How much more does it cost to produce the magazine in colour instead of black-and-white?

10. A student subtracted $(2x^2 + 5x + 10) - (x^2 - 3)$ like this:

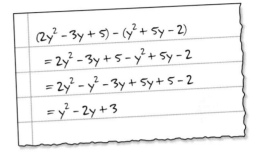

   a) Use substitution to show that the answer is incorrect.
   b) Identify the errors and correct them.

11. **Assessment Focus** Create a polynomial subtraction question. Answer your question. Check your answer. Show your work.

12. A student subtracted like this:

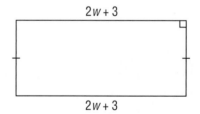

   a) Explain why the solution is incorrect.
   b) What is the correct answer? Show your work.
   c) How could you check that your answer is correct?
   d) What could the student do to avoid making the same mistakes in the future?

13. The perimeter of each polygon is given. Determine each unknown length.
   a) $6w + 14$

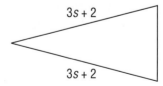

   b) $7s + 7$

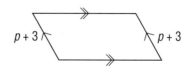

   c) $10p + 8$

14. a) Write two polynomials, then subtract them.
    b) Subtract the polynomials in part a in the reverse order.
    c) How do the answers in parts a and b compare? Why are the answers related this way?

15. Subtract.
    a) $(r^2 - 3rs + 5s^2) - (-2r^2 - 3rs - 5s^2)$
    b) $(-3m^2 + 4mn - n^2) - (5m^2 + 7mn + 2n^2)$
    c) $(5cd + 8c^2 - 7d^2) - (3d^2 + 6cd - 4c^2)$
    d) $(9e + 9f - 3e^2 + 4f^2) -$
       $(-f^2 - 2e^2 + 3f - 6e)$
    e) $(4jk - 7j - 2k + k^2) - (2j^2 + 3j - jk)$

16. The difference of two polynomials is $3x^2 + 4x - 7$.
    One polynomial is $-8x^2 + 5x - 4$.
    a) What is the other polynomial?
    b) Why are there two possible answers to part a?

Take It Further

17. The diagram shows one rectangle inside another rectangle. What is the difference in the perimeters of the rectangles?

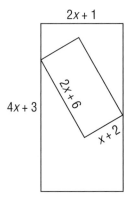

18. One polynomial is subtracted from another. The difference is $-4x^2 + 2x - 5$. Write two polynomials that have this difference. How many different pairs of polynomials can you find? Explain.

Reflect

What strategy or strategies do you use to subtract polynomials?
Why do you prefer this strategy or strategies?

Math Link

Your World

On a suspension bridge, the roadway is hung from huge cables passing through the tops of high towers. Here is a photograph of the Lions Gate Bridge in Vancouver. The position of any point on the cable can be described by its horizontal and vertical distance from the centre of the bridge. The vertical distance in metres is modelled by the polynomial $0.0006x^2$, where x is the horizontal distance in metres.

5.1 **1.** In each polynomial, identify:
the variable, number of terms, coefficients, constant term, and degree.

a) $3m - 5$

b) $4r$

c) $x^2 + 4x + 1$

2. Create a polynomial that meets these conditions:
trinomial in variable m, degree 2, constant term is -5

3. Which polynomial is represented by each set of algebra tiles? Is the polynomial a monomial, binomial, or trinomial? How do you know?

a)

b)

c)

4. Use algebra tiles to represent each polynomial. Sketch the tiles you used.

a) $4n - 2$

b) $-t^2 + 4t$

c) $2d^2 + 3d + 2$

5.2 **5.** For each pair of monomials, which are like terms? Explain how you know.

a) $2x, -5x$ b) $3, 4g$

c) $10, 2$ d) $2q^2, -7q^2$

e) $8x^2, 3x$ f) $-5x, -5x^2$

6. Simplify $3x^2 - 7 + 3 - 5x^2 - 3x + 5$. Explain how you did this.

7. Renata simplified a polynomial and got $4x^2 + 2x - 7$. Her friend simplified the same polynomial and got $-7 + 4x^2 + 2x$. Renata thinks her friend's answer is wrong. Do you agree? Explain.

8. Cooper thinks that $5x - 2$ simplifies to $3x$. Is he correct? Explain. Use algebra tiles to support your explanation.

9. Identify the equivalent polynomials. Justify your answers.

a) $1 + 3x - x^2$

b) $1 + 3x^2 - x^2 + 2x - 2x^2 + x - 2$

c) $x^2 - 3x - 1$

d) $6 + 6x - 6x^2 - 4x - 5 + 2x^2 + x^2 - 4$

e) $3x - 1$

f) $-3x^2 + 2x - 3$

g) $6x^2 - 6x - 6 + x - 5x^2 - 1 + 2x + 4$

h) $3x - x^2 + 1$

5.3
5.4 **10.** Use algebra tiles to add or subtract. Sketch the tiles you used.

a) $(4f^2 - 4f) + (-2f^2)$

b) $(3r^2 + 2r + 5) + (-7r^2 + r - 3)$

c) $(-2v + 5) - (-9v + 3)$

d) $(-2g^2 - 12) - (-6g^2 + 4g - 1)$

11. Add or subtract. Use a strategy of your choice.

a) $(3w^2 + 17w) + (12w^2 - 3w)$

b) $(5m^2 - 3) + (m^2 + 3)$

c) $(-3h - 12) - (-9h - 6)$

d) $(6a^2 + 2a - 2) + (-7a^2 + 4a + 11)$

e) $(3y^2 + 9y + 7) - (2y^2 - 4y + 13)$

f) $(-14 + 3p^2 + 2p) - (-5p + 10 - 7p^2)$

12. a) Which polynomial must be added to $5x^2 + 3x - 2$ to get $7x^2 + 5x + 1$?

b) Which polynomial must be subtracted from $5x^2 + 3x - 2$ to get $7x^2 + 5x + 1$?

Justify your answers.

How Can I Summarize What I Have Learned?

Suppose I want to summarize what I know about polynomials.

➤ What tools could I use to do this?

- a Frayer model

- a table

- a concept map

I can use a Frayer model to explain the meaning of a term or concept.

Definition Like terms have the same variable raised to the same exponent.	Facts/Characteristics Like terms are represented by algebra tiles with the same size and shape. I can combine like terms by adding their coefficients.
Like terms	
Examples $-3x$ and $4x$ $5b^2$ and $2b^2$	Non-examples $-3c$ and 4 $5n^2$ and $2n$

I can use a table to show how terms and concepts are alike and different.

Polynomial	Number of Terms	Name by Number of Terms	Degree
12	1	monomial	0
$8a$	1	monomial	1
$-4b^2 + 9$	2	binomial	2
$2c - 7$	2	binomial	1
$3d^2 - 4d + 6$	3	trinomial	2

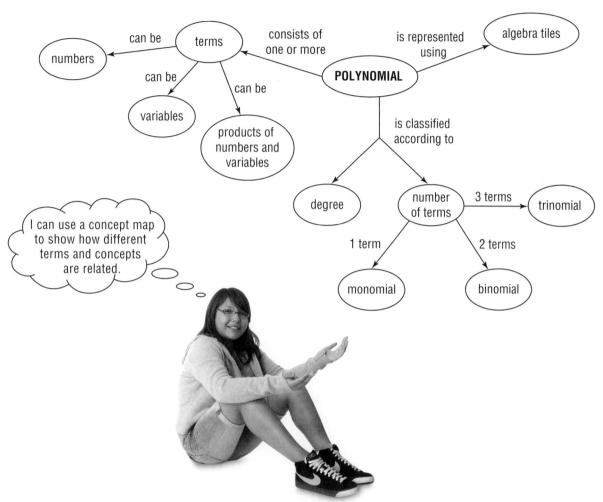

Check

Use the tools *you* find most helpful to summarize the important ideas and concepts you have learned about polynomials.

1. Choose another term or concept. Make a Frayer model to show what you know about that term or concept.

2. What other types of polynomials could you include in the table on page 238?

3. a) What could you add to the concept map above?
   b) Think of another way to draw a concept map about polynomials.

Add to your Frayer model, table, or concept map as you work through this unit.

GAME

Investigating Polynomials that Generate Prime Numbers

A prime number is any whole number, greater than 1, that is divisible by only itself and 1.

In 1772, Leonhard Euler, a Swiss mathematician, determined that the polynomial $n^2 - n + 41$ generates prime numbers for different values of n.

Use a calculator to check that this is true:

➤ Choose a value of n between 1 and 10.
   Substitute this number for n in the polynomial.
   Is the number you get a prime number?
   How do you know?

➤ Repeat the process for other values of n between 1 and 10.

➤ Choose a value of n between 10 and 40.
   Substitute this number for n in the polynomial.
   Is the number you get a prime number?
   How do you know?

➤ Repeat the process for other values of n between 10 and 40.

➤ Substitute $n = 41$. Is the number you get a prime number?
   How can you tell?

➤ List the values of n and the resulting primes in a table.

In 1879, E. B. Escott, an American mathematician, determined the polynomial $n^2 - 79n + 1601$ for generating prime numbers.
Test this polynomial:

➤ Substitute different values of n, and check that the numbers you get are prime. List the values of n and the resulting primes in a table. What patterns do you see?

➤ Substitute $n = 80$. Did you get a prime number? Explain.

➤ Determine other values of n for which Escott's polynomial does *not* generate prime numbers.

Currently, there is no known polynomial that generates only prime numbers. And, there is no known polynomial that generates all the prime numbers.

➤ Determine a value of n for which each of these polynomials does *not* generate a prime number:
   • $n^2 - n + 41$, other than $n = 41$
   • $n^2 - n + 17$
   • $n^2 + n - 1$

Multiplying and Dividing a Polynomial by a Constant

How does this diagram model the product 3×25?

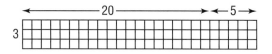

FOCUS

• Use different strategies to multiply and divide a polynomial by a constant.

What property is illustrated by this diagram?

How could you use the diagram above to model division?

Investigate

Use any strategy or materials you wish.

➤ Determine each product. Write a multiplication sentence.
  • $2(3x)$
  • $3(2x + 1)$
  • $2(2x^2 + x + 4)$
  • $-2(3x)$
  • $-3(2x + 1)$
  • $-2(2x^2 + x + 4)$

➤ Determine each quotient. Write a division statement.
  • $9x \div 3$
  • $(8x + 12) \div 4$
  • $(5x^2 + 10x + 20) \div 5$
  • $9x \div (-3)$
  • $(8x + 12) \div (-4)$
  • $(5x^2 + 10x + 20) \div (-5)$

Compare your answers and strategies with those of another pair of students.

If your answers are different, find out why.

Look at your multiplication and division sentences.

What relationships do you see among the original terms and the answers?

How could you use these relationships to multiply and divide without using algebra tiles?

➤ The expression 4(3x) is a product statement.

It represents the product of the constant, 4, and the monomial, 3x.

We can model the product as 4 rows of three x-tiles.

So, $4(3x) = 3x + 3x + 3x + 3x$ This is repeated addition.
$$= 12x$$

We can also model 4(3x) as the area of a rectangle with dimensions 4 and 3x.

So, $4(3x) = 4(3)(x)$
$$= 12x$$

➤ 4(−3x) is the product of 4 and the monomial −3x.

We can model the product as 4 rows of three −x-tiles.

So, $4(-3x) = -3x - 3x - 3x - 3x$
$$= -12x$$

➤ −4(3x) is the opposite of 4(3x).

We can model this by flipping the tiles we used to model 4(3x).

So, $-4(3x) = -(12x)$
$$= -12x$$

We can use the same strategy with algebra tiles to multiply a binomial or a trinomial by a constant. To determine the product symbolically, we use the *distributive property*.

Example 1   Multiplying a Binomial and a Trinomial by a Constant

Determine each product.

a) $3(-2m + 4)$

b) $-2(-n^2 + 2n - 1)$

▶ **Solutions**

Method 1	Method 2
Use algebra tiles.	Use the distributive property.
a) $3(-2m + 4)$	Multiply each term in the brackets by the term outside the brackets.
Display 3 rows of two $-m$-tiles and four 1-tiles.	a) $3(-2m + 4) = 3(-2m) + 3(4)$
	$= -6m + 12$

There are six $-m$-tiles and twelve 1-tiles.
So, $3(-2m + 4) = -6m + 12$

b) $-2(-n^2 + 2n - 1)$
Display 2 rows of one $-n^2$-tile, two n-tiles, and one -1-tile.

b) $-2(-n^2 + 2n - 1)$
$= (-2)(-1n^2) + (-2)(2n) + (-2)(-1)$
$= 2n^2 + (-4n) + 2$
$= 2n^2 - 4n + 2$

This shows $2(-n^2 + 2n - 1)$.

Flip all the tiles.

There are two n^2-tiles, four $-n$-tiles, and two 1-tiles.
So, $-2(-n^2 + 2n - 1) = 2n^2 - 4n + 2$

Multiplication and division are inverse operations. To divide a polynomial by a constant, we reverse the process of multiplication.

➤ The expression $6x \div 3$ is a division statement.
It represents the quotient of the monomial, $6x$, and the constant 3.
To model $6x \div 3$,
we arrange six x-tiles in 3 rows.
Each row contains two x-tiles.
So, $6x \div 3 = 2x$

We can also model $6x \div 3$ as
one dimension of a rectangle with
an area of $6x$ and the other dimension 3.
Then, $6x \div 3 = \dfrac{6x}{3}$
$$= 2x$$

We can use what we know about division as a fraction and integer division to determine the quotient.
$$\dfrac{6x}{3} = \dfrac{6}{3} \times x$$
$$= 2 \times x$$
$$= 2x$$

➤ $(-6x) \div 3$ is the quotient of the monomial, $-6x$, and the constant 3.

Using a model:
We arrange six $-x$-tiles in 3 rows.

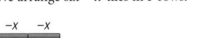

Each row contains two $-x$-tiles.
So, $(-6x) \div 3 = -2x$

Using fractions and integers:
$$(-6x) \div 3 = \dfrac{-6x}{3}$$
Simplify the fraction.
$$(-6x) \div 3 = \dfrac{-6}{3} \times x$$
$$= -2 \times x$$
$$= -2x$$

➤ $6x \div (-3)$ is the quotient of the monomial, $6x$, and the constant -3.
Using fractions and integers:
$$6x \div (-3) = \dfrac{6x}{-3}$$
Simplify the fraction.
$$6x \div (-3) = \dfrac{6}{-3} \times x$$
$$= -2 \times x$$
$$= -2x$$

Example 2   **Dividing a Binomial and a Trinomial by a Constant**

Determine each quotient.

a) $\dfrac{4s^2 - 8}{4}$

b) $\dfrac{-3m^2 + 15mn - 21n^2}{-3}$

▶ **Solutions**

Method 1	**Method 2**

Method 1

a) $\dfrac{4s^2 - 8}{4}$

Use algebra tiles.
Arrange four s^2-tiles and eight -1-tiles in 4 equal rows.

In each row, there is one s^2-tile and two -1-tiles.

So, $\dfrac{4s^2 - 8}{4} = s^2 - 2$

b) $\dfrac{-3m^2 + 15mn - 21n^2}{-3}$

Think multiplication.
What do we multiply -3 by to get
$-3m^2 + 15mn - 21n^2$?
$(-3) \times ? = -3m^2 + 15mn - 21n^2$
Since $(-3) \times 1 = -3$,
then $(-3) \times (1m^2) = -3m^2$
Since $(-3) \times (-5) = 15$,
then $(-3) \times (-5mn) = +15mn$
Since $(-3) \times 7 = -21$,
then $(-3) \times (+7n^2) = -21n^2$
So, $\dfrac{-3m^2 + 15mn - 21n^2}{-3} = m^2 - 5mn + 7n^2$

Method 2

a) $\dfrac{4s^2 - 8}{4}$

Write the quotient expression as the sum of 2 fractions.

$\dfrac{4s^2 - 8}{4} = \dfrac{4s^2}{4} + \dfrac{-8}{4}$

Simplify each fraction.

$= \dfrac{4}{4} \times s^2 + (-2)$

$= 1 \times s^2 - 2$

$= s^2 - 2$

b) $\dfrac{-3m^2 + 15mn - 21n^2}{-3}$

Write the quotient expression as the sum of 3 fractions.

$\dfrac{-3m^2 + 15mn - 21n^2}{-3}$

$= \dfrac{-3m^2}{-3} + \dfrac{15mn}{-3} + \dfrac{-21n^2}{-3}$

Simplify each fraction.

$= m^2 + (-5mn) + (7n^2)$

$= m^2 - 5mn + 7n^2$

1. How could you use multiplication to verify the quotient in a division question?

2. Why can we not use algebra tiles to divide when the divisor is negative?

Practice

Check

3. Write the multiplication sentence modelled by each set of algebra tiles.

a)

b)

c)

d)

4. For each set of algebra tiles in question 3, write a division sentence.

5. a) Which of these products is modelled by the algebra tiles below?
i) $2(-2n^2 + 3n + 4)$
ii) $2(2n^2 - 3n + 4)$
iii) $-2(2n^2 - 3n + 4)$

b) In part a, two of the products were not modelled by the algebra tiles. Model each product. Sketch the tiles you used.

6. Which of these quotients is modelled by the algebra tiles below?

a) $\dfrac{8t - 12}{-4}$

b) $\dfrac{-8t - 12}{4}$

c) $\dfrac{8t - 12}{4}$

Apply

7. a) Multiply.
i) $3(5r)$ ii) $-3(5r)$
iii) $(5r)(3)$ iv) $-5(3r)$
v) $-5(-3r)$ vi) $(-3r)(5)$

b) In part a, explain why some answers are the same.

c) For which products in part a could you have used algebra tiles? For each product, sketch the tiles you could use.

8. a) Divide.
i) $\dfrac{12k}{4}$ ii) $(-12k) \div 4$
iii) $\dfrac{12k}{-4}$ iv) $(-12k) \div (-4)$

b) In part a, explain why some answers are the same.

c) For which quotients in part a could you have used algebra tiles? For each quotient, sketch the tiles you could use.

9. Write the multiplication sentence modelled by each rectangle.

a)

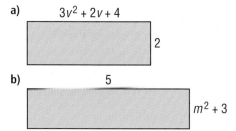
$3v^2 + 2v + 4$

2

b)

5

$m^2 + 3$

10. For each rectangle in question 9, write a division sentence.

11. Use algebra tiles to determine each product. Sketch the tiles you used. Record the product symbolically.
  a) $7(3s + 1)$
  b) $-2(-7h + 4)$
  c) $2(-3p^2 - 2p + 1)$
  d) $-6(2v^2 - v + 5)$
  e) $(-w^2 + 3w - 5)(3)$
  f) $(x^2 + x)(-5)$

12. Here is a student's solution for this question:

$-2(4r^2 - r + 7) = -2(4r^2) - 2(r) - 2(7)$
$\qquad\qquad\qquad = -8r^2 - 2r - 16$

Identify the errors in the solution, then write the correct solution.

13. Use algebra tiles to determine each quotient. Sketch the tiles you used. Record the product symbolically.
  a) $\dfrac{12p - 18}{6}$ **b)** $\dfrac{-6q^2 - 10}{2}$
  c) $\dfrac{5h^2 - 20h}{5}$ **d)** $\dfrac{4r^2 - 16r + 6}{2}$
  e) $\dfrac{-8a^2 + 4a - 12}{4}$ **f)** $\dfrac{6x^2 + 3x + 9}{3}$

14. Here is a student's solution for this question:
Divide: $(-14m^2 - 28m + 7) \div (-7)$

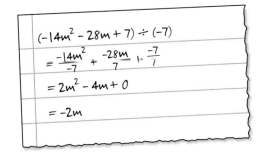

$(-14m^2 - 28m + 7) \div (-7)$

$= \dfrac{-14m^2}{-7} + \dfrac{-28m}{7} + \dfrac{-7}{1}$

$= 2m^2 - 4m + 0$

$= -2m$

Identify the errors in the solution, then write the correct solution.

15. Use any strategy to determine each product.
  a) $-3(-4u^2 + 16u + 8)$
  b) $12(2m^2 - 3m)$
  c) $(5t^2 + 2t)(-4)$
  d) $(-6s^2 - 5s - 7)(-5)$
  e) $4(-7y^2 + 3y - 9)$
  f) $10(8n^2 - n - 6)$

16. Use any strategy to determine each quotient.
  a) $\dfrac{24d^2 - 12}{12}$
  b) $\dfrac{8x + 4}{4}$
  c) $\dfrac{-10 + 4m^2}{-2}$
  d) $(25 - 5n) \div (-5)$
  e) $(-14k^2 + 28k - 49) \div 7$
  f) $\dfrac{30 - 36d^2 + 18d}{-6}$
  g) $\dfrac{-26c^2 + 39c - 13}{-13}$

17. Which pairs of expressions are equivalent? Explain how you know.
  a) $5j^2 + 4$ and $5(j + 4)$
  b) $10x^2$ and $3x(x + 7)$
  c) $15x - 10$ and $5(-2 + 3x)$
  d) $-3(-4x - 1)$ and $12x^2 - 3x$
  e) $-5(3x^2 - 7x + 2)$ and $-15x^2 + 12x - 10$
  f) $2x(-3x - 7)$ and $-6x^2 - 14x$

18. Assessment Focus

a) Determine each product or quotient.

  i) $(3p)(4)$ ii) $\dfrac{-21x}{3}$

  iii) $(3m^2 - 7)(-4)$

  iv) $\dfrac{-2f^2 + 14f - 8}{2}$

  v) $(6y^2 - 36y) \div (-6)$

  vi) $(-8n + 2 - 3n^2)(3)$

b) List the products and quotients in part a that can be modelled with algebra tiles. Justify your selection.

c) Sketch the tiles for one product and one quotient in part a.

19. a) Determine each product.

  i) $2(2x + 1)$ ii) $2(1 - 2x)$

     $3(2x + 1)$ $3(1 - 2x)$

     $4(2x + 1)$ $4(1 - 2x)$

     $5(2x + 1)$ $5(1 - 2x)$

b) Describe the patterns in part a.

c) Predict the next 3 products in each list in part a. How do you know the products are correct?

d) Suppose you extended the lists in part a upward. Predict the preceding 3 products in each list.

20. a) The perimeter of an equilateral triangle is represented by the polynomial $15a^2 + 21a + 6$.
Determine the polynomial that represents the length of one side.

b) Determine the length of one side when $a = 4$ cm.

21. Square A has side length $4s + 1$. Square B has a side length that is 3 times as great as the side length of square A.

a) What is the perimeter of each square? Justify your answers.

b) Write a polynomial, in simplest form, to represent the difference in the perimeters of squares A and B.

22. Determine each product.

a) $2(2x^2 - 3xy + 7y^2)$

b) $-4(pq + 3p^2 + 3q^2)$

c) $(-2gh + 6h^2 - 3g^2 - 9g)(3)$

d) $5(-r^2 + 8rs - 3s^2 - 5s + 4r)$

e) $-2(4t^2 - 3v^2 + 19tv - 6v - t)$

23. Determine each quotient.

a) $(3n^2 - 12mn + 6m^2) \div 3$

b) $\dfrac{-6rs - 16r - 4s}{-2}$

c) $\dfrac{10gh - 30g^2 - 15h}{5}$

d) $(12t^2 - 24ut - 48t) \div (-6)$

Take It Further

24. The area of a circle is given by the monomial πr^2.

Write, then simplify a polynomial for the shaded area in this diagram:

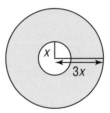

Reflect

How are multiplying and dividing a polynomial by a constant related?
Use examples to explain.

FOCUS

- Use different strategies to multiply and divide a polynomial by a monomial.

You can use the strategies you know for multiplying and dividing a polynomial by a constant to multiply and divide a polynomial by a monomial.

Investigate

You may need algebra tiles.

➤ Determine each product.
Use a strategy of your choice.
Write a multiplication sentence.

- $2a(5a)$
- $4b(3b - 2)$
- $-3c(-5c + 1)$

➤ Determine each quotient.
Use a strategy of your choice.
Write a division sentence.

- $\dfrac{3g^2 + 9g}{3g}$
- $\dfrac{-18f^2 + 12f}{6f}$
- $\dfrac{24d^2 + 8d}{-4d}$

Reflect & Share

Compare your answers and strategies with those of another pair of students.
If you have different answers, find out why.
If you used different strategies, explain your strategies and choice of strategies.
How can you use multiplication to check your quotients?

➤ The expression $(2c)(4c)$ is the product of two monomials.
We interpret the product with algebra tiles arranged to form a rectangle with dimensions $2c$ and $4c$.

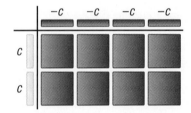

To help build the rectangle, we place guiding tiles to represent each dimension. Then we fill in the rectangle with tiles.

We need eight c^2-tiles to build the rectangle.
So, $(2c)(4c) = 8c^2$

➤ The expression $(2c)(-4c)$ is the product of a positive and a negative monomial.
We form a rectangle with guiding tiles: two c-tiles along one dimension and four $-c$-tiles along the other dimension.
We know that the product of a positive number and a negative number is negative.
So, when we fill in the rectangle, we use $-c^2$-tiles.

We need eight $-c^2$-tiles to build this rectangle.
So, $(2c)(-4c) = -8c^2$

We use similar strategies to multiply a binomial by a monomial.

➤ The expression $-4c(2c - 3)$ is the product of a monomial and a binomial.
We form a rectangle with guiding tiles:
• four $-c$-tiles along one dimension; and
• two c-tiles and three -1-tiles along the other dimension

The product of two numbers with opposite signs is negative.
So, when we place a tile in a row and column headed by guiding tiles with opposite signs, the tile is negative.

The product of two numbers with the same sign is positive.
So, when we place a tile in a row and column headed by guiding tiles with the same sign, the tile is positive.

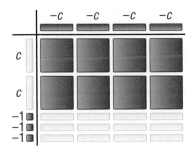

There are eight $-c^2$-tiles and twelve c-tiles.
So, $-4c(2c - 3) = -8c^2 + 12c$

Example 1   Multiplying a Binomial by a Monomial

Determine each product.

a) $2x(3x + 4)$ **b)** $-2x(-3x + 4)$

▶ **Solutions**

Method 1	Method 2

Method 1

a) $2x(3x + 4)$

Use algebra tiles to make a rectangle with dimensions $2x$ and $3x + 4$.

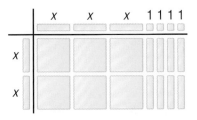

Six x^2-tiles and eight x-tiles fill the rectangle.
So, $2x(3x + 4) = 6x^2 + 8x$

Method 2

a) $2x(3x + 4)$

Use an area model.
Sketch a rectangle with dimensions $2x$ and $3x + 4$.
Divide the rectangle into 2 smaller rectangles.

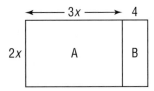

Rectangle A has area: $2x(3x) = 6x^2$
Rectangle B has area: $2x(4) = 8x$
The total area is: $6x^2 + 8x$
So, $2x(3x + 4) = 6x^2 + 8x$

b) $-2x(-3x + 4)$

Use algebra tiles.

Form a rectangle with guiding tiles:

- two $-x$-tiles along one dimension; and
- three $-x$-tiles and four 1-tiles along the other dimension

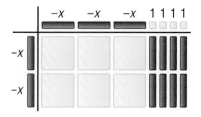

Six x^2-tiles and eight $-x$-tiles fill the rectangle.

So, $-2x(-3x + 4) = 6x^2 - 8x$

b) $-2x(-3x + 4)$

Use the distributive property.

Multiply each term in the brackets by the term outside the brackets.

$$-2x(-3x + 4) = -2x(-3x) + (-2x)(4)$$
$$= 6x^2 - 8x$$

To divide a polynomial by a monomial, we reverse the process of multiplying these polynomials.

➤ To determine the quotient of $\dfrac{8x^2}{4x}$, arrange eight x^2-tiles in a rectangle with one dimension $4x$.

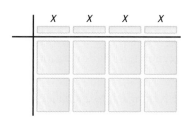

Along the left side of the rectangle, the guiding tiles are x-tiles.

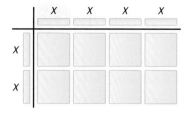

There are 2 guiding x-tiles.

So, $\dfrac{8x^2}{4x} = 2x$

➤ To determine the quotient of $\dfrac{-6w^2 + 9w}{3w}$, arrange six $-w^2$-tiles and nine w-tiles in a rectangle with one dimension $3w$.

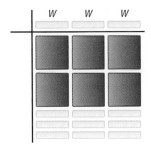

Along the left side of the rectangle:
- the guiding w-tiles are negative because they must have the sign opposite to that of the guiding tiles along the top of the rectangle
- the guiding 1-tiles are positive because they must have the same sign as the guiding tiles along the top of the rectangle

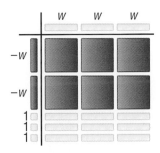

There are 2 guiding $-w$-tiles and 3 guiding 1-tiles.

So, $\dfrac{-6w^2 + 9w}{3w} = -2w + 3$

Determine each quotient.

a) $\dfrac{-10m^2}{2m}$

b) $\dfrac{30k^2 - 18k}{-6k}$

▶ **Solutions**

Method 1	Method 2
a) $\dfrac{-10m^2}{2m}$ Use algebra tiles. Arrange ten $-m^2$-tiles in a rectangle with one dimension $2m$. The guiding tiles along the other dimension represent $-5m$.  So, $\dfrac{-10m^2}{2m} = -5m$	a) $\dfrac{-10m^2}{2m}$ Think multiplication. $2m \times ? = -10m^2$ Since $2 \times (-5) = -10$ and $m \times m = m^2$ Then $2m \times (-5m) = -10m^2$ So, $\dfrac{-10m^2}{2m} = -5m$
b) $\dfrac{30k^2 - 18k}{-6k}$ Think multiplication. $-6k \times ? = 30k^2 - 18k$ Since $-6k \times (-5k) = 30k^2$ and $-6k \times (+3) = -18k$ Then $-6k \times (-5k + 3) = 30k^2 - 18k$ So, $\dfrac{30k^2 - 18k}{-6k} = -5k + 3$	b) $\dfrac{30k^2 - 18k}{-6k}$ Write the quotient expression as the sum of two fractions. $\dfrac{30k^2 - 18k}{-6k} = \dfrac{30k^2}{-6k} + \dfrac{-18k}{-6k}$ Simplify each fraction. $\dfrac{30k^2 - 18k}{-6k} = \dfrac{30}{-6} \times \dfrac{k^2}{k} + \dfrac{-18}{-6} \times \dfrac{k}{k}$ $= (-5) \times k + 3 \times 1$ $= -5k + 3$

Discuss the ideas

1. Why can we not use repeated addition to model the product $(2c)(4c)$?

2. Why can we not use an area model to multiply when there are negative terms in the product statement?

3. How could we check that a quotient is correct?

Check

4. Write the multiplication sentence modelled by each set of algebra tiles.

a)

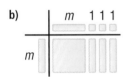

b)

c)

5. For each set of algebra tiles in question 4, write a division sentence.

6. Which of these multiplication sentences is modelled by the algebra tiles below?

a) $2n(n + 2)$

b) $2(2n^2 + 1)$

c) $2n(2n + 1)$

7. Write the multiplication sentence modelled by each rectangle.

a)

b)

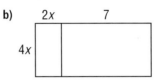

8. For each rectangle in question 7, write a division sentence.

Apply

9. a) Multiply.

i) $(3m)(4m)$ ii) $(-3m)(4m)$

iii) $(3m)(-4m)$ iv) $(-3m)(-4m)$

v) $(4m)(3m)$ vi) $(4m)(-3m)$

b) In part a, explain why there are only two answers.

c) For which products in part a could you have used algebra tiles? For each product, sketch the tiles you could use.

10. a) Divide.

i) $\dfrac{12x}{2x}$ ii) $\dfrac{12x}{-2x}$

iii) $\dfrac{-12x}{2x}$ iv) $\dfrac{-12x}{-2x}$

v) $\dfrac{12x^2}{2x}$ vi) $\dfrac{12x^2}{2x^2}$

vii) $\dfrac{-12x^2}{2x^2}$ viii) $\dfrac{12x^2}{-2x^2}$

b) In part a, explain why some quotients are equal.

c) For which quotients in part a could you have used algebra tiles? For each quotient, sketch the tiles you could use.

11. Multiply or divide as indicated.

a) $(2r)(-6r)$

b) $(-16n^2) \div (-8n)$

c) $(-5g)(7g)$

d) $\dfrac{40k}{-10k}$

e) $(9h)(3h)$

f) $\dfrac{48p^2}{12p}$

g) $18u^2 \div (-3u^2)$

h) $\dfrac{-24d^2}{-8d^2}$

12. Use any strategy to determine each product.

a) $2x(x + 6)$

b) $3t(5t + 2)$

c) $-2w(3w - 5)$

d) $-x(2 + 8x)$

e) $3g(-5 - g)$

f) $(4 + 3y)(2y)$

g) $(-7s - 1)(-y)$

h) $(-3 + 6r)(2r)$

13. A student thinks that the product $2x(x + 1)$ is $2x^2 + 1$. Choose a model. Use the model to explain how to get the correct answer.

14. Here is a student's solution for this question:
Multiply: $(-2d + 9)(-3d)$

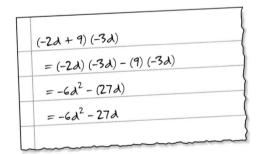

Identify the errors in the solution, then write the correct solution.

15. a) Describe two different strategies to simplify $\dfrac{3r^2 - 12r}{3r}$.

b) Which strategy do you find easier? Explain.

16. Use any strategy to determine each quotient.

a) $\dfrac{10x^2 + 4x}{2x}$

b) $(6x^2 + 4x) \div x$

c) $\dfrac{6y + 3y^2}{3y}$

d) $\dfrac{40x^2 - 16x}{8x}$

e) $\dfrac{15g - 10g^2}{5g}$

f) $\dfrac{-12k - 24k^2}{3k}$

g) $(24h^2 + 36h) \div (-4h)$

h) $(-8m^2 + 18m) \div (-2m)$

17. Assessment Focus

a) Determine each product or quotient. Use a different strategy each time.

i) $\dfrac{15n^2 + 5n}{5n}$

ii) $-3r(4 - 7r)$

iii) $(-16s^2 + 4s) \div (-2s)$

iv) $(t - 9)(4t)$

b) Choose one product and one quotient in part a. Use a different strategy to solve each problem. In each case, which strategy do you prefer? Explain why.

18. a) Use algebra tiles to model the quotient $\dfrac{12x^2 + 12x}{2x}$. Determine the quotient.

b) The polynomial $12x^2 + 12x$ can be represented by the areas of rectangles with different dimensions. Sketch and label the dimensions for as many different rectangles as you can. For each rectangle, write a division statement.

19. a) Write a polynomial to represent the area of each rectangle in the diagram below.

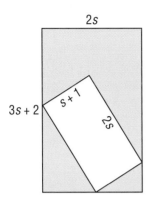

b) Determine a polynomial for the shaded area. Justify your strategy.

c) Determine the area in part b when $s = 2.5$ cm.

20. Determine each product.

a) $3m(2n + 4)$

b) $(-5 + 3f)(-2g)$

c) $7m(-6p + 7m)$

d) $(-8h - 3k)(4k)$

e) $(-2t + 3r)(4t)$

f) $(-g)(8h - 5g)$

21. Determine each quotient.

a) $(12x^2 + 6xy) \div 3x$

b) $\dfrac{12gh + 6g}{2g}$

c) $(-27p^2 + 36pq) \div 9p$

d) $\dfrac{40rs - 35r}{-5r}$

e) $\dfrac{14n^2 + 42np}{-7n}$

Take It Further

22. Determine a polynomial for the area of this shape. Justify your answer.

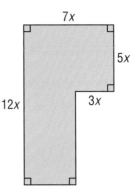

23. a) The polynomial $54s^2$ represents the surface area of a cube. Determine a polynomial that represents the area of one face.

b) Use your answer to part a. Determine the length of an edge of the cube.

24. The product $2\pi r(r + h)$ represents the surface area of a cylinder.

a) Determine the product.

b) To check your work, determine the surface area of a cylinder with radius 5 cm and height 3 cm two ways:

• using the product

• using your answer to part a

25. Simplify:
$[(2x^2 - 8x + 3xy + 5) + (24x^2 - 16x - 12xy)] \div 4x$

Reflect

Explain how the strategies for dividing a polynomial by a monomial are related to the strategies for multiplying a polynomial by a monomial. Include examples in your explanation.

Polynomials

▶ A polynomial is one term or the sum of terms whose variables have whole-number exponents; for example, $2m^2 + 3m - 5$

▶ The numerical value of a term is its coefficient.

▶ A term that consists of only a number is a constant term.

▶ The degree of a polynomial in the variable m is the highest power of m in the polynomial.

▶ A polynomial with: 1 term is a monomial; 2 terms is a binomial; and 3 terms is a trinomial.

Algebra Tiles

We can represent a polynomial with algebra tiles. $2p^2 + 2p - 3$

Like Terms

Like terms are represented by the same type of algebra tile. In symbolic form, like terms have the same variables raised to the same exponent. Like terms can be added or subtracted. $3x^2$ and $2x^2$ are like terms, but $-x$ and 3 are not.

$3x^2$: $2x^2$: $3x^2 + 2x^2$ simplifies to $5x^2$.

$-x$:    3: ▢▢▢ $-x + 3$ cannot be simplified.

Operations with Polynomials

We can use algebra tiles to model operations with polynomials, then record the answers symbolically.

▶ To add polynomials, combine like terms:
$$(3r^2 + 5r) + (2r^2 - r) = 3r^2 + 5r + 2r^2 - r$$
$$= 5r^2 + 4r$$

▶ To subtract polynomials, use a strategy for subtracting integers:
$$(3r^2 + 5r) - (2r^2 - r) = 3r^2 + 5r - (2r^2) - (-r)$$
$$= 3r^2 - 2r^2 + 5r + r$$
$$= r^2 + 6r$$

▶ To multiply a polynomial by a monomial, multiply each term of the polynomial by the monomial: $2t(5t - 3) = 2t(5t) + 2t(-3)$
$$= 10t^2 - 6t$$

▶ To divide a polynomial by a monomial, divide each term of the polynomial by the monomial:
$$\frac{21x^2 - 14x}{7x} = \frac{21x^2}{7x} - \frac{14x}{7x}$$
$$= 3x - 2$$

5.1 **1.** Use algebra tiles to model each polynomial. Sketch the tiles you used.

    a) $2u^2 + 5u$ **b)** $4n^2 - 2n - 3$

2. Identify the variables, coefficients, and constant terms in each polynomial.

    a) $4w - 3$ **b)** $5v^2 + 3$ **c)** $5y - 6 - y^2$

3. Classify each polynomial below:

    i) according to the number of terms
    ii) according to its degree

    a) $3f + 5$ **b)** $-2g^2$ **c)** $5h - 6 - h^2$

4. Use algebra tiles to model the polynomial that fits each description. Sketch the tiles you used.

    a) a second-degree trinomial in the variable y, the coefficients of the variable when the polynomial is written in descending order are -1 and -3, and with constant term 4

    b) a first-degree binomial in the variable x, with constant term 4, and the coefficient of the other term is -3

5. Identify the equivalent polynomials. Explain how you know they are equivalent.

    a) $-3x^2 + 3x - 11$ **b)** $3x^2 + 4x$
    c) $-2 - x$ **d)** $7 + 5x$
    e) $5x + 7$ **f)** $x - 2$
    g) $4x + 3x^2$ **h)** $3x - 11 - 3x^2$

6. Which polynomial is modelled by each set of algebra tiles?
State the degree of the polynomial.

    a)

    b)

    c)

7. Jennie does not understand how the terms $2k$ and k^2 are different. Use algebra tiles to model these terms and explain the difference.

8. For each polynomial, write an equivalent polynomial.

    a) $-1 - 2h$ **b)** $3j + 2j^2 - 4$ **c)** $-5p + p^2$

5.2 **9.** Identify like terms.

    a) $5x^2, 3y^2, -2x^2, 5x, 2y$
    b) $-8x, 5x, 8, -2, -x, 11$

10. Match each algebra tile model below with its corresponding polynomial.

    a) $n^2 - n + 3$ **b)** $-w^2 - 3$
    c) $-2t$ **d)** $2q + 2$
    e) $2r^2 - 2r + 1$

11. Write an expression with 5 terms that has only 3 terms when simplified.

12. Simplify by combining like terms.
  a) $3x + 4 - 2x - 8 + 3x - 3$
  b) $4y^2 - 2y + 3y - 11y^2$
  c) $2a^2 + 7a - 3 - 2a^2 - 4a + 6$
  d) $2a^2 + 3a + 3a^2 - a^2 - a - 4a^2$

5.3
5.4

13. Students who have trouble with algebra often make these mistakes.
  ➤ They think: $x + x = x^2$
  ➤ They think: $(x)(x) = 2x$
  Use algebra tiles to explain the correct answers.

14. Write the polynomial sum or difference modelled by each set of tiles. Determine the sum or difference.
  a)

  b)
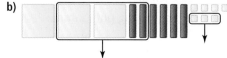

15. Add or subtract as indicated.
  a) $(p^2 + 3p + 5) + (3p^2 + p + 1)$
  b) $(3q^2 + 3q + 7) - (2q^2 + q + 2)$
  c) $(6 - 3r + 7r^2) - (9 + 4r + 3r^2)$
  d) $(5s + 3 - s^2) + (5 + 3s - 2s^2)$
  e) $(-4t^2 - 3t + 9) - (-2t^2 - 5t - 1)$
  f) $(-9u^2 - 5) - (-3u^2 - 9)$
  g) $(3a^2 + 5ab - 7b^2) + (3b^2 - 10ab - 7a^2)$
  h) $(10xy - 3y^2 + 2x) - (5y - 4x^2 + xy)$

16. The sum of two polynomials is $15c + 6$. One polynomial is $3c - 7$. What is the other polynomial? Explain how you found it.

17. Match each sum or difference of polynomials with its answer. Justify your choices.

A	$(5x^2 - 2) + (2x^2 + 4)$	P	$4x^2 + 2x - 1$
B	$(x^2 - 3x) - (4x^2 - x)$	Q	$7x^2 + 2$
C	$(x^2 + 2x + 3) + (3x^2 - 4)$	R	$x^2 + 2x - 1$
D	$(3x^2 - x + 2) - (2x^2 - 3x + 3)$	S	$-3x^2 - 2x$
E	$(-3x - 2) - (3x - 2)$	T	$-6x$

18. The difference of two polynomials is $3d^2 - 7d + 4$.
  One polynomial is $-8d^2 - 5d + 1$.
  a) What is the other polynomial? Explain how you found it.
  b) How many different answers can you find?

19. Write a polynomial for the perimeter of each shape. Simplify the polynomial. Determine each perimeter when $a = 3$ cm.
  a)
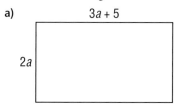
  b)
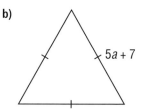

5.5

20. Write the multiplication sentence modelled by each set of algebra tiles.
  a)

  b)

21. For each set of algebra tiles in question 20, write a division sentence.

22. Determine each product or quotient. Use any strategy you wish.
  a) $10k \div 2$ **b)** $5(-4x^2)$
  c) $2(-3m + 4)$ **d)** $\dfrac{-6n^2}{3}$
  e) $-3(4s - 1)$ **f)** $\dfrac{9 - 12m}{3}$
  g) $5(-7 + 2x)$
  h) $-2(1 - 2n + 3n^2)$
  i) $2(x + 3x^2)$
  j) $(-6p^2 - 6p + 4) \div (-2)$
  k) $\dfrac{15 - 21q + 6q^2}{-3}$
  l) $(2 + 5n - 7n^2)(-6)$

23. Determine each product or quotient.
  a) $(xy - x^2 + y^2)(-2)$
  b) $(12m^2 - 6n + 8m) \div (-2)$
  c) $\dfrac{-18pq + 3p^2 - 9q}{3}$
  d) $4(2r^2 - 3r + 4s - 5s^2)$

5.6 **24.** Write the multiplication sentence modelled by each diagram.
  a)

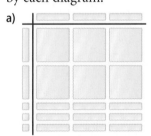

  b)

  | | 8a | 3 |
  5a

25. Write a division sentence for each diagram in question 24.

26. Determine each product.
  a) $(7s)(2s)$ **b)** $(-3g)(-5g)$
  c) $m(3m + 2)$ **d)** $-5t(t - 3)$
  e) $7z(-4z - 1)$ **f)** $(-3f - 5)(-2f)$
  g) $-5k(3 - k)$ **h)** $y(1 - y)$

27. This diagram shows one rectangle inside another.

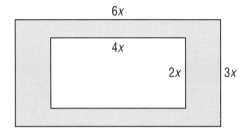

  a) Determine the area of each rectangle.
  b) Determine the area of the shaded region. Explain your strategy.

28. Determine each quotient.
  a) $24j \div (-6j)$ **b)** $\dfrac{24x}{3x}$
  c) $\dfrac{-36x^2}{-9x}$ **d)** $(-8a^2 - 12a) \div 4a$
  e) $(-8c + 4c^2) \div 4c$ **f)** $\dfrac{14y^2 - 21y}{-7y}$

29. a) The area of a rectangular deck is $(8d^2 + 20d)$ square metres. The deck is $4d$ metres long. Determine a polynomial that represents the width of the deck.
  b) What are the dimensions and area of the deck when d is 4 metres?

1. a) Which polynomial in t do these tiles represent?

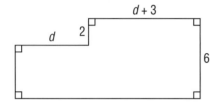

b) Classify the polynomial by degree and by the number of terms.

c) Identify the constant term and the coefficient of the t^2-term.

2. a) Write a polynomial for the perimeter of this shape. Simplify the polynomial.

b) Determine the perimeter of the shape when $d = 5$ m.

3. Sketch algebra tiles to explain why:

a) $3x + 2x$ equals $5x$ **b)** $(3x)(2x)$ equals $6x^2$

4. A student determined the product $3r(r + 4)$.
The student's answer was $3r^2 + 4$.
Use a model to explain whether the student's answer is correct.

5. Add or subtract as indicated. What strategy will you use each time?

a) $(15 - 3d) + (3 - 15d)$ **b)** $(9h + 3) - (9 - 3h^2)$

c) $(2y^2 + 5y - 6) + (-7y^2 + 2y - 6)$ **d)** $(7y^2 + y) - (3y - y^2)$

6. Multiply or divide as indicated. What strategy will you use each time?

a) $25m(3m - 2)$ **b)** $-5(3v^2 - 2v - 1)$

c) $(8x^2 - 4x) \div 2x$ **d)** $\dfrac{-6 + 3g^2 - 15g}{-3}$

7. Determine two polynomials with:

a) a sum of $3x^2 - 4x - 2$

b) a difference of $3x^2 - 4x - 2$

8. A rectangle has dimensions $5s$ and $3s + 8$.

a) Sketch the rectangle and label it with its dimensions.

b) What is the area of the rectangle?

c) What is the perimeter of the rectangle?

You will need a copy of a 100-chart.

1	2	3	4	5	6	7	8	9	10
11	12	13	14	15	16	17	18	19	20
21	22	23	24	25	26	27	28	29	30
31	32	33	34	35	36	37	38	39	40
41	42	43	44	45	46	47	48	49	50
51	52	53	54	55	56	57	58	59	60
61	62	63	64	65	66	67	68	69	70
71	72	73	74	75	76	77	78	79	80
81	82	83	84	85	86	87	88	89	90
91	92	93	94	95	96	97	98	99	100

➤ Choose any 3 by 3 square of numbers on the chart.
Add the numbers in each diagonal.
What do you notice?

➤ Choose a different 3 by 3 square.
Add the numbers in each diagonal.
How do your results compare?

➤ Determine a relationship between the number at the
centre of any 3 by 3 square and the sum of the numbers
in a diagonal.

➤ Let x represent the number at the centre of any 3 by 3 square.
Write a polynomial, in terms of x, for each number at
the four corners of the square.

➤ Add the polynomials in each diagonal. What is the sum?
How does this explain the relationship you found earlier?

➤ Suppose you know the sum of the numbers in a diagonal of a
3 by 3 square. How could you determine the number at the centre
of the square?

➤ What do you think is the relationship between the number at the centre
of a 5 by 5 square and the sum of the numbers in a diagonal? What about
a 7 by 7 square? Make a prediction, then use polynomials to check.

Your work should show:
• each 3 by 3 square and the related calculations
• a relationship between the number at the centre and the sum
• how this relationship changes as the size of the square changes

Reflect
on Your Learning

What did you find easy about polynomials? What did
you find difficult? What strategies might you use to
overcome these difficulties?

Linear Equations and Inequalities

The Pep Club promotes school spirit at athletic events and school activities. The members of the club need new uniforms. They are thinking of selling healthy snacks at lunch time to raise the money needed. What information does the Pep Club need to gather? What math might the members use?

What You'll Learn

- Model and solve problems using linear equations.
- Explain and illustrate strategies to solve linear inequalities.

Why It's Important

Linear equations and inequalities occur in everyday situations involving ratios and rates, geometry formulas, scientific contexts, and financial applications. Using an equation or inequality to solve a problem is an important problem-solving strategy.

Key Words

- inverse operations
- inequality

6.1 Solving Equations by Using Inverse Operations

FOCUS

• Model a problem with a linear equation, use an arrow diagram to solve the equation pictorially, and record the process symbolically.

The top row of the arrow diagram shows the steps to remove a flat tire on a car. What steps are needed to put on a new tire?

How are these steps related to the steps to remove the flat tire?

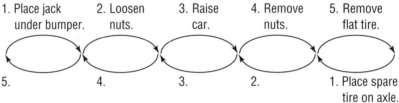

1. Place jack under bumper.   2. Loosen nuts.   3. Raise car.   4. Remove nuts.   5. Remove flat tire.

5.   4.   3.   2.   1. Place spare tire on axle.

Investigate

> This arrow diagram shows the operations applied to the start equation $x = -7$ to build the end equation $3x + 8 = -13$.

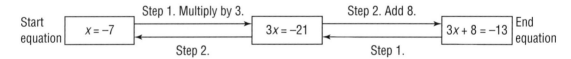

Start equation | Step 1. Multiply by 3. | $x = -7$ | $3x = -21$ | Step 2. | Step 2. Add 8. | $3x + 8 = -13$ | End equation | Step 1.

Copy and complete the diagram. What are Steps 1 and 2 in the bottom row? What operations must be applied to the end equation to return to the start equation?

> Choose a rational number to complete your own start equation: $x = \square$
Multiply or divide each side of the equation by the same number.
Write the resulting equation.
Add or subtract the same number from each side of the equation.
Write the resulting equation. This is the end equation.
Trade end equations with your partner.
Determine your partner's start equation. Record the steps in your solution.

Share your end equations with another pair of classmates.
Determine each other's start equations. What strategies did you use?
How are the steps used to get from the start equation to the end equation related to the steps used to reverse the process?

Inverse operations "undo" or reverse each other's results.
Addition and subtraction are inverse operations.
Multiplication and division are also inverse operations.

We can use inverse operations to solve many types of equations. To do this, we
determine the operations that were applied to the variable to build the equation.
We then use inverse operations to isolate the variable by "undoing" these operations.

For example, to solve $x + 2.4 = 6.5$:

➤ Start with x.

Identify the operation applied to x to produce
the expression $x + 2.4$; that is, add 2.4 to get:
$x + 2.4$

➤ Since $x + 2.4$ is equal to 6.5, apply the inverse operation
on 6.5 to isolate x; that is, subtract 2.4 to get:
$x + 2.4 - 2.4 = 6.5 - 2.4$
So, $x = 4.1$

Build equation

```
          +2.4
     ┌───────────┐
  ┌─────┐     ┌───────┐
  │  x  │     │ x+2.4 │
  └─────┘     └───────┘
  ┌─────┐     ┌───────┐
  │ 4.1 │     │  6.5  │
  └─────┘     └───────┘
     └───────────┘
          -2.4
```
Solve equation

Example 1	**Writing Then Solving One-Step Equations**

For each statement below, write then solve an equation to determine each number.
Verify the solution.

a) Three times a number is -3.6.

b) A number divided by 4 is 1.5.

► *A Solution*

a) Let n represent the number. Then, 3 times n is -3.6.
The equation is: $3n = -3.6$

Inverse Operations

Build equation

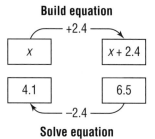

Solve equation

Algebraic Solution

$3n = -3.6$
Undo the multiplication.
Divide each side by 3.
$$\frac{3n}{3} = \frac{-3.6}{3}$$
$$n = -1.2$$

Verify the solution: $3 \times (-1.2) = -3.6$, so the solution is correct.

b) Let m represent the number. Then, m divided by 4 is 1.5.
The equation is: $\frac{m}{4} = 1.5$

Inverse Operations

Build equation

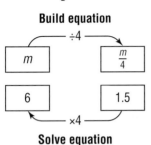

Solve equation

Algebraic Solution

$$\frac{m}{4} = 1.5$$

Undo the division.
Multiply each side by 4.

$$4 \times \frac{m}{4} = 4 \times 1.5$$
$$m = 6$$

Verify the solution: $\frac{6}{4} = 1.5$, so the solution is correct.

To "undo" a sequence of operations, we perform the inverse operations in the reverse order. For example, compare the steps and operations to wrap a present with the steps and operations to unwrap the present.

Wrap present

| 1. Put present in box. | 2. Wrap box. | 3. Put on bow. |

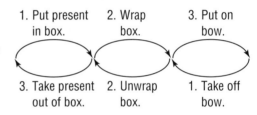

| 3. Take present out of box. | 2. Unwrap box. | 1. Take off bow. |

Unwrap present

Example 2   Solving a Two-Step Equation

Solve, then verify each equation.

a) $4.5d - 3.2 = -18.5$ **b)** $\frac{r}{4} + 3 = 7.2$

▶ *A Solution*

a) $4.5d - 3.2 = -18.5$

Inverse Operations

Build equation

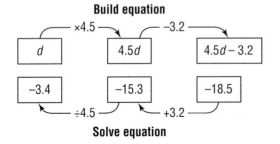

Solve equation

Algebraic Solution

$$4.5d - 3.2 = -18.5$$

Add 3.2 to each side.

$$4.5d - 3.2 + 3.2 = -18.5 + 3.2$$
$$4.5d = -15.3$$

Divide each side by 4.5.

$$\frac{4.5d}{4.5} = \frac{-15.3}{4.5}$$
$$d = -3.4$$

To verify the solution, substitute $d = -3.4$ into $4.5d - 3.2 = -18.5$.

Left side $= 4.5d - 3.2$ Right side $= -18.5$

$\quad\quad\quad = 4.5 \times (-3.4) - 3.2$

$\quad\quad\quad = -15.3 - 3.2$

$\quad\quad\quad = -18.5$

Since the left side equals the right side, $d = -3.4$ is correct.

b) $\frac{r}{4} + 3 = 7.2$

Inverse Operations   **Algebraic Solution**

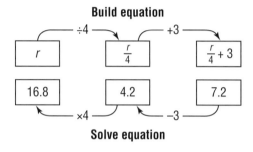

$$\frac{r}{4} + 3 = 7.2$$

Subtract 3 from each side.

$$\frac{r}{4} + 3 - 3 = 7.2 - 3$$

$$\frac{r}{4} = 4.2$$

Multiply each side by 4.

$$4 \times \frac{r}{4} = 4 \times 4.2$$

$$r = 16.8$$

To verify the solution, substitute $r = 16.8$ into $\frac{r}{4} + 3 = 7.2$.

Left side $= \frac{r}{4} + 3$ Right side $= 7.2$

$\quad\quad\quad = \frac{16.8}{4} + 3$

$\quad\quad\quad = 4.2 + 3$

$\quad\quad\quad = 7.2$

Since the left side equals the right side, $r = 16.8$ is correct.

We can use equations to model and solve problems. With practice, you can determine the inverse operations required to solve the equation mentally. In many situations, there may be more than one way to solve the equation.

Math Link

Science

When a freighter unloads its cargo, it replaces the mass of cargo with an equal mass of sea water. This mass of water will keep the ship stable. The volume of sea water added is measured in litres. To relate the volume of water to its mass, we use this formula for density, D:

$D = \frac{M}{V}$, where M = mass, and V = volume

Once a freighter has been unloaded, it is filled with 5 million litres of water. The density of sea water is 1.030 kg/L. What mass of water was added? Solve the equation $1.030 = \frac{M}{5\,000\,000}$ to find out.

Example 3   **Using an Equation to Model and Solve a Problem**

A rectangle has length 3.7 cm and perimeter 13.2 cm.

a) Write an equation that can be used to determine the width of the rectangle.

b) Solve the equation.

c) Verify the solution.

▶ **Solutions**

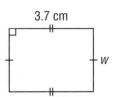

a) Let w centimetres represent the width of the rectangle. The perimeter of a rectangle is twice the sum of the length and width. So, the equation is: $13.2 = 2(3.7 + w)$

b) Solve the equation.

Method 1

Use inverse operations.

$13.2 = 2(3.7 + w)$

Think:

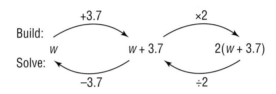

$$13.2 = 2(3.7 + w)$$ Divide each side by 2.

$$\frac{13.2}{2} = \frac{2(3.7 + w)}{2}$$

$$6.6 = 3.7 + w$$ Subtract 3.7 from each side.

$$6.6 - 3.7 = 3.7 + w - 3.7$$

$$2.9 = w$$

Method 2

Use the distributive property, then inverse operations.

$13.2 = 2(3.7 + w)$ Use the distributive property to expand $2(3.7 + w)$.

$13.2 = 2(3.7) + 2(w)$

$13.2 = 7.4 + 2w$

$13.2 - 7.4 = 7.4 + 2w - 7.4$ Subtract 7.4 from each side.

$5.8 = 2w$ Divide each side by 2.

$\frac{5.8}{2} = \frac{2w}{2}$

$2.9 = w$

c) Check: The perimeter of a rectangle with length 3.7 cm and width 2.9 cm is:

$2(3.7 \text{ cm} + 2.9 \text{ cm}) = 2(6.6 \text{ cm})$

$= 13.2 \text{ cm}$

The solution is correct. The width of the rectangle is 2.9 cm.

Example 4   **Using an Equation to Solve a Percent Problem**

Seven percent of a number is 56.7.

a) Write, then solve an equation to determine the number.

b) Check the solution.

▶ *A Solution*

a) Let n represent the number. Then, 7% of the number is 7% $\times$ n, or $0.07n$.
   An equation is: $0.07n = 56.7$

   $0.07n = 56.7$ Divide each side by 0.07.

   $\dfrac{0.07n}{0.07} = \dfrac{56.7}{0.07}$ Use a calculator.

   $n = 810$

   The number is 810.

b) 7% of 810 $= 0.07 \times 810$

   $\qquad\qquad\quad = 56.7$

   So, the solution is correct.

Discuss the ideas

1. How are inverse operations used to solve an equation?
   How can you verify your solution of an equation?

2. When you build or solve an equation, why must you apply the
   operations or inverse operations to both sides of the equation?

3. When you verify the solution to an equation, why should you
   substitute the solution in the original equation?

4. When you solve a two-step equation using inverse operations,
   how is the order in which you apply the inverse operations
   related to the order in which you would build the end equation?

Practice

Check

5. Solve each equation by copying and
   completing the arrow diagram.
   How do you know that your solution
   is correct?

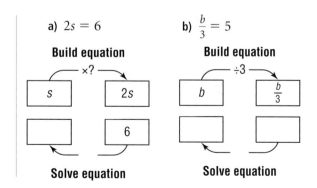

a) $2s = 6$

b) $\dfrac{b}{3} = 5$

c) $5e = -35$

Build equation

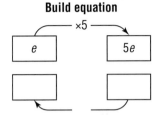

Solve equation

d) $\frac{x}{2} = -7$

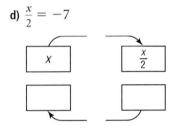

e) $-9w = 2.7$

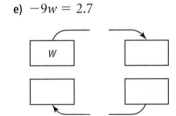

f) $\frac{c}{5} = -1.2$

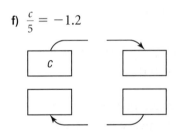

6. Solve each equation by copying and completing the arrow diagram. How do you know that your solution is correct?

a) $3x + 2 = 8$

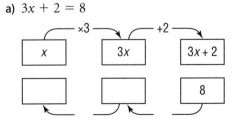

b) $-5a - 6 = 7$

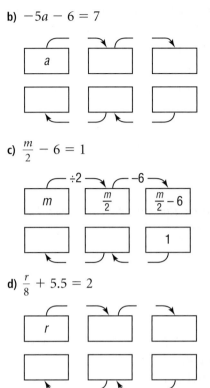

c) $\frac{m}{2} - 6 = 1$

d) $\frac{r}{8} + 5.5 = 2$

7. A student tried to solve the equation $-5m = 15$ by adding 5 to each side. Explain what is wrong with the student's method.
Show the correct way to solve the equation.

Apply

8. Solve each equation.
Which strategy did you use?
Verify the solution.

a) $4x = 9.6$

b) $10 = 3b - 12.5$

c) $-5.25x = -210$

d) $-0.5 = -2x + 8.1$

e) $250 + 3.5n = 670$

f) $-22.5 = -2c - 30.5$

9. For each statement below, write then solve an equation to determine the number. Verify the solution.
   a) Two times a number is -10.
   b) Three times a number, plus 6.4, is 13.9.
   c) Four times a number is -8.8.
   d) Ten is equal to two times a number, plus 3.6.

10. Solve each equation. Verify the solution.
    a) $\frac{c}{3} = 15$
    b) $\frac{m}{6} - 1.5 = -7$
    c) $-1.5 = \frac{n}{4}$
    d) $5 = \frac{q}{-2} - 5$
    e) $\frac{2c}{5} = 1.2$
    f) $1.2 = \frac{2a}{3} + 5.1$

11. For each statement below, write then solve an equation to determine the number. Verify the solution.
    a) A number divided by 4 is -7.
    b) Three, plus a number divided by 5 is 6.
    c) One-half of a number is 2.5.
    d) One-third of a number, minus 4, is 2.

12. Jenna says that, to build the equation $-2b + 4 = -\frac{3}{4}$, she multiplied each side of the start equation by -2, then added 4 to each side. Can Jenna's partner solve this equation by dividing each side by -2, then subtracting 4 from each side? Explain why or why not.

13. Erica is thinking of a number. If you divide her number by 3 then subtract 13.5, the result is 2.8.
    a) Let b represent Erica's number. Write an equation to determine this number.
    b) Solve the equation.
    c) Verify the solution.

14. A parallelogram has one shorter side of length 1.2 cm and perimeter 6.6 cm.

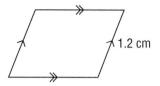

1.2 cm

   a) Write an equation that can be used to determine the length of the longer side.
   b) Solve the equation.
   c) Verify the solution.

15. Twelve percent of a number is 39.48.
    a) Write, then solve an equation to determine the number.
    b) Check the solution.

16. Stephanie has a job in sales. She earns a monthly salary of $2500, plus a commission of 8% of her sales. One month, Stephanie earns a total of $2780. This can be represented by the equation
    $2780 = 2500 + 0.08s$,
    where s is Stephanie's sales in dollars.
    a) Solve the equation to determine Stephanie's sales for that month.
    b) Verify the solution.

17. Steve works in a clothing store. He earns $1925 a month, plus a commission of 10% of his sales. One month, Steve earned $2725.
    a) Choose a variable to represent Steve's sales in dollars, then write an equation to determine Steve's sales that month.
    b) Solve the equation. What were Steve's sales?

18. Solve each equation. Verify the solution.
    a) $5(x - 7) = -15$
    b) $2(m + 4) = 11$
    c) $-3(t - 2.7) = 1.8$
    d) $7.6 = -2(-3 - y)$
    e) $8.4 = -6(a + 2.4)$

19. Assessment Focus Vianne took 4 bottles of water and 6 bottles of juice to a family picnic. Each bottle of juice contained 0.5 L. The total volume of water and juice was 4.42 L. What was the volume of 1 bottle of water?
   a) Choose a variable and write an equation for this situation.
   b) Solve the equation.
   c) Verify the solution.
   Show your work.

20. On a test, a student solved these equations:

$$a) \quad 3(x - 2.4) = 4.2$$
$$3(x) - 3(2.4) = 3(4.2)$$
$$3x - 7.2 = 12.6$$
$$3x - 7.2 + 7.2 = 12.6 + 7.2$$
$$3x = 19.8$$
$$\frac{3x}{3} = \frac{19.8}{3}$$
$$x = 6.6$$

$$b) \quad 5 - \frac{1}{2}x = 3$$
$$5 - \frac{1}{2}x - 5 = 3 - 5$$
$$\frac{1}{2}x = -2$$
$$x = -1$$

What mistakes did the student make? Write a correct solution for each equation.

21. A large pizza with tomato sauce and cheese costs $7.50, plus $1.50 for each additional topping. A customer orders a large pizza and is charged $16.50. How many toppings did the customer order?
   a) Write an equation to solve the problem.
   b) Solve the problem. Verify the solution.

22. An item increased in price by $4.95. This is a 9% increase. What did the item cost before the price increase?
   a) Write an equation to solve the problem.
   b) Solve the equation. Verify your solution.

Take It Further

23. The expression $180(n - 2)$ represents the sum of the interior angles in a polygon with n sides. Suppose the sum of its interior angles is 1080°. How many sides does the polygon have?
   a) Write an equation to solve the problem.
   b) Kyler solves the equation after using the distributive property to simplify $180(n - 2)$. Show the steps in Kyler's solution.
   c) Esta solves the equation by undoing the operations that were used to build the equation. Show the steps in Esta's solution.
   d) Whose method do you prefer? Explain.

24. Solve each equation. Verify the solution.
   a) $4x + \frac{37}{5} = -17$ b) $8m - \frac{6}{7} = \frac{176}{7}$
   c) $\frac{3}{4} - 5p = \frac{67}{6}$ d) $\frac{22}{8} + 10g = \frac{62}{5}$

Reflect

Choose a reversible routine from daily life. Explain why reversing the routine means undoing each step in the reverse order. Explain how this idea can be used to solve an equation. Include an example.

FOCUS

• Model a problem
  with a linear
  equation, use
  balance strategies
  to solve the
  equation pictorially,
  and record the
  process
  symbolically.

Tracey has to solve the equation $4a + 6 = 7a$.
Could she use an arrow diagram to model this equation?
How could these balance scales help Tracey?

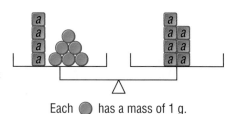

Each ⬤ has a mass of 1 g.

Investigate ⟨2⟩

Use a model or strategy of your choice to solve this equation: $5a + 7 = 2a + 1$
Record the solution algebraically.
How do you know that your solution is correct?

Compare your strategies and solutions with those of another
pair of classmates.
If you used different strategies, explain your strategy and
choice of strategy.
What are the advantages and disadvantages of each strategy?
Which strategies did not work?

Connect

To solve an equation, we need to isolate the variable on one side of the equation.

In Lesson 6.1, we isolated the variable by reversing the operations acting on the variable.
However, this strategy can only be used when the variable occurs once in the equation.

Another way to isolate the variable is to use a balance strategy modelled by balance
scales. The scales remain balanced when we do the same thing to each side.

| **Example 1** | **Modelling Equations with Variables on Both Sides** |

a) Solve: $6x + 2 = 10 + 4x$

b) Verify the solution.

▶ **A Solution**

a) Rearrange the equation so that both terms containing the variable are on the same side of the equation. Then isolate the variable to solve the equation.

Pictorial Solution   Algebraic Solution

Draw balance scales. On the left pan, draw masses to represent $6x + 2$. On the right pan, draw masses to represent $10 + 4x$.

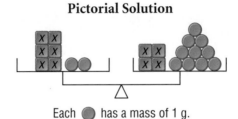

Each ● has a mass of 1 g.

$$6x + 2 = 10 + 4x$$

Remove four x masses from each pan.

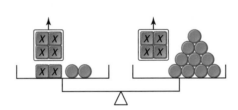

$$6x - 4x + 2 = 10 + 4x - 4x$$
$$2x + 2 = 10$$

Remove two 1-g masses from each pan.

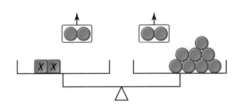

$$2x + 2 - 2 = 10 - 2$$
$$2x = 8$$

Divide the masses in each pan into 2 equal groups. Each x-mass in the left pan corresponds to a group of 4 g in the right pan.

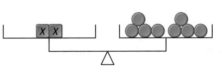

$$\frac{2x}{2} = \frac{8}{2}$$
$$x = 4$$

b) Check: Substitute $x = 4$ in each side of the equation.

Left side $= 6x + 2$ Right side $= 10 + 4x$

$\qquad = 6(4) + 2$ $= 10 + 4(4)$

$\qquad = 24 + 2$ $= 10 + 16$

$\qquad = 26$ $= 26$

Since the left side equals the right side, $x = 4$ is correct.

We cannot easily use a balance scales model when any term in an equation is negative. But we can use algebra tiles to model and solve the equation. We use the principle of balance by adding the same tiles to each side or subtracting the same tiles from each side.

Example 2   Using Algebra Tiles to Solve an Equation

Solve: $-3c + 7 = 2c - 8$

▶ *A Solution*

Algebra Tile Model	Algebraic Solution

Algebra Tile Model

Model the equation with tiles.

Add two $-c$-tiles to each side to get the terms containing c on the same side. Remove zero pairs.

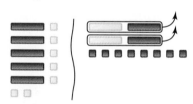

Add seven -1-tiles to each side to get the constant terms on the same side. Remove zero pairs.

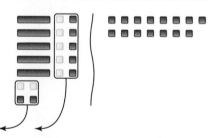

Arrange the remaining tiles on each side into 5 groups.

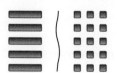

One $-c$-tile is equal to -3.

Flip the tiles. One c-tile is equal to 3.

Algebraic Solution

$$-3c + 7 = 2c - 8$$

$$-3c + 7 - 2c = 2c - 8 - 2c$$
$$-5c + 7 = -8$$

$$-5c + 7 - 7 = -8 - 7$$
$$-5c = -15$$

$$-1c = -3$$

$$c = 3$$

Equations with rational numbers in fraction or decimal form cannot be modelled easily with balance scales. However, we can solve these equations by doing the same thing to each side of the equation to isolate the variable. We may:

➤ Add the same quantity to each side.
➤ Subtract the same quantity from each side.
➤ Multiply or divide each side by the same non-zero quantity.

Example 3   Solving Equations with Rational Coefficients

Solve each equation, then verify the solution.

a) $\dfrac{122}{r} = 3,\ r \neq 0$ b) $\dfrac{2a}{3} = \dfrac{4a}{5} + 7$

➤ A Solution

Create an equivalent equation without fractions.

a) To clear the fraction, multiply each side by the denominator.

$$\frac{122}{r} = 3 \qquad\qquad \text{Multiply each side by } r.$$

$$r \times \frac{122}{r} = 3 \times r \qquad\qquad \text{Think: } \frac{r}{1} \times \frac{122}{r} = \frac{122}{1}$$

$$122 = 3r \qquad\qquad \text{Divide each side by 3.}$$

$$\frac{122}{3} = \frac{3r}{3}$$

$$\frac{122}{3} = r$$

So, $r = \dfrac{122}{3}$, or $40\,\dfrac{2}{3}$, or $40.\overline{6}$

Check: Substitute $r = \dfrac{122}{3}$ in the original equation.

Left side $= \dfrac{122}{r}$ Right side $= 3$

$$= \frac{122}{\frac{122}{3}}$$

$$= \frac{122}{1} \times \frac{3}{122}$$

$$= 3$$

Since the left side equals the right side, $r = \dfrac{122}{3}$ is correct.

b) To clear the fractions, multiply each side by the common denominator.

$$\frac{2a}{3} = \frac{4a}{5} + 7 \qquad\qquad \text{Multiply each side by the common denominator 15.}$$

$$15 \times \frac{2a}{3} = 15\left(\frac{4a}{5} + 7\right) \qquad\qquad \text{Use the distributive property.}$$

$$\overset{5}{\cancel{15}} \times \frac{2a}{\underset{1}{\cancel{3}}} = \overset{3}{\cancel{15}} \times \frac{4a}{\underset{1}{\cancel{5}}} + 15 \times 7$$

$$10a = 12a + 105 \qquad\qquad \text{Subtract } 12a \text{ from each side.}$$

$$10a - 12a = 12a + 105 - 12a$$

$$-2a = 105 \qquad\qquad \text{Divide each side by } -2.$$

$$\frac{-2a}{-2} = \frac{105}{-2}$$

$$a = -52\frac{1}{2}, \text{ or } -52.5$$

Check: Substitute $a = -52.5$ in each side of the original equation.

Left side $= \frac{2a}{3}$ 　　　　　　　　Right side $= \frac{4a}{5} + 7$

$\quad\quad = \frac{2(-52.5)}{3}$ 　　　　　　　　$\quad\quad = \frac{4(-52.5)}{5} + 7$

$\quad\quad = -35$ 　　　　　　　　　　$\quad\quad = -42 + 7$

　　　　　　　　　　　　　　　　$\quad\quad = -35$

Since the left side equals the right side, $a = -52.5$ is the correct solution.

Example 4　Using an Equation to Model and Solve a Problem

A cell phone company offers two plans.

Plan A: 120 free minutes, $0.75 per additional minute
Plan B: 30 free minutes, $0.25 per additional minute

Which time for calls will result in the same cost for both plans?

a) Model the problem with an equation.
b) Solve the problem.
c) Verify the solution.

▶ *A Solution*

a) Let t minutes represent the time for calls.

For Plan A, you pay only for the time that is greater than 120 min.
So, the time you pay for is $(t - 120)$ min.
Each minute costs $0.75, so the cost in dollars is: $0.75(t - 120)$
For Plan B, you pay only for the time that is greater than 30 min.
So, the time you pay for is $(t - 30)$ min.
Each minute costs $0.25, so the cost in dollars is: $0.25(t - 30)$
When these two costs are equal, the equation is:
$0.75(t - 120) = 0.25(t - 30)$

b)　　　　　$0.75(t - 120) = 0.25(t - 30)$　　　　Use the distributive property.
$0.75(t) + 0.75(-120) = 0.25(t) + 0.25(-30)$
　　　　$0.75t - 90 = 0.25t - 7.5$　　　　Subtract $0.25t$ from each side.
$0.75t - 0.25t - 90 = 0.25t - 0.25t - 7.5$
　　　　$0.50t - 90 = -7.5$　　　　Add 90 to each side.
$0.50t - 90 + 90 = -7.5 + 90$
　　　　　$0.50t = 82.5$　　　　Divide each side by 0.50.
　　　　　$\frac{0.50t}{0.50} = \frac{82.5}{0.50}$
　　　　　　$t = 165$

The cost is the same for both plans when the time for calls is 165 min.

c) For Plan A, you pay for: 165 − 120, or 45 min
The cost is: 45 × \$0.75 = \$33.75
For Plan B, you pay for: 165 − 30, or 135 min
The cost is: 135 × \$0.25 = \$33.75
These costs are equal, so the solution is correct.

Discuss the ideas

1. Why can we not use an arrow diagram to solve an equation with a variable term on each side?

2. When you solve an equation with variables on both sides of the equation, does it matter if you isolate the variable on the left side or the right side of the equation? Explain.

3. For an equation such as $\frac{122}{r} = 3$, why do we include the statement that $r \neq 0$?

Practice

Check

4. Write the equation represented by each picture. Solve the equation. Record the steps algebraically.

a)

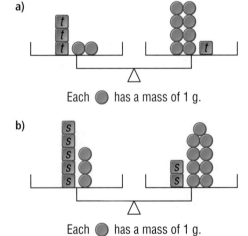

Each ⬤ has a mass of 1 g.

b)

Each ⬤ has a mass of 1 g.

5. Hammy uses algebra tiles to solve the equation $3f - 2 = f + 4$. These pictures show the steps in the solution:

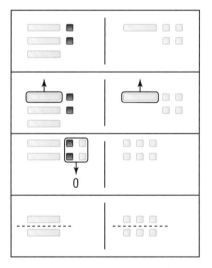

a) Explain the action taken in each step.
b) Record each step algebraically.

6. Use algebra tiles to solve each equation. Record the steps.

a) $4g = 7 - 3g$

b) $4k + 4 = -2k - 8$

c) $-4a - 3 = 3 - a$

d) $3h - 5 = 7 - 3h$

Apply

7. a) Solve each equation.

i) $\frac{6}{h} = 2, h \neq 0$ ii) $\frac{-6}{h} = 2, h \neq 0$

iii) $-2 = \frac{6}{h}, h \neq 0$ iv) $\frac{6}{-h} = 2, h \neq 0$

v) $-2 = \frac{-6}{h}, h \neq 0$ vi) $\frac{6}{-h} = -2, h \neq 0$

b) Explain why there are only 2 solutions to all the equations in part a.

8. Solve each equation. What strategy did you use? Verify the solution.

a) $2.4 = \frac{4.8}{s}, s \neq 0$

b) $\frac{-5.4}{t} = 1.8, t \neq 0$

c) $-6.5 = \frac{-1.3}{w}, w \neq 0$

9. Ten divided by a number is -3. Write, then solve an equation to determine the number. Verify the solution.

10. Solve each equation. What strategy did you use? Verify the solution.

a) $-12a = 15 - 15a$

b) $10.6y = 2.1y - 27.2$

c) $-10.8 + 7z = 5z$

d) $6u - 11.34 = 4.2u$

e) $-20.5 - 2.2b = -7.2b$

f) $-5.3p = -9 - 8.9p$

11. Solve each equation. Verify the solution.

a) $2 - 3n = 2n + 7$

b) $13 - 3q = 4 - 2q$

c) $-2.4a + 3.7 = -16.1 + 3.1a$

d) $8.8v + 2.1 = 2.3v - 16.1$

e) $-2.5x - 2 = -5.7x + 6$

f) $6.4 - 9.3b = 25.3 - 3.9b$

12. Two rental halls are considered for a wedding.

Hall A costs $50 per person.

Hall B costs $2000, plus $40 per person. Determine the number of people for which the halls will cost the same to rent.

a) Model this problem with an equation.

b) Solve the problem.

c) Verify the solution.

13. Five subtract 3 times a number is equal to 3.5 times the same number, subtract 8. Write, then solve an equation to determine the number. Verify the solution.

14. A part-time sales clerk at a store is offered two methods of payment.

Plan A: $1500 per month with a commission of 4% on his sales

Plan B: $1700 per month with a commission of 2% on his sales

Let s represent the sales in dollars.

a) Write an expression to represent the total earnings under Plan A.

b) Write an expression to represent the total earnings under Plan B.

c) Write an equation to determine the sales that result in the same total earnings from both plans.

d) Solve the equation. Explain what the answer represents.

15. Verify each student's work.
If the solution is incorrect, write a correct and complete solution.

a) Student A:

$$2.2x = 7.6x + 27$$
$$2.2x - 7.6x = 7.6x + 27 - 7.6x$$
$$-5.4x = 27$$
$$\frac{-5.4x}{-5.4} = \frac{27}{-5.4}$$
$$x = 5$$

b) Student B:

$$-2.3x - 2.7 = 2.2x + 11.7$$
$$-2.3x - 2.7 + 2.2x = 2.2x + 11.7 + 2.2x$$
$$-0.1x - 2.7 = 11.7$$
$$-0.1x - 2.7 + 2.7 = 11.7 + 2.7$$
$$-0.1x = 14.4$$
$$\frac{-0.1x}{-0.1} = \frac{14.4}{-0.1}$$
$$x = -144$$

16. a) Solve each pair of equations.

i) $\frac{x}{27} = 3; \frac{27}{x} = 3, x \neq 0$

ii) $\frac{a}{36} = 12; \frac{36}{a} = 12, a \neq 0$

b) How are the steps to solve for a variable in the denominator of a fraction similar to the steps used to solve for a variable in the numerator? How are they different? Explain.

17. Solve each equation. Verify the solution.

a) $4(g + 5) = 5(g - 3)$

b) $3(4j + 5) = 2(-10 + 5j)$

c) $2.2(h - 5.3) = 0.2(-32.9 + h)$

d) $0.04(5 - s) = 0.05(6 - s)$

18. **Assessment Focus** Hendrik has a choice of 2 companies to rent a car.

Company A charges $199 per week, plus $0.20 per kilometre driven.

Company B charges $149 per week, plus $0.25 per kilometre driven.

Determine the distance that Hendrik must drive for the two rental costs to be the same.

a) Model this problem with an equation.

b) Solve the problem.

c) Verify the solution.

Show your work.

19. Solve each equation.

a) $\frac{7}{2}(m + 12) = \frac{5}{2}(20 + m)$

b) $\frac{1}{3}(5 - 3t) = \frac{5}{6}(t - 2)$

c) $\frac{3}{2}(1 + 3r) = \frac{2}{3}(2 - 3r)$

d) $\frac{2}{3}(6x + 5) = \frac{4}{5}(20x - 7)$

20. Both Dembe and Bianca solve the equation:

$$\frac{x}{3} + \frac{x}{4} = x - \frac{1}{6}$$

Dembe clears the fractions by multiplying each side by 12. Bianca clears the fractions by multiplying each side by 24.

a) Solve the equation using each student's method. Compare the solutions.

b) When you solve an equation involving fractions, why is it a good idea to multiply each side by the least common denominator?

21. Solve each equation. Verify the solution.

a) $\dfrac{x}{4} + \dfrac{7}{4} = \dfrac{5}{6}$

b) $\dfrac{5x}{16} - \dfrac{5}{4} = \dfrac{x}{4}$

c) $2 - \dfrac{x}{24} = \dfrac{5x}{24} + 1$

d) $\dfrac{25}{9} + \dfrac{x}{9} = \dfrac{7x}{6} - \dfrac{5}{2}$

Take It Further

22. In volleyball, statistics are kept about players. The equation $B = M + \dfrac{1}{2}A$ can be used to calculate the total blocks made by a player. In the equation, B is the total blocks, M is the number of solo blocks, and A is the number of assisted blocks. Marlene has 9 total blocks and 4 solo blocks. How many assisted blocks did Marlene make? How do you know that your answer is correct?

23. A cell phone company offers two different plans.

Plan A
Monthly fee of $28
30 free minutes
$0.45 per additional minute

Plan B
Monthly fee of $40
No free minutes
$0.25 per minute

a) Write an equation to determine the time in minutes that results in the same monthly cost for both plans.

b) Solve the equation.

c) Verify the solution.

Reflect

List some strategies for solving an equation. For each strategy, provide an example of an equation and its solution.

Math Link

Science

Ohm's Law relates the resistance, R ohms, in an electrical circuit to the voltage, V volts, across the circuit and the current, I amperes, through the circuit: $R = \dfrac{V}{I}$

For a light bulb, when the voltage is 120 V and the resistance is 192 Ω, the current in amperes can be determined by solving this equation: $192 = \dfrac{120}{I}$

How Can I Use My Problem-Solving Skills?

Suppose I have to solve this problem:
  The sale price of a jacket is $41.49.
  The original price has been
  reduced by 17%.
  What was the original price?

➤ What do I know?
  • The sale price is $41.49.
  • This is 17% less than the original price.

➤ What strategy could I use to solve the problem?
  • I could write, then solve an equation.
    Let d dollars represent the original price.
    17% of d is $0.17d$.
    A word equation is:
    (original price) − (17% of original price) is $41.49
    An algebraic equation is:

$1d - 0.17d = 41.49$	Combine the terms in d.
$0.83d = 41.49$	Divide each side by 0.83.
$\dfrac{0.83d}{0.83} = \dfrac{41.49}{0.83}$	
$d \doteq 49.99$	

  • I could write, then solve a proportion.
    Let d dollars represent the original price, which is 100%.
    Since the price has been reduced by 17%,
    the sale price is 100% − 17%, or 83% of the original price.
    So, the ratio of sale price to original price is equal
    to the ratio of 83% to 100%.
    As a proportion: $\dfrac{41.49}{d} = \dfrac{83}{100}$

$\dfrac{41.49}{d} = \dfrac{83}{100}$	Multiply each side by 100.
$100 \times \dfrac{41.49}{d} = 100 \times \dfrac{83}{100}$	
$\dfrac{4149}{d} = 83$	Multiply each side by d.
$d \times \dfrac{4149}{d} = 83 \times d$	
$4149 = 83d$	Divide each side by 83.
$\dfrac{4149}{83} = \dfrac{83d}{83}$	
$49.99 \doteq d$	

• I could draw a diagram to help me reason the answer.

```
0                                    $41.49      ?
|———————————————————————————————————|——————|
0                                    83%    100%
```

The original price is 100%.
Since the price has been reduced by 17%,
the sale price is 100% − 17%,
or 83% of the original price.
83% of the original price is $41.49

So, 1% of the original price is $\dfrac{\$41.49}{83}$

And, 100%, which is the original price $= \dfrac{\$41.49}{83} \times 100$

$$= \dfrac{\$4149}{83}$$

$$\doteq \$49.99$$

The original price was $49.99.

Check: The discount is:
17% of $49.99 = 0.17 × $49.99
$= \$8.50$
Sale price = original price − discount
$= \$49.99 - \$8.50$
$= \$41.49$
This is the same as the given sale price, so the answer is correct.

➤ Look back.
Which method do you find easiest? Why?
Would you have solved the problem a different way?
If your answer is yes, show your method.

Check

1. The price of gasoline increased by 6%. The new price is $1.36/L.
What was the price of gasoline before it increased?

2. Make up your own percent problem. Solve your problem.
Trade problems with a classmate, then solve your classmate's problem.
Compare your strategies for answering both problems.

Mid-Unit Review

1. For each equation, write the first operation you would use to isolate the variable. Justify your choice of operation.

a) $-3j = 9.6$ b) $\frac{1}{4}r - 2 = 4$

c) $2(-3x + 1.5) = 6$ d) $3 = -2n + 9$

2. Marshall creates this arrow diagram to show the steps in the solution of $\frac{m}{10} + 20.3 = 45.5$.

Build equation

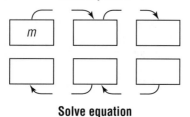

Solve equation

a) Copy and complete the arrow diagram.
b) Record the solution algebraically.

3. Sheila is charged a fare of $27.70 for a cab ride to her friend's house. The fare is calculated using a flat fee of $2.50, plus $1.20 per kilometre. What distance did Sheila travel?

a) Let k kilometres represent the distance travelled. Write an equation to solve the problem. Solve the problem.
b) Verify the solution.

4. An isosceles triangle has two equal sides of length 2.7 cm and perimeter 7.3 cm.

2.7 cm

a) Write an equation that can be used to determine the length of the third side.
b) Solve the equation.
c) Verify the solution.

5. Solve each equation. Verify the solution.

a) $\frac{k}{3} = -1.5$

b) $10.5 = 3b - 12.5$

c) $5(x - 7.2) = 14.5$

d) $8.4 = 1.2b$

e) $2 + \frac{n}{3} = 2.8$

f) $-8 = 0.4(3.2 + h)$

6. Write the equation modelled by these balance scales. Solve the equation. Verify the solution.

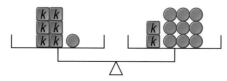

Each ⬤ has a mass of 1 g.

7. Solve each equation. Verify the solution.

a) $\frac{56}{a} = -3.5, a \neq 0$

b) $8w - 12.8 = 6w$

c) $-8z + 11 = -10 - 5.5z$

d) $\frac{5x}{2} = 11 + \frac{2x}{3}$

e) $0.2(5 - 2r) = 0.3(1 - r)$

f) $12.9 + 2.3y = 4.5y + 19.5$

g) $\frac{2}{5}(m + 4) = \frac{1}{5}(3m + 9)$

8. Skateboards can be rented from two shops in a park.

Shop Y charges $15 plus $3 per hour
Shop Z charges $12 plus $4 per hour

Determine the time in hours for which the rental charges in both shops are equal.
a) Write an equation to determine the time.
b) Solve the equation.
c) Verify the solution.

Equation Persuasion

How to Play

1. Each player picks a secret integer between -9 and 9.
Use the secret integer to write an equation of the form:
$n = \text{secret integer}$

2. Remove the face cards from the deck.
Each player draws 3 cards from the deck, one at a time.

Suit	Meaning
♣	Add the number on the card to each side of the equation.
♠	Add the indicated number of ns to each side of the equation.
♦	Multiply each side of the equation by the number on the card.
♥	Subtract the number on the card from each side of the equation.

You will need

• a deck of playing cards

Number of Players

• 2

Goal of the Game

• To solve and verify your partner's end equation

For example:

• Suppose you choose a secret number of -2 and draw these three cards in the given order: 4 of ♣, 3 of ♠, and 5 of ♦.

• Secretly perform the operations indicated by the cards on the start equation: $n = -2$

Add 4 to each side of the equation: $\qquad n + 4 = 2$

Add $3n$ to each side of the equation: $\qquad 4n + 4 = 2 + 3n$

Multiply each side by 5: $\qquad 5(4n + 4) = 5(2 + 3n)$

This is the end equation.

3. Trade end equations with your partner.
Solve each other's end equation.

4. If you solved your partner's equation correctly, you receive 5 points. You get an additional 5 points if you verify the solution. But, if you gave your partner an incorrect end equation, you get 0 points.

5. The first player to get 50 points wins.

6.3 Introduction to Linear Inequalities

FOCUS

• Write and graph inequalities.

We use an **inequality** to model a situation that can be described by a range of numbers instead of a single number. When one quantity is less than or equal to another quantity, we use this symbol: ≤

When one quantity is greater than or equal to another quantity, we use this symbol: ≥

Which of these inequalities describes the time, t minutes, for which a car could be legally parked?

$t > 30$
$t \geq 30$
$t < 30$
$t \leq 30$

Inequality signs
< less than
> greater than

Investigate

Define a variable and write an inequality for each situation.

a) **SPEED LIMIT 55**

b) **Height Restriction**
You must be at least 102 cm to go on this ride.

c)  Store at temperatures below 4°C

d)
Canadian Home Video **14ᴬ** Rating

Reflect & Share

Compare your inequalities with those of another pair of classmates. If the inequalities are different, how can you find out which is correct? Work together to describe three other situations that involve inequalities. Write an inequality for each situation.

Connect

Here are some examples of inequality statements:

➤ One expression is less than another; a is less than 3: $a < 3$

➤ One expression is greater than another; b is greater than -4: $b > -4$

➤ One expression is less than or equal to another;
   c is less than or equal to $\frac{3}{4}$: $c \le \frac{3}{4}$

➤ One expression is greater than or equal to another;
   d is greater than or equal to -5.4: $d \ge -5.4$

Many real-world situations can be modelled by inequalities.

Example 1   **Writing an Inequality to Describe a Situation**

Define a variable and write an inequality to describe each situation.

a) Contest entrants must be at least 18 years old.

b) The temperature has been below $-5°C$ for the last week.

c) You must have 7 items or less to use the express checkout line
   at a grocery store.

d) Scientists have identified over 400 species of dinosaurs.

➤ **A Solution**

a) Let a represent the age of a contest entrant.
   "At least 18" means that entrants must be 18, or 19, or 20, and so on.
   So, a can equal 18 or be greater than 18.
   The inequality is $a \ge 18$.

b) Let t represent the temperature in degrees Celsius.
   For the temperature to be "below $-5°C$", it must be less than $-5°C$.
   The inequality is $t < -5$.

c) Let n represent the number of items.
   The number of items must be 7 or less than 7.
   The inequality is $n \le 7$.

d) Let s represent the number of species of dinosaurs.
   "Over 400" means greater than 400.
   The inequality is $s > 400$.

A linear equation is true for only one value of the variable.
A linear inequality may be true for many values of the variable.
The solution of an inequality is any value of the variable that makes the inequality true.
There are usually too many numbers to list, so we may show them on a number line.

Example 2 **Determining Whether a Number Is a Solution of an Inequality**

Is each number a solution of the inequality $b \geq -4$? Justify the answers.

a) -8 b) -3.5 c) -4 d) -4.5 e) 0

▶ *Solutions*

Method 1

Use a number line. Show all the numbers on a line.
The solution of $b \geq -4$ is all numbers that are greater than or equal to -4.

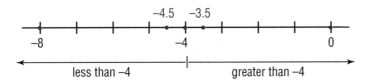

For a number to be greater than -4, it must lie to the right of -4.

a) -8 is to the left of -4, so -8 is not a solution.

b) -3.5 is to the right of -4, so -3.5 is a solution.

c) -4 is equal to itself, so it is a solution.

d) -4.5 is to the left of -4, so -4.5 is not a solution.

e) 0 is to the right of -4, so 0 is a solution.

Method 2

Use substitution. Substitute each number for b in the inequality $b \geq -4$.
Determine whether the resulting inequality is true or false.

a) Since $-8 \geq -4$ is false, -8 is not a solution.

b) Since $-3.5 \geq -4$ is true, -3.5 is a solution.

c) Since $-4 = -4$, -4 is a solution.

d) Since $-4.5 \geq -4$ is false, -4.5 is not a solution.

e) Since $0 \geq -4$ is true, 0 is a solution.

We can illustrate the solutions of an inequality by graphing them on a number line.

For $a > 3$, the solution is all numbers greater than 3. Since 3 is not part of the solution, we draw an open circle at 3 to indicate this.

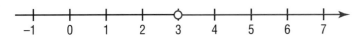

For $b \leq -5$, the solution is all numbers less than or equal to -5. Since -5 is part of the solution, we draw a shaded circle at -5 to indicate this.

Example 3 | **Graphing Inequalities on a Number Line**

Graph each inequality on a number line.

Write 4 numbers that are solutions of the inequality.

a) $t > -5$ b) $-2 \geq x$ c) $0.5 \leq a$ d) $p < -\dfrac{25}{3}$

▶ **A Solution**

a) $t > -5$

Any number greater than -5 satisfies the inequality.

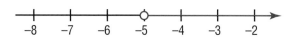

Four possible solutions are:

$-4, -2.1, 0, \dfrac{1}{2}$

b) $-2 \geq x$ means that -2 is greater than or equal to x,
or x is less than or equal to -2; that is, $x \leq -2$

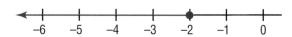

Four possible solutions are:
$-2, -4\dfrac{1}{4}, -6.8, -100$

c) $0.5 \leq a$ means that 0.5 is less than or equal to a,
or a is greater than or equal to 0.5; that is, $a \geq 0.5$

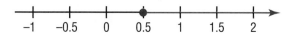

Four possible solutions are:
$0.5, 2, 3\dfrac{3}{4}, 1000$

d) $p < -\dfrac{25}{3}$

$-\dfrac{25}{3}$ is $-8\dfrac{1}{3}$.

The solution is all numbers that are less than $-8\dfrac{1}{3}$.

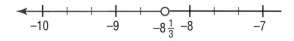

Four possible solutions are:
$-9, -15.8, -20\dfrac{2}{5}, -99$

1. How is the solution of an inequality different from the solution of an equation?

2. How do you know whether to use an open circle or a shaded circle in the graph of an inequality?

Practice

Check

3. Is each inequality true or false? Explain your reasoning.
a) $5 < 8$
b) $-5 < -8$
c) $5 < -8$
d) $5 < 5$
e) $5 \leq 5$
f) $0 \geq -5$
g) $5.01 < 5.1$
h) $\frac{1}{5} < \frac{1}{8}$

4. Use a symbol to write an inequality that corresponds to each statement.
a) x is less than -2.
b) p is greater than or equal to 6.
c) y is negative.
d) m is positive.

5. Is each number a solution of $x < -2$? How do you know?
a) 0
b) -6.9
c) -2.001
d) -3
e) -2
f) $-\frac{1}{2}$

6. Write 4 numbers that are solutions of each inequality.
a) $b > 5$
b) $7 > x$
c) $-2 \leq v$
d) $w \leq -12$

Apply

7. Determine whether the given number is a solution of the inequality. If the number is not a solution, write an inequality for which the number is a solution.
a) $w < 3$; 3
b) $-3.5 < y$; 0
c) $m \geq 5\frac{1}{2}$; 5.05
d) $a \leq -2$; -15

8. Define a variable and write an inequality to model each situation.
a) A coffee maker can hold no more than 12 cups of water.
b) You must be at least 15 years old to obtain a learner's permit to drive in Nunavut.
c) The maximum seating capacity of a school bus is 48 students.
d) Over 2500 people participate in the charity bike-a-thon each year.
e) The shoe store sells sizes no larger than 13.

9. Match each equation or inequality with the graph of its solution below. Justify your choice.
a) $m > 3$
b) $p = 3$
c) $k \leq 3$
d) $t < 3$
e) $v \geq 3$
f) $3 < n$
g) $3 \geq h$
h) $3 \leq s$

i)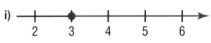

ii)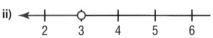

iii)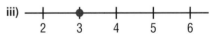

iv)

v)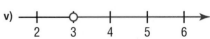

10. Tom and Stevie write the inequality whose solution is shown on this graph:

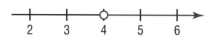

Tom writes $a > 4$. Stevie writes $4 < b$. Can both of them be correct? Explain.

11. Assessment Focus

a) For each situation, define a variable and write an inequality to describe the situation.

   i) In Canada, a child under 23 kg must ride in a car seat.

   ii) A silicone oven mitt is heat resistant to temperatures up to 485°C.

   iii) The minimum wage in Alberta is $8.40 an hour.

b) Graph the solution of each inequality on a number line.

12. Write an inequality whose solution is graphed on the number line. In each case, are 1 and -3 solutions of the inequality? Explain.

a)
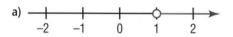

b)
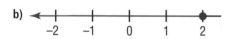

c)
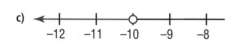

13. Graph the solution of each inequality on a number line.

a) $w > 5.5$ b) $x \le -2$

c) $z > -6$ d) $a < 6.8$

e) $b \le 6.8$ f) $c > \dfrac{2}{3}$

g) $d \le -\dfrac{2}{3}$ h) $x \le \dfrac{18}{5}$

Take It Further

14. Joel is producing a one-hour TV show. An advertiser wants at least 12 min of commercials, and the station will not allow more than 20 min of commercials. Graph the possible show times on a number line. Write two inequalities to describe the situation.

15. The words "over," "under," "maximum," "minimum," "at least," and "no more than" can describe inequalities.

a) Which symbol describes each word?

b) Give a real-world situation that could be described by each word. Write the situation as an inequality.

16. Use a symbol to write an inequality for this statement: y is not negative. Justify your inequality.

Reflect

An inequality can be described with words, symbols, or a graph. Which representation do you find easiest to understand? Explain. Include an example in your explanation.

Solving Linear Inequalities by Using Addition and Subtraction

Jamina places masses on balance scales. Why is the right pan lower than the left pan?
Will the right pan remain lower than the left pan in each situation?

- Jamina places 2 g on each pan.
- Jamina removes 3 g from each pan.

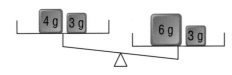

Investigate

②

➤ Write two different numbers.
Write the symbol $<$ or $>$ between the numbers to make an inequality.
➤ Choose another number. Add that number to each side of the inequality.
Is the resulting inequality still true?
➤ Repeat the preceding step 3 more times with different numbers.
➤ Subtract the same number from each side of the original inequality.
Is the inequality still true?
➤ Repeat the preceding step 3 more times with different numbers.

Reflect & Share

Compare your results with those of another pair of classmates.
When the same number is added to or subtracted from each side of an inequality, is the resulting inequality still true? Explain.
How could you use this property to solve the inequality $x + 5 \geq 11$?
Work together to solve the inequality.
How do you know that your solution is correct?

We can use a number line to investigate the effect of adding to and subtracting from each side of an inequality.

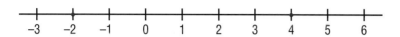

> −2 is less than 4 because −2 is to the left of 4 on a number line.

➤ Adding the same number to each side of an inequality

$$-2 < 4 \qquad \text{Add 2 to each side.}$$
$$-2 + 2 < 4 + 2$$
$$0 < 6 \qquad \text{This resulting inequality is true.}$$

➤ Subtracting the same number from each side of an inequality

$$-2 < 4 \qquad \text{Subtract 1 from each side.}$$
$$-2 - 1 < 4 - 1$$
$$-3 < 3 \qquad \text{This resulting inequality is true.}$$

When we add the same number to, or subtract the same number from, each side of an inequality, the points move left or right, but their relative positions do not change.

The examples above illustrate this property of inequalities:
➤ When the same number is added to or subtracted from each side of an inequality, the resulting inequality is still true.

To solve an inequality, we use the same strategy as for solving an equation: isolate the variable by adding to or subtracting from each side of the inequality. Compare the following solutions of an equation and a related inequality.

Equation

$$h + 3 = 5$$
$$h + 3 - 3 = 5 - 3$$
$$h = 2$$

There is only one solution: $h = 2$

Inequality

$$h + 3 < 5$$
$$h + 3 - 3 < 5 - 3$$
$$h < 2$$

There are many solutions; too many to list. Any number that is less than 2 is a solution; for example, $0, -5.7, -3452$, and so on

Example 1 **Solving an Inequality**

a) Solve the inequality: $6.2 \leq x - 4.5$ b) Verify the solution.   c) Graph the solution.

▶ *A Solution*

a) $6.2 \leq x - 4.5$ Add 4.5 to each side.

$6.2 + 4.5 \leq x - 4.5 + 4.5$

$10.7 \leq x$

b) The solution of the inequality $10.7 \leq x$ is all numbers greater than or equal to 10.7.
Choose several numbers greater than 10.7; for example, 11, 20, 30
Substitute $x = 11$ in the original inequality.

Left side = 6.2   Right side = $x - 4.5$

$= 11 - 4.5$

$= 6.5$

Since $6.2 < 6.5$, the left side is less than the right side,
and $x = 11$ satisfies the inequality.
Substitute $x = 20$ in the original inequality.

Left side = 6.2   Right side = $x - 4.5$

$= 20 - 4.5$

$= 15.5$

Since $6.2 < 15.5$, the left side is less than the right side,
and $x = 20$ satisfies the inequality.
Substitute $x = 30$ in the original inequality.

Left side = 6.2   Right side = $x - 4.5$

$= 30 - 4.5$

$= 25.5$

Since $6.2 < 25.5$, the left side is less than the right side,
and $x = 30$ satisfies the inequality.
Since all 3 substitutions verify the inequality,
it suggests that $x \geq 10.7$ is correct.

c) Graph the solution on a number line.

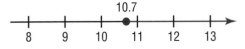

It is impossible to check all of the solutions of an inequality. We verified the
inequality in *Example 1* by selecting several numbers from the solution and
substituting them into the original inequality. Since the resulting statements were
true, this suggests that the solution is correct.

A term containing a variable represents a number, so this term can be added to
or subtracted from each side of an inequality.

| Example 2 | Using an Inequality to Model and Solve a Problem |

Jake plans to board his dog while he is away on vacation.
- Boarding house A charges $90 plus $5 per day.
- Boarding house B charges $100 plus $4 per day.

For how many days must Jake board his dog for boarding house A to be less expensive than boarding house B?

a) Choose a variable and write an inequality that can be used to solve this problem.

b) Solve the problem.

c) Graph the solution.

▶ A Solution

a) Let d represent the number of days Jake boards his dog. For house A: $90 + $5/day can be written, in dollars, as $90 + 5d$. For house B: $100 + $4/day can be written, in dollars, as $100 + 4d$. For house A to be less expensive than house B, $90 + 5d$ must be less than $100 + 4d$. So, an inequality is: $90 + 5d < 100 + 4d$

b)
$$90 + 5d < 100 + 4d$$ Subtract $4d$ from each side.
$$90 + 5d - 4d < 100 + 4d - 4d$$
$$90 + d < 100$$ Subtract 90 from each side.
$$90 - 90 + d < 100 - 90$$
$$d < 10$$

Boarding house A is less expensive if Jake leaves his dog there for less than 10 days.

c) $d < 10$

In *Example 2*, the number line begins with a circle at 0 because a dog cannot be boarded for a negative number of days.

Discuss the ideas

1. Why is it impossible to check all the solutions of an inequality?

2. When a solution of an equation is verified, we say that the solution is correct. When a solution of an inequality is verified, we can only say that this suggests the solution is correct. Why?

3. Suppose the solution of an inequality is $r \geq 5.6$. How would you choose suitable values of r to substitute to check?

Check

4. Which operation will you perform on each side of the inequality to isolate the variable?

a) $a + 4 > 3$ b) $0 < -\dfrac{2}{3} + m$

c) $r - 4 \geq -3$ d) $k - 4.5 \leq 5.7$

e) $s + \dfrac{3}{10} \leq -3$ f) $6.1 > 4.9 + z$

5. What must you do to the first inequality to get the second inequality?

a) $x - 2 > 8$
$$x > 10$$

b) $12.9 \leq y + 4.2$
$$y \geq 8.7$$

c) $p - \dfrac{1}{2} \leq \dfrac{1}{2}$
$$p \leq 1$$

6. State three values of x that satisfy each inequality: one integer, one fraction, and one decimal.

a) $x + 3 \geq 7$ b) $x - 3 \leq 7$

c) $x + 7 < 3$ d) $x - 3 > 7$

Apply

7. Match each inequality with the graph of its solution. Is 3 a possible solution of each inequality? How can you find out?

a) $c - 2 > 2$ b) $8 \geq -5 + w$

c) $1 > r + 8$ d) $7 + m \leq -2$

   i)

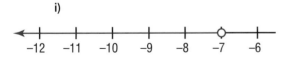

   ii)

iii)

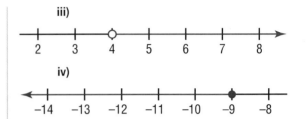

iv)

8. Solve each inequality. Graph the solution. Verify the solution.

a) $x + 5 > 2$ b) $-9 \geq y - 3$

c) $4 + a \leq 8$ d) $2 > x + 7$

e) $k + 8 < -13$ f) $q - 2.5 < 3.9$

9. Solve each inequality. Graph the solution. Show the steps in the solution. Verify the solution by substituting 3 different numbers in each inequality.

a) $4t - 19 < 24 + 3t$

b) $3x < 2x - 11$

c) $5x - 7 < 4x + 4$

d) $2 + 3a \leq 2a - 5$

e) $1.7p + 2.8 \geq 0.7p - 7.6$

f) $2y + 13.3 \geq y - 24.1$

10. A student says $b \geq -9$ is the solution of $-7 \geq b + 2$ because substituting -9 into the original inequality gives the true statement $-7 \geq -7$. Do you agree? Justify your answer.

11. a) Solve the equation: $7.4 + 2p = p - 2.8$

b) Solve the inequality: $7.4 + 2p \geq p - 2.8$

c) Compare the processes in parts a and b. How is solving an inequality like solving the related equation? How is it different?

d) Compare the solutions in parts a and b. How is the solution of an inequality like the solution of the related equation? How is it different?

12. Joel currently has a balance of $212.35 in his bank account. He must maintain a minimum balance of $750 in the account to avoid paying a monthly fee. How much money can Joel deposit into his account to avoid paying this fee?

a) Choose a variable, then write an inequality that can be used to solve this problem.

b) Solve the problem.

c) Graph the solution.

13. Teagan is saving money to buy a snowmobile helmet. One weekend, she earned $20 to add to her savings, but she still did not have the $135.99 she needed for the helmet.

a) Choose a variable, then write an inequality to represent this situation.

b) Solve the inequality. What does the solution represent?

c) Verify the solution and graph it on a number line.

14. Assessment Focus Marie has $4.85. She wants to buy a muffin and a cake at a bake sale. The cake is on sale for $3.45. How much can Marie spend on a muffin?

a) Choose a variable, then write an inequality to solve the problem.

b) Use the inequality to solve the problem.

c) Graph the solution on a number line.

d) A deluxe muffin costs $1.45. Can Marie afford to buy this muffin? Justify your answer.

Show your work.

Take It Further

15. a) Solve each inequality. Graph the solution.

    i) $2a - 5 \geq 2 + 3a$

    ii) $0.7p - 7.6 \leq 1.7p + 2.8$

b) What strategies did you use to solve the inequalities in part a?

c) Compare your solution and graphs in part a with the solutions to questions 9d and 9e. Explain the differences.

16. a) Graph each inequality. Describe the solution in words.

    i) $x < -2.57$

    ii) $b \geq -10.25$

    iii) $p \leq 1.005$

b) Explain how the graphs of these inequalities are different from those that you have graphed before.

c) Which is a more accurate way to describe a solution: using an inequality or using a graph? Explain.

Reflect

How is solving an inequality by using addition or subtraction similar to solving an equation by using addition or subtraction? How is it different? Use an example in your explanation.

6.5 Solving Linear Inequalities by Using Multiplication and Division

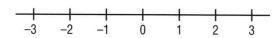

FOCUS

• Use multiplication and division to solve inequalities.

How does the position of a number on a number line determine whether it is greater than or less than another number?
How does this explain why $2 < 3$ but $-2 > -3$?

$$-3 \quad -2 \quad -1 \quad 0 \quad 1 \quad 2 \quad 3$$

Investigate

In the patterns below, each side of the inequality $12 > 6$ is multiplied or divided by the same non-zero number.

Multiplication Pattern

$$12 > 6$$
$$12(-3) \square 6(-3)$$
$$12(-2) \square 6(-2)$$
$$12(-1) \square 6(-1)$$
$$12(1) \square 6(1)$$
$$12(2) \square 6(2)$$
$$12(3) \square 6(3)$$

Division Pattern

$$12 > 6$$
$$12 \div (-3) \square 6 \div (-3)$$
$$12 \div (-2) \square 6 \div (-2)$$
$$12 \div (-1) \square 6 \div (-1)$$
$$12 \div 1 \square 6 \div 1$$
$$12 \div 2 \square 6 \div 2$$
$$12 \div 3 \square 6 \div 3$$

➤ Copy and simplify each expression in the patterns.
➤ Replace each $\square$ with $<$ or $>$ to create a true statement.
➤ Compare the inequality signs in the pattern with the inequality sign in $12 > 6$.
   When did the inequality sign stay the same?
   When did the inequality sign change?

Share your results with another pair of classmates.
What happens to an inequality when you multiply or divide each side by:
• a positive number?
• a negative number?
Work together to explain these results.

Connect

We can use a number line to investigate the effect of multiplying and dividing each side of an inequality by the same number.

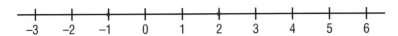

Consider the inequality: $-1 < 2$

Multiply each side by 3.

$$-1 < 2$$
$$(-1)(3) < (2)(3)$$
$$-3 < 6$$

Divide each side by 3.

$$-1 < 2$$
$$(-1) \div 3 < 2 \div 3$$
$$-\frac{1}{3} < \frac{2}{3}$$

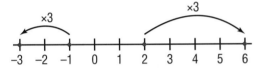

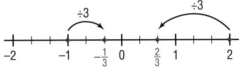

Multiply each side by -3.

$$-1 < 2$$
$$(-1)(-3) > (2)(-3)$$
$$3 > -6$$

We must reverse the inequality sign for each inequality to remain true.

Divide each side by -3.

$$-1 < 2$$
$$(-1) \div (-3) > 2 \div (-3)$$
$$\frac{1}{3} > -\frac{2}{3}$$

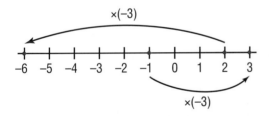

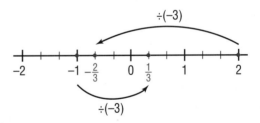

The examples above illustrate these properties of inequalities:

➤ When each side of an inequality is multiplied or divided by the same positive number, the resulting inequality is still true.

➤ When each side of an inequality is multiplied or divided by the same negative number, the inequality sign must be reversed for the inequality to remain true.

To solve an inequality, we use the same strategy as for solving an equation. However, when we multiply or divide by a negative number, we reverse the inequality sign.

Example 1 | Solving a One-step Inequality

Solve each inequality. Graph each solution.

a) $-5s \leq 25$

b) $7a < -21$

c) $\dfrac{y}{-4} > -3$

d) $\dfrac{k}{3} \geq -2$

▶ *A Solution*

a) $-5s \leq 25$

As you divide each side by -5,
reverse the inequality sign.

$\dfrac{-5s}{-5} \geq \dfrac{25}{-5}$

$s \geq -5$

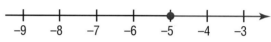

b) $7a < -21$

Divide each side by 7.

$\dfrac{7a}{7} < \dfrac{-21}{7}$

$a < -3$

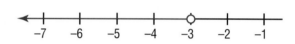

c) $\dfrac{y}{-4} > -3$

As you multiply each side by -4,
reverse the inequality sign.

$-4\left(\dfrac{y}{-4}\right) < -4\,(-3)$

$y < 12$

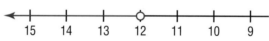

d) $\dfrac{k}{3} \geq -2$

Multiply each side by 3.

$3\left(\dfrac{k}{3}\right) \geq 3(-2)$

$k \geq -6$

Example 2   **Solving a Multi-Step Inequality**

a) Solve this inequality: $-2.6a + 14.6 > -5.2 + 1.8a$

b) Verify the solution.

▶ **A Solution**

a)

$$-2.6a + 14.6 > -5.2 + 1.8a \qquad \text{Subtract 14.6 from each side.}$$
$$-2.6a + 14.6 - 14.6 > -5.2 - 14.6 + 1.8a$$
$$-2.6a > -19.8 + 1.8a \qquad \text{Subtract } 1.8a \text{ from each side.}$$
$$-2.6a - 1.8a > -19.8 + 1.8a - 1.8a$$
$$-4.4a > -19.8 \qquad \text{Divide each side by } -4.4 \text{ and reverse}$$
$$\frac{-4.4a}{-4.4} < \frac{-19.8}{-4.4} \qquad \text{the inequality sign.}$$
$$a < 4.5$$

b) The solution of the inequality $a < 4.5$ is all numbers less than 4.5.
Choose several numbers less than 4.5; for example, 4, 0, −2

Substitute $a = 4$ in the original inequality.

Left side $= -2.6a + 14.6$ Right side $= -5.2 + 1.8a$
$\qquad\qquad = -2.6(4) + 14.6$ $= -5.2 + (1.8)(4)$
$\qquad\qquad = -10.4 + 14.6$ $= -5.2 + 7.2$
$\qquad\qquad = 4.2$ $= 2$

Since $4.2 > 2$, the left side is greater than the right side,
and $a = 4$ satisfies the inequality.

Substitute $a = 0$ in the original inequality.

Left side $= -2.6a + 14.6$ Right side $= -5.2 + 1.8a$
$\qquad\qquad = -2.6(0) + 14.6$ $= -5.2 + (1.8)(0)$
$\qquad\qquad = 14.6$ $= -5.2$

Since $14.6 > -5.2$, the left side is greater than the right side,
and $a = 0$ satisfies the inequality.

Substitute $a = -2$ in the original inequality.

Left side $= -2.6a + 14.6$ Right side $= -5.2 + (1.8)(-2)$
$\qquad\qquad = -2.6(-2) + 14.6$ $= -5.2 - 3.6$
$\qquad\qquad = 5.2 + 14.6$ $= -8.8$
$\qquad\qquad = 19.8$

Since $19.8 > -8.8$, the left side is greater than the right side,
and $a = -2$ satisfies the inequality.

Since all 3 substitutions verify the inequality, it suggests that $a < 4.5$ is correct.

Example 3   **Using an Inequality to Model and Solve a Problem**

A super-slide charges $1.25 to rent a mat and $0.75 per ride. Haru has $10.25. How many rides can Haru go on?

a) Choose a variable, then write an inequality to solve this problem.

b) Solve the problem.

c) Graph the solution.

▶ **A Solution**

a) Let n represent the number of rides that Haru can go on.
The cost of n rides is $1.25 + 0.75n$.
This must be less than or equal to $10.25.
So, the inequality is:
$1.25 + 0.75n \le 10.25$

b) $\qquad 1.25 + 0.75n \le 10.25$ Subtract 1.25 from each side.

$1.25 - 1.25 + 0.75n \le 10.25 - 1.25$

$\qquad\qquad 0.75n \le 9$ Divide each side by 0.75.

$$\frac{0.75n}{0.75} \le \frac{9}{0.75}$$

$$n \le 12$$

Haru can go on 12 or fewer rides.

c) Since the number of rides is a whole number, the number line is drawn with a shaded circle at each solution.

Discuss the ideas

1. How is multiplying or dividing each side of an inequality by the same positive number different from multiplying or dividing each side by the same negative number?

2. What is an advantage of substituting 0 for the variable to verify the solution of an inequality? Can you always substitute 0? Explain.

Check

3. Predict whether the direction of the inequality sign will change when you perform the indicated operation on each side of the inequality.

a) $-9 < -2$; Multiply by 4.

b) $14.5 > 11.5$; Multiply by -3.

c) $6 > -12$; Divide by -4.

d) $-4 < 10$; Divide by 4.

Check your predictions. Were you correct? Explain.

4. Do not solve each inequality. Determine which of the given numbers are solutions of the inequality.

a) $4w < 3$; $-2, 0, 2.5$

b) $3d \geq 5d + 10$; $-5, 0, 5$

5. a) State whether you would reverse the inequality sign to solve each inequality. Then solve and graph the inequality.

i) $10 - y \leq 4$ ii) $3c > -12$

iii) $-6x < 30$ iv) $\dfrac{m}{-2} < 3$

b) Refer to your solutions in part a. State three values of the variable that satisfy each inequality: one integer, one fraction, and one decimal.

6. A student says that if $c > 9$, then $-3c > -27$. Do you agree? Justify your answer.

Apply

7. Solve each inequality. Verify the solution by substituting 3 different numbers in each inequality.

a) $4 - 2t < 7$

b) $-5x + 2 > 24$

c) $2m + 3 \leq -7$

d) $-4x - 2 > 10$

8. Write, then solve an inequality to show how many cars you would have to wash at $5 a car to raise at least $300.

9. Solve each inequality. Graph the solution.

a) $1 - k \leq 4 + k$

b) $2 + 3g < g - 5$

c) $4.5 - 2.5a > 6$

d) $4.7b - 9 \geq 11 - 1.3b$

e) $-6.4 + 3.6s \leq 1.8s + 1.7$

f) $-2.5v + 4.7 \geq -3.8v + 1.58$

10. The Student Council decides to raise money by organizing a dance. The cost of hiring the video-DJ is $1200 and the Student Council is charging $7.50 per ticket. How many tickets can be sold to make a profit of more than $1500?

a) Choose a variable and write an inequality to solve this problem.

b) Use the inequality to solve the problem.

c) Verify the solution and graph it on a number line.

11. Solve each inequality. Graph the solution.

a) $1 + \dfrac{3}{4}x > 17$

b) $-2 \leq -6 + \dfrac{1}{4}c$

c) $4 - \dfrac{2}{3}d \geq \dfrac{5}{6}d - 5$

d) $\dfrac{3}{5}f - \dfrac{1}{2} < 2 + f$

12. Solve each inequality. Show the steps in the solution. Verify the solution by substituting 3 different numbers in each inequality.

a) $4a - 5 \geq a + 2$

b) $15t - 17 \geq 21 - 4t$

c) $10.5z + 16 \leq 12.5z + 12$

d) $7 + \dfrac{1}{3}b \leq 2b + 22$

13. Jake takes a taxi to tour a city. He is charged $2.50, plus $1.20 per kilometre.
Jake has $12.00. How far can he travel?
a) Choose a variable and write an inequality for this problem.
b) Solve the inequality.
Explain the solution in words.
c) Verify the solution.
d) Graph the solution.

14. Assessment Focus
a) Solve the equation: $2 - \frac{3}{4}w = 3w + \frac{1}{2}$

b) Solve the inequality: $2 - \frac{3}{4}w \geq 3w + \frac{1}{2}$
c) Compare the processes in parts a and b. How is solving an inequality like solving the related equation? How is it different?
d) Compare the solutions in parts a and b. How is the solution of an inequality like the solution of the related equation? How is it different?
Show your work.

15. Janelle plans to replace the light bulbs in her house with energy saver bulbs.
A regular light bulb costs $0.55 and has an electricity cost of $0.004 20 per hour.
An energy saver bulb costs $5.00 and has an electricity cost of $0.001 05 per hour.
For how many hours of use is it cheaper to use an energy saver bulb than a regular bulb?
a) Write an inequality for this problem.
b) Solve the inequality.
Explain the solution in words.
c) Verify the solution.
d) Graph the solution.

16. Solve each inequality. Graph the solution.
a) $3(0.4h + 5) > 4(0.2h + 7)$
b) $-2(3 - 1.5n) \leq 3(2 - n)$
c) $-4(2.4v - 1.4) \geq -2(0.8 + 1.2v)$
d) $-5(3.2 + 2.3z) < 2(-1.5z - 4.75)$

Take It Further

17. Solve each inequality.
Verify and graph the solution.
a) $\frac{3}{2}a + \frac{1}{2} < \frac{7}{3}a - \frac{3}{4}$
b) $\frac{3}{5}(5.2 - 3m) > -\frac{7}{10}(2m + 7.5)$

18. A business must choose a company to print a promotional brochure.
Company A charges $900 plus $0.50 per copy.
Company B charges $1500 plus $0.38 per copy.
a) How many brochures must be printed for the cost to be the same at both companies?
b) How many brochures must be printed for Company A to be less expensive?
c) How many brochures must be printed for Company B to be less expensive?
d) Explain the strategies you used to solve these problems.

Reflect

A student says, "Solving inequalities is different from solving equations only when you multiply or divide each side of the inequality by a negative number."
Do you agree with this statement? Explain.

Solving Equations

▶ An equation is a statement that one quantity is equal to another.
To solve an equation means to determine the value of the variable that makes the right side of the equation equal to the left side.

▶ To solve an equation, isolate the variable on one side of the equation. We use inverse operations or a balance strategy of performing the same operation on both sides of the equation. This can include:
  • adding the same quantity to each side of the equation
  • subtracting the same quantity from each side of the equation
  • multiplying or dividing each side of the equation by the same non-zero quantity

▶ Algebra tiles, arrow diagrams, and balance scales help model the steps in the solution.

Solving Inequalities

▶ An inequality is a statement that:
  • one quantity is less than another; for example, $-4 < 3.2a$
  • one quantity is greater than another; for example, $\frac{3}{2}b + 8 > -7$
  • one quantity is greater than or equal to another; for example, $3.4 - 2.8c \geq 1.3c$
  • one quantity is less than or equal to another; for example, $-\frac{5}{8}d + \frac{1}{4} \leq \frac{3}{4} - \frac{1}{2}d$

▶ The solutions of an inequality are the values of the variable that make the inequality true. We can graph the solutions of an inequality on a number line; for example, $f \geq 3.5$:

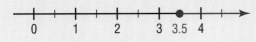

and $g < -\frac{7}{4}$:

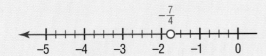

▶ The inequality sign reverses when you multiply or divide each side of the inequality by the same negative number.

6.1 **1. a)** Copy and complete each arrow diagram to solve each equation.

b) Record the steps in the arrow diagram symbolically.

i) $8h = 7.2$

ii) $\frac{t}{5} = -7$

iii) $5c - 1 = 2.4$

2. Both Milan and Daria solve this equation:
$4(3.2s + 5.7) = -6$

a) Milan uses inverse operations to undo the steps used to build the equation. Show the steps in Milan's solution.

b) Daria uses the distributive property, then inverse operations. Show the steps in Daria's solution.

c) Describe an advantage and a disadvantage of each method.

3. Solve each equation. Verify the solution.

a) $-20.5 = 3b + 16.7$

b) $\frac{t}{3} + 1.2 = -2.2$

c) $-8.5 = 6.3 - \frac{w}{2}$

d) $-2.3(x + 25.5) = -52.9$

4. A kite has longer sides of length 3.1 cm and a perimeter of 8.4 cm.

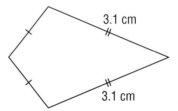

3.1 cm

3.1 cm

a) Write an equation that can be used to determine the length of a shorter side.

b) Solve the equation.

c) Verify the solution.

6.2 **5.** Write the equation represented by these balance scales:

Each ● has a mass of 1 g.

Solve the equation. Record the steps algebraically.

6. Write the equation modelled by these algebra tiles:

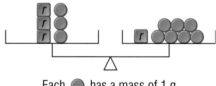

Use algebra tiles to solve the equation. Record the steps algebraically.

7. Solve each equation. Verify the solution.

a) $\frac{-72}{a} = -4.5, a \neq 0$

b) $-\frac{1}{3} + 2m = -\frac{1}{5}$

c) $12.5x = 6.2x + 88$

d) $2.1g - 0.3 = -3.3g - 30$

e) $\frac{3}{2}x + \frac{4}{3} = \frac{5}{8}x + \frac{5}{2}$

f) $5.4(2 - p) = -1.4(p + 2)$

8. Kevin is planning to rent a car for one week. Company A charges $200 per week, with no charge for the distance driven. For the same car, Company B charges a $25 administration fee plus $0.35 per kilometre. Determine the distance driven that will result in equal costs at the two companies.

   a) Define a variable and write an equation that can be used to solve the problem.

   b) Use the equation to solve the problem.

   c) Verify the solution.

9. A student solves this equation:

$3.5(2v - 5.4) = 2.5(3v - 1.2)$

$7v - 5.4 = 7.5v - 1.2$

$7v - 7.5v - 5.4 = 7.5v - 7.5v - 1.2$

$0.5v - 5.4 + 5.4 = -1.2 + 5.4$

$0.5v = 4.2$

$\dfrac{0.5v}{0.5} = \dfrac{4.2}{0.5}$

$v = 8.4$

What mistakes did the student make? Rewrite a correct and complete solution. How do you know your solution is correct?

6.3 **10.** Define a variable, then write an inequality that describes each situation.

   a) Persons under 18 are not admitted.

   b) A person must be at least 90 cm tall to go on an amusement park ride.

   c) Horton can spend a maximum of $50.

   d) A game is recommended for players 5 years and older.

11. Write the inequality represented by each number line.

   a)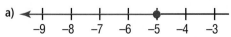

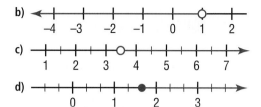

12. a) Graph each inequality on a number line.

   i) $a < -5.2$ **ii)** $b \le 8.5$

   iii) $c > -\dfrac{5}{3}$ **iv)** $d \ge \dfrac{25}{4}$

   b) For each inequality in part a, are -3 and 5 possible solutions? Justify your answer.

6.4
6.5 **13.** Determine 3 values of the variable that satisfy each inequality: one integer, one fraction, and one decimal.

   a) $h - 2 < -5$ **b)** $3k > -9$ **c)** $5 - y > 0$

14. State whether each operation on the inequality $-2x > 5$ will reverse the inequality sign.

   a) Multiply each side by 4.

   b) Add -5 to each side.

   c) Subtract -2 from each side.

   d) Divide each side by -6.

15. The cost of a prom is $400 to rent a hall, and $30 per person for the meal. The prom committee has $10 000. How many students can attend?

   a) Define a variable and write an inequality to model this problem.

   b) Solve the inequality, then graph the solution.

16. Solve each inequality. Verify and graph the solution.

   a) $7 + y < 25$ **b)** $-7y < 14$

   c) $\dfrac{x}{4} > -2.5$ **d)** $5.2 - y < -5.5$

   e) $13.5 + 2y \le 18.5$ **f)** $24 + 3a \le -6 + 7a$

1. Use a model of your choice to illustrate the steps to solve this equation:

$15 + 2d = 5d + 6$

Explain each step and record it algebraically.

2. Solve each equation.

a) $-3x - 0.7 = -7$

b) $\frac{26}{x} = 5 - 1.5$

c) $\frac{r}{3} + 5.4 = -3.2$

d) $2.4w - 5.6 = 3.7 + 1.9w$

e) $\frac{1}{4}c - \frac{7}{2} = \frac{1}{2}c + \frac{3}{4}$

f) $4.5(1.2 - m) = 2.4(-2m + 2.1)$

3. To cater a lunch, Tina's Catering charges $100, plus $15 per meal.
Norman's Catering charges $25, plus $20 per meal.
Determine the number of meals that will result in equal costs
at the two companies.

a) Define a variable, then write an equation that can be used
to solve this problem.

b) Solve the equation. Verify the solution.

4. Solve each inequality. Verify, then graph the solution.

a) $5 - t > 3$

b) $3(t + 2) \geq 11 - 5t$

c) $\frac{m}{4} + 5 \leq \frac{1}{2} - m$

5. A car rental company charges $24.95 per day plus $0.35 per kilometre.
A business person is allowed $50 each day for travel expenses.
How far can the business person travel without exceeding her daily budget?

a) Define a variable, then write an inequality to solve the problem.

b) Solve the problem. Graph the solution.
How do you know that your answer is correct?

6. Two students wrote these solutions on a test. Identify the errors.
Write a correct and complete algebraic solution.

a) $\frac{1}{4}c - 2 = 3$

$4 \times \frac{1}{4}c - 2 = 4 \times 3$

$c - 2 = 12$

$c = 14$

b) $x + 4 < -8 - 2x$

$x + 4 - 4 > -8 - 2x - 4$

$x > -12 - 2x$

$x + 2x > -12 - 2x + 2x$

$3x > 12$

$x > 4$

There are 25 students in the school's Pep Club.

1. The Pep Club can buy new uniforms from
   2 different suppliers:
   Company A charges $500, plus $22 per uniform.
   Company B charges $360, plus $28 per uniform.
   a) Define a variable, then write an equation that
      can be used to determine the number of
      uniforms that will result in equal costs at both
      companies.
   b) Solve the equation. Verify the solution.
   c) Which company should the Pep Club choose?
      Justify your recommendation.
   d) How much money must the Pep Club raise to
      purchase the uniforms?

2. The Pep Club decides to raise the money for the
   uniforms by selling snacks at lunch time. The snacks
   cost the Pep Club $6.00 for a box of 30.
   a) Determine the cost per snack.
   b) The Pep Club makes a profit of $0.25 on each snack sold. Suppose the club
      does raise the money it needs. Define a variable, then write an inequality
      that can be used to determine how many snacks might have been sold.
      How many boxes of snacks did the members of the Pep Club need?
   c) Solve the inequality.
   d) Verify the solution.

Your work should show:
- an equation and inequality and how you determined them
- how you determined the solutions of the equation and the inequality
- clear explanations of your reasoning

Reflect
on Your Learning

How is solving a linear inequality like solving a linear equation?
How is it different?
Include examples in your explanation.

1 **1.** Which numbers are perfect squares?
Determine the square root of each perfect
square. Estimate the square root of each
non-perfect square.

a) 3.6   **b)** 0.81   **c)** $\frac{16}{25}$

d) 0.0004   **e)** $\frac{224}{9}$ **f)** 4.41

g) 2.56   **h)** 0.24

2 **2.** Simplify, then evaluate each expression.

a) $(-8)^4 \times (-8)^3 \div (-8)^6$

b) $(9^4 \times 9^3)^0$

c) $[(-2)^5]^3 - [(-3)^3]^2$

d) $[(-4)^1 + (-4)^2 - (-4)^3] \times$
$(-4)^5 \div (-4)^4$

e) $\frac{3^5}{3^2} - (-3)^2$

3 **3.** Evaluate.

a) $1\frac{5}{8} + \left(-4\frac{1}{6}\right)$ **b)** $-3\frac{2}{5} - 7\frac{3}{4}$

c) $(-1.3)(3.4)$ **d)** $\left(-2\frac{1}{10}\right) \div \left(-5\frac{2}{5}\right)$

e) $-8.3 + 6.7 \times (-3.9)$

f) $1\frac{1}{2} \times \left[\left(-\frac{1}{3}\right) + \frac{1}{4}\right]$

g) $[-7.2 - (-9.1)] \div 0.5 + (-0.8)$

4 **4.** The pattern in this table continues.

Term Number, n	Term Value, v
1	5
2	7
3	9
4	11

a) Describe the patterns in the table.

b) Write an equation that relates v to n.

c) Verify the equation by substituting values
from the table.

d) Determine the value of the 24th term.

e) Which term number has a value of 233?

5. **a)** Create a table of values for the linear
relation $y = 3x - 2$.

b) Describe the patterns in the table.

c) Graph the data.

6. **a)** Does each equation describe a vertical
line, a horizontal line, or an oblique line?
How do you know?

  i) $2x = 5$

 ii) $y + 2 = -1$

iii) $x + y = 3$

b) Graph each line in part a.
Explain your work.

7. Match each equation with a graph below.
Justify your answers.

a) $x + 2y = 5$ **b)** $2x + y = 5$ **c)** $2x - y = 5$

Graph A

Graph B

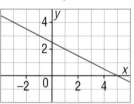

Graph C

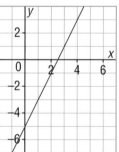

8. Carl is cycling across Canada. This graph shows the distance he covers in 10 days.

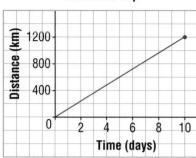

Carl's Bike Trip

a) Estimate how many days it will take Carl to cycle 700 km.

b) Predict how far Carl will cycle in 13 days.

9. Name the coefficients, variable, and degree of each polynomial. Identify the constant term if there is one.

a) $3x - 6$ b) $4n^2 - 2n + 5$

c) 19 d) $-a^2 + 7 - 21a$

10. Simplify each polynomial.

a) $2a - 4 - 9a + 5$

b) $3y - 2y^2 + 4 - y + 3y^2 - 8$

c) $9c - 4cd + d - 6cd + 4 - 7c$

d) $4m^2 - 3n^2 + 2m - 3n + 2m^2 + n^2$

11. Add or subtract the polynomials.

a) $(3s^2 - 2s + 6) + (7s^2 - 4s - 3)$

b) $(8x^2 - 5x + 2) - (5x^2 + 3x - 4)$

c) $(9t - 4 + t^2) + (6 - 2t^2 + 5t)$

d) $(1 + 4n - n^2) - (3n - 2n^2 + 7)$

e) $(6y^2 + 3xy - 2x^2 + 1) +$
$(3x^2 - 2y^2 - 8 + 6xy)$

f) $(8a - 6b - 3a^2 - 2ab) -$
$(4b^2 - 7ab + 9b - 6)$

12. Determine each product or quotient.

a) $9(3s^2 - 7s + 4)$

b) $\dfrac{35 - 49w^2 - 56w}{-7}$

c) $7m(3m - 9)$

d) $(-12d^2 + 18d) \div (-6d)$

13. Solve each equation. Verify the solution.

a) $9x = 7.2$ b) $-2.7 = \dfrac{a}{4}$

c) $6.5s - 2.7 = -30$ d) $\dfrac{c}{4} - 0.2 = 5.8$

e) $6(n - 8.2) = -18.6$ f) $-8 = \dfrac{7}{c}, c \neq 0$

g) $22 - 7d = -8 - 2d$

h) $3.8v - 17.84 = 4.2v$

i) $2(t - 8) = 4(2t - 19)$

j) $\dfrac{3}{4}(2r - 4) = \dfrac{1}{5}(36 - r)$

14. a) Graph each inequality on a number line.

i) $a \leq 3$ ii) $-4.5 < b$

iii) $c < -\dfrac{7}{4}$ iv) $d \geq 2\dfrac{1}{3}$

b) State whether -4 and 2 are possible solutions for each inequality in part a. Justify your answer.

15. Solve each inequality. Graph the solution. Verify the solution.

a) $x + 7 < 3$ b) $-3x > 6$

c) $b - 4.8 \geq -1.5$ d) $\dfrac{n}{-8} + 2 \leq -7$

e) $7m + 23 \leq 6m - 15$

f) $6.5 - 0.2t > 8$

g) $-5(4 - 0.8s) \geq 3(19 - s)$

16. Daphne will sell her video game system for $140 to Surinder. She also offers to sell him video games for $15 each. Surinder has saved $210 in total. How many video games can Surinder buy from Daphne?

a) Write an inequality to solve this problem.

b) Solve the inequality. Verify the solution.

Similarity and Transformations

Here are some flags of different countries and Canadian provinces. Some of these flags have line symmetry.

Picture each flag lying on your desk.

Which flags have a line of symmetry that is:

- vertical?
- horizontal?
- oblique?

Identify any flag that has more than one line of symmetry. Which flag has the most lines of symmetry?

What You'll Learn

- Draw and interpret scale diagrams.
- Apply properties of similar polygons.
- Identify and describe line symmetry and rotational symmetry.

Why It's Important

Architects, engineers, designers, and surveyors use similarity and scale diagrams routinely in their work. Symmetry can be seen in art and nature. An understanding of symmetry helps us to appreciate and find out more about our world, and to create works of art.

Key Words

- scale diagram
- corresponding lengths
- scale factor
- proportion
- similar polygons
- corresponding angles
- corresponding sides
- rotational symmetry
- order of rotation
- angle of rotation symmetry

Suppose I have to solve this problem:

Determine the unknown measures of the angles and sides in △ABC. The given measures are rounded to the nearest whole number.

I think of what I already know about triangles.

I see that AB and AC have the same hatch marks; this means the sides are equal.

AC = AB

So, AC = 5 cm

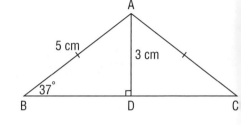

I know that a triangle with 2 equal sides is an isosceles triangle.

So, △ABC is isosceles.

An isosceles triangle has 2 equal angles that are formed where the equal sides intersect the third side.

I use 3 letters to describe an angle.

So, ∠ACD = ∠ABD

$= 37°$

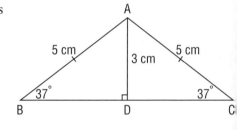

Since △ABC is isosceles, the height AD is the perpendicular bisector of the base BC.

So, BD = DC and ∠ADB = 90°

I can use the Pythagorean Theorem in △ABD to calculate the length of BD.

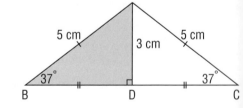

$$AD^2 + BD^2 = AB^2$$
$$3^2 + BD^2 = 5^2$$
$$9 + BD^2 = 25$$
$$9 - 9 + BD^2 = 25 - 9$$
$$BD^2 = 16$$
$$BD = \sqrt{16}$$
$$BD = 4$$

BD = 4 cm

So, BC = 2 × 4 cm

     = 8 cm

I know that the sum of the angles in a triangle is 180°.

So, I can calculate the measure of ∠BAC.

$\angle BAC + \angle ACD + \angle ABD = 180°$

$\angle BAC + 37° + 37° = 180°$

$\angle BAC + 74° = 180°$

$\angle BAC + 74° - 74° = 180° - 74°$

$\angle BAC = 106°$

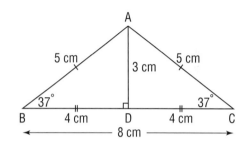

My friend Janelle showed me a different way to calculate.

She recalled that the line AD is a line of symmetry for an isosceles triangle.

So, ΔABD is congruent to ΔACD.

This means that ∠BAD = ∠CAD

Janelle calculated the measure of ∠BAD in ΔABD.

$\angle BAD + 37° + 90° = 180°$

$\angle BAD + 127° = 180°$

$\angle BAD + 127° - 127° = 180° - 127°$

$\angle BAD = 53°$

Then, $\angle BAC = 2 × 53°$

     $= 106°$

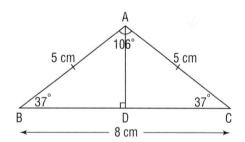

Check

1. Calculate the measure of each angle.

  a) ∠ACB   **b)** ∠GEF and ∠GFE   **c)** ∠HJK and ∠KHJ

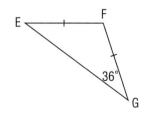
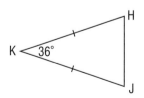

Scale Diagrams and Enlargements

How are these photos alike?
How are they different?

FOCUS

• Draw and interpret scale diagrams that represent enlargements.

Investigate ②

You will need 0.5-cm grid paper.
Here is an actual size drawing of a memory card for a digital camera and an enlargement of the drawing.

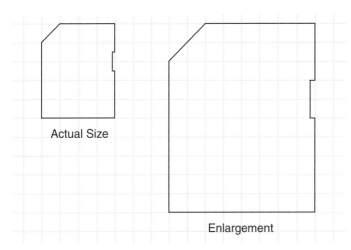

Actual Size

Enlargement

➤ Copy the drawings on grid paper.
Measure the lengths of pairs of matching sides on the drawings.
Label each drawing with these measurements.

➤ For each measurement, write the fraction: $\dfrac{\text{Length on enlargement}}{\text{Length on actual size drawing}}$
Write each fraction as a decimal.
What do you notice about these numbers?

Compare your numbers with those of another pair of students.
Work together to draw a different enlargement of the memory card.
Determine the fraction $\dfrac{\text{Length on enlargement}}{\text{Length on actual size drawing}}$ for this
new enlargement.

Connect

A diagram that is an enlargement or a
reduction of another diagram is called
a **scale diagram.**
Here is letter F and a scale diagram of it.

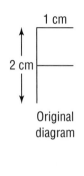

Original
diagram

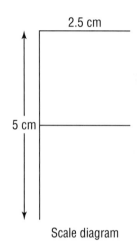

Scale diagram

Compare the matching lengths in the scale diagram and in the original diagram.

$\dfrac{\text{Length of vertical segment on the scale diagram}}{\text{Length of vertical segment on the original diagram}} = \dfrac{5 \text{ cm}}{2 \text{ cm}}$

$= 2.5$

$\dfrac{\text{Length of horizontal segment on scale diagram}}{\text{Length of horizontal segment on original diagram}} = \dfrac{2.5 \text{ cm}}{1 \text{ cm}}$

$= 2.5$

> This equation is called a **proportion** because it is a statement that two ratios are equal.

Each length on the original diagram is multiplied by 2.5 to get the matching length
on the scale diagram. Matching lengths on the original diagram and the scale
diagram are called **corresponding lengths.**

The fraction $\dfrac{\text{Length on scale diagram}}{\text{Length on original diagram}}$ is called the **scale factor** of
the scale diagram.
A scale factor can be expressed as a fraction or as a decimal.
For the diagram above, the scale factor is $\dfrac{5}{2}$, or 2.5.
Pairs of corresponding lengths have the same scale factor, so we say that
corresponding lengths are *proportional.*
Each segment of the enlargement is longer than the corresponding segment on the
original diagram, so the scale factor is greater than 1.

Example 1   **Using Corresponding Lengths to Determine the Scale Factor**

This drawing of a mosquito was printed
in a newspaper article about the West Nile Virus.
The actual length of the mosquito is 12 mm.
Determine the scale factor of the diagram.

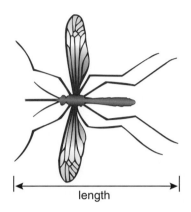

length

▶ *A Solution*

Measure the length on the scale drawing of the mosquito,
to the nearest millimetre.
The length is 4.5 cm, which is 45 mm.

> To calculate the scale
> factor, the units of length
> must be the same.

The scale factor is: $\dfrac{\text{Length on scale diagram}}{\text{Length of mosquito}} = \dfrac{45 \text{ mm}}{12 \text{ mm}}$

$= 3.75$

The scale factor is 3.75.

Example 2   **Using a Scale Factor to Determine Dimensions**

This photo of longhouses has dimensions 9 cm by 6 cm.
The photo is to be enlarged by a scale factor of $\dfrac{7}{2}$.
Calculate the dimensions of the enlargement.

Solutions

To determine a length on the scale diagram, multiply the corresponding length on the original diagram by the scale factor.

Method 1	Method 2
Use mental math. Length of enlargement: $\frac{7}{2} \times 9$ cm $= \frac{7 \times 9 \text{ cm}}{2}$ $\quad = 31.5$ cm Width of enlargement: $\frac{7}{2} \times 6$ cm $= \frac{7 \times 6 \text{ cm}}{2}$ $\quad = 21$ cm The dimensions of the enlargement are 31.5 cm by 21 cm.	Use a calculator. Write $\frac{7}{2}$ as 3.5. Length of enlargement: 3.5×9 cm $= 31.5$ cm Width of enlargement: 3.5×6 cm $= 21$ cm The dimensions of the enlargement are 31.5 cm by 21 cm.

Example 3 — Drawing a Scale Diagram that Is an Enlargement

Draw a scale diagram of this metal bracket. Use a scale factor of 1.5.

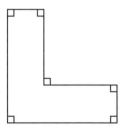

Solutions

Method 1

Use a photocopier. Write the scale factor 1.5 as a percent: 150%
Set the zoom feature on the photocopier to 150%. Copy the diagram.

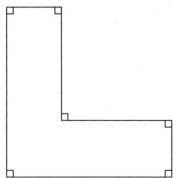

Measure the length of each line segment in the given diagram.
Determine the length of each line segment in the scale diagram
by multiplying each length on the original diagram by 1.5.

1.5 × 3 cm = 4.5 cm
1.5 × 2 cm = 3 cm
1.5 × 1 cm = 1.5 cm

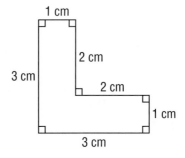

Use a ruler and a protractor to draw a scale diagram with the new lengths above.
The angles in the scale diagram match the angles in the given diagram.

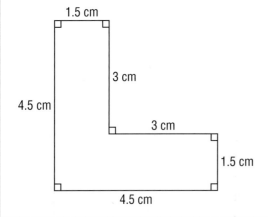

Discuss the ideas

1. Explain what is meant by the term "scale factor" for a scale diagram.

2. When you calculate a scale factor, why is it important to have the same units for the lengths on the original diagram and the scale diagram?

3. Suppose you are given two diagrams. How can you tell if one diagram is a scale drawing of the other diagram?

Practice

Check

4. Determine the scale factor for each scale diagram.

a)

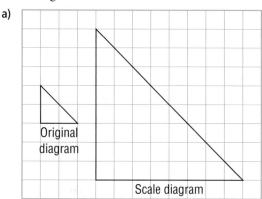

Original diagram

Scale diagram

b)

Original diagram

Scale diagram

5. Scale diagrams of different squares are to be drawn. The side length of each original square and the scale factor are given. Determine the side length of each scale diagram.

	Side length of original square	Scale factor
a)	12 cm	3
b)	82 mm	$\frac{5}{2}$
c)	1.55 cm	4.2
d)	45 mm	3.8
e)	0.8 cm	12.5

Apply

6. A photo of a surfboard has dimensions 17.5 cm by 12.5 cm. Enlargements are to be made with each scale factor below. Determine the dimensions of each enlargement. Round the answers to the nearest centimetre.
 a) scale factor 12   b) scale factor 20
 c) scale factor $\frac{7}{2}$ d) scale factor $\frac{17}{4}$

7. Here is a scale diagram of a salmon fry. The actual length of the salmon fry is 30 mm. Measure the length on the diagram to the nearest millimetre. Determine the scale factor for the scale diagram.

length

8. The head of a pin has diameter 2 mm. Determine the scale factor of this photo of the pinhead.

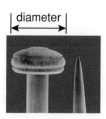

diameter

9. This view of the head of a bolt has the shape of a regular hexagon. Each angle is 120°. Use a protractor and ruler to draw a scale diagram of the bolt with scale factor 2.5.

10. Draw your initials on 0.5-cm grid paper. Use different-sized grid paper to draw two different scale diagrams of your initials. For each scale diagram, state the scale factor.

11. Assessment Focus For each set of diagrams below, identify which of diagrams A, B, C, and D are scale diagrams of the shaded shape. For each scale diagram you identify:

    i) State the scale factor.

    ii) Explain how it is a scale diagram.

a)

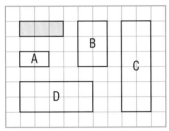

b)

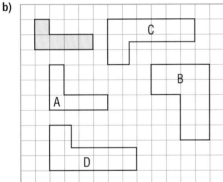

12. One frame of a film in a projector is about 50 mm high. The film is projected onto a giant screen. The image of the film frame is 16 m high.

    a) What is the scale factor of this enlargement?

    b) A penguin is 35 mm high on the film. How high is the penguin on the screen?

13. Look in a newspaper, magazine, or on the Internet. Find an example of a scale diagram that is an enlargement and has its scale factor given. What does the scale factor indicate about the original diagram or object?

14. Draw a scale diagram of the shape below with scale factor 2.5.

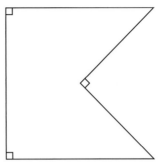

15. On a grid, draw ΔOAB with vertices O(0, 0), A(0, 3), and B(4, 0).

    a) Draw a scale diagram of ΔOAB with scale factor 3 and one vertex at C(3, 3). Write the coordinates of the new vertices.

    b) Is there more than one answer for part a? If your answer is no, explain why no other diagrams are possible. If your answer is yes, draw other possible scale diagrams.

Take It Further

16. One micron is one-millionth of a metre, or 1 m = 10^6 microns.

    a) A human hair is about 200 microns wide. How wide is a scale drawing of a human hair with scale factor 400? Give your answer in as many different units as you can.

    b) A computer chip is about 4 microns wide. A scale diagram of a computer chip is 5 cm wide. What is the scale factor?

Reflect

Suppose you are given a scale diagram. Why is it important to know the scale factor?

FOCUS
• Draw and interpret scale diagrams that represent reductions.

Here is a map of Victoria Island from the Internet.
What is the scale on the map? How is the scale used?

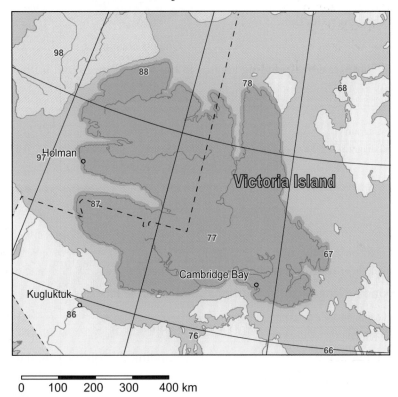

0   100   200   300   400 km

Investigate

You will need 2-cm grid paper and 0.5-cm grid paper.

➤ Trace your hand on the 2-cm grid paper. Copy this outline of your hand onto the 0.5-cm grid paper. Be as accurate as you can.

➤ On both drawings, measure and label the length of each finger.

For each finger, determine the fraction: $\dfrac{\text{Length on 0.5-cm grid paper}}{\text{Length on 2-cm grid paper}}$

Write each fraction as a decimal to the nearest hundredth.

What do you notice about the decimals?

Reflect & Share

Compare your answers with those of another pair of classmates.
Are the numbers the same? Should they be the same? Explain.
How does this work relate to the scale diagrams of the previous lesson?

A scale diagram can be smaller than the original diagram. This type of scale diagram is called a *reduction*.

Here is a life-size drawing of a button and a scale diagram that is a reduction.

Scale diagram

Original diagram

We measure and compare corresponding lengths in the scale diagram and in the original diagram.

$$\frac{\text{Diameter of scale diagram}}{\text{Diameter of original diagram}} = \frac{2\text{ cm}}{3\text{ cm}}$$

$$= \frac{2}{3}$$

$$\frac{\text{Height of heart on scale diagram}}{\text{Height of heart on original diagram}} = \frac{0.4\text{ cm}}{0.6\text{ cm}}$$

$$= \frac{0.4}{0.6}$$ Write an equivalent fraction.

$$= \frac{2}{3}$$

The fraction $\dfrac{\text{Length on scale diagram}}{\text{Length on original diagram}}$ is the scale factor of the scale diagram.

Pairs of corresponding lengths are proportional, and the scale factor is $\dfrac{2}{3}$.

The equation $\dfrac{\text{Length on scale diagram}}{\text{Length on original diagram}} = \dfrac{2}{3}$ is a proportion.

Each side of the reduction is shorter than the corresponding side on the original diagram, so the scale factor is less than 1.

| **Example 1** | **Drawing a Scale Diagram that Is a Reduction** |

Draw a scale diagram of this octagon. Use a scale factor of 0.25.

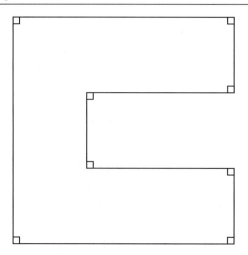

Method 1

Measure the length of each line segment in the octagon.

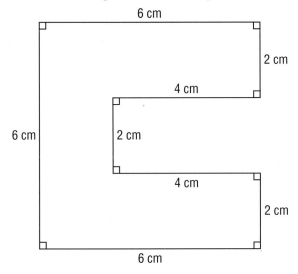

Determine the length of each line segment in the scale diagram by multiplying each length by 0.25.

0.25×2 cm $= 0.5$ cm

0.25×4 cm $= 1$ cm

0.25×6 cm $= 1.5$ cm

Use a ruler and protractor to draw a scale diagram with the new lengths above.
The angles in the scale diagram match the angles in the original diagram.

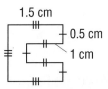

Method 2

Use a photocopier.
Write the scale factor 0.25 as a percent: 25%
Set the zoom feature on the photocopier to 25%.
Copy the diagram.

A scale may be given as a ratio. For example, suppose the scale on a scale diagram of a house is 1:150. This means that 1 cm on the diagram represents 150 cm, or 1.5 m on the house.

Example 2   **Using a Scale on a Scale Diagram to Determine Lengths**

Here is a scale diagram of the top view of a truck.

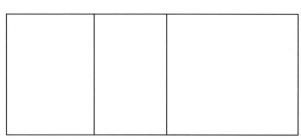

Scale 1:50

The length of the truck is 4 m.

a) The front and back wheels of the truck are 3.85 m apart.
   How far apart should the wheels be on the scale diagram?

b) What is the width of the truck?

▶ *A Solution*

The scale is 1:50. This means that 1 cm on the diagram represents 50 cm on the truck.
So, the scale factor is $\frac{1}{50}$.

a) The front and back wheels of the truck are 3.85 m apart.

   Each distance on the scale diagram is $\frac{1}{50}$ of its distance on the truck.

   So, on the scale diagram, the distance between the wheels is:
   $$\frac{1}{50} \times 3.85 \text{ m} = \frac{3.85 \text{ m}}{50}$$
   $$= 0.077 \text{ m}$$

   Convert this length to centimetres: 0.077 m = 0.077 × 100 cm, or 7.7 cm
   On the scale diagram, the wheels are 7.7 cm apart.

b) Measure the width of the truck on the scale diagram.
   The width is 3.2 cm.
   Each actual measure is 50 times as great as the measure on the scale diagram.
   So, the actual width of the truck is: 50 × 3.2 cm = 160 cm
   The truck is 160 cm wide; that is 1.6 m wide.

1. What is a reduction? How is it like an enlargement?
   How is it different?

2. What is a proportion? When can it be used to solve a problem
   involving reductions?

3. How can you tell whether a scale diagram is an enlargement or
   a reduction?

Check

4. Write each fraction in simplest form, then express it as a decimal.

a) $\frac{25}{1000}$ b) $\frac{5}{125}$ c) $\frac{2}{1000}$ d) $\frac{3}{180}$

5. Determine the scale factor for each reduction as a fraction or a decimal.

a)
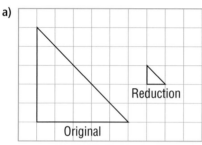

b)
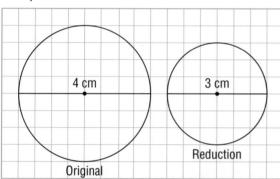

6. For each pair of circles, the original diameter and the diameter of the reduction are given. Determine each scale factor as a fraction or a decimal.

	Diameter of Actual Circle	Diameter of Reduction
a)	50 cm	30 cm
b)	30 cm	20 cm
c)	126 cm	34 cm
d)	5 m	2 cm
e)	4 km	300 m

Apply

7. Here are two drawings of a dog. Determine the scale factor of the reduction as a fraction and as a decimal.

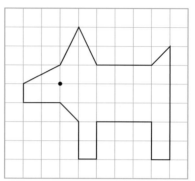
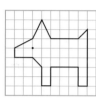

8. Which of rectangles A, B, and C is a reduction of the large rectangle? Justify your answer.

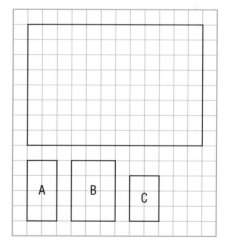

9. Which two polygons have pairs of corresponding lengths that are proportional? Identify the scale factor for the reduction.

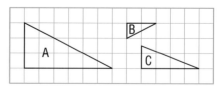

10. Which two polygons have pairs of corresponding lengths that are proportional? Identify the scale factor for the reduction.

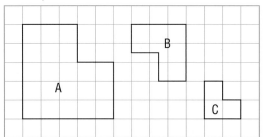

11. A reduction of each object is to be drawn with the given scale factor. Determine the corresponding length in centimetres on the scale diagram.
  a) A desk has length 75 cm. The scale factor is $\frac{1}{3}$.
  b) A bicycle has a wheel with diameter about 60 cm. The scale factor is $\frac{3}{50}$.
  c) A surfboard has length 200 cm. The scale factor is 0.05.
  d) A sailboat has length 8 m. The scale factor is 0.02.
  e) A canyon has length 12 km. The scale factor is 0.000 04.

12. Copy each diagram on 1-cm grid paper. Draw a reduction of each diagram with the given scale factor.
  a) scale factor $\frac{3}{4}$

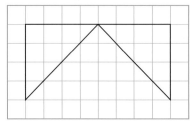

  b) scale factor $\frac{2}{3}$

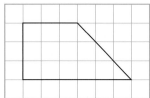

13. Here is a scale diagram of an outdoor hockey rink. The rink is 32 m long.

Scale 1:400

  a) Each hockey net is 1.82 m long. Suppose you had to include the hockey nets on the scale diagram. How long would each hockey net be on the diagram?
  b) What is the width of the rink?

14. A volleyball court measures approximately 18 m by 9 m. Make a scale drawing of the court using a scale factor of $\frac{1}{200}$. Show any calculations you made.

15. A lacrosse field measures 99 m by 54 m. Make a scale drawing of the field using a scale factor of 0.002. Show any calculations you made.

16. Your teacher will give you the dimensions of your classroom. Choose a scale factor and justify its choice. Draw a scale diagram of your classroom. Include as much detail as possible.

17. Assessment Focus Draw a scale diagram of any room in your home. Show as much detail as possible by including items in the room. Show any calculations you make and record the scale factor.

18. Look in a newspaper, magazine, or on the Internet. Find an example of a scale diagram that is a reduction and has its scale factor given. What does the scale factor indicate about the original diagram or object?

19. Ask your teacher for a scale diagram of the room shown below. The length of the room is 7.5 m.

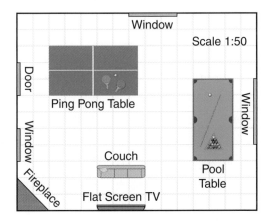

a) Determine the scale factor.
b) What are the actual dimensions of:
   i) the ping pong table?
   ii) the pool table?
c) What is the actual size of the flat screen television?
d) Moulding is to be placed around the ceiling. It costs $4.99/m. How much will the moulding cost?

20. A 747 jet airplane is about 70 m long. A plastic model of this plane is 28 cm long.
a) Determine the scale factor of the model.
b) On the model, the wingspan is 24 cm. What is the wingspan on the 747 plane?
c) On the model, the tail is 7.6 cm high. What is the height of the tail on the 747 plane?

Take It Further

21. The approximate diameter of each planet in our solar system is given below.
Earth: 12 760 km; Jupiter: 142 800 km;
Mars: 6790 km; Mercury: 4880 km;
Neptune: 49 500 km; Saturn: 120 600 km;
Uranus: 51 120 km; Venus: 12 100 km
Create a scale drawing that includes all the planets. Justify your choice of scale factor. Label each planet with its actual diameter.

Reflect

A scale factor is the ratio of a length on a scale diagram to the actual length.
When you know two of these three values, how can you determine the third value?
Include an example in each case.

Drawing Scale Diagrams

Geometry software can be used to enlarge or reduce a shape.
Use available geometry software.

If you need help at any time, use the software's *Help* menu.

➤ Construct a rectangle. Select the rectangle.
Use the scale feature of the software to enlarge the
rectangle.

FOCUS

• Use different technologies to produce enlargements and reductions.

The rectangle has been enlarged by a scale factor of
1.5, or 150%.

➤ Construct a quadrilateral. Select the quadrilateral.
  Use the scale feature to reduce the quadrilateral.

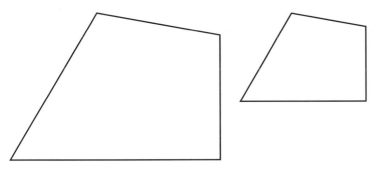

The quadrilateral has been reduced by a scale factor of $\frac{3}{5}$, or 60%.

Check

1. Construct a shape. Choose an enlargement scale factor, then enlarge your shape. Calculate the ratios of the corresponding sides of the enlargement and the original shape. What can you say about the ratios?

2. Construct a shape. Choose a reduction scale factor, then reduce your shape. Calculate the ratios of the corresponding sides of the reduction and the original shape. What can you say about the ratios?

3. Print the diagrams of the enlargement and reduction. Trade diagrams with a classmate. Identify the scale factor for each of your classmate's scale diagrams.

4. Try these other ways of enlarging and reducing a shape:
   • an overhead projector
   • a photocopier
   • a Draw tool in a software program

Which pair of polygons below show an enlargement or a reduction?
Explain your choice.

FOCUS

• Recognize and draw
  similar polygons, then
  use their properties to
  solve problems.

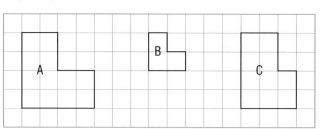

Investigate

You will need 0.5-cm grid paper, 2-cm grid paper,
a ruler, and a protractor.

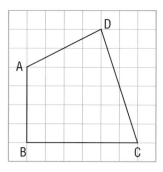

➤ Choose a scale factor. Draw an enlargement of
  quadrilateral ABCD.
  Label the new quadrilateral A′B′C′D′.
  Measure the side lengths to the nearest millimetre
  and the angles to the nearest degree.
  Copy and complete this table:

Lengths of Sides (mm)	AB	A′B′	BC	B′C′	CD	C′D′	DA	D′A′

Measures of Angles (°)	∠A	∠A′	∠B	∠B′	∠C	∠C′	∠D	∠D′

➤ Choose a scale factor. Draw a reduction of quadrilateral ABCD.
  Label the new quadrilateral A″B″C″D″. Copy and complete this table:

Lengths of Sides (mm)	AB	A″B″	BC	B″C″	CD	C″D″	DA	D″A″

Measures of Angles (°)	∠A	∠A″	∠B	∠B″	∠C	∠C″	∠D	∠D″

➤ Copy the table below. Use your results from the first 2 tables to complete this table. Write the ratios of the lengths of the sides as decimals to the nearest hundredth.

$\dfrac{AB}{A'B'}$	$\dfrac{BC}{B'C'}$	$\dfrac{CD}{C'D'}$	$\dfrac{DA}{D'A'}$	$\dfrac{AB}{A''B''}$	$\dfrac{BC}{B''C''}$	$\dfrac{CD}{C''D''}$	$\dfrac{DA}{D''A''}$

➤ What do you notice about the measures of the matching angles?
What do you notice about the ratios of matching sides?

Compare your results with those of another pair of students.
Work together to draw two other quadrilaterals that have sides and angles related the same way as your quadrilaterals.
How does this work relate to scale drawings that show enlargements and reductions?

Connect

When one polygon is an enlargement or a reduction of another polygon, we say the polygons are **similar**. Similar polygons have the same shape, but not necessarily the same size.

Here are two similar pentagons.

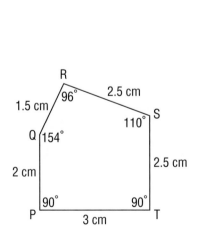
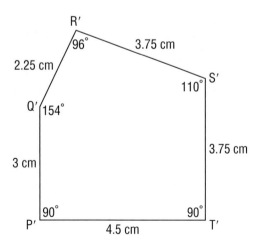

Matching angles are **corresponding angles**.
Matching sides are **corresponding sides**.
We list the corresponding angles and the pairs of corresponding sides.

Corresponding Sides			Corresponding Angles	
PQ = 2 cm	P′Q′ = 3 cm	$\dfrac{P'Q'}{PQ} = \dfrac{3}{2} = 1.5$	∠P = 90°	∠P′ = 90°
QR = 1.5 cm	Q′R′ = 2.25 cm	$\dfrac{Q'R'}{QR} = \dfrac{2.25}{1.5} = 1.5$	∠Q = 154°	∠Q′ = 154°
RS = 2.5 cm	R′S′ = 3.75 cm	$\dfrac{R'S'}{RS} = \dfrac{3.75}{2.5} = 1.5$	∠R = 96°	∠R′ = 96°
ST = 2.5 cm	S′T′ = 3.75 cm	$\dfrac{S'T'}{ST} = \dfrac{3.75}{2.5} = 1.5$	∠S = 110°	∠S′ = 110°
TP = 3 cm	T′P′ = 4.5 cm	$\dfrac{T'P'}{TP} = \dfrac{4.5}{3} = 1.5$	∠T = 90°	∠T′ = 90°

In similar polygons:
- pairs of corresponding sides have lengths in the same ratio; that is, the lengths are proportional, and
- the corresponding angles are equal

Pentagon P′Q′R′S′T′ is an enlargement of pentagon PQRST with a scale factor of $\dfrac{3}{2}$, or 1.5. Or, we can think of pentagon PQRST as a reduction of pentagon P′Q′R′S′T′ with a scale factor of $\dfrac{2}{3}$.

We say: pentagon PQRST is similar to P′Q′R′S′T′.
We write: pentagon PQRST ~ pentagon P′Q′R′S′T′

▶ **Properties of Similar Polygons**
When two polygons are similar:
- their corresponding angles are equal, and
- their corresponding sides are proportional.

It is also true that if two polygons have these properties, then the polygons are similar.

Quadrilateral ABCD ~ quadrilateral PQRS

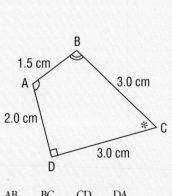

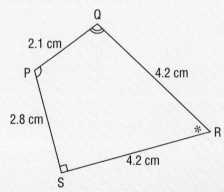

$$\dfrac{AB}{PQ} = \dfrac{BC}{QR} = \dfrac{CD}{RS} = \dfrac{DA}{SP}$$

Example 1 | **Identifying Similar Polygons**

Identify pairs of similar rectangles. Justify the answer.

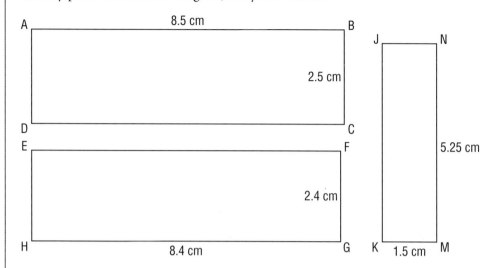

▶ *A Solution*

The measure of each angle in a rectangle is 90°.
So, for any two rectangles, their corresponding angles are equal.
For each pair of rectangles, determine the ratios of corresponding sides.
Since the opposite sides of a rectangle are equal, we only need to check the ratios
of corresponding lengths and corresponding widths.

For rectangles ABCD and EFGH:

$$\frac{AB}{EF} = \frac{8.5}{8.4} \qquad \frac{BC}{FG} = \frac{2.5}{2.4}$$
$$= 1.011\ldots \qquad = 1.041\overline{6}$$

These numbers show that the corresponding sides are not proportional.
So, rectangles ABCD and EFGH are not similar.

For rectangles ABCD and JKMN:

$$\frac{AB}{JK} = \frac{8.5}{5.25} \qquad \frac{BC}{KM} = \frac{2.5}{1.5}$$
$$= 1.619\ldots \qquad = 1.\overline{6}$$

These numbers show that the corresponding sides are not proportional.
So, rectangles ABCD and JKMN are not similar.

For rectangles EFGH and JKMN:

$$\frac{EF}{JK} = \frac{8.4}{5.25} \qquad \frac{FG}{KM} = \frac{2.4}{1.5}$$
$$= 1.6 \qquad = 1.6$$

These numbers show that the corresponding sides are proportional.
So, rectangles EFGH and JKMN are similar.

Example 2   **Drawing a Polygon Similar to a Given Polygon**

a) Draw a larger pentagon that is similar to this pentagon.

b) Draw a smaller pentagon that is similar to this pentagon.

Explain why the pentagons are similar.

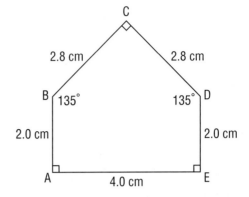

▶ *A Solution*

a) Draw an enlargement. Choose a scale factor greater than 1, such as 2.

Let the similar pentagon be A′B′C′D′E′.

Multiply each side length of ABCDE by 2 to get the corresponding side lengths of A′B′C′D′E′.

A′B′ = 2 × AB	B′C′ = 2 × BC	E′A′ = 2 × EA
= 2 × 2.0 cm	= 2 × 2.8 cm	= 2 × 4.0 cm
= 4.0 cm	= 5.6 cm	= 8.0 cm

Since DE = AB,   Since CD = BC,
then D′E′ = A′B′   then C′D′ = B′C′
      = 4.0 cm   = 5.6 cm

The corresponding angles are equal. So:

$\angle A' = \angle A$ $\angle B' = \angle B$
    $= 90°$ $= 135°$

$\angle C' = \angle C$ $\angle D' = \angle D$
    $= 90°$ $= 135°$

$\angle E' = \angle E$
    $= 90°$

Use a ruler and protractor to draw pentagon A′B′C′D′E′.

The pentagons are similar because corresponding angles are equal and corresponding sides are proportional. That is, the length of each side of the enlargement is 2 times the length of the corresponding side of the original pentagon.

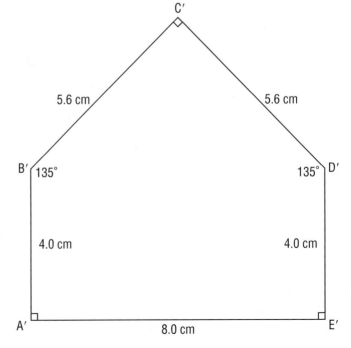

b) Draw a reduction. Choose a scale factor that is less than 1, such as $\frac{1}{2}$.

Let the similar pentagon be A′B′C′D′E′.

Multiply each side length of ABCDE by $\frac{1}{2}$ to get the corresponding side lengths of A′B′C′D′E′.

$A'B' = \frac{1}{2} \times AB$ $\qquad$ $B'C' = \frac{1}{2} \times BC$ $\qquad$ $E'A' = \frac{1}{2} \times EA$

$\qquad = \frac{1}{2} \times 2.0$ cm $\qquad\quad = \frac{1}{2} \times 2.8$ cm $\qquad\quad = \frac{1}{2} \times 4.0$ cm

$\qquad = 1.0$ cm $\qquad\qquad\quad = 1.4$ cm $\qquad\qquad\quad = 2.0$ cm

$\quad$ Since DE = AB, $\qquad$ Since CD = BC,

$\quad$ then D′E′ = A′B′ $\qquad$ then C′D′ = B′C′

$\qquad\qquad = 1.0$ cm $\qquad\qquad\quad = 1.4$ cm

The corresponding angles are equal. So:

$\angle A' = \angle A$ $\qquad$ $\angle B' = \angle B$ $\qquad$ $\angle C' = \angle C$ $\qquad$ $\angle D' = \angle D$ $\qquad$ $\angle E' = \angle E$

$\quad = 90°$ $\qquad\qquad = 135°$ $\qquad\qquad = 90°$ $\qquad\qquad = 135°$ $\qquad\qquad = 90°$

Use a ruler and protractor to draw pentagon A′B′C′D′E′.
The pentagons are similar because corresponding angles are equal and corresponding sides are proportional.
That is, the length of each side of the reduction is $\frac{1}{2}$ the length of the corresponding side of the original pentagon.

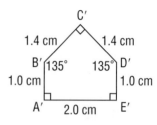

Example 3 $\quad$ **Solving Problems Using the Properties of Similar Polygons**

These two octagonal garden plots are similar.

a) Calculate the length of GH.

b) Calculate the length of NP.

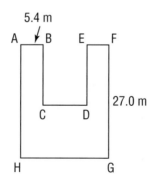

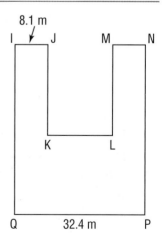

▶ **A Solution**

a) To calculate GH, consider polygon ABCDEFGH as a reduction of polygon IJKLMNPQ.

The scale factor of the reduction is the ratio of corresponding sides, such as:

$$\frac{AB}{IJ} = \frac{5.4}{8.1}$$

Write a ratio of corresponding sides that includes GH.

GH corresponds to PQ, so a ratio is $\frac{GH}{PQ}$.

Substitute: PQ = 32.4, then $\frac{GH}{PQ} = \frac{GH}{32.4}$

This ratio is equal to the scale factor.

Use the ratio and scale factor to write a proportion.

$$\frac{GH}{32.4} = \frac{5.4}{8.1}$$

Solve the proportion to determine GH. Multiply each side by 32.4.

$$32.4 \times \frac{GH}{32.4} = 32.4 \times \frac{5.4}{8.1}$$

$$GH = \frac{32.4 \times 5.4}{8.1}$$

$$GH = 21.6$$

GH is 21.6 m long.

b) To calculate NP, consider polygon IJKLMNPQ as an enlargement of polygon ABCDEFGH. The scale factor of the enlargement is the ratio of corresponding sides, such as: $\frac{IJ}{AB} = \frac{8.1}{5.4}$

Write a ratio of corresponding sides that includes NP.

NP corresponds to FG, so a ratio is $\frac{NP}{FG}$. This ratio is equal to the scale factor.

Substitute: FG = 27.0, then $\frac{NP}{FG} = \frac{NP}{27.0}$

Write a proportion.

$$\frac{NP}{27.0} = \frac{8.1}{5.4}$$

Solve the proportion to determine NP. Multiply each side by 27.0.

$$27.0 \times \frac{NP}{27.0} = 27.0 \times \frac{8.1}{5.4}$$

$$NP = \frac{27.0 \times 8.1}{5.4}$$

$$= 40.5$$

NP is 40.5 m long.

Discuss the ideas

1. How is drawing a similar polygon like drawing a scale diagram?

2. All rectangles have corresponding angles equal.
   a) When would two rectangles be similar?
   b) When would two rectangles *not* be similar?

3. How can you tell whether two polygons are similar?

Check

4. Calculate the side length, in units, in each proportion.

a) $\dfrac{AB}{8} = \dfrac{3}{2}$ b) $\dfrac{BC}{25} = \dfrac{12}{15}$

c) $\dfrac{CD}{4} = \dfrac{63}{28}$ d) $\dfrac{DE}{7} = \dfrac{24}{30}$

5. Calculate the value of the variable in each proportion.

a) $\dfrac{x}{2.5} = \dfrac{7.5}{1.5}$ b) $\dfrac{y}{21.4} = \dfrac{23.7}{15.8}$

c) $\dfrac{z}{12.5} = \dfrac{0.8}{1.2}$ d) $\dfrac{a}{0.7} = \dfrac{1.8}{24}$

6. Identify similar quadrilaterals. List their corresponding sides and corresponding angles.

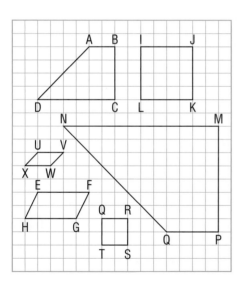

7. Use grid paper. Construct a quadrilateral similar to quadrilateral MNPQ.

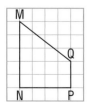

8. Use isometric dot paper. Construct a hexagon similar to hexagon ABCDEF.

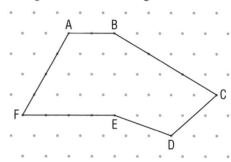

Apply

9. Are any of these rectangles similar? Justify your answer.

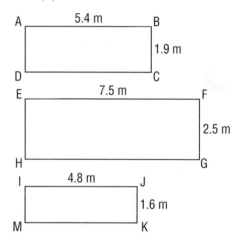

10. For each polygon below:
  i) Draw a similar larger polygon.
  ii) Draw a similar smaller polygon.
  Explain how you know the polygons are similar.

a)   b)

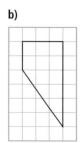

11. Are the polygons in each pair similar? Explain how you know.

a)

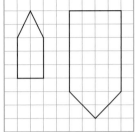

b)

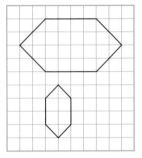

12. **Assessment Focus** Use grid paper. Construct rectangles with these dimensions: 3 units by 4 units, 6 units by 8 units, 9 units by 12 units, and 12 units by 15 units

a) i) Which rectangle is not similar to the other rectangles? Explain your reasoning.

ii) Draw two different rectangles that are similar to this rectangle. Show your work.

b) The diagonal of the smallest rectangle has length 5 units. Use proportions to calculate the lengths of the diagonals of the other two similar rectangles.

13. A rectangular door has height 200 cm and width 75 cm. It is similar to a door in a doll's house. The height of the doll's house door is 25 cm.

a) Sketch and label both doors.

b) Calculate the width of the doll's house door.

14. Each side of pentagon B is twice as long as a side of pentagon A.

Are the pentagons similar? Explain.

15. Use dot paper.

a) Draw two different:

i) equilateral triangles

ii) squares

iii) regular hexagons

b) Are all regular polygons of the same type similar? Justify your answer.

Take It Further

16. Are all circles similar? Justify your answer.

17. Draw two similar rectangles.

a) What is the ratio of their corresponding sides?

b) What is the ratio of their areas?

c) How are the ratios in parts a and b related?

d) Do you think the relationship in part c is true for all similar shapes? Justify your answer.

Reflect

What is meant by the statement that two polygons are similar? How would you check whether two polygons are similar?

7.4

Similar Triangles

FOCUS
* Use the properties of similar triangles to solve problems.

Identify two triangles in this diagram. How could you find out if they are similar?

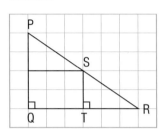

Investigate

6

You will need a ruler, compass, and protractor.
Each pair of students works with one of the three triangles below.

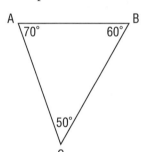

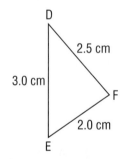

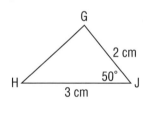

➤ Construct an enlargement of the triangle you chose. Label its vertices.
   Construct a reduction of the triangle. Label its vertices.
➤ Measure and record the angles of all your triangles. What do you notice?
➤ Measure and record the ratios of the lengths of corresponding sides for:
   • the original triangle and its enlargement
   • the original triangle and its reduction
   Write each ratio as a fraction, then as a decimal to the nearest tenth.
   What do you notice about the decimals?
➤ What can you say about the triangles you worked with?

Compare your results with those of another group of classmates.
What do you need to know about two triangles to be able to identify
whether they are similar?

When two polygons are similar:
- the measures of corresponding angles must be equal *and*
- the ratios of the lengths of corresponding sides must be equal.

A triangle is a special polygon. When we check whether two triangles are similar:
- the measures of corresponding angles must be equal; *or*
- the ratios of the lengths of corresponding sides must be equal

▶ **Properties of Similar Triangles**

To identify that ΔPQR and ΔSTU are similar, we only need to know that:
- ∠P = ∠S and ∠Q = ∠T and ∠R = ∠U; *or*
- $\dfrac{PQ}{ST} = \dfrac{QR}{TU} = \dfrac{PR}{SU}$

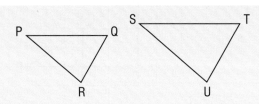

These triangles are similar because:

∠A = ∠Q = 75°

∠B = ∠R = 62°

∠C = ∠P = 43°

When we name two similar triangles, we order the letters to match the corresponding angles.

We write: ΔABC ~ ΔQRP

Then we can identify corresponding sides:

AB corresponds to QR.

BC corresponds to RP.

AC corresponds to QP.

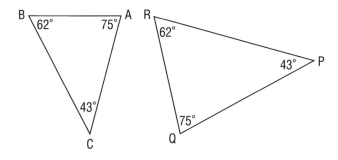

Math Link

Your World

Satellite imagery consists of photographs of Earth taken from space. The images are reductions of regions on Earth. The quality of an image depends upon the instrument used to obtain it and on the altitude of the satellite. The Landsat 7 satellite can create images of objects as small as 10 cm long.

Example 1   **Using Corresponding Sides to Name Similar Triangles**

Identify the similar triangles.
Justify your answer.

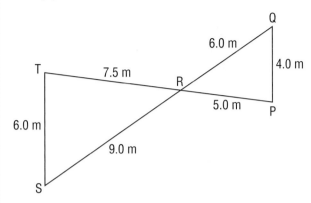

▶ **A Solution**

Since we know the side lengths of the triangles,
we identify the corresponding sides.
In ΔPQR, from shortest to longest: PQ, PR, QR
In ΔSTR, from shortest to longest: ST, TR, RS
Find out if the corresponding sides are proportional.

$$\frac{ST}{PQ} = \frac{6.0}{4.0} = 1.5$$

$$\frac{TR}{PR} = \frac{7.5}{5.0} = 1.5$$

$$\frac{RS}{QR} = \frac{9.0}{6.0} = 1.5$$

Since the corresponding sides are proportional, the triangles are similar.
P and T are the vertices where the two shorter sides in each triangle meet,
so ∠P corresponds to ∠T.
Similarly, ∠Q corresponds to ∠S and ∠TRS corresponds to ∠QRP.
So, ΔPQR ~ ΔTSR

In *Example 1*, we can say that ΔTSR is an enlargement of ΔPQR
with a scale factor of 1.5.
Or, since $1.5 = \frac{3}{2}$, we can also say that ΔPQR is a reduction of ΔTSR
with a scale factor of $\frac{2}{3}$.
We can use the properties of similar triangles to solve problems
that involve scale diagrams.
These problems involve lengths that cannot be measured directly.

Example 2   **Using Similar Triangles to Determine a Length**

At a certain time of day, a person who is 1.8 m tall has a shadow 1.3 m long. At the same time, the shadow of a totem pole is 6 m long. The sun's rays intersect the ground at equal angles. How tall is the totem pole, to the nearest tenth of a metre?

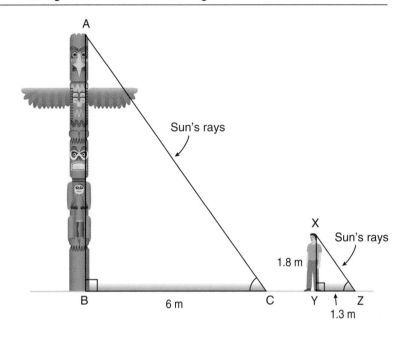

▶ *A Solution*

The sun's rays form two triangles with the totem pole, the person, and their shadows.

If we can show the triangles are similar, we can use a proportion to determine the height of the totem pole.

Assume both the totem pole and the person are perpendicular to the ground, so:

$\angle B = \angle Y = 90°$

The sun's rays make equal angles with the ground, so: $\angle C = \angle Z$

Since two pairs of corresponding angles are equal, the angles in the third pair must also be equal because the sum of the angles in each triangle is 180°.

So, $\angle A = \angle X$

Since 3 pairs of corresponding angles are equal, $\triangle ABC \sim \triangle XYZ$

So, $\triangle ABC$ is an enlargement of $\triangle XYZ$ with a scale factor of $\frac{6}{1.3}$.

Write a proportion that includes the unknown height of the totem pole, AB.

$\quad \dfrac{AB}{XY} = \dfrac{6}{1.3}$ \qquad Substitute XY = 1.8.

$\quad \dfrac{AB}{1.8} = \dfrac{6}{1.3}$ \qquad To solve for AB, multiply each side by 1.8.

$1.8 \times \dfrac{AB}{1.8} = \dfrac{6}{1.3} \times 1.8$

$\quad\quad AB = \dfrac{6 \times 1.8}{1.3}$

$\quad\quad\quad \doteq 8.308$

The height of the totem pole is about 8.3 m.

Example 3 | **Using Overlapping Similar Triangles to Determine a Length**

A surveyor wants to determine the width of a lake at two points on opposite sides of the lake. She measures distances and angles on land, then sketches this diagram. How can the surveyor determine the length HN to the nearest metre?

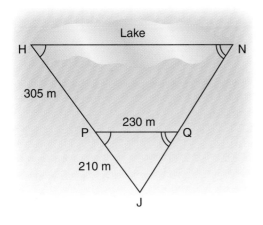

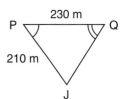

▶ *A Solution*

Identify the two triangles, then draw them separately.
Consider △HNJ and △PQJ. From the diagram:

$\angle NHJ = \angle QPJ$

$\angle HNJ = \angle PQJ$

$\angle J$ is the common angle to both triangles.

Since 3 pairs of corresponding angles are equal,

△HNJ ∼ △PQJ

Two corresponding sides are:

HJ = 305 m + 210 m   and   PJ = 210 m
   = 515 m

So, △HNJ is an enlargement of △PQJ

with a scale factor of $\dfrac{515}{210}$.

Write a proportion that includes the unknown length HN.

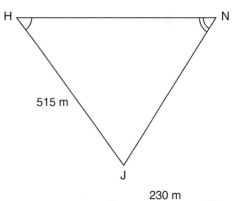

$\dfrac{HN}{PQ} = \dfrac{515}{210}$ Substitute PQ = 230.

$\dfrac{HN}{230} = \dfrac{515}{210}$ To solve for HN, multiply each side by 230.

$230 \times \dfrac{HN}{230} = \dfrac{515}{210} \times 230$

$HN = \dfrac{515 \times 230}{210}$

$\doteq 564.0476$

The width of the lake, HN, is about 564 m.

Example 4   **Using Triangles Meeting at a Vertex to Determine a Length**

A surveyor used this scale diagram to determine the width of a river. The measurements he made and the equal angles are shown. What is the width, AB, to the nearest tenth of a metre?

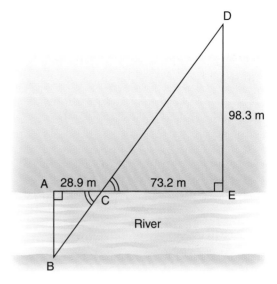

▶ **A Solution**

Consider △ABC and △EDC.
From the diagram:
∠A = ∠E
∠B = ∠D
∠ACB = ∠ECD
Since 3 pairs of corresponding angles are equal, △ABC ~ △EDC
Two corresponding sides are:
AC = 28.9 m   and   EC = 73.2 m
So, △ABC is a reduction of △EDC with a scale factor of $\frac{28.9}{73.2}$.

Write a proportion that includes the unknown length AB.

$\dfrac{AB}{ED} = \dfrac{28.9}{73.2}$ Substitute ED = 98.3.

$\dfrac{AB}{98.3} = \dfrac{28.9}{73.2}$ To solve for AB, multiply each side by 98.3.

$98.3 \times \dfrac{AB}{98.3} = \dfrac{28.9}{73.2} \times 98.3$

$AB = \dfrac{28.9 \times 98.3}{73.2}$

$\doteq 38.8097$

The width of the river, AB, is about 38.8 m.

Discuss the ideas

1. How can you tell that two triangles are similar?

2. When two triangles are similar, how do you identify the corresponding sides?

3. Suppose you know that two triangles are similar. How do you write the proportion to determine the length of an unknown side?

Check

4. Which triangles in each pair are similar? How do you know?

a)

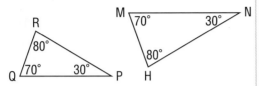

b)

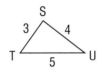

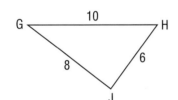

c)

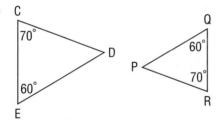

d)

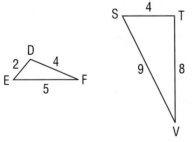

5. In each diagram, identify two similar triangles. Explain why they are similar.

a)

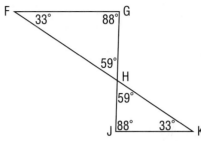

b)

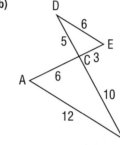

c)

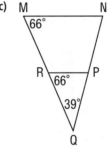

Apply

6. Determine the length of AB in each pair of similar triangles.

a)

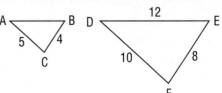

b)

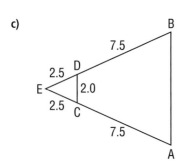

c)

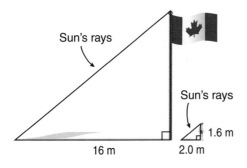

7. Jaquie is 1.6 m tall. When her shadow is 2.0 m long, the shadow of the school's flagpole is 16 m long. How tall is the flagpole, to the nearest tenth of a metre?

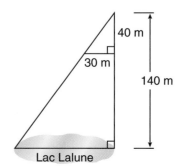

8. Assessment Focus Work with a partner. Use the method described in question 7. Choose an object whose height you cannot measure directly.
a) Draw a labelled diagram.
b) Indicate which triangles are similar.
c) Determine the height of the object. Show your work.

9. Tina wants to estimate the heights of two trees. For each tree, she stands so that one end of her shadow coincides with one end of the shadow of the tree. Tina's friend measures the lengths of her shadow and the tree's shadow. Tina is 1.7 m tall.

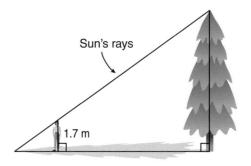

a) Tina's shadow is 2.4 m and the first tree's shadow is 10.8 m. What is the height of the tree?
b) Tina's shadow is 0.8 m and the second tree's shadow is 12.8 m. What is the height of the tree?

10. When the shadow of a building is 16 m long, a 4-m fence post casts a shadow 3 m long.
a) Sketch a diagram.
b) How tall is the building?

11. This scale diagram shows the measurements a surveyor made to determine the length of Lac Lalune. What is this length? How do you know?

12. To help calculate the distance PQ across a river, Emil drew the diagram below based on measurements he made. What is the distance across the river?

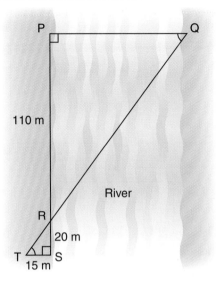

Take It Further

13. Phillipe places a mirror M on the ground 6.0 m from a tree. When he is 1.7 m from the mirror, he can see the top of the tree in the mirror. His eyes are 1.5 m above the ground. The diagram below shows the equal angles. How can you use similar triangles to determine the height of the tree to the nearest tenth of a metre?

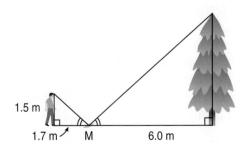

14. The foot of a ladder is 3 m from the base of a wall. The ladder just touches the top of a 1.4-m fence that is 2.4 m from the wall. How high up the wall does the ladder reach? How do you know?

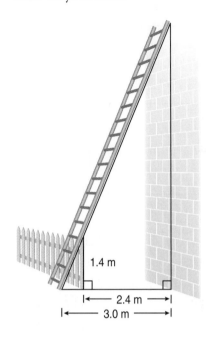

15. In the diagram below, how high are the two supports x and y for the conveyor belt?

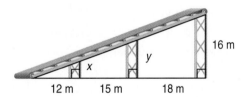

Reflect

How do the properties of similar triangles help you to determine distances that cannot be measured directly? Include an example in your explanation.

7.1 **1.** A photo of a gymnast is to be enlarged. The dimensions of the photo are 15 cm by 10 cm. What are the dimensions of the enlargement with a scale factor of $\frac{7}{5}$?

2. A computer chip has dimensions 15 mm by 8 mm. Here is a scale drawing of the chip.

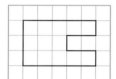

a) Determine the scale factor of the diagram.
b) Draw a scale diagram of the chip with a scale factor of 8.

7.2 **3.** a) Copy this polygon on 1-cm grid paper.

b) Draw a scale diagram of the polygon with a scale factor of $\frac{3}{5}$. Show any calculations you made.

4. This top view of a swimming pool is drawn on 0.5-cm grid paper. The dimensions of the pool are 60 m by 40 m. Determine the scale factor of the reduction as a fraction or a decimal.

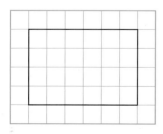

7.3 **5.** These quadrilaterals have corresponding angles equal.

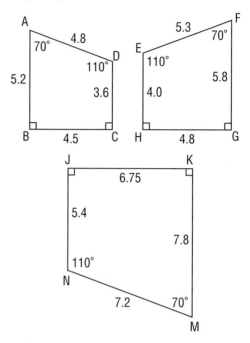

a) Are any of these quadrilaterals similar? Justify your answer.
b) Choose one quadrilateral. Draw a similar quadrilateral. How do you know the quadrilaterals are similar?

6. A window has the shape of a hexagon.

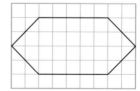

Draw a hexagon that is similar to this hexagon. Explain how you know the hexagons are similar.

7.4 **7.** A tree casts a shadow 8 m long. At the same time a 2-m wall casts a shadow 1.6 m long.
a) Sketch a diagram.
b) What is the height of the tree?

Reflections and Line Symmetry

How can you use this photograph to show what you know about line symmetry?

Investigate

Your teacher will give you a large copy of the shapes below.

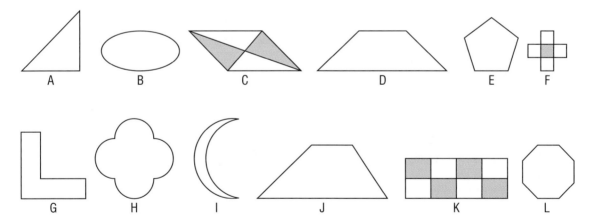

Which shapes have the same number of lines of symmetry?

Sort the shapes according to the number of lines of symmetry they have.

Which shapes do not have line symmetry? How can you tell?

Share your sorting with another pair of students.

Compare strategies for identifying the lines of symmetry.

The pentagon ABCDE has one line of symmetry AG, because AG divides the pentagon ABCDE into two congruent parts: polygon ABCG is congruent to polygon AEDG.

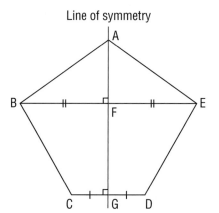

Line of symmetry

Also, each point on one side of the line of symmetry has a corresponding point on the other side of the line. These two points are the same distance, or *equidistant* from the line of symmetry: points B and E correspond, BF = FE, and BE ⊥ AG.

A line of symmetry is also called a *line of reflection*. If a mirror is placed along one side of a shape, the reflection image and the original shape together form one larger shape. The line of reflection is a line of symmetry of this larger shape.

Original shape

Original shape and its reflection image

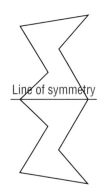

Line of symmetry

Example 1   **Identifying Lines of Symmetry in Tessellations**

Identify the lines of symmetry in each tessellation.

a)

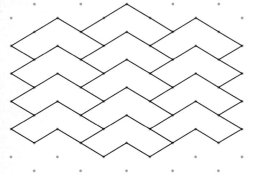

b)

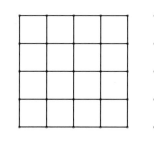

► **A Solution**

a) The red line is the line of symmetry for this tessellation. Each point on one side of the line has a corresponding point on the other side. The pattern on one side of the line of symmetry is a mirror image of the pattern on the other side.

b) This tessellation has 4 lines of symmetry. For each line, a point on one side of the line has a matching point on the other side. And, the pattern on one side of the line is a mirror image of the pattern on the other side.

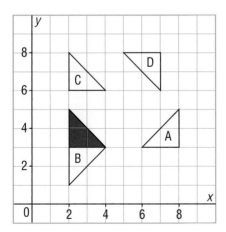

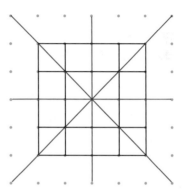

Two shapes may be related by a line of reflection.

Example 2	**Identifying Shapes Related by a Line of Reflection**

Identify the triangles that are related to the red triangle by a line of reflection. Describe the position of each line of symmetry.

▶ A Solution

Triangle A is the reflection image of the red triangle in the blue line through 5 on the *x*-axis.
Triangle B is the reflection image of the red triangle in the red line through 3 on the *y*-axis.
Triangle C is not a reflection image of the red triangle.
Triangle D is the reflection image of the red triangle in the green line through the points $(9, 1)$ and $(1, 9)$.

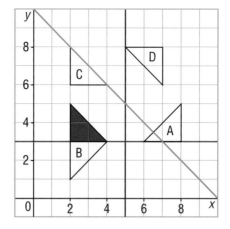

We can use a coordinate grid to draw shapes and their reflection images.

Example 3   Completing a Shape Given its Line of Symmetry

Quadrilateral ABCD is part of a larger shape.
- Draw the image of ABCD after each reflection below.
- Write the coordinates of the larger shape formed by ABCD and its image.
- Describe the larger shape and its symmetry.
a) a reflection in the horizontal line through 2 on the *y*-axis
b) a reflection in the vertical line through 6 on the *x*-axis
c) a reflection in an oblique line through $(0, 0)$ and $(6, 6)$

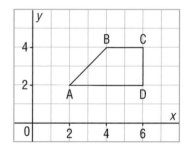

▶ A Solution

The red line is the line of reflection. Each image point is the same distance from this line as the corresponding original point.

a)

Point	Image
A(2, 2)	A(2, 2)
B(4, 4)	B′(4, 0)
C(6, 4)	C′(6, 0)
D(6, 2)	D(6, 2)

The larger shape ABCC′B′ has coordinates: A(2, 2), B(4, 4), C(6, 4), C′(6, 0), B′(4, 0)
This shape is a pentagon with line symmetry. The line of symmetry is the red line.

b)

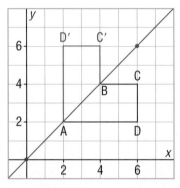

Point	Image
A(2, 2)	A′(10, 2)
B(4, 4)	B′(8, 4)
C(6, 4)	C(6, 4)
D(6, 2)	D(6, 2)

The larger shape ABB′A′ has coordinates: A(2, 2), B(4, 4), B′(8, 4), A′(10, 2)
This shape is an isosceles trapezoid with line symmetry. The line of symmetry is the red line.

c)

Point	Image
A(2, 2)	A(2, 2)
B(4, 4)	B(4, 4)
C(6, 4)	C′(4, 6)
D(6, 2)	D′(2, 6)

The larger shape AD′C′BCD has coordinates: A(2, 2), D′(2, 6), C′(4, 6), B(4, 4), C(6, 4), D(6, 2)
This shape is a concave hexagon with line symmetry. The line of symmetry is the red line.

Discuss the ideas

1. How do you identify whether a shape has a line of symmetry?

2. How are a line of reflection and a line of symmetry related?

Practice

Check

3. You may have seen these hazardous substance warning symbols in the science lab. Which symbols have line symmetry? How many lines of symmetry?

a)

b)

c)

d)

e)

f)

Apply

4. Identify the lines of symmetry in each tessellation.

a)

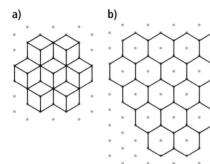

b)

5. Copy each polygon on grid paper. It is one-half of a shape. Use the red line as a line of symmetry to complete the shape by drawing its other half. Label the shape with the coordinates of its vertices.

a)

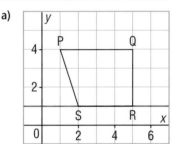

b)

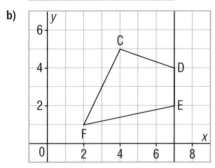

c)

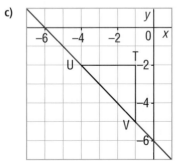

6. State the number of lines of symmetry in each design.

a) a tessellation created by M.C. Escher

b) a Haida button blanket

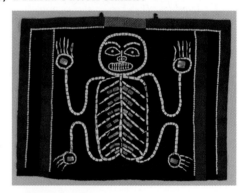

7. **Assessment Focus**

a) Draw a triangle on a grid.

b) Choose one side of the triangle as a line of reflection.

   i) Draw the reflection image.

   ii) Label the vertices of the shape formed by the original triangle and its image.

   iii) Write the coordinates of each vertex.

   iv) How many lines of symmetry does the shape have?

c) Repeat part b for each of the other two sides of the triangle. Do you always get the same shape? Explain.

d) Repeat parts a to c for different types of triangles.

e) Which types of triangle always produce a shape that is a quadrilateral with line symmetry? Justify your answer.

8. Quadrilateral PQRS is part of a larger shape.

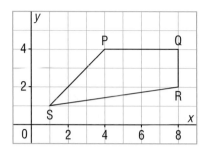

After each reflection below:
- Draw the image of PQRS.
- Write the coordinates of the larger shape formed by PQRS and its image.
- Describe the larger shape and its symmetry.

a) a reflection in the horizontal line through 4 on the y-axis

b) a reflection in the vertical line through 8 on the x-axis

c) a reflection in the oblique line through $(1, 1)$ and $(4, 4)$

9. a) Graph these points on grid paper:
A$(-3, 0)$, B$(-1, 1)$, C$(0, 3)$,
D$(1, 1)$, E$(3, 0)$.
Join the points to form polygon ABCDE.

b) Reflect the polygon in the x-axis. Draw and label its image.

c) Write the coordinates of the shape formed by the polygon and its image.

d) How many lines of symmetry does this shape have? How do you know?

10. Identify the pentagons that are related to the blue pentagon by a line of reflection. Describe the position of each line of symmetry.

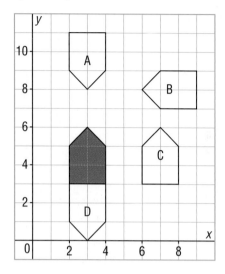

Take It Further

11. a) On a grid, plot the points P$(2, 2)$, Q$(6, 2)$, and R$(4, 4)$. Join the points to form $\triangle$PQR.

b) Reflect $\triangle$PQR in the line through the points $(0, 4)$ and $(4, 0)$. Draw the reflection image.

c) Reflect $\triangle$PQR in the line through the points $(0, -4)$ and $(4, 0)$. Draw the reflection image.

d) Reflect $\triangle$PQR in the x-axis. Draw the reflection image.

e) Look at the shape formed by the triangle and all its images. How many lines of symmetry does this shape have?

Reflect

When you see two shapes on a grid, how can you tell if they are related by a line of reflection?

Include examples of shapes that are related and are not related this way.

GAME

Make Your Own Kaleidoscope

The kaleidoscope was invented in 1816. It uses mirrors placed at different angles to produce patterns with symmetry.

To make a simple kaleidoscope, use masking tape to join two mirrors so they stand at an angle.

Place your mirrors on the arms of each angle below.
Sketch and describe what you see.
Include any lines of symmetry in your sketch.

You will need

- 2 small rectangular mirrors
- masking tape

1.

2.

3.

4.

5.

6.

7.6 Rotations and Rotational Symmetry

FOCUS

- Draw and classify shapes with rotational symmetry.

Look at these photographs.
How are the windmills the same?
How are they different?

Investigate

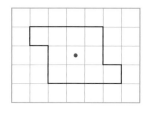

You will need a protractor, a sharp pencil, tracing paper, and grid paper or isometric dot paper.

➤ Each of you chooses one of these shapes and copies it on grid paper or dot paper.

 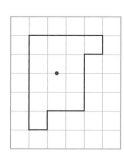

➤ Trace your shape and place the tracing to coincide with the shape.
Place a pencil point on the red dot.
Rotate the tracing, counting the number of times the tracing coincides with the original shape, until you make a complete turn.

➤ Repeat the rotation. This time, measure and record the angle you turned the tracing through each time.

➤ Work together to draw a shape that coincides with itself 4 times as you rotate it.

Share your results with another group.
What is the relationship between the number of times the shape coincided with itself and the angle you turned it through each time?

A tracing of this shape is rotated about its centre. We draw a line segment to help identify the angle the shape turned through before it coincided with itself.

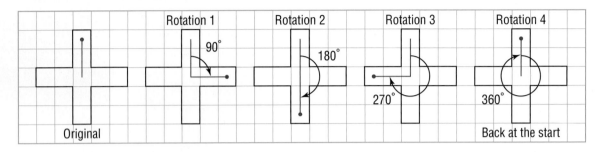

The shape coincided with itself 4 times in one complete turn; that is, during a rotation of 360°.

A shape has **rotational symmetry** when it coincides with itself after a rotation of less than 360° about its centre.
The number of times the shape coincides with itself, during a rotation of 360°, is the **order of rotation.** The shape above has *rotational symmetry of order* 4.

For each match, the shape rotated through 90°.
We say the **angle of rotation symmetry** is 90°. This is $\frac{360°}{4}$.

> In general, for rotational symmetry:
> the angle of rotation symmetry $= \dfrac{360°}{\text{the order of rotation}}$

A shape that requires a rotation of 360° to return to its original position does not have rotational symmetry. A shape cannot have rotational symmetry of order 1.

Example 1   Identifying Shapes with Rotational Symmetry

Determine which hexagons below have rotational symmetry.
State the order of rotation and the angle of rotation symmetry.

a)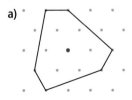

b)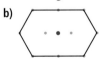

c)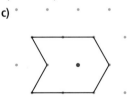

► *A Solution*

For each hexagon:
- Join one vertex to the red dot.
- Trace the hexagon.
- Rotate the tracing about the red dot and record the order of rotation.
- Calculate the angle of rotation symmetry.

a) The order of rotation is 3.
The angle of rotation symmetry is: $\dfrac{360°}{3} = 120°$

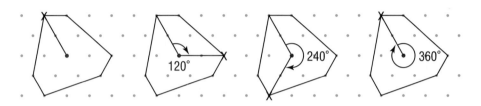

b) The order of rotation is 2.
The angle of rotation symmetry is: $\dfrac{360°}{2} = 180°$

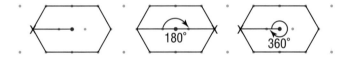

c) This hexagon is rotated one complete turn
before it coincides with itself.
It does not have rotational symmetry.

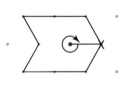

A rotation is another type of transformation.
We use a square grid to draw rotation images after a rotation
of 90°, or any multiple of 90°, such as 180° and 270°.
We use isometric dot paper to draw rotation images after a rotation
of 60°, or any multiple of 60°, such as 120° and 180°.

Example 2 **Drawing Rotation Images**

a) Rotate pentagon ABCDE
   90° clockwise about vertex E.
   Draw the rotation image.

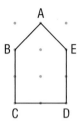

b) Rotate trapezoid FGHJ
   120° counterclockwise
   about vertex F.
   Draw the rotation image.

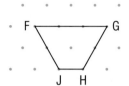

▶ *A Solution*

Trace each shape and label the vertices on the tracing.

a) Rotate pentagon ABCDE 90°
   clockwise about E. Side ED
   moves from being vertical to
   being horizontal.

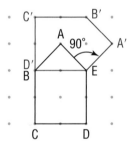

b) Rotate trapezoid FGHJ
   120° counterclockwise
   about F. The angle between
   FG and FG′ is 120°.

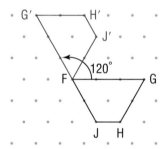

Example 3 **Identifying Symmetry after Rotations**

a) Rotate rectangle ABCD:
   i) 90° clockwise about vertex A
   ii) 180° clockwise about vertex A
   iii) 270° clockwise about vertex A
   Draw and label each rotation image.
b) Look at the shape formed by the rectangle and all its images.
   Identify any rotational symmetry in this shape.

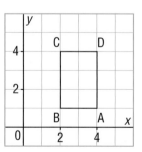

▶ *A Solution*

a) Trace rectangle ABCD and label the vertices.

   i) Rotate ABCD 90° clockwise about A.
   Vertical side AD becomes horizontal side AG.
   The rotation image is AEFG.

   ii) Rotate ABCD 180° clockwise about A.
   Vertical side AD becomes vertical side AK.
   The rotation image is AHJK.

   iii) Rotate ABCD 270° clockwise about A.
   Vertical side AD becomes horizontal side AP.
   The rotation image is AMNP.

b) The resulting shape BCDEFGHJKMNP has rotational symmetry of order 4 about point A.

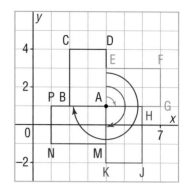

Discuss the ideas

1. How do you determine whether a shape has rotational symmetry?

2. How can you determine:
   a) the order of rotational symmetry?
   b) the angle of rotation symmetry?

3. How is rotational symmetry related to rotation images?

Practice

Check

4. What is the angle of rotation symmetry for a shape with each order of rotational symmetry?
   a) 3   **b)** 5   **c)** 9   **d)** 12

5. What is the order of rotational symmetry for each angle of rotation symmetry?
   a) 60°   **b)** 20°   **c)** 45°   **d)** 36°

6. What is the order of rotational symmetry and angle of rotation symmetry for each regular polygon?
   a) an equilateral triangle

   b) a regular pentagon

c) a square

d) a regular octagon

Apply

7. Does each picture have rotational symmetry? If it does, state the order and the angle of rotation symmetry.

a)

b)

8. Does each shape have rotational symmetry about the red dot? If it does, state the order and the angle of rotation symmetry.

a)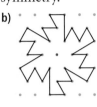
b)

9. Copy each shape on grid paper. Draw the rotation image after each given rotation.

a) 90° clockwise about E
b) 180° about M

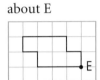

c) 270° counterclockwise about Y

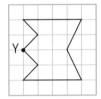

10. Copy each shape on isometric dot paper. Draw the rotation image after each given rotation.

a) 60° clockwise about G

b) 120° counterclockwise about B

11. Identify and describe any rotational symmetry in each design.

a)

b)

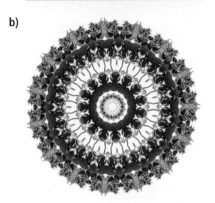

12. This octagon is part of a larger shape that is to be completed by a rotation of 180° about the origin.

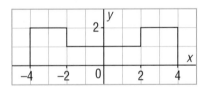

a) On a coordinate grid, draw the octagon and its image.

b) Outline the shape formed by the octagon and its image. Describe any rotational symmetry in this shape. Explain why you think the symmetry occurred.

13. Assessment Focus Rotate each shape.

a) rectangle ABCD

   i) 180° about vertex A

   ii) 180° about centre E

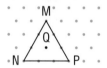

b) square FGHJ counterclockwise through

   i) 90° about vertex F

   ii) 90° about centre K

c) equilateral triangle MNP clockwise through

   i) 120° about vertex M

   ii) 120° about centre Q

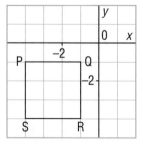

d) How are the images in each of parts a, b, and c the same? How are they different? Explain what you notice.

14. a) Rotate square PQRS clockwise about vertex P through:

   i) 90°   ii) 180°   iii) 270°

Draw and label each rotation image.

b) Outline the shape formed by the square and all its images. Identify any rotational symmetry. Explain what you notice.

15. Triangle ABC is part of a larger shape that is to be completed by three rotations.

a) Rotate ΔABC clockwise about vertex C through: i) 90° ii) 180° iii) 270° Draw and label each rotation image.

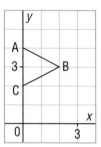

b) List the coordinates of the vertices of the larger shape formed by the triangle and its images. Describe any rotational symmetry.

Take It Further

16. a) Draw a polygon on a coordinate grid. Choose an angle of rotation and a centre of rotation to complete a larger polygon with order of rotation: i) 2 ii) 4 List the coordinates of the centre of rotation, and the vertices of the larger polygon.

b) Draw a polygon on isometric dot paper. Choose an angle of rotation and a centre of rotation to complete a larger polygon with order of rotation: i) 3 ii) 6

Reflect

How do you decide if a given shape has rotational symmetry?

If it does, how do you determine the order of rotation and the angle of rotation symmetry?

Include an example in your explanation.

7.7 Identifying Types of Symmetry on the Cartesian Plane

FOCUS

• Identify and classify line and rotational symmetry.

What symmetry do you see in each picture?

Investigate

③

You will need grid paper and tracing paper.

➤ Plot these points on a coordinate grid: A(1, 3), B(3, 1), and C(5, 5)
  Join the points to form △ABC.
➤ Each of you chooses one of these transformations:
  • a translation 2 units right and 2 units down
  • a rotation of 180° about vertex C
  • a reflection in a line through AB
  Draw the image for the transformation you chose.
  Record the coordinates of each vertex on the image.
  On a separate piece of paper, record any symmetry in the triangle and its image.
➤ Trade grids with a member of your group.
  Identify any symmetry in the triangle and its image.

Compare the types of symmetry you found.
Did any grid show both rotational symmetry and line symmetry?
Explain why both types of symmetry occurred.
Which grid showed only one type of symmetry?

Connect

On this grid, rectangle A has been rotated 180° about E(−1, 2) to produce its image, rectangle B.

We can extend our meaning of line symmetry to relate the two rectangles.

The line through −1 on the *x*-axis is a line of symmetry for the two rectangles.

Each point on rectangle A has a corresponding point on rectangle B.

These points are equidistant from the line of symmetry.

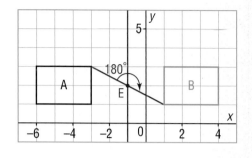

When a shape and its transformation image are drawn, the resulting diagram may show:

- no symmetry
- line symmetry
- rotational symmetry
- both line symmetry and rotational symmetry

Example 1   Determining whether Shapes Are Related by Symmetry

For each pair of rectangles ABCD and EFGH, determine whether they are related by symmetry.

a)

b)

c)

► *A Solution*

a) There is no line on which a mirror can be placed so that one rectangle is the reflection image of the other. So, the rectangles are not related by line symmetry. Trace the rectangles. Use guess and check to determine if a centre of rotation exists. When ABCD is rotated 180° about the point S(0, 3), ABCD coincides with GHEF. So, the rectangles are related by rotational symmetry of order 2 about S(0, 3).

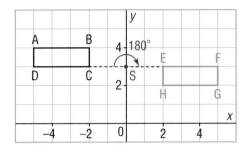

b) Each point on ABCD has a corresponding point on EFGH. These points are equidistant from the *x*-axis. So, the two rectangles are related by line symmetry; the *x*-axis is the line of symmetry. Trace the rectangles. Use guess and check to determine if a centre of rotation exists. When a tracing of ABCD is rotated 180° about the point P(−2.5, 0), ABCD coincides with GHEF. So, the two rectangles are related by rotational symmetry.

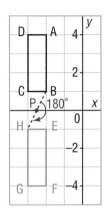

c) When ABCD is rotated 90° clockwise about point J(−5, 4), ABCD coincides with FGHE. Then, the polygon formed by both rectangles together has rotational symmetry of order 4 about point J. So, the two rectangles are related by rotational symmetry.

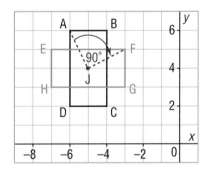

| **Example 2** | **Identifying Symmetry in a Shape and Its Transformation Image** |

Draw the image of rectangle ABCD after each transformation. Write the coordinates of each vertex and its image. Identify and describe the type of symmetry that results.

a) a rotation of 180° about the origin
b) a reflection in the *x*-axis
c) a translation 4 units right and 1 unit down

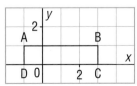

▶ **Solution**

a) Use tracing paper to rotate ABCD 180° about the origin.

Point	Image
A(−1, 1)	A′(1, −1)
B(3, 1)	B′(−3, −1)
C(3, 0)	C′(−3, 0)
D(−1, 0)	D′(1, 0)

The octagon ABCD′A′B′C′D, formed by both rectangles together, has rotational symmetry of order 2 about the origin, and no line symmetry.

b) Reflect ABCD in the *x*-axis.

Point	Image
A(−1, 1)	A′(−1, −1)
B(3, 1)	B′(3, −1)
C(3, 0)	C(3, 0)
D(−1, 0)	D(−1, 0)

The rectangle ABB′A′, formed by both rectangles, has rotational symmetry of order 2 about the point (1, 0). It also has 2 lines of symmetry: the *x*-axis and the vertical line through 1 on the *x*-axis.

c) Translate ABCD 4 units right and 1 unit down.

Point	Image
A(−1, 1)	A′(3, 0)
B(3, 1)	B′(7, 0)
C(3, 0)	C′(7, −1)
D(−1, 0)	D′(3, −1)

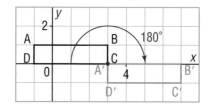

The two rectangles do not form a shape; but they have a common vertex at C (or A′). The two rectangles are related by rotational symmetry of order 2 about the point C(3, 0). There is no line of symmetry relating the rectangles.

In *Example 2,* we could write the translation 4 units right and 1 unit down in a shorter form as R4, D1. In this shorter form, a translation of 7 units left and 2 units up would be written as L7, U2.

Example 3 | **Identifying Symmetry in Shapes and their Translation Images**

Draw the image of pentagon PQRST
after each translation below.
Label the vertices of the pentagon and its image,
and list their coordinates.
If each diagram has symmetry, describe it.
If each diagram does not have symmetry,
explain how you know.

a) a translation L2   **b)** a translation L2, D3

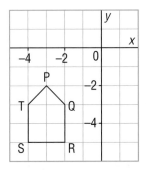

▶ *A Solution*

a) Translate each vertex of pentagon PQRST 2 units left.

Point	Image
P(−3, −2)	P′(−5, −2)
Q(−2, −3)	T(−4, −3)
R(−2, −5)	S(−4, −5)
S(−4, −5)	S′(−6, −5)
T(−4, −3)	T′(−6, −3)

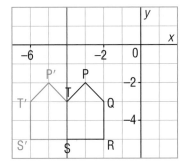

The diagram has line symmetry because the vertical line
through ST is a line of reflection.
The diagram does not have rotational symmetry because there is no point
about which it can be rotated so that it coincides with itself.

b) Translate each vertex of pentagon PQRST 2 units left and 3 units down.

Point	Image
P(−3, −2)	P′(−5, −5)
Q(−2, −3)	Q′(−4, −6)
R(−2, −5)	R′(−4, −8)
S(−4, −5)	S′(−6, −8)
T(−4, −3)	T′(−6, −6)

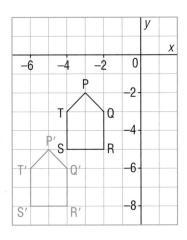

The diagram does not have line symmetry because
there is no line on which a mirror can be placed so
that one pentagon is the reflection image of the other.
The diagram does not have rotational symmetry
because there is no point about which it can be
rotated so that it coincides with itself.

1. How can you tell if two shapes are related by line symmetry?

2. How can you tell if two shapes are related by rotational symmetry?

Practice

Check

3. Describe the rotational symmetry and line symmetry of each shape.

a) a parallelogram

b) a rhombus

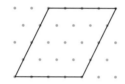

c) an isosceles trapezoid

d) a kite

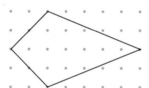

4. Describe the rotational symmetry and line symmetry of each wheel cover. On a copy of the wheel covers, mark the centre of rotation and the line of reflection.

a)

b)

c)

d)

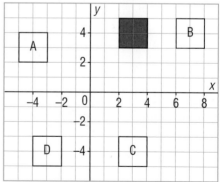

5. Describe the symmetry of each face of a die. Copy each face. Mark the centre of rotation and the lines of symmetry.

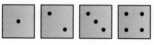

Apply

6. Look at the squares below.

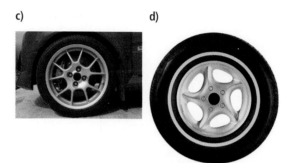

Which of squares A, B, C, and D are related to the red square:

a) by rotational symmetry about the origin?

b) by line symmetry?

7. For each diagram, determine whether the two polygons are related by line symmetry, by rotational symmetry about the origin, or by both.

a)

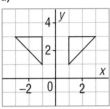

b)

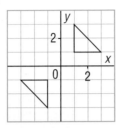

c)

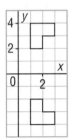

d)

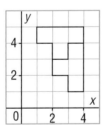

8. For each diagram, determine whether the two octagons are related by line symmetry, by rotational symmetry, by both types of symmetry, or by neither.

a)

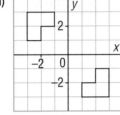

b)

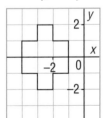

9. Triangle F′G′H′ is the image of ΔFGH after a rotation about the origin. Identify any symmetry.

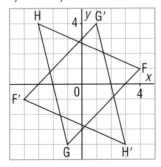

10. Identify and describe the types of symmetry in each piece of artwork.

a)

b)

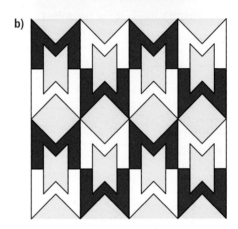

11. Copy each shape on grid paper.
   • Draw the image after the translation given.
   • Label each vertex with its coordinates.
   • Does each diagram have line and rotational symmetry?
     If your answer is yes, describe the symmetry.
     If your answer is no, describe how you know.

a) 6 units up

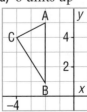

b) 4 units right

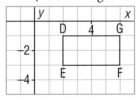

12. Assessment Focus

  a) On a grid, draw ΔCDE with vertices
     C(2, 3), D(−2, −1), and E(3, −2).

  b) Draw the translation image ΔC'D'E'
     after the translation R1, U3.

  c) Label all the vertices with their ordered pairs.

  d) Explain why the translation does not
     result in line or rotational symmetry.

  e) Find a translation that does result in one
     type of symmetry. Draw the image.
     How do you know the diagram has
     symmetry?

  Show your work.

13. a) Draw the image of parallelogram CDEF
     after each transformation below.

  b) The parallelogram and its image form a
     diagram. If each diagram has symmetry,
     describe it. If each diagram does not have
     symmetry, describe how you know.

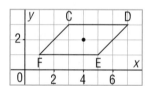

  i) a rotation of 90° clockwise about (4, 2)

  ii) a reflection in the horizontal line
      through 1 on the *y*-axis

  iii) a translation R4

14. The digits 0 to 9 on a digital clock are made
up from horizontal and vertical segments.

  a) Sketch each digit on dot paper. Identify
     any symmetry it has.

  b) For each digit with line symmetry, plot a
     part of the digit on grid paper and draw a
     line of symmetry so that the digit can be
     completed by a reflection.

  c) For each digit with rotational symmetry,
     plot a part of the digit on grid paper.
     Locate the point about which the digit
     can be completed by a rotation.

  d) Is there a pair of digits that are related by
     line or rotational symmetry? Justify your
     answer by plotting the digits on a
     Cartesian plane.

15. This hexagon is part
of a larger shape that
is completed by
rotating the hexagon
180° about the origin.

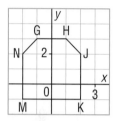

  a) Draw the rotation image.

  b) List the coordinates of the vertices of the
     larger shape.

  c) Describe the symmetry in the larger
     shape.

Take It Further

16. The 24-hour clock represents midnight as
00:00 and three-thirty A.M. as 03:30. The time
03:30 has line symmetry with a horizontal
line of reflection. List as many times from
midnight onward that have line symmetry,
rotational symmetry, or both. Describe the
symmetry for each time you find.

Reflect

When you see a shape and its transformation image on a grid, how do you identify
line symmetry and rotational symmetry? Include examples in your explanation.

Scale Diagrams

For an enlargement or reduction, the scale factor is: $\dfrac{\text{Length on scale diagram}}{\text{Length on original diagram}}$

An enlargement has a scale factor > 1. A reduction has a scale factor < 1.

Similar Polygons

Similar polygons are related by an enlargement or a reduction. When two polygons are similar:

▶ their corresponding angles are equal:

$\angle A = \angle E; \angle B = \angle F; \angle C = \angle G; \angle D = \angle H$

and

▶ their corresponding sides are proportional:

$$\dfrac{AB}{EF} = \dfrac{BC}{FG} = \dfrac{CD}{GH} = \dfrac{DA}{HE}$$

Any of the ratios $\dfrac{AB}{EF}, \dfrac{BC}{FG}, \dfrac{CD}{GH}$, and $\dfrac{DA}{HE}$ is the scale factor.

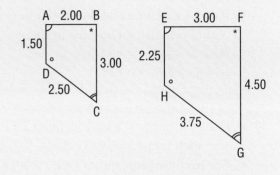

Similar Triangles

When we check whether two triangles are similar:

▶ their corresponding angles must be equal:

$\angle P = \angle S$ and $\angle Q = \angle T$ and $\angle R = \angle U$

or

▶ their corresponding sides must be proportional:

$$\dfrac{PQ}{ST} = \dfrac{QR}{TU} = \dfrac{PR}{SU}$$

Any of the ratios $\dfrac{PQ}{ST}, \dfrac{QR}{TU}$, and $\dfrac{PR}{SU}$ is the scale factor.

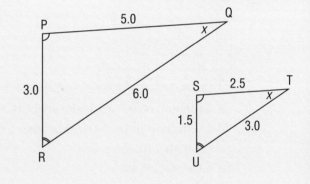

Line Symmetry

A shape has line symmetry when a line divides the shape into two congruent parts so that one part is the image of the other part after a reflection in the line of symmetry.

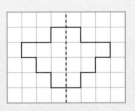

Rotational Symmetry

A shape has rotational symmetry when it coincides with itself after a rotation of less than 360° about its centre. The number of times the shape coincides with itself is the order of rotation.

The angle of rotation symmetry $= \dfrac{360°}{\text{the order of rotation}}$

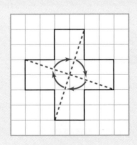

Review

1. This photo of participants in the Arctic Winter Games is to be enlarged.

Measure the photo. What are the dimensions of the enlargement for each scale factor?

a) 3   b) 2.5   c) $\frac{3}{2}$ d) $\frac{21}{5}$

2. Draw this pentagon on 1-cm grid paper. Then draw an enlargement of the shape with a scale factor of 2.5.

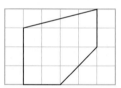

3. A full-size pool table has dimensions approximately 270 cm by 138 cm. A model of a pool table has dimensions 180 cm by 92 cm.

a) What is the scale factor for this reduction?

b) A standard-size pool cue is about 144 cm long. What is the length of a model of this pool cue with the scale factor from part a?

4. Here is a scale diagram of a ramp. The height of the ramp is 1.8 m. Measure the lengths on the scale diagram. What is the length of the ramp?

5. Gina plans to build a triangular dog run against one side of a dog house. Here is a scale diagram of the run. The wall of the dog house is 2 m long. Calculate the lengths of the other two sides of the dog run.

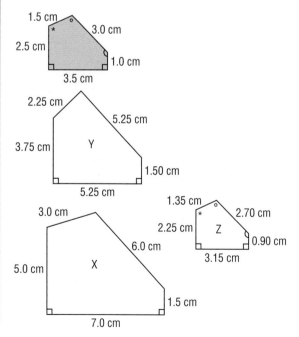

Wall of dog house

6. Which pentagon is similar to the red pentagon? Justify your answer.

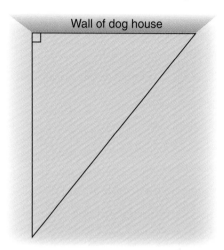

1.5 cm   3.0 cm
2.5 cm   1.0 cm
3.5 cm

2.25 cm   5.25 cm
3.75 cm   Y
1.50 cm
5.25 cm

1.35 cm   2.70 cm
2.25 cm   Z   0.90 cm
3.15 cm

3.0 cm
5.0 cm   X   6.0 cm
1.5 cm
7.0 cm

7. These two courtyards are similar.

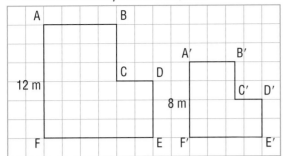

Determine each length.
a) BC   b) B'C'   c) A'B'

8. These two quadrilaterals are similar.

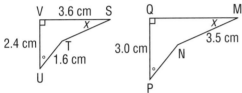

Calculate the length of: **a)** PN **b)** TS

7.4

9. To determine the distance, *d*, across a pond, Ari uses this diagram. What is the distance across the pond?

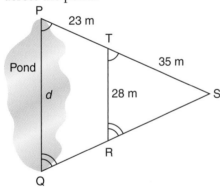

10. This scale diagram shows a surveyor's measurements taken to determine the distance across a river. What is the approximate distance across the river?

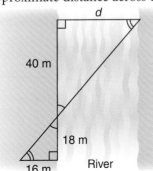

11. How can you use similar triangles to calculate the distance *x* in this scale diagram?

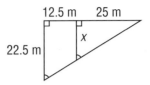

7.5

12. Which of these traffic signs have line symmetry? How many lines of symmetry in each case?

a)
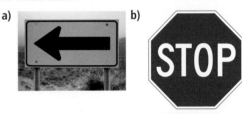

b)

c)
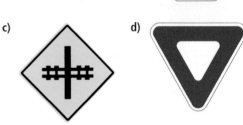

d)

13. Hexagon ABCDEF is a part of a larger shape. Copy the hexagon on a grid.

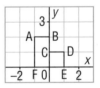

a) Complete the shape by reflecting the hexagon:
  i) in the *y*-axis
  ii) in the *x*-axis
  iii) in the line through $(-2, -1)$ and $(2, 3)$
b) Complete the shape with a translation R2.
c) List the ordered pairs of the vertices of each completed shape.
d) State whether each completed shape has line symmetry.

14. What is the order of rotational symmetry of each shape? How do you know?

a)

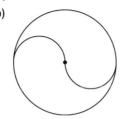

b)

c)

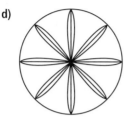

d)

15. Rectangle ABCD is part of a larger shape that is to be completed by a transformation image.

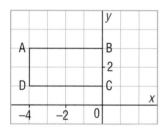

a) Rotate rectangle ABCD as indicated, then draw and label each image.
   i) 90° counterclockwise about the point $(-4, 2)$
   ii) 180° about vertex B
   iii) 270° counterclockwise about the point $(-2, 2)$

b) Which diagrams in part a have rotational symmetry? How do you know?

16. Look at the diagrams in question 15. Which diagrams have line symmetry? How do you know?

17. For each diagram, determine whether the two pentagons are related by any symmetry. Describe each type of symmetry.

a)

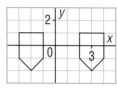

b)

18. Identify and describe the types of symmetry in each piece of artwork.

a)

b)

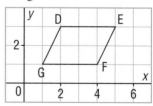

19. a) Translate quadrilateral DEFG as indicated, then draw and label each image.

   i) L4, D2   ii) R1, U2

b) Does each translation result in line symmetry or rotational symmetry? If your answer is yes, describe the symmetry. If your answer is no, explain why there is no symmetry.

1. These two quadrilaterals are similar.

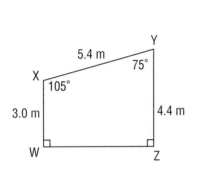
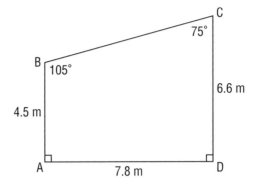

   a) Calculate the length of BC.
   b) Calculate the length of WZ.
   c) Draw an enlargement of quadrilateral WXYZ with scale factor 2.
   d) Draw a reduction of quadrilateral ABCD with scale factor $\frac{1}{3}$.

2. Scott wants to calculate the height of a tree. His friend measures Scott's shadow as 3.15 m. At the same time, the shadow of the tree is 6.30 m. Scott knows that he is 1.7 m tall.
   a) Sketch two triangles Scott could use to calculate the height of the tree.
   b) How do you know the triangles are similar?
   c) What is the height of the tree?

3. Use isometric dot paper or grid paper.
   a) Draw these shapes: equilateral triangle, square, rectangle, parallelogram, trapezoid, kite, and regular hexagon
   b) For each shape in part a:
      i) Draw its lines of symmetry.
      ii) State the order and angle of rotation symmetry.
   c) Draw a shape that has line symmetry but not rotational symmetry.
   d) Draw a shape that has rotational symmetry but not line symmetry.

4. Plot these points on a grid: A(2, 1), B(1, 2), C(1, 4), D(2, 5), E(3, 4), F(3, 2)
   For each transformation below:
      i) Draw the transformation image.
      ii) Record the coordinates of its vertices.
      iii) Describe the symmetry of the diagram formed by the original shape and its image.
   a) a rotation of 90° clockwise about the point G(2, 3)
   b) a translation R2
   c) a reflection in the line $y = 2$

Unit Problem — Designing a Flag

Part 1

At sea, flags are used to display messages or warnings. Here are some nautical flags.

➤ Describe the symmetries of each flag in as much detail as possible.

➤ Classify the flags according to the numbers of lines of symmetry.

Part 2

Design your own flag.

The flag may be for a country, an organization, or it may be a flag with a message. It must have line symmetry and rotational symmetry.

➤ Describe the symmetries in your flag.

The actual flag must be at least 3 m by 2 m.

➤ Draw a scale diagram of your flag, including the scale factor you used.

➤ Describe what your flag will be used for.

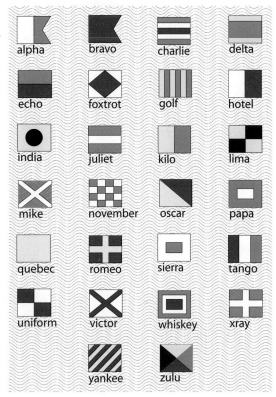

Your work should show:

• a description and classification of the symmetries of the nautical flags
• a scale diagram of your flag, in colour, including the scale factor
• a description of the symmetries in your flag
• a description of what your flag will be used for

Reflect on Your Learning

How does knowledge of enlargements and reductions in scale diagrams help you understand similar polygons?

How are line symmetry and rotational symmetry related to transformations on a grid?

Circle Geometry

We see circles in nature and in design.
What do you already know about circles?

What You'll Learn

Circle properties that relate:
- a tangent to a circle and the radius of the circle
- a chord in a circle, its perpendicular bisector, and the centre of the circle
- the measures of angles in circles

Why It's Important

Knowing the properties of circles and the lines that intersect them helps us to use circles in designs, to calculate measurements involving circles, and to understand natural objects that are circular.

Key Words

- tangent
- point of tangency
- chord
- arc
- minor arc
- major arc
- central angle
- inscribed angle
- subtended
- inscribed polygon
- supplementary angles

383

8.1

Properties of Tangents to a Circle

FOCUS

• Discover the relationship between a tangent and a radius, then solve related problems.

This wheel is rolling in a straight line on a flat surface.
The wheel touches the ground at only one point.
Visualize the red spoke extended to the ground.
What angle does the spoke appear to make with the ground?

Investigate

You will need a compass, protractor, and ruler.

➤ Construct a large circle and draw a radius.
Draw a line that touches the circle only at the endpoint of the radius.
Measure the angle between the radius and the line.
➤ Repeat the previous step for other radii and lines that touch the circle at an endpoint of a radius. Record your results.
Repeat the procedure for other circles.
Write a statement about what you observe.

Compare your results with those of another pair of students.
What is the mean value of the angles you measured?
What do you think is the measure of the angle between the line you drew and the radius of each circle?

Imagine fixing one end of a ruler and rotating the ruler across a circle.

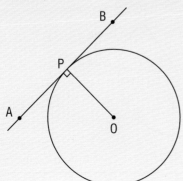

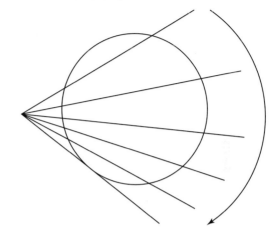

As one edge of the ruler sweeps across the circle, it intersects the circle at 2 points.
Just as the ruler leaves the circle, it intersects the circle at 1 point.
The edge of the ruler is then a tangent to the circle.

A line that intersects a circle at only one point is a
tangent to the circle.
The point where the tangent intersects the circle is
the **point of tangency**.

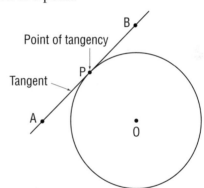

Line AB is a tangent to the circle with centre O.
Point P is the point of tangency.

▶ **Tangent-Radius Property**

A tangent to a circle is perpendicular to the radius at the point of tangency.
That is, ∠APO = ∠BPO = 90°

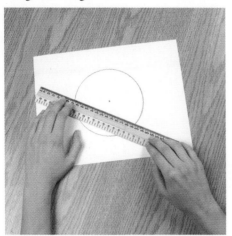

Example 1   Determining the Measure of an Angle in a Triangle

Point O is the centre of a circle
and AB is a tangent to the circle.
In $\triangle OAB$, $\angle AOB = 63°$
Determine the measure of $\angle OBA$.

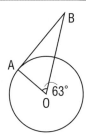

▶ A Solution

Let $x°$ represent the measure of $\angle OBA$.
Since AB is a tangent to the circle, $\angle OAB = 90°$
The sum of the angles in $\triangle OAB$ is 180°.
So, $x° + 90° + 63° = 180°$
$$x° = 180° - 90° - 63°$$
$$= 27°$$
So, $\angle OBA = 27°$

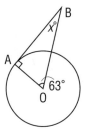

Example 2   Using the Pythagorean Theorem in a Circle

Point O is the centre of a circle
and CD is a tangent to the circle.
CD = 15 cm and OD = 20 cm
Determine the length of the radius OC.
Give the answer to the nearest tenth.

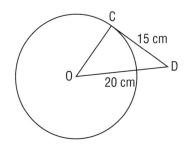

▶ A Solution

Since CD is a tangent, $\angle OCD = 90°$
Use the Pythagorean Theorem in right $\triangle OCD$ to calculate OC.
Let d represent the length of OC.
$$d^2 + CD^2 = OD^2$$
$$d^2 + 15^2 = 20^2$$
$$d^2 + 225 = 400$$
$$d^2 = 400 - 225$$
$$d^2 = 175$$
$$d = \sqrt{175}$$
$$d \doteq 13.23$$
The radius of the circle is about 13.2 cm long.

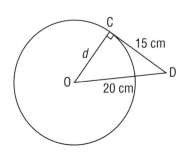

| Example 3 | Solving Problems Using the Tangent and Radius Property |

An airplane, A, is cruising at an altitude of 9000 m.
A cross section of Earth is a circle with
radius approximately 6400 km.
A passenger wonders how far she is from a point H
on the horizon she sees outside the window.
Calculate this distance to the nearest kilometre.

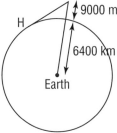

A Solution

The line of sight AH from the passenger to the horizon
is a tangent to the circle at H.

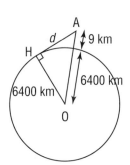

9000 m = 9 km

Since the tangent AH is perpendicular to the
radius OH at the point of tangency H,
ΔAHO is a right triangle, with ∠OHA = 90°.
Use the Pythagorean Theorem to calculate AH.
Let d represent the length of AH.

$$d^2 + 6400^2 = (6400 + 9)^2$$
$$d^2 + 6400^2 = 6409^2$$
$$d^2 = 6409^2 - 6400^2$$
$$d = \sqrt{6409^2 - 6400^2}$$
$$d \doteq 339.53$$

The passenger is about 340 km from the horizon.

1. A line may look as if it is a tangent to a circle but it may not be. How can you determine if the line is a tangent?

2. The Pythagorean Theorem was used in *Examples 2* and *3*. When is the Pythagorean Theorem useful for solving problems involving tangents?

Practice

Check

3. In each diagram, point O is the centre of each circle. Which lines are tangents?

a)
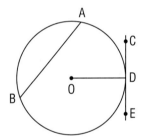

b)
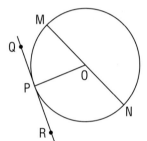

4. Point Q is a point of tangency. Point O is the centre of each circle. What is each value of $d°$?

a)
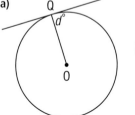

b)
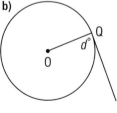

5. Point P is a point of tangency and O is the centre of each circle. Determine each value of $x°$.

a)
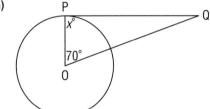

b)   c)
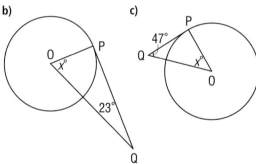

6. Point P is a point of tangency and O is the centre of each circle. Determine each value of a.

a)
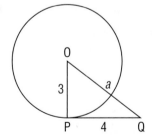

b)

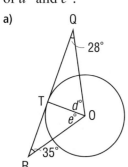

c)

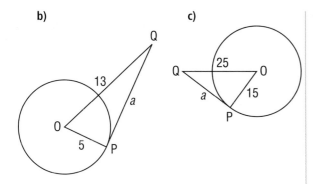

b)

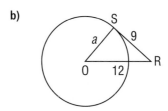

9. Point S is a point of tangency and O is the centre of the circle. Determine the values of *a* and *b* to the nearest tenth.

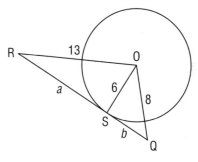

Apply

7. Point T is a point of tangency and O is the centre of each circle. Determine each value of $d°$ and $e°$.

a)

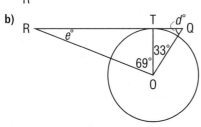

b)

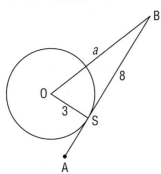

8. Point S is a point of tangency and O is the centre of each circle. Determine each value of *a* to the nearest tenth.

a)

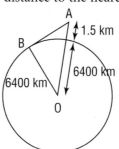

10. Look around the classroom or think of what you might see outside the classroom. Provide an example to illustrate that the tangent to a circle is perpendicular to the radius at the point of tangency.

11. Both AB and CD are tangents to a circle at P and Q. Use what you know about tangents and radii to explain how to locate the centre of the circle. Justify your strategy.

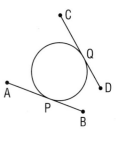

12. A small aircraft, A, is cruising at an altitude of 1.5 km. The radius of Earth is approximately 6400 km. How far is the plane from the horizon at B? Calculate this distance to the nearest kilometre.

13. A skydiver, S, jumps from a plane at an altitude of 3 km. The radius of Earth is approximately 6400 km. How far is the horizon, H, from the skydiver when she leaves the plane? Calculate this distance to the nearest kilometre.

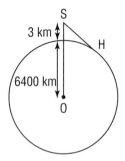

14. Point O is the centre of the circle. Point B is a point of tangency. Determine the values of *x*, *y*, and *z*°. Give the answers to the nearest tenth where necessary. Justify the strategies you used.

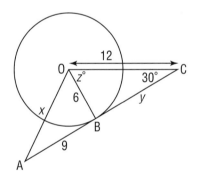

15. **Assessment Focus**

a) From any point outside a circle, how many tangents do you think you can draw to the circle?
Explain your reasoning.

b) Construct a circle. Choose a point outside the circle. Check your answer to part a. How do you know you have drawn as many tangents as you can?

c) How do you know that the lines you have drawn are tangents?
Show your work.

16. a) Construct a circle and draw two radii. Draw a tangent from the endpoint of each radius so the two tangents intersect at point N. Measure the distance from N to each point of tangency. What do you notice?

b) Compare your answer to part a with that of your classmates. How do the lengths of two tangents drawn to a circle from the same point outside the circle appear to be related?

c) Points A and C are points of tangency and O is the centre of the circle. Calculate the values of *x* and *y* to the nearest tenth. Do the answers confirm your conclusions in part b? Explain.

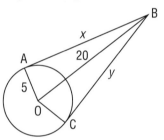

17. A circular mirror with radius 20 cm hangs by a wire from a hook. The wire is 30 cm long and is a tangent to the mirror in two places. How far above the top of the mirror is the hook? How do you know?

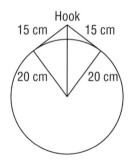

18. A communications satellite orbits Earth at an altitude of about 600 km. What distance from the satellite is the farthest point on Earth's surface that could receive its signal? Justify the strategy you used.

19. Two cylindrical rods are bound with a strap. Each rod has diameter 12 cm. How long is the strap? Give the answer to the nearest tenth of a centimetre. (The circumference C of a circle with diameter d is given by $C = \pi d$.)

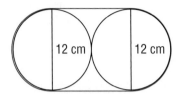

20. What is the radius of the largest circle that can be cut from a square piece of paper whose diagonal is 24 cm long?

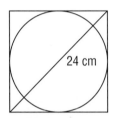

24 cm

21. A cylindrical pipe touches a wall and the ceiling of a room. The pipe is supported by a brace. The ends of the brace are 85 cm from the wall and ceiling. Apply what you discovered in question 16. What is the diameter of the pipe? Give the answer to the nearest centimetre.

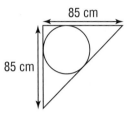

85 cm

85 cm

22. Each of 3 logs has diameter 1 m.
   a) What is the minimum length of strap needed to wrap the logs?
   b) Would this minimum length be the actual length of strap used? Explain.

Reflect

What do you know about a tangent and a radius in a circle? How can you use this property? Include examples in your explanation.

Math Link

Literacy

Sometimes a conversation goes off topic when the subject being discussed makes one person think of a related idea. For example, a discussion about Olympic athletes may prompt someone to think of and describe her exercise plan. When this happens, we say the discussion has "gone off on a tangent." How does this everyday occurrence relate to the meaning of the word "tangent" in math?

Properties of Chords in a Circle

FOCUS

• Relate a chord, its perpendicular bisector, and the centre of the circle, then solve problems.

These pictures show the sun setting.
Imagine the sun as it touches the horizon.
How is the centre of the sun related to the horizon?

Investigate

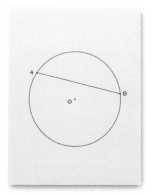

You will need scissors, a compass, protractor, and ruler.

➤ Construct then cut out a large circle. Label the centre of the circle O.

➤ Choose two points A and B on the circle. Join these points to form line segment AB. Make sure AB does *not* go through the centre of the circle.

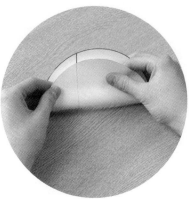

➤ Fold the circle so that A coincides with B. Crease the fold, open the circle, and draw a line along the fold. Mark the point C where the fold line intersects AB. What do you notice about the angles at C? What do you notice about line segments AC and CB?

➤ Repeat the steps above for two other points D and E on the circle.

Compare your results with those of another pair of classmates.

What appears to be true about each line segment and its related fold line?

What name could you give each fold line?

Through which point do both fold lines appear to pass?

Connect

A line segment that joins two points on a circle is a **chord**.
A diameter of a circle is a chord through the centre of the circle.

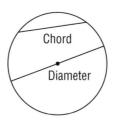

The chord, its perpendicular bisector, and the centre of the circle are related.

A perpendicular bisector intersects a line segment at 90° and divides the line segment into two equal parts.

▶ **Perpendicular to Chord Property 1**
The perpendicular from the centre of a circle to a chord bisects the chord; that is, the perpendicular divides the chord into two equal parts.
Point O is the centre of the circle.
When ∠OCB = ∠OCA = 90°,
then AC = CB

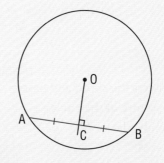

▶ **Perpendicular to Chord Property 2**
The perpendicular bisector of a chord in a circle passes through the centre of the circle.
When ∠SRP = ∠SRQ = 90° and PR = RQ,
then SR passes through O, the centre of the circle.

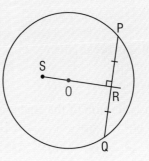

> ◗ **Perpendicular to Chord Property 3**
> A line that joins the centre of a circle and
> the midpoint of a chord is perpendicular
> to the chord.
> When O is the centre of a circle and EG = GF,
> then ∠OGE = ∠OGF = 90°

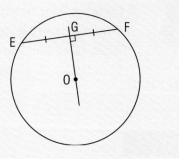

We can use these 3 properties to solve problems involving chords in a circle.

Example 1   **Determining the Measure of Angles in a Triangle**

Point O is the centre of a circle,
and line segment OC bisects chord AB.
∠OAC = 33°
Determine the values of $x°$ and $y°$.

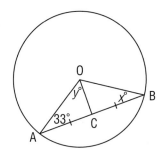

▶ A Solution

Since OC bisects the chord and passes
through the centre of the circle,
OC is perpendicular to AB.
So, ∠ACO = 90°
And, since the radii are equal, OA = OB,
ΔOAB is isosceles.

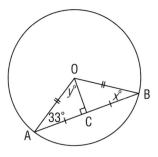

Since ΔOAB is isosceles, then
∠OBA = ∠OAB
So, $x° = 33°$
In ΔOAC, use the sum of the angles in a triangle.
$$y° + 33° + 90° = 180°$$
$$y° = 180° - 90° - 33°$$
$$= 57°$$

Many line segments can be drawn from O,
the centre of a circle, to a chord AB.
The *distance* from O to AB is defined as the shortest distance.
This distance is the length of the perpendicular from O to AB;
that is, the length of OC.

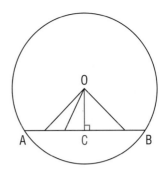

Example 2 **Using the Pythagorean Theorem in a Circle**

Point O is the centre of a circle.
AB is a diameter with length 26 cm.
CD is a chord that is 10 cm from the centre of the circle.
What is the length of chord CD?
Give the answer to the nearest tenth.

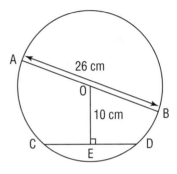

▶ *A Solution*

The distance of a chord from the centre of a circle
is the perpendicular distance from the centre to the chord.
Since OE is perpendicular to chord CD,
then OE bisects CD, and CE = ED
To use the Pythagorean Theorem, join OC to form right $\triangle OCE$.
OC is a radius, so OC is $\frac{1}{2}$ of AB, which is $\frac{1}{2}$ of 26 cm, or 13 cm.
Use the Pythagorean Theorem in $\triangle OCE$ to calculate CE.
Let the length of CE be represented by x.

$$OC^2 = x^2 + OE^2$$
$$13^2 = x^2 + 10^2$$
$$169 = x^2 + 100$$
$$169 - 100 = x^2$$
$$69 = x^2$$
$$x = \sqrt{69}$$
$$x \doteq 8.307$$

So, CE $\doteq$ 8.307 cm

Chord CD = 2 × CE
$\doteq$ 2 × 8.307 cm
$=$ 16.614 cm

Chord CD is about 16.6 cm long.

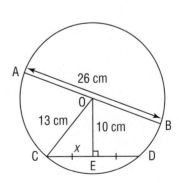

A horizontal pipe has a circular cross section, with centre O. Its radius is 20 cm.
Water fills less than one-half of the pipe.
The surface of the water AB is 24 cm wide.
Determine the maximum depth of the water, which is the depth CD.

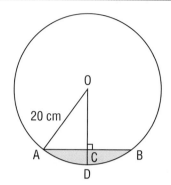

▶ *A Solution*

The depth CD = OD − OC
OD is the radius, 20 cm.

Since OC is perpendicular to AB, then AC = $\frac{1}{2}$ of AB,
which is $\frac{1}{2}$ of 24 cm, or 12 cm.

To determine OC, use the Pythagorean Theorem in △OAC.
Let x represent the length of OC.

$AC^2 + x^2 = OA^2$
$12^2 + x^2 = 20^2$
$144 + x^2 = 400$
$\quad\quad x^2 = 400 - 144$
$\quad\quad x^2 = 256$
$\quad\quad x = \sqrt{256}$
$\quad\quad x = 16$

CD = OD − OC
$\quad$ = 20 cm − 16 cm
$\quad$ = 4 cm

The maximum depth of the water is 4 cm.

Discuss the ideas

1. In a circle, how are these 3 items related?
   - the centre of the circle
   - a chord of a circle
   - the perpendicular bisector of the chord

2. A diameter of a circle is a chord of the circle. How is the answer to question 1 affected if the chord is a diameter?

Check

Give the answers to the nearest tenth where necessary.

3. Point O is the centre of each circle. Determine the values of $d°$, e, and f.

a)

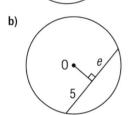

b)

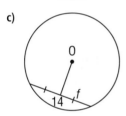

c)

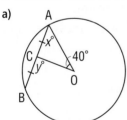

4. Point O is the centre of each circle. Determine each value of $x°$ and $y°$.

a)

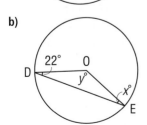

b)

c)

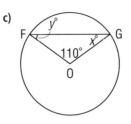

5. Point O is the centre of each circle. Determine each value of a and b.

a)

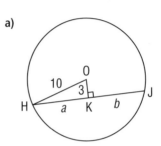

b)

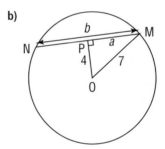

Apply

6. Point O is the centre of the circle. Determine the value of b. Which circle properties did you use?

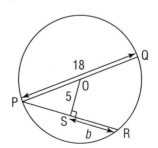

7. Point O is the centre of each circle. Determine each value of *r*. Which extra line segments do you need to draw first? Justify your solutions.

a)

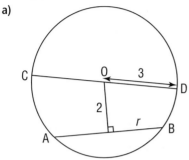

b)

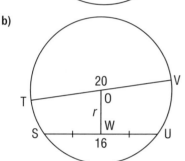

8. Construct a large circle, centre O.

a) Draw, then measure a chord in the circle. How far is the chord from O?

b) Draw other chords that are the same length as the chord you drew in part a. For each chord you draw, measure its distance from O. What do you notice?

c) Compare your results with those of other students. What appears to be true about congruent chords in a circle?

9. Trace a circular object to draw a circle without marking its centre. Draw two chords in the circle. Use what you have learned in this lesson to locate the centre of the circle. Justify your strategy.

10. Point O is the centre of each circle. Determine each value of *s*. Which circle properties did you use?

a)

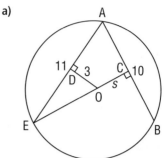

b)

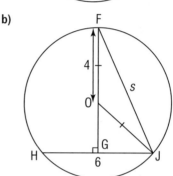

11. A circle has diameter 25 cm. How far from the centre of this circle is a chord 16 cm long? Justify your answer.

12. Assessment Focus

A circle has diameter 14 cm.

a) Which of the following measures could be lengths of chords in this circle? Justify your answers. How could you check your answers?

   i) 5 cm   ii) 9 cm

   iii) 14 cm   iv) 18 cm

b) For each possible length you identified in part a, determine how far the chord is from the centre of the circle.

Show your work. State which circle properties you used.

13. Draw and label a diagram to illustrate that the perpendicular to a chord from the centre of a circle bisects the chord.

14. A chord is 6 cm long. It is 15 cm from the centre of a circle. What is the radius of the circle?

15. A circle has diameter 13 cm. In the circle, each of two chords is 8 cm long.
   a) What is the shortest distance from each chord to the centre of the circle?
   b) What do you notice about these congruent chords?

16. An archaeologist discovers a fragment of a circular plate on a dig at a prehistoric site. She wants to sketch the missing portion of the plate to determine how large it was. Trace the image of the plate fragment. Locate the centre of the plate. Use a compass to complete the sketch of the plate. Explain your work.

17. A radar station R tracks all ships in a circle with radius 50.0 km. A ship enters this radar zone and the station tracks it for 62.5 km until the ship passes out of range. What is the closest distance the ship comes to the radar station? Justify your answer.

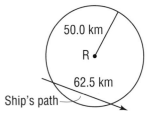

18. A pedestrian underpass is constructed beneath a roadway using a cylindrical pipe with radius 1.8 m. The bottom of the pipe will be filled and paved. The headroom at the centre of the path is 2.8 m. How wide is the path?

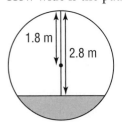

Take It Further

19. A spherical fish bowl has diameter 26 cm. The surface of the water in the bowl is a circle with diameter 20 cm.
   a) What is the maximum depth of the water?
   b) How many different answers are there for part a? Explain.

Reflect

What is the relationship among the centre of a circle, a chord, and the perpendicular bisector of the chord? Use an example to show how this relationship can help you calculate some measures in circles.

Verifying the Tangent and Chord Properties

Dynamic geometry software on a computer or a graphing calculator can be used to verify the circle properties in Lessons 8.1 and 8.2.

The diagrams show what you might see as you conduct the investigations that follow.

To verify the tangent property

FOCUS

• Use dynamic geometry software to verify the tangent and chord properties in a circle.

1. Construct a circle. If the software uses a point on the circle to define the circle, make sure you do not use this point for any further steps.

2. Construct a point on the circle. If the software has a "Draw Tangent" tool, use it to draw a tangent at the point you constructed.

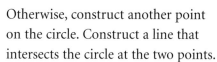
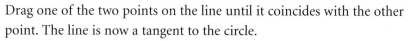

   Otherwise, construct another point on the circle. Construct a line that intersects the circle at the two points. Drag one of the two points on the line until it coincides with the other point. The line is now a tangent to the circle.

3. Construct a line segment to join the centre of the circle and the point of tangency. What does this line segment represent?

4. To measure the angle between the tangent and radius, you need a second point on the tangent. Construct a second point if the software does not do this automatically.

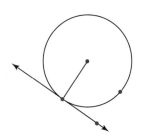

5. Use the software's measurement tools to measure the angle between the radius and tangent. Does the angle measure match what you have learned about a tangent and radius? If not, suggest a reason why.

6. Draw other tangents to the circle and the radii that pass through the points of tangency. Measure the angle between each tangent and radius. What do you notice?

7. Drag either the circle or its centre to investigate the property for circles of different sizes. What is always true about the angle between a tangent to a circle and a radius at the point of tangency?

To verify the chord property

1. Construct a circle.

2. Construct a line segment to join two points on the circle.

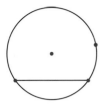

3. Construct a line perpendicular to the segment through the centre of the circle.

4. Use measurement tools to measure the distance between each endpoint of the chord and the point of intersection of the chord and the perpendicular. What do you notice?

5. Drag the endpoints of the chord to different positions on the circle to check the results for other chords. What do you notice?

6. Drag the circle or its centre to investigate the property for circles of different sizes. What is always true about a perpendicular from the centre of a circle to a chord in the circle?

Check

1. Suppose you have constructed a circle and one of its radii. Suggest a way, different from those mentioned above, to construct a tangent at the endpoint of the radius. Construct several circles, radii, and tangents to demonstrate your ideas.

2. Use the geometry software to verify these properties of chords.
   a) Construct a chord. Construct its midpoint. Construct a perpendicular through the midpoint. Through which point does the perpendicular bisector of the chord pass?
   b) Construct a chord. Construct its midpoint. Construct a line segment from the midpoint to the centre of the circle. What is the measure of the angle between the chord and this line segment?

GAME

Seven Counters

How to Play

Your teacher will give you a larger copy of this game board:

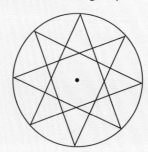

You will need
- a copy of the game board
- 7 counters

Number of Players
- 1 or 2

Goal of the Game
- To place all seven counters on the game board

1. Place a counter on a vertex of the star in the game board. Slide the counter along any segment of the star to place it at another vertex. The counter is now fixed.
2. Continue placing counters by sliding them from one vertex to another until no more counters can be placed. A counter cannot be placed on the game board if no vertex has a line segment along which the counter can move.
3. If you play with a partner, take turns to place counters and work together to decide on a winning strategy.
4. If you play against a partner, work independently to see who can place more counters.
5. It is possible to place all seven counters on the board, leaving one vertex of the star open.
   Keep trying until you have succeeded!
6. Explain your winning strategy.

Give the answers to the nearest tenth where necessary.

8.1 **1.** Point O is the centre of each circle and P is a point of tangency. Determine each value of $x°$ and $y°$.
Which circle properties did you use?

a)

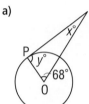

b)

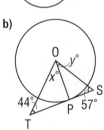

2. Point O is the centre of a circle and point P is a point of tangency. Determine the value of a. Explain your strategy.

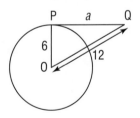

3. A metal disc is to be cut from a square sheet with side length 50 cm.
How far from a corner of the sheet is the centre of the disc? Justify your strategy.

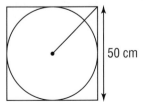

8.2 **4.** Point O is the centre of the circle. Determine the value of $m°$.

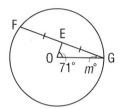

5. Point O is the centre of each circle. Determine each value of x.

a)

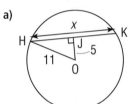

b)

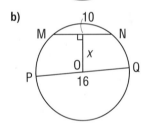

6. A circle has diameter 32 cm. A chord AB is 6 cm from O, the centre of the circle.
a) Sketch a diagram.
b) What is the length of the chord? Which circle properties did you use to find out?

7. Water is flowing through a pipe with radius 14 cm. The maximum depth of the water is 9 cm. What is the width, PQ, of the surface of the water?

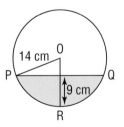

Properties of Angles in a Circle

- Discover the properties of inscribed angles and central angles, then solve related problems.

Shooting angle

A soccer player attempts to get a goal. In a warm-up, players line up parallel to the goal line to shoot on the net. Does each player have the same shooting angle? Is there an arrangement that allows the players to be spread out but still have the same shooting angle?

Investigate

You will need a compass, ruler, and protractor.

➤ Construct a large circle, centre O.
   Choose two points A and B on the circle.
   Choose a third point C on the circle.
   Join AC and BC.
   Measure ∠ACB. Join AO and OB.
   Measure the smaller ∠AOB.
   Record your measurements.

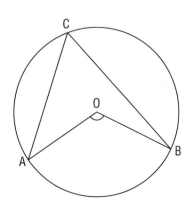

➤ Repeat the previous step for other points A, B, and C on the circle and for other circles.

➤ Construct another large circle.
  Mark 5 points A, B, C, D, and E, in order, on the circle.
  Join AB, AC, AD, and EB, EC, ED.
  Measure ∠ABE, ∠ACE, and ∠ADE.
  Record your measurements.

➤ Repeat the previous step for other circles.

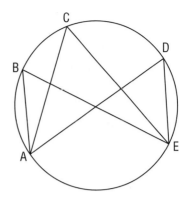

Compare your results with those of another pair of students.
What relationship did you discover between the angle at the centre
of a circle and the angle on the circle?
What relationship did you discover among the angles on a circle?

Connect

➤ A section of the circumference of a circle is an **arc**.
  The shorter arc AB is the **minor arc**.
  The longer arc AB is the **major arc**.

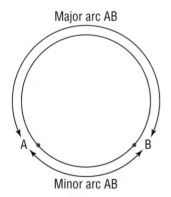

Major arc AB

Minor arc AB

➤ The angle formed by joining the endpoints of an arc
  to the centre of the circle is a **central angle**;
  ∠AOB is a central angle.

  The angle formed by joining the endpoints of an arc
  to a point on the circle is an **inscribed angle**;
  ∠ACB is an inscribed angle.

  The inscribed and central angles in this circle
  are **subtended** by the minor arc AB.

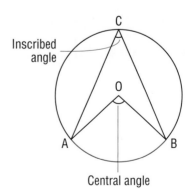

Inscribed angle

Central angle

Central Angle and Inscribed Angle Property

In a circle, the measure of a central angle subtended
by an arc is twice the measure of an inscribed angle
subtended by the same arc.

$\angle POQ = 2 \angle PRQ$, or

$\angle PRQ = \frac{1}{2} \angle POQ$

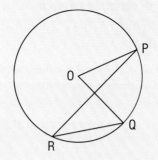

The above property is true for any inscribed angle.

Inscribed Angles Property

In a circle, all inscribed angles subtended
by the same arc are congruent.

$\angle PTQ = \angle PSQ = \angle PRQ$

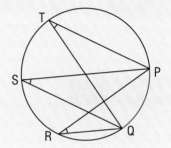

➤ The two arcs formed by the endpoints of a
diameter are semicircles.
The central angle of each arc is a straight angle,
which is 180°.
The inscribed angle subtended by a semicircle
is one-half of 180°, or 90°.

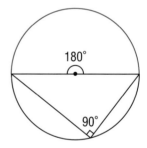

Angles in a Semicircle Property

All inscribed angles subtended by
a semicircle are right angles.
Since $\angle AOB = 180°$,
then $\angle AFB = \angle AGB = \angle AHB = 90°$

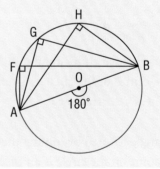

We say: The angle *inscribed* in a semicircle is a right angle.
We also know that if an inscribed angle is 90°, then it is subtended by a semicircle.

Example 1   **Using Inscribed and Central Angles**

Point O is the centre of a circle.
Determine the values of $x°$ and $y°$.

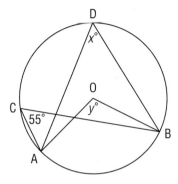

▶ *A Solution*

Since ∠ADB and ∠ACB are inscribed angles
subtended by the same arc AB,
these angles are congruent.
So, $x° = 55°$
Both the central ∠AOB and the
inscribed ∠ACB are subtended by minor arc AB.
So, the central angle is twice the inscribed angle.
That is, ∠AOB = 2∠ACB
$$y° = 2 \times 55°$$
$$= 110°$$

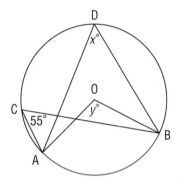

Example 2   **Applying the Property of an Angle Inscribed in a Semicircle**

Rectangle ABCD has its vertices on a circle with radius 8.5 cm.
The width of the rectangle is 10.0 cm. What is its length?
Give the answer to the nearest tenth.

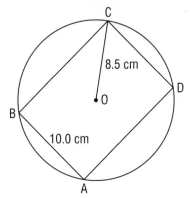

▶ *A Solution*

The length of the rectangle is AD.
Each angle of the rectangle is 90°.
So, each angle is subtended by a semicircle:
∠ADC is subtended by semicircle ABC.
This means that each diagonal of the rectangle
is a diameter of the circle:
AC is a diameter.

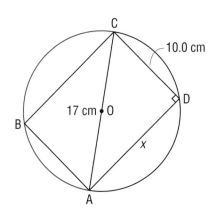

The radius of the circle is 8.5 cm,
so AC = 2 × 8.5 cm, or 17 cm.

Use the Pythagorean Theorem in right ΔADC to calculate AD.
Let the length of AD be represented by x.
$x^2 + CD^2 = AC^2$
$x^2 + 10^2 = 17^2$
$x^2 + 100 = 289$
$\quad\quad x^2 = 289 - 100$
$\quad\quad x^2 = 189$
$\quad\quad\ x = \sqrt{189}$
$\quad\quad\quad \doteq 13.748$
The rectangle is about 13.7 cm long.

A polygon whose vertices lie on a circle is an **inscribed polygon**.
In *Example 2*, rectangle ABCD is an *inscribed rectangle*.
Rectangle ABCD is *inscribed* in the circle.

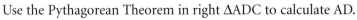

| Example 3 | Determining Angles in an Inscribed Triangle |

Triangle ABC is inscribed in a circle, centre O.
∠AOB = 100° and ∠COB = 140°
Determine the values of $x°$, $y°$, and $z°$.

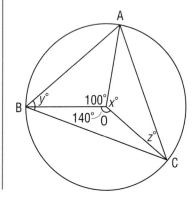

▶ *A Solution*

The sum of the central angles in a circle is 360°.

So, $100° + 140° + x° = 360°$

$$240° + x° = 360°$$
$$x° = 360° - 240°$$
$$= 120°$$

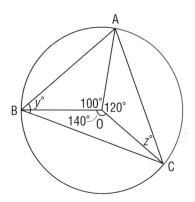

$\angle ABC$ is an inscribed angle and
$\angle AOC$ is a central angle
subtended by the same arc.

So, $\angle ABC = \frac{1}{2} \angle AOC$

$$y° = \frac{1}{2} \times 120°$$
$$= 60°$$

OA and OC are radii, so $\triangle OAC$ is isosceles,
with $\angle OAC = \angle OCA = z°$
The sum of the angles in a triangle is 180°.
So, in $\triangle OAC$,

$$120° + z° + z° = 180°$$
$$120° + 2z° = 180°$$
$$2z° = 180° - 120°$$
$$= 60°$$
$$z° = \frac{60°}{2}$$
$$= 30°$$

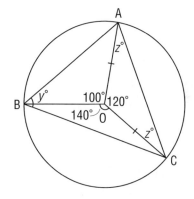

Discuss the ideas

1. How can the circle properties in this lesson help you decide where soccer players need to stand to have the same shooting angle on goal?

2. Suppose a circle has an inscribed angle. How do you identify the arc that subtends the angle?

Check

3. In each circle, identify an inscribed angle
and the central angle subtended by the
same arc.

a)

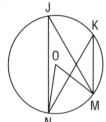

b)

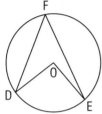

c)

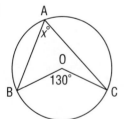

4. Point O is the centre of each circle.
Determine each value of $x°$.

a)

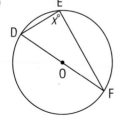

b)

c)

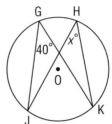

d)

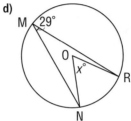

Apply

5. Point O is the centre of each circle. Label
each vertex. Determine each value of $y°$
and $z°$. Which circle properties did you use?

a)

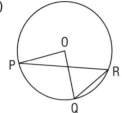

b)

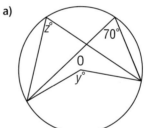

c)

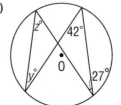

6. Point O is the centre of each circle. Label each vertex. Determine each value of $x°$ and $y°$. Which circle properties did you use?

a)

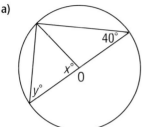

b)

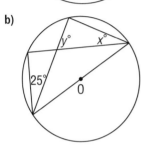

7. Construct a circle and two diameters PR and QS. Join the endpoints of the diameters to form quadrilateral PQRS.
   a) What type of quadrilateral is PQRS? Use what you have learned in this lesson to justify your answer.
   b) What type of quadrilateral is PQRS when the diagonals are perpendicular? Construct a diagram to check your answer.

8. Draw and label a diagram to illustrate:
   a) the measure of the central angle in a circle is equal to twice the measure of an inscribed angle subtended by the same arc
   b) the inscribed angles subtended by the same arc of a circle are equal

9. Rectangle PQRS is inscribed in a circle with radius 7 cm. The length of the rectangle is 12 cm.
   a) Sketch a diagram.

b) What is the width of the rectangle? Give the answer to the nearest tenth. Justify your solution.

10. Assessment Focus Geometry sets often include *set squares*. A set square is a plastic right triangle. Trace around a circular object. Explain how you can use a set square and what you know about the angle in a semicircle to locate the centre of the circle. Justify your solution.

11. Point O is the centre of each circle. Label each vertex. Determine each value of $x°$ and $y°$. Which circle properties does each question illustrate?

a)

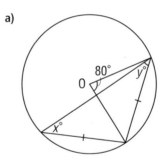

b)

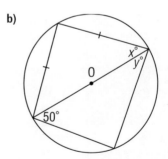

c)

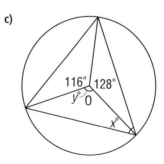

12. In *Investigate* on page 404, point C was on the major arc AB of a circle, centre O. Suppose C was on the minor arc AB. Do the circle properties that relate inscribed angles and central angles still apply? Investigate to find out. Justify your answer.

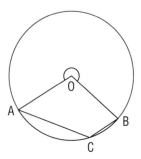

13. Some hockey players are approaching the goal. Two of them are the same distance from the end boards. Rana's shooting angle is 30° while Raji's is 35°.
a) Sketch a diagram.
b) Who is closer to the middle of the ice? Explain your reasoning.

Take It Further

14. The *Seven Counters* game board on page 402 is an 8-pointed star inscribed in a circle. The vertices are equally spaced around the circle. What is the measure of the inscribed angle at each vertex of the star? Justify your solution.

15. The measure of ∠ACE between a tangent DE and the diameter AC at the point of tangency C is 90°. The measure of ∠ABC inscribed in a semicircle is also 90°.

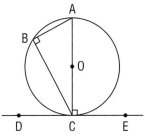

a) How does the angle between a tangent and a chord appear to be related to the inscribed angle on the opposite side of the chord? That is, how is ∠QRS related to ∠QPR? Are ∠PRT and ∠PQR related in a similar way? Explain your reasoning.

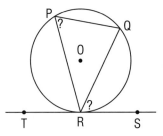

b) Construct and measure accurate diagrams to verify the relationship in part a.

Reflect

Make a poster that summarizes the properties of angles in a circle.

Verifying the Angle Properties

Dynamic geometry software on a computer or a graphing calculator can be used to verify the circle properties in Lesson 8.3.

The diagrams show what you might see as you conduct the investigations that follow.

To verify the property of inscribed and central angles

1. Construct a circle.

2. Mark three points on the circle.
   Label them A, B, and C.
   Label the centre of the circle O.

3. Join AB and BC. Join OA and OC.

4. Measure $\angle ABC$ and $\angle AOC$.
   What do you notice?

5. Drag point C around the circle. Do *not* drag it between points A and B.
   Does the measure of $\angle ABC$ change?
   What property does this verify?

6. Drag point A or B around the circle. What do you notice about the angle measure relationship?

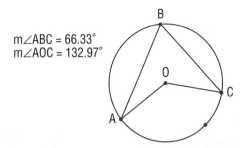

m∠ABC = 66.33°
m∠AOC = 132.97°

To verify the property of inscribed angles subtended by the same arc

1. Construct a circle.

2. Mark four points on the circle. Label them A, B, C, D in order. Label the centre of the circle O.

3. Join AB, AC, BD, and CD.

4. Measure ∠ABD and ∠ACD. What do you notice?

5. Drag point C around the circle. What do you notice about the angle measures? What property does this verify?

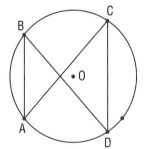

m∠ABD = 41.67°
m∠ACD = 41.67°

Check

1. In the first investigation, you dragged point C around the major arc AB. Predict what would happen if you dragged C to the minor arc AB. Use the software to confirm your prediction.

2. Use the software to confirm that all right triangles can be inscribed in a circle. Justify your strategy.

How Do I Best Learn Math?

Suppose I have to investigate two triangles like these in a circle.

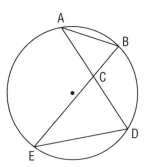

➤ I could work alone or with others.

- Keena says, "I prefer to think things through on my own."
- Jetta says, "I like to discuss my ideas with a partner."
- Tyrell says, "I like to work in a group to get lots of ideas."

➤ I use what I know about angles.

- Keena's method:
  I drew and labelled a diagram like the one above, then measured the angles in the triangles.
  I made sure that the diagram is big enough to be able to measure the angles with a protractor.
  I recorded the angle measures on the diagram.
  I noticed that pairs of angles in the two triangles are equal:

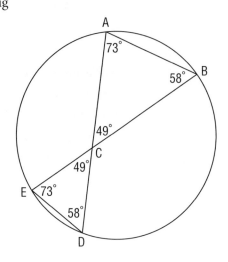

  $\angle ABE = \angle ADE = 58°$
  $\angle BAD = \angle BED = 73°$
  $\angle ACB = \angle ECD = 49°$

  So, the triangles are similar.
  $\triangle ABC \sim \triangle EDC$

- Jetta's method:

  I reasoned from what I have learned
  about angles in a triangle.
  Arc AE subtends inscribed angles
  at B and at D.
  So, ∠ABE = ∠ADE
  Arc BD subtends inscribed angles
  at A and at E.
  So, ∠BAD = ∠BED
  Since two pairs of angles in the two triangles
  are equal, the angles in the third pair must also
  be equal, because the sum of the angles in any triangle is 180°.
  So, ∠ACB = ∠ECD
  Since 3 pairs of corresponding angles in two triangles are equal,
  the triangles are similar.
  ΔABC ~ ΔEDC

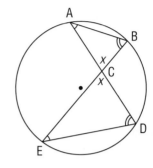

- Tyrell's method:

  I used geometry software.
  I drew a circle and two intersecting chords.
  I then joined the ends of the chords
  to form two triangles.
  I labelled the vertices of the triangles.
  I used the software to measure the angles.
  I rounded the angle measures shown
  on the screen to the nearest degree.

  From the screen, I noticed that
  these angles are equal:
  ∠ABE = ∠ADE = 70°
  ∠BAD = ∠BED = 43°
  ∠ACB = ∠ECD = 67°

  Since 3 pairs of corresponding angles in
  two triangles are equal,
  the triangles are similar.
  ΔABC ~ ΔEDC

m∠ABE = 70.27°
m∠ADE = 70.27°
m∠BAD = 42.90°
m∠BED = 42.90°
m∠ACB = 66.82°
m∠ECD = 66.82°

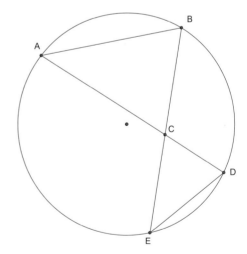

Check

1. Choose the way you best learn math.
   Investigate whether all rectangles can be inscribed in a circle.

▶ A tangent to a circle is perpendicular to the radius at the point of tangency.
That is, $\angle APO = \angle BPO = 90°$

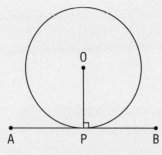

▶ The perpendicular from the centre of a circle to a chord bisects the chord.
When $\angle OBC = \angle OBA = 90°$, then $AB = BC$

▶ A line segment that joins the centre of a circle to the midpoint of a chord is perpendicular to the chord.
When O is the centre of a circle and $AB = BC$, then $\angle OBC = \angle OBA = 90°$

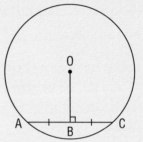

▶ The perpendicular bisector of a chord in a circle passes through the centre of the circle.
When $\angle OBC = \angle OBA = 90°$, and $AB = BC$, then the centre O of the circle lies on DB.

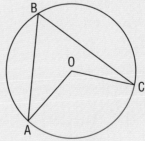

▶ The measure of a central angle subtended by an arc is twice the measure of an inscribed angle subtended by the same arc.
$\angle AOC = 2\angle ABC$, or
$\angle ABC = \frac{1}{2} \angle AOC$

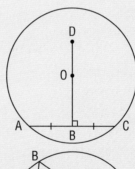

▶ All inscribed angles subtended by same arc are congruent.
$\angle ACB = \angle ADB = \angle AEB$

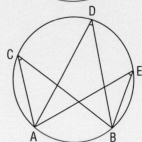

▶ All inscribed angles subtended by
a semicircle are right angles.
$\angle ACB = \angle ADB = \angle AEB = 90°$

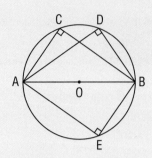

Review

Give the answers to the nearest tenth where
necessary.

8.1 **1.** Point O is the centre of each circle.
Segments PT and QT are tangents.
Determine each value of $x°$, $y°$, a, and b.
Show your work.

a)

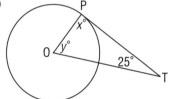

b)

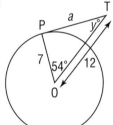

c)

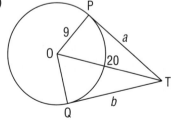

2. A circular mirror is suspended by a wire
from a hook, H. Point O is the centre of the
circle and is 16 cm below H. Explain how
you know that the wire is *not* a tangent to
the circle at P and at Q.

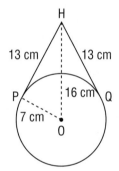

3. Draw a circle with centre O. Mark a point P
on the circle. Explain how to draw a
tangent to the circle. Which circle property
did you use?

4. A circular plate is supported so it touches
two sides of a shelf. The diameter of the
plate is 20 cm. How far is the centre O of
the plate from the inside corner C of the
shelf? Which circle properties helped you
find out?

5. Point O is the centre of each circle.
Determine each value of *x*.
Justify your answers.

a)
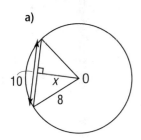

b)
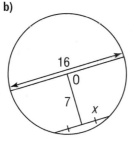

6. A dream catcher with diameter 22 cm is
strung with a web of straight chords.
One of these chords is 18 cm long.
a) Sketch a diagram.
b) How far is the chord from the centre of
the circle? Justify your solution strategy.

7. Point O is the centre of each circle.
Determine each value of *x*° and *y*°.
Which circle properties did you use?

a)
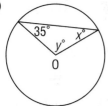

b)
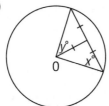

8. A square has side length 5 cm. It is
inscribed in a circle, centre O.
What is the length of the radius of the
circle? How do you know?

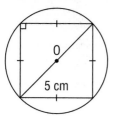

9. Point O is the centre of each circle.
Determine each value of *x*° and *y*°.
Justify your answers.

a)
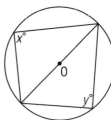

b)
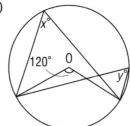

c)
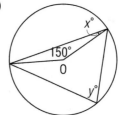

10. A rectangle is inscribed in a circle, centre O
and diameter 36.0 cm. A shorter side of
the rectangle is 10.0 cm long. What is the
length of a longer side? How do you know?

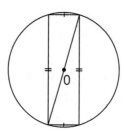

1. Point O is the centre of the circle.
   Point P is a point of tangency.
   Determine the values of x and $y°$.
   Give reasons for your answers.

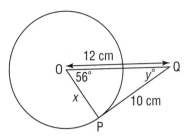

2. Point O is the centre of the circle.
   Determine the values of $x°$, $y°$, and $z°$.
   Which circle properties did you
   use each time?

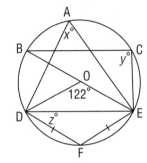

3. A circle has diameter 6.0 cm. Chord AB is 2.0 cm from the centre of the circle.
   a) Sketch a diagram.
   b) How long is the chord AB?
   c) Another chord, CD, in the circle is 2.5 cm from the centre of the circle.
      Is chord CD longer or shorter than chord AB? Justify your answer.

4. Use what you know about inscribed and central angles to explain why the angle
   inscribed in a semicircle is 90°.

5. Where is the longest chord in any circle? How do you know? Draw a diagram to
   illustrate your answer.

6. A circle has diameter 16 cm.
   a) Which of the following measures could be distances of chords from the
      centre of this circle? How could you check your answers?

      i) 4 cm   ii) 6 cm   iii) 8 cm   iv) 10 cm
   b) For each possible distance you identified in part a,
      determine the length of the chord.

7. a) Construct a circle and mark points P and Q to form major and minor arcs PQ.
   b) Construct inscribed ∠PRQ subtended by minor arc PQ.
   c) Construct inscribed ∠PSQ subtended by major arc PQ.
   d) How are ∠PRQ and ∠PSQ related? Justify your answer.

Unit Problem · Circle Designs

Many works of art, designs, and objects in nature are based on circles.

Work with a partner to generate a design for a corporate or team logo.

Part 1

Sketch a design that uses circles, tangents, and chords. Use your imagination to relate circles to a business or sports team.

Part 2

Work with geometry tools or computer software to draw your design.

Measure and label all angles and lengths that demonstrate the circle properties.

Some lines or features at this stage may disappear or be covered by the final coloured copy. So, ensure you have a detailed design copy to submit that demonstrates your understanding of the geometry.

Part 3

Produce a final copy of your design. You may cover or alter the underlying geometry features at this point if it enhances your design.

Your work should show:
*   sketches of your design
*   a detailed, labelled copy of your design that shows circle geometry properties
*   written explanations of the circle properties you used in your design
*   a final coloured copy of your design with an explanation of its purpose, if necessary

Reflect
on Your Learning

Explain how knowing the circle properties from this unit can help you determine measurements of lengths and angles in circles.

Probability and Statistics

Are you an average teenager? How could you find out how your answers to these questions compare with those of the average Canadian teenager?

How many hours a week do you spend playing sports?

How are you most likely to communicate with your friends?

What You'll Learn

- Understand the role of probability in society.
- Identify and address problems related to data collection.
- Use either a population or a sample to answer a question.
- Develop and implement a plan to collect, display, and analyze data.

Why It's Important

People make decisions based on data. People can make informed decisions if they understand what the data really mean and where they come from, and are confident the data are accurate.

How do your likes, dislikes, opinions, and lifestyle compare with those of your friends?

Key Words

- population
- census
- sample
- valid conclusions
- rubric

This season, Haley made 44 out of 50 basketball shots she attempted.
What is the probability Haley will sink the next shot?
What assumptions do you make?

Investigate

From the statements below, identify the different probabilities that Jean-Guy considers in a day. List an assumption associated with each statement. Explain how the situation would change if that assumption were not true.

➤ Jean-Guy noticed that, in the last month, 70% of the time the bus was 3 minutes late. So, he takes his time with breakfast today.

➤ Lately, Jean-Guy's math teacher checks homework 4 days a week. So, Jean-Guy makes sure he has time to complete his homework today.

➤ At school, Jean-Guy and his friends agree that their lacrosse team has a 95% chance of making the finals.

➤ In health class, Jean-Guy's teacher reads a magazine that claims 172 out of 1000 male smokers develop lung cancer, but only 13 out of 1000 males who do not smoke develop lung cancer.

Share your assumptions with those of another pair of students. Discuss which assumptions you think are the most likely and least likely to be true.
Which probability could have been most influenced by personal opinion? How do you think the other probabilities were determined? Explain.

Probability refers to the likelihood that an event will occur.

By collecting and analyzing data, predictions can be made about the likelihood that a certain event will occur. For example, meteorologists study past weather data to make predictions about future conditions. A 40% probability of snow means that under similar conditions in the past it snowed 40% of the time, or 4 times out of 10.

A probability of 40% can be expressed as 4 out of 10, $\frac{4}{10}$, or 0.4.

When you flip a coin, there is a 0.5 probability the coin will land heads up. Despite this probability, you may feel strongly that the coin will land tails up. In this case, you have made a *subjective judgment*.

Example 1   **Identifying Decisions Based on Probabilities and Judgments**

Explain how each decision is based on theoretical probability, experimental probability, subjective judgment, or any combination of these.

a) It is Ausma's experience that 4 out of 5 times the prize in the cereal box is found at the bottom of the box. So, Ausma opens the bottom of the cereal box to find her prize.

b) Two friends are rolling a die. Out of eight rolls made, a "4" came up 7 times. Amith predicts the next roll will likely not be a "4," since each number has an equal chance of being rolled. Maria decides the die is unfair since 7 out of 8 rolls revealed a "4."

▶ *A Solution*

a) Ausma's decision to open the bottom of the cereal box to find her prize is based on past experience. This is an example of experimental probability.

b) Amith's decision that the next roll will likely not be a "4" is based on theoretical probability. Amith knows that the probability of rolling each number is 1 out of 6, so the probability of rolling any number other than a "4" is 5 out of 6.
Based on previous rolls, Maria has noticed that the experimental probability of rolling a "4" is 7 out of 8. She knows that each number should have an equal probability of being rolled. So, she makes a subjective judgment that the die must be unfair.

Often, we make predictions about an outcome based on assumptions associated with a given probability.

If these assumptions change, the prediction may not match the outcome.

Example 2   **Explaining How Assumptions Affect a Probability**

In past baseball games, Alice made 2 hits for every 5 times she went up to bat.

a) In the next game, suppose Alice goes up to bat. What is the probability that she will get a hit? What assumptions are you making?

b) For each assumption, explain how the predicted outcomes might change if the assumption changes.

▶ *A Solution*

a) The experimental probability of Alice hitting the ball is 2 out of 5, or 40%. We assume that the next team Alice plays against is at the same level of ability as previous teams she has played.

b) If the opposing team is more able, then Alice will probably make fewer hits. The likelihood that Alice has a hit would be less than 2 out of 5. If the opposing team is less able, then Alice will probably have more than 2 hits. In this case, the likelihood that Alice has a hit would be greater than 2 out of 5.

Sometimes a probability can be used to support opposing views.

Example 3   **Using a Probability to Support Opposing Views**

Jon wants to learn how to snowboard but does not want to take lessons. His mother insists that Jon take lessons. Jon and his mother find an article that claims:

> 68% of snowboarding injuries occur during beginner lessons

Explain how both Jon and his mother can use this statistic to support their opinions.

► A Solution

68% of snowboarding injuries occur during beginner lessons. Jon's mother can argue that this statistic proves lessons are important because beginners are prone to accidents. Jon can argue that this statistic is a good reason not to take lessons because the likelihood of getting injured during the lesson is high.

Discuss the ideas

1. When you toss a coin, what assumptions are you making when you say the probability of it landing heads up is $\frac{1}{2}$?

2. Car insurance for teenagers is more expensive than for adults because the probability of an accident is greater for teenage drivers. What assumptions is an insurance company making when it charges a teenage driver more for insurance?

Practice

Check

3. Indicate whether each decision is based on theoretical probability, experimental probability, or subjective judgment. Explain how you know.
   a) The last two times Andrei won a prize at a coffee shop, he ordered a medium hot chocolate. Andrei never won when he ordered a large hot chocolate, so today he orders a medium hot chocolate.
   b) Instead of buying her own lottery ticket, Martha pools her money with the people at work to buy more tickets and increase her chances of winning.
   c) Anita boards the last car of a train because, in the past, the last car always had available seats.
   d) Doug will not travel by airplane even though experts say it is safer to fly than drive.

4. What assumptions is each person making?
   a) Based on past math quizzes, Claudia says she has a 90% chance of getting a perfect score on her next math quiz.
   b) Six times out of ten, Omar gets stuck in traffic when he leaves work. So, he calculates that his chances for getting stuck in traffic today after work are 60%.

Apply

5. The weather forecast is 70% chance of rain. Winona had planned to go canoeing. Explain how the decision she makes may be based either on probability or on subjective judgment.

6. The student council has a draw for a prize during the school dance. Lei decides not to enter the draw because all of his classmates have entered and he feels unlucky today. Is Lei's decision based on probability, on subjective judgment, or both? Explain.

7. One year, the probability of *not* recovering a stolen vehicle in Montreal was 44%. How could politicians use this fact to argue that:
a) more money should be allotted to searching for stolen vehicles
b) more money should not be allotted, and instead should go to different causes

8. Vanessa observes her birdfeeder at the same time each day for a week. She notes that 32 of the 100 birds which visit the feeder are cardinals. She concludes that, in general, there is a 32% probability a bird visiting the feeder will be a cardinal.
a) What assumptions did Vanessa make?
b) If each assumption changes, how might the predicted outcome change?

9. Kathryn read this headline:

Poll reveals 30% support Bradford, 70% support Choo in next election

Kathryn says that if she polled the next 10 people she passed on the street, 7 of them would be voting for Choo.
a) What assumption is Kathryn making?
b) Explain what the effect might be if the assumption were not true.

10. A DNA match was found between a blood sample and a suspect. A forensic scientist testifies that there is a 1 in 7000 chance the blood sample is from someone other than the suspect. Describe how two lawyers could use this statistic to support different positions.

11. **Assessment Focus** An advertisement for acne treatment boasts:

a) Explain how a teenager's decision on whether to try this acne treatment could be based on probability and subjective judgment.
b) If the teenager does decide to try the acne treatment, what assumptions might he be making? For each assumption, explain how the predicted outcome of the treatment might change if the assumption changes.

12. a) Provide 2 examples of how statistics are used in the media to sell a product.
b) Why do advertisers use numbers in these ads? Do you think using statistical data makes the ads more effective?
c) For each example, list some assumptions associated with the statistic.

13. Look at newspapers, magazines, or on the internet. Give 2 examples of how politicians or environmentalists use probability.

14. Shaquille O'Neal's free throw percentage during one season was 62%. A teacher points out that this means each time Shaquille attempted a free throw during that season, his probability of making the shot was 62%. A student then says:

"Shaquille either makes the shot or he doesn't. So, isn't the probability 50%?"

Explain the flaw in the student's thinking.

15. Research 2 occupations that use probability. Explain the role of probability in each occupation.

16. The annual Farmer's Almanac makes predictions about long range weather patterns. Investigate to find out how these predictions are made. What assumptions is the almanac making?

17. According to Transport Canada, in 2004, there were 34 fatalities due to air travel and 2730 fatalities due to road travel.
   a) What impression does this information give? How might this information be misleading?
   b) What additional information would you need to determine whether travelling by plane or by car is safer?

Reflect

Think of 2 decisions that could be influenced by probabilities.
What assumptions would you be making about each probability?
How might the probabilities be different if the assumptions were not true?

Math Link

Your World

Probabilities are used in risk assessment. To compare the safety of certain sport utility vehicles (SUVs) and minivans, researchers subjected both to crash tests while the vehicles moved at 56 km/h. Here are the results:

Probability of:	SUV	Minivan
life threatening head injury	16%	2%
life threatening chest injury	20%	4%
life threatening leg injury	35%	1%

How might insurance companies use this information?
How might car manufacturers use this information?

GAME

Cube Master

You will need
- more than 30 cubes (blue, green, and red)
- a container for the cubes

Number of Players
- 4

Goal of the Game
- Use experimental probability and subjective judgment to estimate the numbers of coloured cubes in a container.

How to Play

1. Choose a "dealer". The dealer selects any 30 cubes. (For example, the dealer could choose 5 red cubes, 12 green cubes, and 13 blue cubes.)
   No other player should know how many cubes of each colour were selected.
   The dealer places the 30 cubes in a container.
2. Each player records a guess of how many cubes of each colour are in the container.
   Players should not share these guesses.
3. The players take turns selecting one cube from the container, then returning the cube.
   (The dealer makes sure the players cannot see what is in the container.)
   Players note which colour was selected each time.
   Stop after 10 cubes have been selected and returned.
4. Players now adjust their initial guesses by considering the colours of the cubes selected.
5. Repeat Steps 3 and 4 two more times.
6. Players compare their final estimates with the actual numbers of cubes to calculate their points.
   The player with the fewest points wins.

For example:

	Actual Number of Cubes	Player's Final Estimate	Number of Points (Difference between actual number and estimate)
Red	5	4	1
Green	12	11	1
Blue	13	15	2
Total Number of Points:			4

7. Repeat the game until everyone has had the opportunity to be the dealer.

Share your strategies with the other players.
Whose strategy worked best? Why?

Potential Problems with Collecting Data

FOCUS

• Describe how the collection of data may be adversely affected.

Suppose your friend asks you, "Who do you think will win the Western Hockey League (WHL) playoffs?"

What might affect your answer to this question?

Investigate

Choose one person in the group to be the leader.

The leader will read the questions below, while the others write down their answers.

The leader should ask the questions exactly as they are written, without explanation.

1. How large is this textbook? (Point to this textbook when asking the question.)
2. Do you think students are working too much because of the large amount of homework assigned?
3. What is your favourite genre of music? Choose one from: Rock, Pop, Country

Share all the answers with the group.

Did you interpret the questions the same way as your group? Why?

Describe any problems with each question.

Rewrite each question to avoid these problems.

Share your rewritten questions with another group.

Discuss how the rewritten questions avoid potential problems.

How might a poorly worded question affect data collection?

What sort of wording should someone collecting data use?

What sort of wording should that person avoid?

There are several factors that might lead to problems with data collection.

Potential Problem	What It Means	Example
Bias	The question influences responses in favour of, or against the topic of the data collection.	Suppose a person asks: *Don't you think the price of a movie ticket is too high?* This person has a bias against the current ticket price, and the bias influences how the survey question is written.
Use of Language	The use of language in a question could lead people to give a particular answer.	If you ask: *Don't you think the price of a movie ticket is too high?*, the question may lead people to answer yes. A better question would be: *Do you think the price of a movie ticket is too high, too low, or fair?*
Timing	*When* the data are collected could lead to particular results.	A survey is conducted to find opinions on the need for a vehicle to have winter tires. The results may be different if the survey is conducted in August instead of February.
Privacy	If the topic of the data collection is personal, a person may not want to participate or may give an untrue answer on purpose. Anonymous surveys may help.	People may not want to participate in a study on weight if it means stepping on a scale in front of other people.
Cultural Sensitivity	Cultural sensitivity means that you are aware of other cultures. You must avoid being offensive and asking questions that do not apply to that culture.	Suppose you wanted to know the favourite method of cooking ham, and you asked: *Please circle your favourite method:* *BBQ Bake Fry* This question does not apply to everyone because many people do not eat ham. A better question would be: *If you eat ham, name your favourite method of cooking it.*
Ethics	Ethics dictate that collected data must not be used for purposes other than those told to the participants. Otherwise, your actions are considered unethical.	Suppose you tell your classmates that you want to know their favourite snacks to help you plan your birthday party. If you then use the information to try to sell your classmates their favourite snacks between classes, your actions would be unethical.
Cost	The cost of collecting data must be taken into account.	If you need to pay for printing the questionnaires, or to pay people to collect the data, the cost may be more than you can afford.
Time	The time needed for collecting the data must be considered.	A survey that takes an hour to complete may be too long for most people. This would limit the number of people willing to participate.

Example 1   **Identifying and Eliminating Potential Problems**

For each survey question, explain why a problem may occur and the effect it would have on the results. Suggest how each problem could be avoided.

a) A survey is conducted to find out if citizens think the local government should provide more money for youth activities. The question asked was: "Would you support an increase in taxes to create more skate parks?"

b) A survey is conducted to find out the level of school spirit. Students are polled about their level of school spirit after the soccer team wins the championship.

▶ *A Solution*

a) The use of language in the survey question could be problematic.
The question emphasizes what citizens would lose; that is, their taxes would increase. The question also downplays what citizens would gain by only mentioning skate parks, instead of a variety of activities.
Most people would probably respond by saying they would not support an increase in taxes to build more skate parks.
A better question would be: "Do you think the local government should supply more funds for youth recreational activities?"

b) The timing of the survey question could be problematic.
Since the school's soccer team just won the championship, the level of school spirit would be higher than usual.
The results of the survey may show a higher level of school spirit than if the survey was conducted at another time.
Asking students the same question a month later, when no school event is occurring, should produce more accurate results.

Example 2   **Analyzing Data Collection for Problems**

Kublu and Irniq plan to open a shop in Saskatoon that would sell traditional Inuit crafts.
To ensure Saskatoon is the best place for their business, they want to survey residents to find out how popular Inuit crafts are.
Kublu knows that they would get the most accurate results if each household in Saskatoon is surveyed, but Irniq points out that this is problematic.
Explain why.

► *A Solution*

The number of households in Saskatoon is great. Kublu and Irniq may have problems related to cost and time.

The cost of printing and mailing enough surveys for each household would be very high. Also, Kublu and Irniq should provide an envelope and stamp for each household to return the survey. This would be an additional cost.

The time it would take to print, mail, and collect the surveys for all the households would be too long.

Example 3   Overcoming Potential Problems of Data Collection

Antonia wants to find out if there is a relationship between household income and how much people spent on Christmas presents.
Identify potential problems Antonia may encounter, and explain how she could deal with the problems.

► *A Solution*

Christmas is not celebrated by all cultures, and so the survey question does not apply to everyone. An appropriate opening question for the survey might be: "Do you celebrate Christmas?" If a person responds "No", then he or she will not need to answer the other question in your survey.

Information about income and spending habits is personal, so people may be uncomfortable revealing it. An anonymous survey would be appropriate.

The use of language may influence responses.
Examples of inappropriate or intrusive questions would be:
"How much do you make?" and "How much do you spend?"
A better question might be:
"Is the amount you spend on Christmas presents:
– greater than your weekly income?
– less than your weekly income?
– equal to your weekly income?"

1. How could the use of language affect the data collected? Give an example.

2. Two factors that may influence data collection are *time* and *timing*. What is the difference between these?

Check

3. Name a problem with each data collection.

   a) After the first week of school, your principal asks you and your friends how you are enjoying school.

   b) An online magazine asks readers either to agree or disagree with the statement: "If you find a $20-bill, you turn it in."

   c) Brenda asks her classmates if they think girls should not be allowed to cover their heads in school.

   d) To discover the most popular kind of movie at his school, Carlos plans to ask each student what her or his favourite kind of movie is.

Apply

4. For each scenario in question 3:

   a) Describe the effect each problem would have on the data collection.

   b) How could each problem be overcome?

5. Parinder wanted to find out how often the computers in her school were being used. She asked students the question: "How much time do you spend on the computer each week?"

   a) How do you think her schoolmates will interpret this question?

   b) How could the question be rewritten so it would more accurately reflect what Parinder wants to know?

   c) Who might be interested in her findings? Why?

6. Andrew went to each class in his school and asked for a show of hands to find out how many students had ever been bullied at school. Only 2 students raised their hands.

Andrew concluded that bullying was not a major problem at his school.

   a) Is this a reasonable conclusion? Explain.

   b) Describe a better method for conducting Andrew's survey.

7. Trinity wants to find out how football fans feel about building a new indoor football stadium for a Canadian Football League team. She goes to the stadium to survey fans after a winning game on a warm August evening.

   a) Describe how the timing of her question may influence the responses.

   b) In what setting might the responses be different than those Trinity received?

8. a) Describe how each question reveals a bias of the questioner.

   i) Do you think it is a good idea to use DNA tests to convict a violent criminal?

   ii) Do you think gas guzzling SUVs should be banned?

   iii) Do you think students should be allowed to use spell check because it automatically improves spelling?

   b) Rewrite each question to eliminate the bias. Explain how your question is an improvement.

9. Rebecca was looking for a cell phone service provider. She surveyed her friends and asked who their service providers were. Based on these data, she chose the provider that her friends used more than any other.

a) Do you think Rebecca's question reflected what she wanted to know? Explain.

b) What questions might have helped Rebecca to make a more informed decision?

10. A fashion website is conducting a survey. Sasha answered questions about his favourite brands of clothing, then provided an email address as a login to the site in the future. Shortly after this, his inbox was full of emails advertising a new brand of clothing.

a) Which important factor did the survey designers overlook? How is this problematic?

b) How can the survey designers avoid this problem?

11. Provide an example of data collection where the cost and time needed to complete the collection may lead to problems.

12. a) Write 3 questions people would prefer to answer anonymously.

b) For each question, describe what the results might be if the participants were not anonymous.

13. **Assessment Focus** Bridget wants to find out how much the average grade 9 student spends on clothes each month.

a) Identify potential problems she may encounter related to 3 of these factors: use of language, ethics, cost, time, timing, privacy, cultural sensitivity

b) For each potential problem in part a, explain how Bridget could avoid the problem.

14. a) Describe 2 possible data collections that might be problematic because of the time of year they are conducted.

b) Suggest a better time that each should be conducted.

Take It Further

15. Common methods of surveying are by personal interviews, over the phone, or by email. Identify potential problems associated with each method of surveying.

16. a) Why might questions about Hanukkah be culturally sensitive?

b) Think of 3 more topics that might be culturally sensitive. Explain why.

c) Design a culturally sensitive survey question about one of the topics in part a or b. Explain how you would collect the data to address the cultural sensitivity.

Reflect

Why is it important to identify and overcome sources of potential problems in data collection?

9.3

FOCUS

• Select and defend the choice of using a population or a sample.

To estimate the number of salmon in a river, biologists use a strategy called *mark and recapture*. At one place in the river, biologists capture some fish. Each fish is marked with a tag, then released into the river. At a different place in the river, biologists recapture fish. They track the numbers of marked and unmarked fish caught. They can then estimate the salmon population.

Investigate

Each pair of students will need 50 small pieces of paper.

➤ Create a population of 50 fish by labelling each piece of paper with either "F" for female or "M" for male.

➤ Record the percents of female and male fish in your population.

➤ Fold the pieces of paper and place them in a box.

Trade populations with another pair of students.

➤ Choose a sample of 10 fish from the other pair's population. Record the numbers of male and female fish in your sample. Use this to estimate the percents of male and female fish in the population.

➤ Repeat the preceding step by choosing samples of 20 fish, and then 40 fish.

➤ Did your estimates of the percents of male and female fish change as the sample size changed? Explain.

Compare your estimates with the actual percents recorded by the other pair of students. How did your estimates compare with the actual percents? In general, how did the estimates change as the size of the sample increased?

When collecting data, the **population** is the group about which you are getting information. A **census** is conducted when data are collected from each member of the population. For example, suppose you test game consoles made in a factory for defects, then *all* the game consoles made in the factory are the population. If you test each game console, then you have conducted a census.

A census can be costly, time consuming, and difficult or impossible to complete. So, a census is only used when an issue is important or when the population is small.

If a census is not feasible or necessary then data are collected from a small portion, or **sample**, of the population. When the sample chosen is representative of the population, the data collection provides **valid conclusions**. For example, testing 100 game consoles out of 1000 made each day is a sample. If those consoles tested represent the typical quality of consoles made in the factory, the conclusions of the data collection will be valid.

Care must be taken when determining the appropriate size of the sample. If the sample is large, the data collection could be costly or time consuming. If the sample is small, then it may not be representative of the population.

Example 1   Explaining Why Data Are Collected from Populations

In each case, explain why a population was surveyed instead of a sample.
a) To determine the average number of siblings of his classmates, Carlos surveyed each person in the class.
b) Every 5 years, Statistics Canada conducts a census. One question in the survey is used to determine the ages of the people in each household.

▶ A Solution

a) Carlos knows that surveying the entire population will produce exact results, rather than estimates. So, he chose to survey the entire population, the whole class, because it would not take long or cost him anything.
b) A census was completed because of the importance of the question. The government requires data about the ages of Canadians so that it can budget for services such as day-care centres, schools, and senior citizens' homes.

Example 2 **Reasoning Why and When Samples Should Be Used**

The student leadership team is planning a school dance. To attract grade 9 students to the dance, the team decided to collect data about the preferred music of the grade 9 students. The team set up in the hallway to collect the data. By the end of the day it had surveyed 73% of the grade 9 students.

a) Why do you think the data were collected from a sample instead of the entire population?

b) Will the opinions of the sample likely reflect those of the population? Explain.

▶ *A Solution*

a) There was probably not enough time or people available to ask all grade 9 students. It would also require a lot of effort to find each grade 9 student, especially with absences.

b) Since the majority of students, 73%, were asked, it is likely that their opinions will reflect those of the entire population.

Example 3 **Identifying and Critiquing the Use of Samples**

In each case, identify if data were collected from a sample or a population. Wherever a sample was used, explain if you think the conclusion would be valid.

a) A province considers banning cell phones in all of its schools. To determine the opinions of students on this issue, you poll each student in your school.

b) To determine which politician is expected to win the municipal election, every person over 18 and who is eligible to vote in the election is polled.

c) To determine the average lifetime of a type of light bulb, 150 light bulbs were selected randomly from the production line and tested.

▶ *A Solution*

a) Sample: The population is all students of all schools in the province. By asking only the students in your school, your results are based on a sample. If the students in your school do not represent typical students in the province, the conclusion will not be valid. For example, if all students in your school own cell phones, your conclusion would probably be not to ban cell phones. However, not every student in the province owns a cell phone. So, your results would not be representative of the population.

b) Population: All possible voters are polled.

c) Sample: Since not all light bulbs were tested, the results are based on a sample. It would not make sense for the whole population to be tested, since all light bulbs would be destroyed in the process. There would be no light bulbs left to sell. Since a fairly large number of light bulbs were tested, the results will likely give a good estimate of the lifetime of a light bulb. So, the conclusion about the lifetime of a light bulb is likely valid.

Discuss the ideas

1. What factors do you need to consider when you collect data from either a population or a sample?

2. What does "valid conclusion" mean? Provide an example where the conclusion based on a sample is not valid.

Practice

Check

3. In each case, describe the population.
   a) The management team of a shopping mall in Comox wants to know how to attract more people between the ages of 13 and 25 to the mall.
   b) A juice company wants to determine the average volume of juice in a 1-L carton.
   c) A board of education wants to find out which schools need renovations.
   d) The government wants to determine the average age of First Nations people in Nunavut.

4. In each case, are the data collected from a census or a sample?
   a) To determine the favourite TV show of grade 9 students in a school, all grade 9 students in the school are surveyed.
   b) To find out if customers of a chain of coffee shops are happy with the service, some customers in every shop were surveyed.

Apply

5. Identify the population you would sample to find out opinions on:
   a) bus fares b) the GST c) cost of day care
   d) emergency room wait times

6. Courtney surveys her friends and finds that 68% of them have an MP3 player. She reports that 68% of the grade 9 students have an MP3 player. James surveys the entire grade 9 population and discovers that 51% have an MP3 player.
   a) Whose conclusion is more likely to be valid? Explain.
   b) Why might the other student's conclusion not be valid?

7. For each situation, explain why data are collected from a sample and not a census.
   a) to determine the number of hours an AAA battery will last in a calculator
   b) to determine the number of First Nations children in Canada who speak Cree

8. Should a census or sample be used to collect data about each topic? Explain your choice.
   a) the effectiveness of a new suntan lotion
   b) the popularity of a fruit-flavoured yogurt
   c) the number of grade 9 students in your school with braces
   d) the number of your friends who like to play computer games

9. In each case, do you think the conclusion is valid? Justify your answers.
   a) Irina surveyed 20 students to find out if they eat breakfast. All the students said yes. Irina concluded that everyone in the school eats breakfast.
   b) To test for pesticide pollution, a scientist collects and tests one vial of water from a river. From the results, a local newspaper reporter concludes that there are dangerous levels of pesticide in the river.

10. **Assessment Focus** Suppose you are the manager of a high school cafeteria. You want to create a new breakfast and lunch menu for the students.
    a) What population are you interested in surveying?
    b) Would you survey a sample or population? Explain.
    c) If you had to use a sample, what would you do to make sure your conclusions are valid?

11. In each case, provide an example and justify your choice.
    a) Collecting data from a population, rather than a sample, is more appropriate.
    b) Collecting data from a sample, rather than the entire population, is more appropriate.

Take It Further

12. a) Describe a situation where a sample:
       i) represents a population
       ii) does not represent a population
    b) What changes would you make to the sample in part ii so that the conclusions would be valid?

13. Every 5 years, the *Census of Agriculture* is sent to every farm household across Canada. This census collects data on topics such as crop area, livestock, farm labour, machinery, and expenses. Choose one of these topics. Explain why you think it is important enough for the government to conduct a census.

Reflect

Describe when to use a census and when to use a sample.

Using *Census at School*

Statistics Canada is a government agency that collects data on Canadian citizens. *Census at School* is an international online project that engages students from grades 4 to 12 in statistical enquiry. Data on students from 8 to 18 years old can be found at the *Census at School* website.

You can use *Census at School* to find data about Canadian youth under headings such as:

What is your favourite subject?
How much pressure do you feel because of schoolwork?
What is your favourite physical activity?

There is a link to data from other participating countries such as South Africa and New Zealand.

To use *Census at School*, follow these steps:

1. Open the website. Your teacher will give you the address. Select the appropriate language.

2. You will see the *Census at School* homepage. Click on *Data and results* located in the table on the left of the screen.

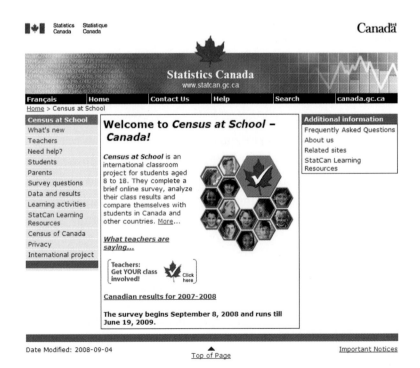

3. Under *Canadian summary results*, you can access data collected over the past several years. Select the latest summary results.

Canadian summary results

Student responses from across the country are collected throughout the school year and analysed during the summer. Then summary data tables are published in the fall.

- Summary results 2007/2008 (including provinces and territories)
- Summary results 2006/2007 (including provinces and territories)
- Summary results for 2005/2006 (including provinces and territories)
  - Highlights: What kids said in the last survey
- Summary results for 2004/2005 (including provinces and territories)
- Summary results for 2003/2004

Note: These results can be viewed by provinces and territories by selecting the *Provinces and territories* link at the top of the page.

Canadian summary results for 2007/2008

- Canada
- Provinces and territories

4. Use the site to answer these questions.

a) What is the most popular mode of transportation to school for Canadian youth? Is this the most popular mode of transportation for each province or territory? Explain.

b) What are the two most popular methods of communication for Canadian students?

c) Which type of charity would most students support if they had $1000 to donate?

d) What percent of students have been bullied 10 times or more in the last month in Manitoba?

5. To find data from other countries, click on the *International project* link on the left of the screen. Next, click on the *CensusAtSchool* link. Then on the next screen click on the link provided.

6. Select the United Kingdom (UK). Click on the link to *Results and Data*. Then, select the *Phase 7 Results* link. What do 14-year-olds feel is the most important issue facing the UK today?

Results and Data
- See the data presented in a variety of formats, eg tables, spreadsheets, graphs.
- Get a RANDOM SAMPLE of the raw census data.
- Access all the different Questionnaires including language versions.

Check

Return to the data for Canadian youth.

1. Select a topic that interests you, and report on your findings.

2. How many elementary and secondary students have participated in Canada's *Census at School*? Do you think this sample would produce valid conclusions? Explain.

9.1 **1.** Before a security company hires someone, that person must pass a lie-detector test. Suppose that a lie detector has a 0.9 probability of identifying a lie.
A person being tested thinks that if he lies 10 times, 9 of those lies will be detected.
a) Name one assumption the person is making.
b) Explain how the predicted outcome might change if the assumption changes.

2. Due to global warming, the West Antarctic Ice Sheet (WAIS) could melt and raise sea levels. Some scientists think there is a 1 in 20 chance that WAIS will collapse in the next 200 years. Explain how this statistic could be used to support opposing positions about the effects of global warming. **9.3**

9.2 **3.** Ca Bol surveys a group of people to find out how they feel about students listening to music while studying.
a) Write a question Ca Bol could use to influence:
  i) the responses in favour of students listening to music while studying
  ii) the responses to oppose students listening to music while studying
b) Write a question that does not show a bias. Explain how this question is more suitable than the questions in part a.

4. Suppose your teacher conducts a survey in class about student smoking.
a) What problems might arise?
b) How would these problems affect the data collected?

5. Ahmed wanted to find out if a person's years of post-secondary education is related to how much the person earns.
a) Describe problems Ahmed might have to overcome related to:
  i) privacy
  ii) cultural sensitivity
  iii) use of language
  iv) cost and time
b) Describe the effect each problem may have on Ahmed's results.

6. Describe a situation where the timing of a question may influence the responses.

7. Which students in your school would you survey for their opinions on each topic?
a) the quality of cafeteria service
b) the cost of a gym uniform
c) the number of student parking spaces
d) the school spirit at football games

8. For each situation, explain why data were not collected by a census.
a) the number of Canadian families with internet access
b) the average cost of DVD players
c) the average mass of a Northern pike in Misaw Lake, Saskatchewan

9. For each topic, would you collect data using a census or a sample?
Justify your choice.
a) to determine the average height of a grade 9 student in your class
b) to determine the reaction to new traffic laws in your province or territory

When we cannot survey an entire population, we choose a sample from the population.

When a political party wants to determine if its candidate is likely to win the next territorial election, it may conduct a telephone survey of a sample of voters. How could the party ensure that the sample is representative of the population?

FOCUS

• Understand and choose an appropriate sample.

Investigate

Suppose a school considers making the cafeteria food more healthy. The school would like you to determine the reactions of the school population.

List 3 ways you could select the sample of people to be questioned.
Discuss and record the advantages and disadvantages of each way.
Choose the most appropriate way of selecting your sample.

Reflect & Share

Share your 3 ways of selecting a sample with another pair of students.
Did you come up with any of the same ways?
Which ways had similar advantages and disadvantages?
Discuss and select the best way from all the possibilities.
Justify your choice.

Here are some common sampling methods:

Simple random sampling

Each member of the population has an equal chance of being selected.

For example, to select a random sample of 5 students from your math class, each student is assigned a number and 5 numbers are drawn from a hat.

Systematic or interval sampling

Every nth member of the population is selected.

This method is often used in manufacturing; for example, every 20th product in an assembly line is tested for quality. If the item is destroyed or unusable after being sampled, then the sample is a *destructive sample*.

Cluster sampling

Every member of each randomly chosen group of the population is selected.

For example, each grade represents a group of the school population. One grade in your school is chosen randomly, and all students in that grade are selected.

Self-selected sampling

Only members who are interested and volunteer will participate.

For example, if a radio station conducts a telephone survey, only people who are interested will call.

Convenience sampling

Only members of the population who are convenient to include are selected.

For example, for a survey about grocery shopping habits, people in a grocery store are approached and questioned.

Stratified random sampling

Some members from each group of the population are randomly selected.

For example, 5 randomly chosen students from each grade in a school could be selected, even if each grade has a different number of students.

Example 1 **Identifying Appropriate Samples**

The student leadership team wants to find out if students would like the cafeteria to have longer hours. Several sampling methods were suggested. Explain whether each sample is appropriate.

a) Every student's name is put into a box, and 100 names are selected randomly to be surveyed.

b) Every 5th person entering the school is selected.

c) Each person on the leadership team asks her or his friends.

d) An announcement is made asking anyone who wishes to participate to fill in a ballot.

▶ **A Solution**

Sampling Method	Is the Sample Appropriate?
a) Simple random sampling	The sample is appropriate because every student has an equal chance of being selected.
b) Systematic sampling	The sample may or may not be appropriate depending on when you ask students. If you ask students who arrive early in the morning, then these students may appreciate the cafeteria having longer hours. The opinions of these students would likely not be representative of the entire student population.
c) Convenience sampling	The sample is likely not appropriate because friends often have similar views on issues.
d) Self-selected sampling	The sample is likely not appropriate because only students who have strong opinions about this topic may respond.

Example 2 **Choosing Appropriate Samples**

A company packages boxes of granola bars. The quality-control manager inspects the first 5 boxes each morning to ensure that each has the same number and types of granola bars.

a) Is this a good way of ensuring quality control? Explain.

b) Suggest 2 other methods of sampling that would be appropriate. Explain why each is appropriate.

▶ **A Solution**

a) This may not be a good way of ensuring quality control because the people working on the assembly line may be more alert in the morning. So, the boxes filled in the mornings may pass inspection. However, the boxes made later in the day, which may not meet the manager's standards, are never inspected.

b) Systematic sampling would allow the manager to inspect several boxes throughout the day. For example, each 50th box could be inspected. Simple random sampling throughout the day would also be appropriate because it ensures each box has an equal chance of being selected.

1. Which sampling methods are least likely to produce valid conclusions? Explain.

2. Which sampling methods are most likely to produce valid conclusions? Explain.

Practice

Check

3. Identify a potential problem with each sampling method.
   a) Suppose you want to know whether most people enjoy shopping. You survey the shoppers at a local mall.
   b) The cook in the school cafeteria surveys the teachers to find out which items to sell.
   c) To determine public opinion on the effectiveness of the local police force, residents in the area with the greatest crime rate are surveyed.
   d) To find out about the exercise habits of Canadian teenagers, a fitness magazine asks its readers to email information about their exercise habits.

Apply

4. Explain whether each sample is appropriate. Justify your answer.
   a) A TV show asks viewers to text their opinions about the decreased speed limit in town.
   b) To determine if customers are pleased with the service in a restaurant, every 8th customer is polled on a given day.
   c) Fifty student ID numbers were randomly selected by a computer. The students with these ID numbers were surveyed about a new school policy.
   d) Ten students were randomly selected from each grade to estimate how many students in the school cycle to school.
   e) To determine if all physical education students would prefer to go skiing or skating on a field trip, one gym class was randomly selected from a list and each student in the class was polled.

5. a) In each case, will the selected sample represent the population? Explain.
   i) To find out if the arena should offer more public skating times, a survey is posted on a bulletin board in the arena and left for patrons to complete.
   ii) To find out the favourite breakfast food of grade 9 students, a survey of 300 randomly-selected grade 9 students was conducted.
   iii) To find out if the soccer league should buy new uniforms for the players, 20 parents of the students in the soccer league were surveyed.
   b) If the sample does not represent the population, suggest another sample that would. Describe how you would select that sample.

6. Describe an appropriate sampling method for each situation. Justify your answers.
   a) The Prime Minister wants to know citizens' opinions about the new budget.
   b) The school newspaper wants to poll students to predict who will be elected student president.

7. To determine citizens' view of new parking fines, the mayor invites listeners to call in during a radio show. Do you think the results will accurately reflect the opinions of all citizens? Explain.

8. Assessment Focus Suppose you want to find out how people feel about lowering the age at which teens can drive.
 a) Describe a sampling method that would not lead to valid conclusions. Justify your choice.
 b) Describe a sampling method you might use, and justify your choice.

9. For each topic, identify a sample of people whose opinions would bias the survey results. Explain your choice.
 a) whether fur from animals should be used for coats
 b) whether households should be fined for not recycling

10. A survey reports: Fifty Canadians say that the most important issue Canadians face is global warming.
 a) Do you think this sample is representative of the population? Explain.
 b) How might this sample have been selected?

 c) Suppose you were to repeat the survey. How would you select a sample? Explain how your choice of sample would represent the population.

Take It Further

11. Some sampling methods produce invalid conclusions more often than they produce valid conclusions. Which sampling methods do you think fit this description? Why do you think these sampling methods are still used?

12. a) Explain how you might obtain each sample.
   i) a simple random sample from the school population
   ii) a systematic sample of cell phones from a factory
   iii) a cluster sample of teenagers from your town
   iv) a stratified random sample of apple trees in an orchard
 b) Suggest a topic of data collection for each sample in part a.

Reflect

When you select a sample to represent a population, what factors must you consider?

Using Spreadsheets and Graphs to Display Data

FOCUS
- Display data on graphs using spreadsheets.

You can use a graph to display your data in a way that is clear and easy to understand.

Spreadsheet software can be used to record and graph data.

These data come from the *Census at School* website:

Which method do you use most often to communicate with friends?

Method of communication	Girls	Boys	All students
	%		
Internet chat or MSN	36.11	35.26	35.7
In person	30.02	35.51	32.65
Telephone (land line)	15.61	13.5	14.6
Cell phone	8.91	7.66	8.31
Text messaging	6.59	3.77	5.23
E-mail	1.73	2.20	1.96
Other	1.03	2.11	1.55

Notes: Secondary students only.
Methods of communication appear in order of frequency for all students.
Source: Statistics Canada, Census at School, 2006/2007.

1. Enter the *Method of communication* and the percent of *All students* into columns and rows.

2. Highlight the data including the column heads. Click the graph/chart icon. Select the circle graph, which is sometimes called a pie chart. Label the graph and all sectors of the circle.
   Your graph might look like this:

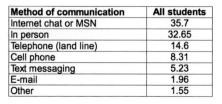

Method of communication	All students
Internet chat or MSN	35.7
In person	32.65
Telephone (land line)	14.6
Cell phone	8.31
Text messaging	5.23
E-mail	1.96
Other	1.55

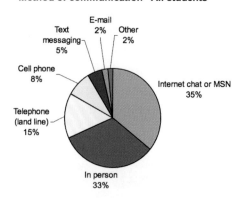

Method of communication - All students

3. You can also display the data using a bar graph. Create a *Vertical bar graph,* sometimes called a *Column graph* for the data. Label the graph and axes. Experiment with the scale of each axis to most clearly display the data.

4. To display the data for *Boys, Girls,* and *All students,* you can make a multiple bar graph.

Enter the data for *Boys* and *Girls* into the next two columns of the spreadsheet. Now highlight all the data and create a bar graph.

Your finished graph might look like this:

Method of communication	All students	Boys	Girls
Internet chat or MSN	35.7	35.26	36.11
In person	32.65	35.51	30.02
Telephone (land line)	14.6	13.5	15.61
Cell phone	8.31	7.66	8.91
Text messaging	5.23	3.77	6.59
E-mail	1.96	2.2	1.73
Other	1.55	2.11	1.03

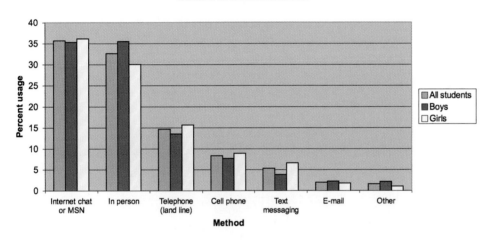

Method of communication

Check

1. List one advantage and one disadvantage of displaying data using each type of graph above.

2. These data are from *Census at School:*

How long does it usually take you to travel to school?

Minutes	Elementary	Secondary
	%	
Less than 10	38.36	18.96
10 to 19	31.83	31.92
20 to 29	12.55	17.96
30 to 44	10.65	16.83
45 to 59	4.16	7.71
60 or more	2.44	6.61

Source: Statistics Canada, Census at School, 2006/2007.

Use an appropriate graph to display the results for all students. Justify your choice of graph.

How Can I Assess My Work?

I can design a **rubric**. A rubric helps me to see how well I understood the task and how good I am at communicating what I know. It lists the content and quality needed for a task; these are called the *criteria* of the task.

My first step to create a rubric is to determine the criteria of the task. Suppose I have to write an article for my school newspaper. The criteria I would look for in the article are:

- Accurate information
- Well organized
- An eye-catching title
- Correct spelling and grammar

I then assess each criterion using one of 4 *levels of achievement*:

- Not yet adequate
- Adequate
- Proficient
- Excellent

I create a grid:

	Not yet adequate	Adequate	Proficient	Excellent
Accurate information				
Correct spelling and grammar				
Well organized				
Eye-catching title				

I then include what I think needs to be done to achieve each level.

	Not yet adequate	Adequate	Proficient	Excellent
Accurate information	uses few facts that are not enough to explain the topic (1-2 facts)	uses some facts to explain the topic (3-4 facts)	uses most of the available facts to explain the topic (5-7 facts)	uses all the available facts to explain the topic (8 facts)
Correct spelling and grammar		has some spelling and grammatical errors (4-6 errors)	has few spelling and grammatical errors (1-3 errors)	has no spelling or grammatical errors (0 errors)
Well organized	ideas are not in an order that makes sense	ideas are partly in an order that makes sense		all ideas are in an order that makes sense
Eye-catching title	attempts to write a title, but it is not clear and will not attract readers	writes a title that is clear, but may not attract many readers	writes a title that is clear and effective at attracting many readers	writes a title that is very clear and is outstanding at attracting all readers

Check

1. What descriptions might go in the grey areas?

Apply

2. a) Create a rubric to evaluate your day at school. Use the criteria below.

	Not yet adequate	Adequate	Proficient	Excellent
Homework was done				
On time for classes				
Paid attention				
Helped others				

b) Trade rubrics with a classmate. Suggest how to improve your classmate's rubric.

9.5 Designing a Project Plan

FOCUS

• Develop a project plan for data collection.

Have you been stopped in the shopping mall by a person with a clipboard and been asked to answer questions for a survey?
Have you ever answered the telephone at home in the evening and been asked if you would take part in a survey?
Or, have you completed an online survey?
If so, what types of questions were you asked?

Investigate

Suppose your school board would like to know if there is a relation between the number of hours a student works at a part-time job and her or his academic success. Design a plan that the school board could follow to collect the data.

Reflect & Share

Share your plan with that of another group.
How are your plans similar? How are your plans different?
Do your plans avoid potential problems? Explain.
If not, make adjustments to your plan.

Connect

Here are 5 possible steps to consider when you design a plan for data collection:
1. **Prepare a question.** The wording should avoid biases, and be culturally sensitive. If the survey question is personal, the participants should be anonymous.
2. **Identify the population, and possibly choose a sample.** If you select a sample, ensure it represents the population. Consider the time and cost involved in collecting data from your population or sample.
3. **Collect the data.** Consider the timing of your data collection: does it avoid potential problems?
4. **Analyze and display the data.** Choose an appropriate display for the data, such as a table, circle graph, bar graph, or line graph.
5. **Design a rubric.** This should help you evaluate the important components of your project.

Suppose a frozen yogurt company considers adding a new flavour to its menu. Decide how to conduct a survey to determine whether the new flavour should be added to the menu.

▶ *A Solution*

Follow the steps:

1. The survey question might be:

Rate the taste of this new flavour of frozen yogurt on a scale of 1 to 5.

1	2	3	4	5
Strongly Dislike	*Dislike*	*No Opinion*	*Like*	*Strongly Like*

2. The population is all people who eat frozen yogurt and may purchase it from this company. A sample of the population might be every 10th customer who comes into a store one day from when it opens to when it closes.

3. To collect the data, the company must have a server who offers every 10th customer a free sample, poses the survey question, and records the responses.

4. To analyze the data, determine the number of people who chose each rating. This can be displayed on a circle graph. Then calculate the mean rating.

5. Evaluate the process you followed to determine if the data are valid and that you have accounted for all possible biases.

Discuss the ideas

1. Why is it important to plan before you collect data?

2. How can a rubric help you reflect on your plan?

Practice

In this lesson, you will prepare a project plan for your data collection. In the Unit Problem, you will carry out the data collection, analyze and display your results, then draw conclusions.

Developing a Project Plan

3. a) Choose a topic that interests you. Prepare a question you want to answer about that topic.

b) Explain how the wording of your question avoids bias.

c) Is your topic a sensitive one for different cultures? If so, how will you deal with this?

d) Test your question on a classmate. Make any necessary changes.

4. a) Describe the population for your data collection.

b) Will you collect data from the population or a sample? If you work with a sample, how will you select the sample to ensure it represents the population?

c) Explain how your choice of population or sample takes into account the time and cost of the project.

5. Explain how you will collect the data. As part of your answer, discuss:
- how the timing of your data collection will not cause a problem
- any privacy considerations

6. How might you display your data? Justify your choice.

Creating a Rubric for Your Project

7. Create a rubric for your project. In the Unit Problem, you will collect the data and present your findings. Your rubric must assess the following criteria:
- the survey question
- the choice of sample or population
- how the data were collected
- the display of your data
- the conclusions you made
- your presentation

Your rubric should have 4 levels of achievement.

Assessing Your Plan

8. a) Trade project plans with a classmate. Look for potential problems in your classmate's plan. Suggest ways of improving the plan.

b) Incorporate your classmate's comments into your plan.

Reflecting on Your Plan

9. People often make predictions about the results of their data collection. Sometimes these predictions are based on data from the past or personal experience. Make a prediction about your results. Explain why you think it might be true.

10. Why is this topic of interest to you? Who else might be interested in the results?

Reflect

Which step in developing your plan did you find most challenging? Explain.

Your World

Every five years, Statistics Canada completes a census by collecting data from every household in Canada. Statistics Canada also requires one in five households to provide more detailed information about themselves. These data are used to help us better understand our country, including its natural resources, educational needs, and the economic situations of people living in various regions. Since the same or similar questions are asked every 5 years, the data can show what changes have taken place in our population over time.

Study Guide

Probability

▶ Probability is the likelihood an event will occur. For example, a weather forecast says that the probability of rain is 60%. This assumes that the predicted weather conditions do not change. If they do change, then the likelihood of rain may also change.

▶ Decisions based on probabilities may be a combination of theoretical probability, experimental probability, and subjective judgment. People may make different decisions based on one probability. For example, one person may consider a 60% probability of rain as being too high, and cancel a planned outdoor event. Another person may say that a 40% probability it will not rain is good enough to proceed with the event.

Collecting data

▶ Problems may arise if a person does not consider:
   – bias
   – use of language
   – ethics
   – cost and time
   – timing
   – privacy
   – cultural sensitivity

▶ The population is the group from which you are getting information.

▶ When a census is conducted, data are collected from the entire population.

▶ When data are collected from only part of the population, a *sample* is used. This sample must be representative of the population.

▶ Valid conclusions are obtained when the sample results represent those of the population.

9.1 **1.** Two weeks before a municipal election, a survey produced these data about voters' preferences for a new mayor.

Preference for Mayor	Number of Votes
Vivian Rogers	19
Fred Yao	11
Mustafa Abaz	34
Undecided	6

a) Based on these data, predict which candidate will win.

b) What assumptions are you making? For each assumption, explain what would happen if the assumption changes.

2. A volleyball team has won all 5 games it played this season.
Darrell thinks that the team will lose its next game because he believes their winning streak cannot last.
The players on the team believe that the team has a 100% chance of winning the next game.
Explain how probability and subjective judgment may be influencing these opinions.

3. A local hospital is raising money by selling lottery tickets. The chances of winning are advertised as 1 in 3. Explain how someone can use this probability to support:
a) purchasing a ticket
b) not purchasing a ticket

4. Find an example where statistics are used in an advertisement to try to convince consumers that one product is better than another. Suppose the statistic is true. What assumptions are you making about how the data were collected?

9.2 **5.** a) In each case, identify any problems.
i) To determine people's reactions to a possible increase in minimum wage, a student asked: "Don't you agree that minimum wage should increase?"
ii) For a class project, a student needed to determine if college students were maintaining healthy weights. After the student completed the project, she gave a weight loss company the addresses of any overweight participants.
iii) To test the safety of its deluxe car model, a company subjects many cars to different crash tests.
iv) To determine if residents would support the construction of a community outdoor pool, you survey residents by going door-to-door in November.

b) Describe the effect each problem might have on the results of the data collection.

6. Adila wants to know which digital camera is the best buy.
a) What do you think "best buy" means? Design a question that will give Adila the information she wants.
b) Explain how your question avoids bias.

7. For a school project, Raheem wants to find out if there is an increase in teen pregnancy in Canada. Describe the effect of problems Raheem might encounter related to:
a) privacy
b) cultural sensitivity
c) use of language

8. a) Provide an example of a question that could lead to problems because participants are only allowed to choose from 3 possible answers.
b) Reword the question to avoid the potential problems.

9. Provide an example of data you might want to collect, but where the cost and time involved might be problematic.

9.3 **10.** As an operator of a skydiving school, would you suggest a census or a sample when inspecting parachutes for excess wear? Explain.

11. Leah wants to test the lifespan of different brands of batteries.
   a) List reasons why Leah would use a sample for her data collection.
   b) Suggest how she might choose her sample to ensure it represents the population.

12. a) Explain why a sample might be used in each survey.
   i) You wish to find out the most popular sport for teens your age.
   ii) You wish to find out the most popular Internet provider in your area.
   b) Provide an example when a census would be more appropriate for collecting data than a sample.

9.4 **13.** A TV show surveys viewers to determine the popularity of its singers. At the end of each show, viewers cast votes for their favourite singers by calling in at $0.75 per call. Do you think the opinions of the sample will reflect those of the population? Explain.

14. Discuss whether each sampling method should lead to valid conclusions.
   a) A car company subjects every 200th vehicle it manufactures to crash tests.
   b) Six students from each grade are selected randomly to complete a survey about which extracurricular activities the school should offer.
   c) A juice company sets up a booth in a local mall and allows anyone who wishes to participate in a taste test.

15. Describe an appropriate sampling method for each case. Justify your choice.
   a) to predict which political party will win the next election
   b) to determine which brand of tennis racket is preferred

9.5 **16.** Adam wants to find out what brand of chewing gum is recommended by most dentists.
   a) Write an appropriate survey question Adam could use.
   b) Choose an appropriate sample. Explain your choice.
   c) Explain how Adam could collect the data and display the results.
   d) Explain how Adam could express his results as a probability.

1. A coin is tossed 5 times and each time it lands heads up. The coin is to be tossed again. Shawnie says the coin will land heads up. Owen says the coin will land tails up. Jovana says the coin is equally likely to land heads up as tails up. How might these students have made their predictions?

2. Hannah's hockey team won its last 7 out of 8 games. Hannah calculates that the team's probability of winning the next game is $\frac{7}{8} = 0.875$.
   a) What assumptions is Hannah making?
   b) For each assumption, explain how the predicted outcome might be affected if the assumption changes.

3. Manroop wants to survey Canadians to determine how happy or depressed they are.
   a) Describe how the timing of Manroop's survey may influence her results.
   b) Explain how privacy may be a factor in this survey.
      What should Manroop do to ensure the privacy of the participants?
   c) Manroop designs the following question:

   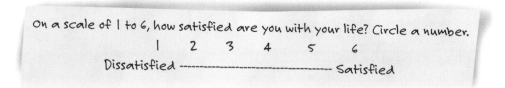

   What problems might Manroop encounter with this question?
   What effects would those problems have on her data?

4. Provide an example of a situation where:
   a) collecting data from a sample is more appropriate than a census
   b) a sample may not result in the same conclusions as a census
   Justify each example.

5. For each case, explain how you would select a sample.
   a) to test the water quality in your school
   b) to determine the most popular brand of toothpaste used by students at your school
   c) to measure the average mass of backpacks of students at your school

6. Emile starts a petition to ask the municipal government to allow all stores to open at 9 A.M. on Sunday morning. What problems might he encounter as he solicits signatures? Describe the effect each problem would have on his results.

What Can You Discover about the World around You?

You will collect data for the project plan you designed in Lesson 9.5.
You will then present your findings and assess your work.

Part 1 Collect and Analyze the Data
➤ Collect the data from your chosen population or sample.
➤ Organize the data. Consider using a spreadsheet.
➤ Make an appropriate graph to display your data.
➤ Analyze your results. What conclusions can you make?

Part 2 Assess Your Data
Use the rubric you made to assess your data collection and make
any necessary changes.

Part 3 Present Your Findings
In your presentation, make sure you answer these questions:
➤ Why did you choose your topic?
➤ What considerations did you make when writing your question?
➤ What considerations did you make when selecting the population or sample?
   If you chose a sample, how did you try to ensure the conclusions would be valid?
➤ Why did you choose to display the data in the way you did?
➤ What conclusions can be made from the data?
➤ Are you surprised by the results? Explain.
➤ Who might be interested in your data and why?
➤ If you were to repeat the project, what steps would you take to improve it? Explain.

Part 4 Assess Your Presentation
Use the rubric to assess your presentation.

Your work should include:
- a project plan from Lesson 9.5
- the display of your data and your conclusions
- answers to the presentation questions
- a rubric used for self-assessment

Reflect on Your Learning

What are the most important considerations when
collecting data? Why? What are the most important
questions to ask about probabilities published in the
media? Explain.

A quilt consists of small blocks that tessellate.

Materials

- ruler
- compass
- pencil crayons or markers
- construction paper
- tape
- dynamic geometry software (*optional*)

Part 1

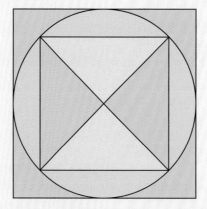

The larger shape in this quilt block is a square with side length 15 cm.

Within the square there is a circle and within this circle there is a smaller square.

➤ What is the side length of the smaller square?

➤ Describe the triangles in the block.

Part 2

Look at these quilt blocks. What shapes do you see?

Block A

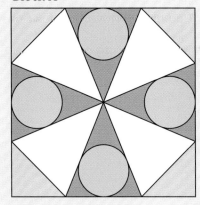

Block B

Part 3

Design a square block with side length 15 cm that will be repeated 3 times
to form a square with side length 30 cm. Use circles as part of your design.
With your four 15-cm blocks, create as many different 30-cm blocks as you can.
Describe the symmetries in each 30-cm block.

Take It Further

Choose a shape other than a square.
Create a block that will tessellate to form a quilt.

1 **1.** Sketch this number line.

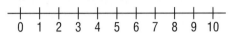

Do *not* use a calculator. Determine or estimate each square root. Where necessary, write the square root to the nearest tenth. Place each square root on the number line.

a) $\sqrt{0.64}$ b) $\sqrt{\dfrac{36}{25}}$ c) $\sqrt{79.7}$ d) $\sqrt{4.41}$

e) $\sqrt{\dfrac{100}{9}}$ f) $\sqrt{\dfrac{89}{90}}$ g) $\sqrt{30.25}$ h) $\sqrt{\dfrac{17}{4}}$

2. Here is a floor plan for a building that is 5 m tall. It has a flat roof. What is the surface area of the building, including its roof, but excluding its floor?

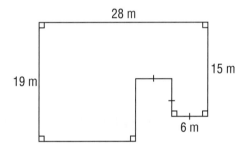

2 **3.** A student answered the following skill-testing question to try to win a prize:
$(-4)^3 - (-2)^4 \div 2^2 + 5^2 \times 7^0$

The student's answer was 5. Did the student win the prize? Show your work.

4. Express as a single power, then evaluate.
$$\left(\dfrac{6^7 \times 6^3}{6^5 \times 6^2}\right)^2$$

3 **5.** During the month of July, Bruce earned $225 cutting lawns and $89.25 weeding flower beds. He spent $223.94 on an MP3 player and purchased 3 DVDs at $22.39 each.

a) Write each amount as a rational number. Justify your choice of sign for each number.

b) Write an addition statement for Bruce's balance at the end of July.

c) What is Bruce's balance?

6. Use a calculator. Evaluate to the nearest hundredth.
$$\dfrac{-17.8 - (-9.6) \div 1.2 + 31.4}{7.6 \times (-4.1) - 2.9}$$

4 **7.** Marcie is rowing at an average speed of 3 m/s. She travels a distance d metres in t seconds.

a) Create a table of values for this relation.

b) Graph the data. Will you join the points on the graph? Explain.

c) Is the relation linear? How do you know?

d) Write an equation that relates d to t.

e) How far does Marcie row in 15 s?

f) How long does it take Marcie to travel 1 km?

8. Colton works for 8 h each week at a sporting goods store. This graph shows how his pay in dollars relates to the number of weeks he works.

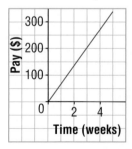

a) Estimate how much Colton earns after 2 weeks.

b) Estimate how long it will take Colton to earn $1000. What assumptions do you make?

c) What conditions could change that would make this graph no longer valid?

9. The difference of two polynomials is $4n^2 - 2n + 5$. One polynomial is $-6n^2 - 7n + 8$.

a) What is the other polynomial? Show your work.

b) Why are there two possible answers to part a?

10. This diagram shows one rectangle inside another.

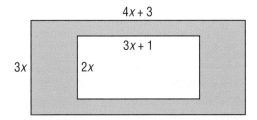

a) Determine the area of the shaded region. Justify your answer.

b) Determine the area of the shaded region when $x = 1.5$ cm.

11. Mountain bikes can be rented from two stores near the entrance to Stanley Park. Store A charges $6.00 per hour, plus $3.50 for a helmet and lock. Store B charges $6.70 per hour and provides a helmet and lock free. Determine the time in hours for which the rental charges in both stores are equal.

a) Write an equation to solve this problem.

b) Solve the equation.

c) Verify the solution.

12. Jerry hires a pedicab to tour a city. He is charged $2.75 plus $0.60 per minute of travel. He has $12.00. How long can he ride in the pedicab?

a) Choose a variable and write an inequality to solve this problem.

b) Solve the inequality. Explain the solution in words.

c) Verify the solution.

d) Graph the solution.

13. This photo is to be enlarged. Determine the dimensions of an enlargement with each scale factor.

a) 2   **b)** $\frac{7}{4}$ **c)** 3.5

14. A hockey rink measures 60 m by 26 m. A model of a hockey rink measures 1.5 m by 0.65 m.

a) What is the scale factor for this reduction?

b) A hockey goal is 1.8 m high and 1.2 m high. What are the dimensions of a goal on the model hockey rink?

15. Bobbi wants to determine the height of a building. When Bobbi's shadow is 2.5 m long, the shadow of the building is 12 m long. Bobbi is 1.7 m tall. What is the height of the building, to the nearest tenth of a metre? Show your work.

16. Trapezoid ABCD is part of a larger shape.

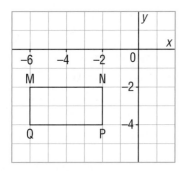

After each reflection below:
- Draw the image of ABCD.
- Describe any symmetry in the shape and its image.

a) a reflection in the horizontal line through 5 on the *y*-axis

b) a reflection in the vertical line through 4 on the *x*-axis

c) a reflection in the oblique line through (0, 6) and (6, 0)

17. a) Does rectangle MNPQ below have rotational symmetry about its centre? If it does, state the order and the angle of rotation symmetry.

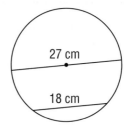

b) Rectangle MNPQ is part of a larger shape. It is to be completed in three different ways, by each rotation below:
- 90° clockwise about the point (−2, −3)
- 180° about vertex Q
- 270° clockwise about the point (−4, −4)

i) Draw each rotation image.

ii) List the coordinates of the larger shape formed by the rectangle and its image each time. Describe any rotational symmetry in this shape.

8 **18.** Point G is a point of tangency and O is the centre of the circle. Determine the length of GH to the nearest tenth of a centimetre.

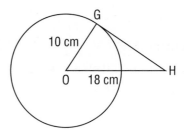

19. A circle has diameter 27 cm. How far from the centre of this circle is a chord 18 cm long? Give your answer to the nearest tenth of a centimetre.

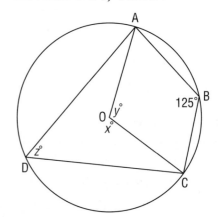

20. Point O is the centre of a circle. Determine the values of $x°$, $y°$, and $z°$.

21. A rectangle is inscribed in a circle with radius 14 cm. The length of the rectangle is 21 cm. Determine the width of the rectangle to the nearest tenth of a centimetre.

22. A regular decagon is inscribed in a circle with radius 20 cm and centre O. The distance from O to each side of the decagon is about 19 cm. What is the perimeter of the decagon to the nearest centimetre?

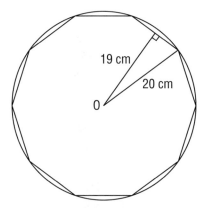

23. Point O is the centre of a circle. Determine the values of $x°$, $y°$, and $z°$.

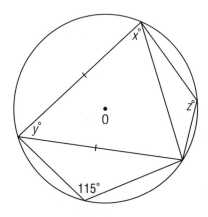

24. A baseball team won 58 of its first 100 games of the season. Bao concludes that there is a 58% probability of the team winning its next game.
   a) What assumptions is Bao making?
   b) For each assumption, explain how the probability might change if the assumption is not true.

25. Zahara is planning a telephone survey to discover how much weekly allowance parents give their children.
   a) Identify potential problems she may encounter related to 3 of these factors: bias, timing, privacy, cultural sensitivity, ethics, time
   b) For each potential problem in part a, explain how Zahara could avoid the problem.

26. An on-line fashion magazine for teens concludes that high school students spend on average $200 per month on clothes.
   a) How do you think the magazine may have conducted the survey?
   b) Do you think the conclusion is valid? Explain.

27. For each situation, explain why data are collected from a sample and not a census.
   a) to determine the mean cost of hockey equipment for teenagers in Canada
   b) to determine the number of Canadian families with at least one cell phone

28. Should a census or sample be used to collect data about each topic? Explain your choice.
   a) to determine the popularity of a new television show
   b) to determine the condition of an airplane's seatbelts

29. Discuss whether each sampling method would lead to valid conclusions.
   a) To determine if the prices of items in a grocery store are appropriate, you survey every 12th customer leaving the store on a given day.
   b) To determine the favourite video game of students in a school, you survey 20 randomly selected students from each grade in the school.

Answers

1.1 Square Roots of Perfect Squares, page 11

3. a) 0.5   **b)** $\dfrac{3}{4}$ or 0.75

    c) $\dfrac{4}{5}$ or 0.8

4. a) 1, 4, 9, 16, 25, 36, 49, 64, 81, 100
    b) 1, 2, 3, 4, 5, 6, 7, 8, 9, 10

5. a) 0.6   **b)** 0.7
    c) 0.9   **d)** 0.4

    e) $\dfrac{1}{6}$ **f)** $\dfrac{5}{3}$

    g) $\dfrac{8}{10} = \dfrac{4}{5}$ **h)** $\dfrac{6}{4} = \dfrac{3}{2}$

6. a) 121, 144, 169, 196, 225, 256, 289, 324, 361, 400
    b) 11, 12, 13, 14, 15, 16, 17, 18, 19, 20

7. a) $\dfrac{13}{4}$ **b)** $\dfrac{20}{14} = \dfrac{10}{7}$

    c) $\dfrac{16}{19}$ **d)** $\dfrac{15}{17}$

    e) 12   **f)** 0.15
    g) 0.11   **h)** 1.8
    i) 0.18   **j)** 0.13

8. a) $0.12 = \dfrac{12}{100}$ is not a perfect square because 12 is
      not a perfect square.
   b) $\sqrt{0.81} = 0.9$, so 0.81 is a perfect square.
   c) $\sqrt{0.25} = 0.5$, so 0.25 is a perfect square.
   d) $\sqrt{1.69} = 1.3$, so 1.69 is a perfect square.
   e) $\dfrac{9}{12}$ is not a perfect square because 12 is not a
      perfect square.
   f) $\dfrac{36}{81}$ is a perfect square because both 36 and 81 are
      perfect squares.
   g) $\dfrac{81}{49}$ is a perfect square because both 81 and 49
      are perfect squares.
   h) $\dfrac{75}{27} = \dfrac{25}{9}$ is a perfect square, because both 25 and
      9 are perfect squares.
   i) $0.081 = \dfrac{81}{1000}$ is not a perfect square because
      1000 is not a perfect square.

j) $\dfrac{25}{10}$ is not a perfect square because 10 is not a
    perfect square.

k) $2.5 = \dfrac{25}{10}$ so it is not a perfect square.

l) $\dfrac{8}{50} = \dfrac{4}{25}$ is a perfect square because both 4 and
    25 are perfect squares.

9. a) 0.09   **b)** 0.0144
    c) 3.61   **d)** 9.61

    e) $\dfrac{4}{9}$ **f)** $\dfrac{25}{36}$

    g) $\dfrac{1}{49}$ **h)** $\dfrac{4}{25}$

10. a) 3.5   **b)** 5.5
    c) 4.5   **d)** 7.5

11. a) i) $36.0 = \dfrac{36}{1}$ is a perfect square.

     ii) $3.6 = \dfrac{36}{10} = \dfrac{18}{5}$ is not a perfect square.

     iii) $0.36 = \dfrac{36}{100} = \dfrac{9}{25}$ is a perfect square.

     iv) $0.036 = \dfrac{36}{1000} = \dfrac{9}{250}$ is not a perfect square.

     v) $0.0036 = \dfrac{36}{10\,000} = \dfrac{9}{2500}$ is a perfect square.

     vi) $0.000\,36 = \dfrac{36}{100\,000} = \dfrac{9}{25000}$ is not a perfect
       square.

    b) i) $\sqrt{36.0} = 6$
      ii) $\sqrt{3.6} \doteq 1.9$
      iii) $\sqrt{0.36} = 0.6$
      iv) $\sqrt{0.036} \doteq 0.19$
      v) $\sqrt{0.0036} = 0.06$
      vi) $\sqrt{0.000\,36} \doteq 0.019$

12. a) i) 300   **ii)** 30
     iii) 0.3   **iv)** 0.03
    b) i) 0.05   **ii)** 0.5
     iii) 50   **iv)** 500

13. a) i) C   **ii)** A
     iii) E   **iv)** B
     v) F   **vi)** D

14. a) 2.4 cm   **b)** 9.6 cm
15. a) 2.5 km   **b)** 3.2 km
    c) 7.84 km^2
16. No. $\sqrt{0.04} = 0.2$
17. b) For example: (3, 4, 5), (9, 12, 15), (12, 16, 20),
      (5, 12, 13), (8, 15, 17)
18. Yes, the squares of all numbers between 0.8 and 0.9
    are between 0.64 and 0.81.

19. a) 3.6 cm **b)** 1 cut

1.2 Square Roots of Non-Perfect Squares, page 18

4. a) 1 and 4; $\sqrt{1} = 1$ and $\sqrt{4} = 2$

b) 9 and 16; $\sqrt{9} = 3$ and $\sqrt{16} = 4$

c) 49 and 64; $\sqrt{49} = 7$ and $\sqrt{64} = 8$

d) 64 and 81; $\sqrt{64} = 8$ and $\sqrt{81} = 9$

e) 81 and 100; $\sqrt{81} = 9$ and $\sqrt{100} = 10$

f) 100 and 121; $\sqrt{100} = 10$ and $\sqrt{121} = 11$

5. a) $\dfrac{49}{100}$ and $\dfrac{64}{100}$; $\sqrt{0.49} = 0.7$ and $\sqrt{0.64} = 0.8$

b) 4 and 9; $\sqrt{4} = 2$ and $\sqrt{9} = 3$

c) 9 and 16; $\sqrt{9} = 3$ and $\sqrt{16} = 4$

d) 49 and 64; $\sqrt{49} = 7$ and $\sqrt{64} = 8$

e) 64 and 81; $\sqrt{64} = 8$ and $\sqrt{81} = 9$

f) 100 and 121; $\sqrt{100} = 10$ and $\sqrt{121} = 11$

6. Estimates will vary, for example:

a) $\sqrt{\dfrac{8}{10}} \doteq 0.9$ **b)** $\sqrt{\dfrac{17}{5}} \doteq \dfrac{9}{5}$

c) $\sqrt{\dfrac{7}{13}} \doteq 0.7$ **d)** $\sqrt{\dfrac{29}{6}} \doteq 2.2$

7. Approximations will vary, for example:

a) $\sqrt{4.5} \doteq 2.1$ **b)** $\sqrt{14.5} \doteq 3.8$

c) $\sqrt{84.5} \doteq 9.2$ **d)** $\sqrt{145.5} \doteq 12.1$

e) $\sqrt{284.5} \doteq 16.9$ **f)** $\sqrt{304.5} \doteq 17.4$

8. a) $\sqrt{29.5} \doteq 5.4$ **b)** $\sqrt{\dfrac{5}{2}} \doteq 1.6$

9. a) The estimate is incorrect. $\sqrt{4.4} \doteq 2.1$

b) The estimate is incorrect. $\sqrt{0.6} \doteq 0.8$

c) The estimate is correct to the nearest tenth.

d) The estimate is incorrect. $\sqrt{0.4} \doteq 0.6$

10. a) Any number between 9 and 16; for example 10.24 and 12.25

b) Any number between 49 and 64; for example 50.41 and 59.29

c) Any number between 144 and 169; for example 158.36 and 166.41

d) Any number between 2.25 and 6.25; for example 3.0 and 3.5

e) Any number between 20.25 and 30.25; for example 22.09 and 29.16

11. a) About 2.1 **b)** About 2.9

c) About 0.4 **d)** About 0.5

e) About 0.8 **f)** About 0.4

g) About 0.2 **h)** About 2.2

12. a) 0.6 **b)** 0.6

c) 1.8 **d)** 2.9

13. a) 1.3 cm **b)** About 2.7 cm

c) About 4.85 cm **d)** 0.7 cm

14. There is no limit to the number of decimals and fractions; for example 0.3025 and $\dfrac{61}{200}$

15.

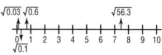

16. a) $\sqrt{0.25}$, $\sqrt{0.5}$, $\sqrt{1.44}$, and $\sqrt{3.6}$ are correctly placed.

b)

17. a) $\sqrt{52.9} \doteq 7.2732$ **b)** $\sqrt{5.29} = 2.3$

c) $\sqrt{2.25} = 1.5$ **d)** $\sqrt{22.5} \doteq 4.7434$

18. a) The numbers are greater than 1.

b) The number must be 0 or 1.

c) The numbers are less than 1.

19. For example:

a) 0.64 **b)** 3

c) $\dfrac{2}{5}$ **d)** 15

20. a) 1.82 km **b)** 2.36 km

21. a) i) About 0.0707 **ii)** About 0.7071

iii) About 7.0711 **iv)** About 70.7107

v) About 707.1068

b) $\sqrt{0.000\,05} \doteq 0.007\,071$

$\sqrt{0.000\,0005} \doteq 0.000\,7071$

$\sqrt{50\,000\,000} \doteq 7071.0678$

$\sqrt{5\,000\,000\,000} \doteq 70\,710.678$

22. Yes. All numbers between 0.775 and 0.781 have squares between 0.6 and 0.61.

23. For example: (1.1, 0.2), (0.6, 0.2) and (0.6, 0.7)

24. a) About 7.8 cm

b) Doubling the side length would increase the area by a factor of 4.

Unit 1: Mid-Unit Review, page 21

1. a) $\sqrt{\dfrac{25}{36}} = \dfrac{5}{6}$ **b)** $\sqrt{0.36} = 0.6$

2. a) 1.96 **b)** $\dfrac{9}{64}$

c) $\dfrac{49}{16}$ **d)** 0.25

3. a) 0.2 **b)** $\dfrac{1}{4}$

c) 1.4   **d)** $\dfrac{2}{9}$

e) 1.3   **f)** $\dfrac{11}{7}$

g) 0.3   **h)** $\dfrac{17}{10}$

4. a) 1.8   **b)** 9.5
   c) 1.6
5. a) 12.2 cm   **b)** 48.8 cm
6. No, the student is incorrect. $\sqrt{0.16} = 0.4$
7. a) $\dfrac{9}{64}$ is a perfect square, since both 9 and 64 are

perfect squares.

b) $3.6 = \dfrac{36}{10}$ is not a perfect square, since 10 is not a

perfect square.

c) $\dfrac{6}{9}$ is not a perfect square, since 6 is not a perfect

square.

d) $5.76 = \dfrac{576}{100}$ is a perfect square, since both 576

and 100 are perfect squares.

8. Estimates will vary, for example:
   a) About 2.4   **b)** About 0.95
   c) About 6.5   **d)** About 5.97
   e) About 0.24   **f)** 0.3
9. a) About 3.0 cm
   b) 4 cm
10. a) Correct   **b)** About 1.3
   c) Correct   **d)** Correct
11. For example:
   a) 20.25, 33.64   **b)** 0.5625, 0.64
   c) 1.69, 1.7   **d)** 0.09, 0.1024
   e) 22.09, 28.09   **f)** 0.0036, 0.0049

Unit 1: Start Where You Are, page 22

1. About 1385 cm^2
2. About 1546 cm^2

1.3 Surface Areas of Objects Made from Right Rectangular Prisms, page 30

4. a) 14 square units   **b)** 18 square units
   c) 22 square units   **d)** 20 square units
   e) 22 square units   **f)** 26 square units
5. a) i) 18 cm^2 **ii)** 18 cm^2
   iii) 18 cm^2
6. a) i) 20 cm^2 **ii)** 20 cm^2
   iii) 22 cm^2

8. a) 68 cm^2 **b)** 144 cm^2
   c) 255.5 cm^2
10. a) 165.03 m^2 **b)** $1609.20
11. 1346 m^2
12. a) 54 square units
   b) 9 ways
   c) i) 6 cubes   **ii)** 12 cubes
   iii) 8 cubes   **iv)** 1 cube
   v) 0 cubes
14. c) 22 cm^2, 24 cm^2, 26 cm^2
16. 110 m^2
17. a) The piece made from 3 cubes has surface area
   14 cm^2; pieces made from 4 cubes have surface
   area 18 cm^2.
   c) 68 faces will not be painted.

1.4 Surface Areas of Other Composite Objects, page 40

3. a) 121 cm^2 **b)** 117 cm^2
   c) 283 cm^2 **d)** 360 cm^2
   e) 256 cm^2
4. a) 58.1 cm^2 **b)** 62.1 m^2
5. a) About 21.9 m^2 **b)** About 58.3 cm^2
6. Including the bottom of base: About 707 cm^2
7. a) 35 m^2
8. a) 5.42 m^2
   b) 2 cans of 1-L wood stain
9. a)

   b) About 2081.3 cm^2
10. a) 2832.3 cm^2 **b)** 3652.1 cm^2
11. 1155 cm^2
12. a) 61.1 m^2
13. a) 3456 cm^2 **b)** 4509 cm^2
14. About 10 700 cm^2
15. a) About 3336 cm^2
   b) i)

   ii) About 4882 cm^2

Unit 1: Review, page 45

1. a) 1.1

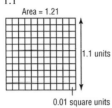

Area = 1.21

1.1 units

0.01 square units

b) $\frac{3}{5}$

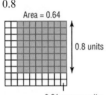

Area = $\frac{9}{25}$

$\frac{3}{5}$ units

$\frac{1}{25}$ square units

c) 0.8

Area = 0.64

0.8 units

0.01 square units

d) $\frac{9}{4}$

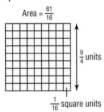

Area = $\frac{81}{16}$

$\frac{9}{4}$ units

$\frac{1}{16}$ square units

e) 1.6

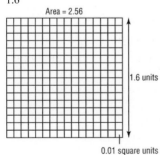

Area = 2.56

1.6 units

0.01 square units

f) $\frac{1}{6}$

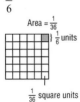

Area = $\frac{1}{36}$

$\frac{1}{6}$ units

$\frac{1}{36}$ square units

g) 0.5

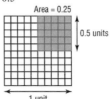

Area = 0.25

0.5 units

1 unit

h) $\frac{10}{8} = \frac{5}{4}$

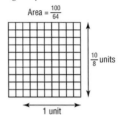

Area = $\frac{100}{64}$

$\frac{10}{8}$ units

1 unit

i) 1.9

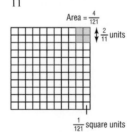

Area = 3.61

1.9 units

0.01 square units

1 unit

j) $\frac{2}{11}$

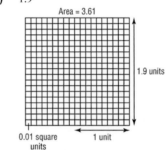

Area = $\frac{4}{121}$

$\frac{2}{11}$ units

$\frac{1}{121}$ square units

k) 1.7

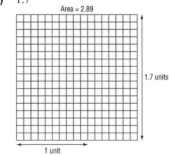

Area = 2.89

1.7 units

1 unit

l) $\dfrac{6}{7}$

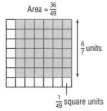

Area $= \dfrac{36}{49}$

$\dfrac{6}{7}$ units

$\dfrac{1}{49}$ square units

2. a) $\dfrac{12}{5}$ **b)** $\dfrac{15}{8}$

c) $\dfrac{14}{9}$ **d)** $\dfrac{18}{11}$

e) 0.14   **f)** 0.17

g) 1.3   **h)** 2.1

3. a) $\dfrac{48}{120}$ is not a perfect square since neither 48 nor 120 are perfect squares.

b) 1.6 is not a perfect square since $1.6 = \dfrac{16}{10}$ and 10 is not a perfect square.

c) $\dfrac{49}{100} = \left(\dfrac{7}{10}\right)^2$ is a perfect square.

d) $0.04 = 0.2^2$ is a perfect square.

e) $\dfrac{144}{24} = 6$ is not a perfect square.

f) $2.5 = \dfrac{25}{10}$ is not a perfect square since 10 is not.

g) $\dfrac{50}{225}$ is not a perfect square since 50 is not.

h) $1.96 = 1.4^2$ is a perfect square.

i) $\dfrac{63}{28}$ simplifies to $\dfrac{9}{4}$, which is a perfect square.

4. a) $\dfrac{9}{25}$ **b)** 2.56

c) $\dfrac{81}{49}$ **d)** 0.64

5. a) 0.9 m   **b)** 0.1 m

c) 2.2 cm   **d)** 2.5 cm

e) 0.4 km   **f)** 1.2 km

6. Estimates will vary, for example:

a) $\sqrt{3.8} \doteq 1.9$, using $\sqrt{1} = 1$ and $\sqrt{4} = 2$

b) $\sqrt{33.8} \doteq 5.8$, using $\sqrt{25} = 5$ and $\sqrt{36} = 6$

c) $\sqrt{133.8} \doteq 11.6$, using $\sqrt{121} = 11$ and $\sqrt{144} = 12$

d) $\sqrt{233.8} \doteq 15.3$, using $\sqrt{225} = 15$ and $\sqrt{256} = 16$

7. Estimates will vary, for example:

a) $\sqrt{\dfrac{77}{10}} \doteq \dfrac{14}{5}$, using $\sqrt{\dfrac{784}{100}} = \dfrac{14}{5}$

b) $\sqrt{\dfrac{18}{11}} \doteq \dfrac{14}{11}$, using $\sqrt{\dfrac{196}{121}} = \dfrac{14}{11}$

c) $\sqrt{\dfrac{15}{39}} \doteq \dfrac{15}{24}$, using $\sqrt{\dfrac{225}{576}} = \dfrac{15}{24}$

d) $\sqrt{\dfrac{83}{19}} \doteq \dfrac{9}{5}$, using $\sqrt{\dfrac{81}{25}} = \dfrac{9}{5}$

e) $\sqrt{\dfrac{28}{103}} \doteq \dfrac{5}{10}$, using $\sqrt{\dfrac{25}{100}} = \dfrac{5}{10}$

f) $\sqrt{\dfrac{50}{63}} \doteq \dfrac{7}{8}$, using $\sqrt{\dfrac{49}{64}} = \dfrac{7}{8}$

8. Estimates will vary, for example:

a) About 2.4   **b)** About 0.6

c) About 0.8   **d)** About 0.6

e) About 4.8   **f)** About 3

9. a) Correct   **b)** Incorrect; $\sqrt{1.6} \doteq 1.3$

c) Incorrect; $\sqrt{156.8} \doteq 12.5$

d) Correct   **e)** Correct

f) Incorrect; $\sqrt{0.7} \doteq 0.8$

10. $\sqrt{27.4}$, $\sqrt{60.8}$

11. a) $\sqrt{3.2}$, $\sqrt{2.3}$, $\sqrt{2.8}$, $\sqrt{1.2}$

b) $\sqrt{125.4}$, $\sqrt{134.5}$, $\sqrt{129.9}$

c) $\sqrt{12.9}$, $\sqrt{15.2}$

d) $\sqrt{5.7}$, $\sqrt{4.8}$, $\sqrt{3.2}$, $\sqrt{2.3}$, $\sqrt{2.8}$

e) $\sqrt{21.2}$, $\sqrt{23.1}$, $\sqrt{29.1}$

f) $\sqrt{237.1}$, $\sqrt{222.1}$, $\sqrt{213.1}$

12. a) About 3.9 cm   **b)** About 3.5 cm

c) 8.5 cm

13. For example:

a) $\dfrac{1}{2}$ **b)** 0.0625

c) 1.97   **d)** $\dfrac{1}{25}$

14. a) i) About 0.0387   **ii)** About 0.3873

      iii) About 3.8730   **iv)** About 38.7298

      v) About 387.2983

15. a) 18 cm^2 **b)** 22 cm^2

c) 26 cm^2

16. a) 51.7 cm^2 **b)** 515.48 m^2

c) 253.28 m^2

17. a)   **b)** 14 824 cm^2

19. **a)** 940.2 cm^2 **b)** 1192.8 cm^2

20. **a)** 30.2 m^2 **b)** 2 containers; $39.90

Unit 1: Practice Test, page 48

1. **a)**

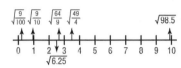

2. **a)** **i)** About 0.65   **ii)** 7.25
    iii) 4.8   **iv)** 14.6
    v) About 11.64

   b) ii, iii, and iv are exact, i and v are approximate

3. For example
   a) 0.25   **b)** 0.04

4. 8.67 km

5. **a)** 68.2 m^2 **b)** $49.84

6. **a)**

   b) 229.7 cm^2

Unit 2 Powers and Exponent Laws, page 50

2.1 What is a Power?, page 55

4. **a)** 2^2 **b)** 3^2
   c) 5^2

5. **a)** 3^3 **b)** 2^3
   c) 5^3

6. **a)** 4^2 **b)** 6×6

   c) 49   **d)** 10^2

e) 81   **f)** 12×12

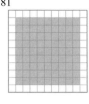
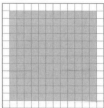

7. **a)** 2   **b)** 4
   c) 8   **d)** −10
   e) −6   **f)** 8

8. **a)** 5   **b)** 4
   c) 1   **d)** 2
   e) 9   **f)** 3

9. **a)** 3×3 **b)** $10 \times 10 \times 10 \times 10$
   c) $8 \times 8 \times 8 \times 8 \times 8$ **d)** $(-6)(-6)(-6)(-6)(-6)$
   e) $-6 \times 6 \times 6 \times 6 \times 6$ **f)** -4×4

10. **a)** 3^2 can be modelled by 9 unit square tiles arranged in a 3 by 3 square. 2^3 can be modelled by 8 unit cubes arranged in a 2 by 2 by 2 cube.
   b) 3^2 represents the area of a square and 2^3 represents the volume of a cube.

11. $6^4 = 6 \times 6 \times 6 \times 6 = 1296$
$4^6 = 4 \times 4 \times 4 \times 4 \times 4 \times 4 = 4096$

12. **a)** 4^4 **b)** 2^3
   c) 5^6 **d)** 10^3
   e) $(-79)^2$ **f)** $-(-2)^8$

13. **a)** $5^2 = 25$ **b)** $3^4 = 81$
   c) $10^5 = 100\,000$ **d)** $-9^3 = -729$
   e) $(-2)^3 = -8$ **f)** $-(-4)^3 = 64$
   g) $(-5)^4 = 625$ **h)** $-5^4 = -625$
   i) $-(-5)^4 = -625$

14. **a)** 8   **b)** 1 000 000
   c) 3   **d)** −343
   e) −343   **f)** 256
   g) −256   **h)** −1296
   i) 1296   **j)** −1296
   k) −125   **l)** −256

15. **a)** **i)** $3^2 = 9$ **ii)** $13.95
   b) **i)** $4^2 = 16$ **ii)** $8.32

16. **a)** 531 441   **b)** −823 543
   c) 48 828 125   **d)** −1 048 576
   e) 43 046 721   **f)** 8 388 608

17. **a)** **i)** $4 \times 4 \times 4 = 64$ **ii)** $-4 \times 4 \times 4 = -64$
    iii) $-(-4 \times 4 \times 4) = 64$
    iv) $(-4 \times 4 \times 4) = -64$

   b) i and iii are positive. ii and iv are negative.

   c) **i)** $4 \times 4 = 16$ **ii)** $-4 \times 4 = -16$
    iii) $-(-4 \times 4) = 16$ **iv)** $(-4 \times 4) = -16$

   d) i and iii are positive. ii and iv are negative.

18. a) All three expressions are the same.

For $(-3)^5$, the negative sign is part of the base, -3.

For (-3^5), the brackets serve no purpose.

b) -4^6 and (-4^6) are the same.

For -4^6, the negative sign is not part of the base.

For $(-4)^6$, the negative sign is part of the base, -4.

19. a) When the exponent is an odd number, for example: $(-3)^5, (-6)^3, (-2)^{17}$

b) When the exponent is an even number, for example: $(-3)^6, (-6)^2, (-2)^{10}$

20. a) 2^2 **b)** 2^4

c) 2^6 **d)** 2^8

e) 2^5 **f)** 2^7

21. a) i) $2^4, 4^2, 16^1$ **ii)** $3^4, 9^2, 81^1$

iii) $2^8, 4^4, 16^2, 256^1$

22. a) Same: same numbers

Different: base and exponent interchanged

b) i) 3^2 **ii)** 2^5

iii) 3^4 **iv)** 4^5

23. $3^5, 6^3, 3^4, 5^2$

24. a) $64 = 8^2$ **b)** $49 = 7^2$

c) $36 = 6^2$ **d)** $25 = 5^2$

e) $16 = 4^2$ **f)** $9 = 3^2$

g) $4 = 2^2$ **h)** $1 = 1^2$

Each number of squares is a square number that decreases as the size of the squares increases.

2.2 Powers of Ten and the Zero Exponent, page 61

4. a) 1 **b)** 1

c) 1 **d)** 1

5. a) 1 **b)** -1

c) -1 **d)** 1

6. a) 10^3 **b)** 10^5

c) 10^9 **d)** 10^4

e) 10^{11}

7. For example: $10^0, 1^4, (-6)^0$

8. a) 10 000 000 **b)** 100

c) 1 **d)** 10 000 000 000

e) 10 **f)** 1 000 000

9. a) 6×10^9 **b)** 2×10^2

c) $(5 \times 10^4) + (1 \times 10^3) + (4 \times 10^2) + (1 \times 10^1) + (5 \times 10^0)$

d) $(6 \times 10^7) + (7 \times 10^5) + (2 \times 10^3) + (8 \times 10^0)$

e) $(3 \times 10^5) + (2 \times 10^3) + (4 \times 10^2) + (1 \times 10^1) + (1 \times 10^0)$

f) $(2 \times 10^6) + (8 \times 10^0)$

10. a) 70 000 000 **b)** 39 057

c) 800 500 200 **d)** 98 000 000 001

e) 1 000 000 000 000 000 **f)** 904 031

11. 5×10^8; 4×10^4; 3×10^6; $(1 \times 10^4) + (7 \times 10^3)$; $(1 \times 10^5) + (3 \times 10^4)$; 6×10^2

12. Negative bases may vary.

Exponent	Power	Standard Form
5	$(-3)^5$	-243
4	$(-3)^4$	81
3	$(-3)^3$	-27
2	$(-3)^2$	9
1	$(-3)^1$	-3
0	$(-3)^0$	1

13. a) $4667 > 4327$ **b)** $24\,240 > 2432$

c) $70\,007\,000 > 777\,777$

14. a) 1 billion $= 10^9$; 100 000 $= 10^5$; 1000 $= 10^3$; 1 $= 10^0$; 100 $= 10^2$; 10 million $= 10^7$

b) $10^0, 10^2, 10^3, 10^5, 10^7, 10^9$

c) You only need to order or compare the exponents.

15. One trillion is 10^{12}, one quadrillion is 10^{15}, and one quintillion is 10^{18}.

2.3 Order of Operations with Powers, page 66

3. a) 10 **b)** 8

c) 16 **d)** 4

e) 8 **f)** 0

g) 36 **h)** 4

i) -14 **j)** -12

4. a) 40 **b)** 50

c) 1000 **d)** 100

e) -200 **f)** -10

g) -8 **h)** 1

5. a) 0 **b)** -1

c) 35 **d)** 125

e) -8 **f)** 1

g) -64 **h)** 8

6. a) i) $4^2 + 4^3 = 80$ **ii)** $5^3 + 5^6 = 15\,750$

b) i) $6^3 - 6^2 = 180$ **ii)** $6^3 - 6^5 = -7560$

7. Correction:

$= 9 + 4 \times 16 + 36$ $(-6)^2$ should be 36, not -36.

$= 9 + 64 + 36$ Calculate 4×16 first, not

$= 109$ $9 + 4$.

8. a) Multiply: $(7)(4)$; 3 **b)** Subtract: $(2 - 5)$; 54

c) Evaluate: $(-3)^2$; 37 **d)** Evaluate: 4^0; -8

e) Divide: $[10 \div (-2)]$; 4

f) Divide: $[18 \div (-6)]$; -54

10. a) -392 **b)** -216

c) -8 **d)** 9

e) 16 **f)** 1

11. The order of operations matches the order in which the multiplication and division are written.

$-4^3 \times 10 - 6 \div 2 = -64 \times 10 - 3 = -640 - 3 = -643$

12. $1035

13. 5 different answers:
$2^3 + (3 \times 4)^2 - 6 = 8 + 144 - 6 = 146$;
$(2^3 + 3) \times 4^2 - 6 = 170$; $2^3 + 3 \times (4^2 - 6) = 38$;
$(2^3 + 3 \times 4^2) - 6 = 50$; $(2^3 + 3 \times 4)^2 - 6 = 394$;
$2^3 + (3 \times 4^2 - 6) = 50$

14. a) 43, 43   **b)** 13, 25
    c) 191, 191   **d)** 72, 7776
    e) 119, 20

15. The student multiplied 3 by 4 instead of squaring
4 first. This does not affect the answer because any
nonzero number with exponent 0 equals 1.
A more efficient solution:

$$-(24 - 3 \times 4^2)^0 \div (-2)^3 = -(1) \div (-8) = \frac{1}{8}$$

16. a) −197 568   **b)** −92 000
    c) −4   **d)** 40.5
    e) 169 744   **f)** −1 185 191

17. $(30 + 9 \times 11 \div 3)^0$

18. a) Marcia
    b) Robbie forgot that the square of −4 is positive.
Nick forgot that the square of −6 is positive.

19. \$84.81

20. a) $(10 + 2) \times 3^2 - 2 = 106$
    b) $10 + 2 \times (3^2 - 2) = 24$
    c) $(10 + 2) \times (3^2 - 2) = 84$
    d) $(10 + 2 \times 3)^2 - 2 = 254$

21. a) $20 \div (2 + 2) \times 2^2 + 6 = 26$
    b) $20 \div 2 + 2 \times (2^2 + 6) = 30$
    c) $20 \div (2 + 2 \times 2^2) + 6 = 8$
    d) $(20 \div 2 + 2) \times (2^2 + 6) = 120$

22. No, Blake did not win the prize.
$5 \times 4^2 - (2^3 + 3^3) \div 5$
$= 5 \times 16 - (8 + 27) \div 5$
$= 80 - 35 \div 5$
$= 80 - 7$
$= 73$

24. a) $1^3 + 2^3 + 3^3 + 4^3 + 5^3 + 6^3 = 21^2$
$1^3 + 2^3 + 3^3 + 4^3 + 5^3 + 6^3 + 7^3 = 28^2$
    b) $3^2 - 1^2 = 2^3$; $6^2 - 3^2 = 3^3$; $10^2 - 6^2 = 4^3$;
$15^2 - 10^2 = 5^3$; $21^2 - 15^2 = 6^3$; $28^2 - 21^2 = 7^3$;
$36^2 - 28^2 = 8^3$

25. For example, use −2 and 3.
    a) $(-2)^2 + 3^2 = 4 + 9 = 13$ **b)** $(-2 + 3)^2 = 1^2 = 1$
    c) The answers are different.
    d) I do not agree. The two expressions are not equal
because the operations are performed in different
orders.

26. Answers may vary. For example:
$4 \div 4 + 4 - 4 = 1$; $4 \div 4 + 4 \div 4 = 2$;
$4 - 4 + 4 - 4^0 = 3$; $4^0 + 4^0 + 4^0 + 4^0 = 4$;
$4 - 4 + 4 + 4^0 = 5$; $4 + 4 - 4^0 - 4^0 = 6$;

$4 + 4^0 + 4^0 + 4^0 = 7$; $(4 + 4) \times 4 \div 4 = 8$;
$4 \div 4 + 4 + 4 = 9$

27. a) **i)** $2^4 = 16$ **ii)** $2^2 = 4$
    iii) $2^5 = 32$ **iv)** $2^3 = 8$
    b) **i)** $28 = 2^4 + 2^3 + 2^2$
    ii) $12 = 2^3 + 2^2$ **iii)** $25 = 2^4 + 2^3 + 2^0$
    iv) $31 = 2^4 + 2^3 + 2^2 + 2^1 + 2^0$
    v) $50 = 2^5 + 2^4 + 2^1$ **vi)** $75 = 2^6 + 2^3 + 2^1 + 2^0$
    c) For example:
    i) $28 = 3^3 + 3^0$ **ii)** $12 = 3^2 + 3^1$
    iii) $25 = 3^2 + 3^2 + 3^1 + 3^1 + 3^0$
    iv) $31 = 3^3 + 3^1 + 3^0$
    v) $50 = 3^3 + 3^2 + 3^2 + 3^1 + 3^0 + 3^0$
    vi) $75 = 3^3 + 3^3 + 3^2 + 3^2 + 3^1$

Unit 2: Mid-Unit Review, page 69

1. a) 196   **b)** 5
    c) −512   **d)** −256
    e) −216   **f)** 256

2.

	Power	Base	Exponent	Repeated Multiplication	Standard Form
a)	4^3	4	3	$4 \times 4 \times 4$	64
b)	2^5	2	5	$2 \times 2 \times 2 \times 2 \times 2$	32
c)	8^6	8	6	$8 \times 8 \times 8 \times 8 \times 8 \times 8$	262 144
d)	7^2	7	2	7×7	49
e)	3^4	3	4	$3 \times 3 \times 3 \times 3$	81

3. a)

Power of 7	Standard Form
7^1	7
7^2	49
7^3	343
7^4	2401
7^5	16 807
7^6	117 649
7^7	823 543
7^8	5 764 801

    b) The pattern in the ones digits is
7, 9, 3, 1, 7, 9, 3, 1, …
    c)

Power of 7	Standard Form
7^9	40 353 607
7^{10}	282 475 249
7^{11}	1 977 326 743

    d) **i)** 1   **ii)** 9
    iii) 7   **iv)** 9

4. a) 1 000 000   **b)** 1
    c) 100 000 000   **d)** 10 000

5. a) 10^9 **b)** 10^0
    c) 10^2 **d)** 10^5

6. a) 1   **b)** 1

c) -1 **d)** 1

7. 10^4 m^2

8. **a)** Subtract: $(-21 - 6)$; 743

    b) Multiply: (2×3); 33

    c) Subtract: $[5 - (-4)]$; 648

    d) Evaluate the power with exponent 0; 1

    e) Subtract: $(3 - 5)$; 8

    f) Subtract: $(7 - 4)$; -57

9. Sophia is correct. Victor might have included the negative sign in the power -2^4 and evaluated it as 16.

10. $(-3)^3 = -27$, not 27; $(-9)^0 = 1$, not -1

Correction:

$(-2)^4 - (-3)^3 \div (-9)^0 \times 2^3$

$= 16 - (-27) \div 1 \times 8$

$= 16 - (-27) \times 8$

$= 16 - (-216)$

$= 232$

Unit 2: Start Where You Are, page 70

1. **a)** 64.8   **b)** 162

    c) 15   **d)** -9

    e) 2

2. **a)** 1   **b)** 1.0125

    c) 1

2.4 Exponent Laws I, page 76

4. **a)** 5^9 **b)** 10^{13}

    c) $(-3)^6$ **d)** 21^{10}

    e) $(-4)^4$ **f)** 6^{15}

    g) 2^4 **h)** $(-7)^3$

5. **a)** 4^2 **b)** 8^3

    c) 15^{10} **d)** $(-6)^5$

    e) 2^2 **f)** $(-10)^6$

    g) 6^4 **h)** $(-1)^1$

6. **a)** **i)** 1   **ii)** 1

       iii) 1   **iv)** 1

7. **a)** **i)** $3^{13} = 1\ 594\ 323$ **ii)** $3^{13} = 1\ 594\ 323$

8. **a)** 3^2 **b)** $(-4)^{11}$

    c) 6^1 **d)** 4^0

    e) $(-3)^4$

9. **a)** **i)** $(-6)^1 = -6$ **ii)** $(-6)^1 = -6$

10. **a)** $10^4 + 10^4 = 20\ 000$ **b)** $10^6 - 10^3 = 999\ 000$

    c) $10^{11} - 10^9 = 99\ 000\ 000\ 000$

    d) $10^1 + 10^7 = 10\ 000\ 010$

    e) $10^6 = 1\ 000\ 000$ **f)** $10^0 = 1$

    g) $10^6 = 1\ 000\ 000$ **h)** $10^5 = 100\ 000$

    i) $10^5 = 100\ 000$ **j)** $10^2 + 10^2 = 200$

11. **a)** 32   **b)** 248

12. **a)** 10^4 m $\times 10^3$ m $= 10^7$ m^2, or $10\ 000\ 000$ m^2

    b) $2(10^4$ m $+ 10^3$ m$) = 22\ 000$ m

c) **i)** 10^7 m $\times 10^0$ m; 10^6 m $\times 10^1$ m; 10^5 m $\times 10^2$ m; 10^4 m $\times 10^3$ m

    ii) $2(10^7$ m $+ 10^0$ m$) = 20\ 000\ 002$ m

            $2(10^6$ m $+ 10^1$ m$) = 2\ 000\ 020$ m

            $2(10^5$ m $+ 10^2$ m$) = 200\ 200$ m

            $2(10^4$ m $+ 10^3$ m$) = 22\ 000$ m

13. **a)** -32 **b)** 91

    c) 21   **d)** -12

    e) 80   **f)** -272

    g) -10

15. **a)** The student multiplied the exponents instead of adding them. Correction: $4^3 \times 4^4 = 4^7$

    b) The student divided the exponents instead of subtracting them.

    Correction: $\dfrac{(-7^6)}{(-7^3)} = \dfrac{-7^6}{-7^3} = \dfrac{7^6}{7^3} = 7^3$

    c) The student used the exponent laws but the bases are different. Correction: $3^2 \times 2^3 = 9 \times 8 = 72$

    d) The student multiplied the exponents in the divisor instead of adding them.

    Correction: $\dfrac{5^8}{5^4 \times 5^2} = \dfrac{5^8}{5^6} = 25$

    e) The student added all the exponents even though only 2 of them were parts of products of powers. Correction: $1^2 + 1^3 \times 1^2 = 1^2 + 1^5 = 1 + 1 = 2$

16. **a)** $10^2 \times 10^1 = 10^3$ **b)** 1000 times as large

17. **a)** **i)** 150   **ii)** 3125

    b) Part ii is a product of two powers that can be simplified using an exponent law.

18. **a)** **i)** 48   **ii)** 4

    b) Part ii is a quotient of two powers that can be simplified using an exponent law.

19. Since the base is negative, the power is negative when the exponent is an odd number.

    a) $(-2)^5$ **b)** $(-2)^5$

    c) $(-2)^2 = 4$ **d)** $(-2)^0 = 1$

    e) $(-2)^2 = 4$ **f)** $(-2)^1$

20. For example: $4^2 \times 2^2$

21. **a)** 1 km $= 10^3$ m $= 10^3 \times 10^2$ cm $= 10^5$ cm

    b) 1 km $= 10^5$ cm $= 10^5 \times 10^1$ mm $= 10^6$ mm

    c) 10^5 m $= (10^5 \div 10^3)$ km $= 10^2$ km

    d) 10^9 mm $= (10^9 \div 10^3)$ m $= 10^6$ m

22. **a)** 10^2 km^2 $= (10^3 \times 10^3) \times 10^2$ m^2 $= 10^8$ m^2

    b) 10^6 cm^2 $= 10^6 \div (10^2 \times 10^2)$ m^2 $= 10^2$ m^2

    c) 10^6 cm^2 $= (10^1 \times 10^1) \times 10^6$ mm^2 $= 10^8$ mm^2

    d) 1 km^2 $= (10^3 \times 10^3) \times (10^2 \times 10^2)$ cm^2 $= 10^{10}$ cm^2

2.5 Exponent Laws II, page 84

4. **a)** $6^3 \times 4^3$ **b)** $2^4 \times 5^4$

    c) $(-2)^5 \times 3^5$ **d)** $25^2 \times 4^2$

e) $11^1 \times 3^1$ **f)** $(-3)^3 \times (-2)^3$

5. a) $8^3 \div 5^3$ **b)** $21^4 \div 5^4$

c) $(-12)^5 \div (-7)^5$ **d)** $\dfrac{10^3}{3^3}$

e) $\dfrac{1^2}{3^2}$ **f)** $\dfrac{27^4}{100^4}$

6. a) 3^8 **b)** 6^9 **c)** 5^3

d) 7^0 **e)** -8^4 **f)** $(-3)^8$

7. $(2^4)^2 = 2^8$; $(2^2)^4 = 2^8$; The results are the same because each expression is the product of 8 factors of 2.

8. a) $3^3 \times (-5)^3$ **b)** $-2^5 \times 4^5$

c) $\dfrac{2^4}{3^4}$ **d)** $\dfrac{(-7)^2}{(-2)^2}$

e) $-(-10)^3 \times 3^3$ **f)** $16^2 \div 9^2$

9. Since $-5^2 = -25$, the base is negative. The power $(-5^2)^3$ is negative when the exponent is an odd number.

10. a) I multiplied first because it was easier than using the power of a product law: $(3 \times 2)^3 = 6^3 = 216$

b) I multiplied first because it was easier than using the power of a product law:
$[(-2) \times 4]^2 = (-8)^2 = 64$

c) I divided first because it was easier than using the power of a quotient law: $\left(\dfrac{9}{-3}\right)^3 = (-3)^3 = -27$

d) I divided first because it was easier than using the power of a quotient law: $\left(\dfrac{8}{2}\right)^2 = 4^2 = 16$

e) I used the zero exponent law: $(12^8)^0 = 1$

f) I used the power of a power law:
$[(-4)^2]^2 = (-4)^4 = 256$

11. $[(-2)^3]^4 = (-2)^{12}$; $(-2)^{12}$ is positive because its exponent is even. $[(-2)^3]^5 = (-2)^{15}$; $(-2)^{15}$ is negative because its exponent is odd.

12. $-(4^2)^3 = -4096$; $(-4^2)^3 = -4096$; $[(-4)^2]^3 = 4096$

13. a) i) $(4 \times 3)^3 = 12^3 = 1728$
$(4 \times 3)^3 = 4^3 \times 3^3 = 64 \times 27 = 1728$

b) i) $[(-2) \times (-5)]^2 = 10^2 = 100$
$[(-2) \times (-5)]^2 = (-2)^2 \times (-5)^2 = 4 \times 25 = 100$

c) i) $\left(\dfrac{6}{2}\right)^4 = 3^4 = 81$

$\left(\dfrac{6}{2}\right)^4 = \dfrac{6^4}{2^4} = \dfrac{1296}{16} = 81$

d) i) $\left(\dfrac{14}{2}\right)^0 = 7^0 = 1$

$\left(\dfrac{14}{2}\right)^0 = \dfrac{14^0}{2^0} = 1$

e) i) $[(-5)^2]^2 = 25^2 = 625$
$[(-5)^2]^2 = (-5)^4 = 625$

f) i) $(2^5)^3 = 32^3 = 32\,768$
$(2^5)^3 = 2^{15} = 32\,768$

14. a) 729   **b)** 256

c) 64   **d)** 1 000 000

e) 1 000 000 000 000   **f)** 144

g) 1   **h)** −512

15. a) The student multiplied the bases and multiplied the powers.
$(3^2 \times 2^2)^3 = 3^6 \times 2^6 = 729 \times 64 = 46\,656$

b) The student added the exponents instead of multiplying them. $[(-3)^2]^3 = (-3)^6 = 729$

c) The student might have thought that 6^1 is 1.
$\left(\dfrac{6^2}{6^1}\right)^2 = (6^1)^2 = 6^2 = 36$

d) The student did not simplify the powers in the brackets correctly.
$(2^6 \times 2^2 \div 2^4)^3 = (2^{6+2-4})^3 = (2^4)^3 = 2^{12} = 4096$

e) The student multiplied the powers in the brackets instead of adding them.
$(10^2 + 10^3)^2 = (100 + 1000)^2 = 1100^2 = 1\,210\,000$

16. a) 1 047 951   **b)** 28

c) 4100   **d)** 46 720

e) −255   **f)** 1 006 561

17. a) 1015   **b)** −59 045

c) 1033   **d)** 59 053

e) −5   **f)** 60 073

18. a) i) $(2 \times 3)^2 = 6^2$

ii) $(2 \times 3)^2 = 2^2 \times 3^2$
iii)

iv) Both rectangles have an area of 36 but they have different dimensions.

b) i) $(2 \times 4)^2 = 8^2$

ii) $(2 \times 4)^2 = 2^2 \times 4^2$
iii)

iv) Both rectangles have an area of 64 but they have different dimensions.

c) **i)** $(3 \times 4)^2 = 12^2$

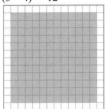

ii) $(3 \times 4)^2 = 3^2 \times 4^2$

iii)

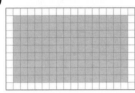

iv) Both rectangles have an area of 144 but they have different dimensions.

d) **i)** $(1 \times 4)^2 = 4^2$

ii) $(1 \times 4)^2 = 1^2 \times 4^2$

iii)

iv) Both rectangles have an area of 16 but they have different dimensions.

19. **a)** 255 583   **b)** 254 819 593
    c) 2 097 152   **d)** 1631
    e) 6560   **f)** 54 899

20. **a)** **i)** 9^2 **ii)** $(3 \times 3)^2$ **iii)** 3^4
    b) **i)** 8^2 **ii)** $(2 \times 4)^2$ **iii)** 2^6

21. **a)** 1, 2, 4, 8, 16, 32, 64, 128, 256, 512, 1024, 2048, 4096

    b) **i)** $2^5 \times 2^6 = 2048$ **ii)** $2^4 \times 2^3 \times 2^5 = 4096$

       iii) $2^{10} \div 2^7 = 8$ **iv)** $\dfrac{2^4 \times 2^8}{2^{10}} = 4$

       v) $(2^3 \times 2^2)^3 = 32\ 768$

       vi) $\left(\dfrac{2^8}{2^6}\right)^4 = 256$

Unit 2: Review, page 87

1. **a)** $4 \times 4 \times 4 = 64$ **b)** $7 \times 7 = 49$
    c) $-(-2)(-2)(-2)(-2)(-2) = 32$
    d) $-3 \times 3 \times 3 \times 3 = -81$
    e) $-1 \times 1 \times 1 \times 1 \times 1 \times 1 \times 1 \times 1 = -1$
    f) $(-1)(-1)(-1)(-1)(-1)(-1)(-1)(-1) = 1$

2. 2^2 can be modelled as the area of a square with side length 2 units. 2^3 can be modelled as the volume of a cube with edge length 2 units.

3. **a)** $3^6 = 729$ **b)** $(-8)^3 = -512$
    c) $-2^7 = -128$ **d)** $12^2 = 144$
    e) $4^5 = 1024$ **f)** $(-5)^4 = 625$

4. 5^8 means $5 \times 5 \times 5 \times 5 \times 5 \times 5 \times 5 \times 5 = 390\ 625$
    8^5 means $8 \times 8 \times 8 \times 8 \times 8 = 32\ 768$

5. 16 min

6. **a)** $-4^2 = -16$; $(-4)^2 = 16$
     The values are different. The brackets indicate that the negative sign is included in the base.
    b) $-2^3 = -8$; $(-2)^3 = -8$
     The values are the same. The brackets indicate that the negative sign is included in the base.

7. **a)** **i)** -9 **ii)** -9
      iii) -9 **iv)** 9
    b) **ii)** The brackets indicate that the negative sign is not part of the base.
       iii) The brackets indicate that the first negative sign is not part of the base and the second negative sign is part of the base.
       iv) The brackets indicate that the negative sign is part of the base.

8. **a)** 10^8 **b)** 10^4
    c) 10^0 **d)** 10^9
    e) 10^3

9. **a)** 7×10^8
    b) $(3 \times 10^2) + (4 \times 10^1) + (5 \times 10^0)$
    c) $(8 \times 10^4) + (2 \times 10^1) + (7 \times 10^0)$

10. **a)**

Power	Repeated Multiplication	Standard Form
3^5	$3 \times 3 \times 3 \times 3 \times 3$	243
3^4	$3 \times 3 \times 3 \times 3$	81
3^3	$3 \times 3 \times 3$	27
3^2	3×3	9
3^1	3	3

    b) The exponents are decreasing by 1; the number of factors is decreasing by 1; each number in standard form is divided by 3 to get the number below it.
    c) $3^0 = 1$

11. **a)** $10^4 \div 10^2 = 10^2$, or 100 times as high
    b) $10^{12} \div 10^7 = 10^5$, or 100 000 times as great

12. **a)** 4729   **b)** 300 208

13. **a)** 90   **b)** -48
    c) 900   **d)** 600

14. **a)** 89   **b)** 175
    c) 0   **d)** 26

e) 73   **f)** 40 000

15. a) i) 1000   **ii)** 2000
     iii) 4000   **iv)** 8000

b) i) $1000 \times 2^4 = 16\ 000$ **ii)** $1000 \times 2^6 = 64\ 000$
     iii) $1000 \times 2^9 = 512\ 000$
     iv) $1000 \times 2^{12} = 4\ 096\ 000$

16. 6 different answers:
$4^3 - (2 \times 3)^4 + 11 = -1221$; $(4^3 - 2) \times 3^4 + 11 = 5033$;
$(4^3 - 2 \times 3)^4 + 11 = 11\ 316\ 507$
$4^3 - (2 \times 3^4 + 11) = -109$; $4^3 - 2 \times (3^4 + 11) = -120$;
$4^3 - (2 \times 3)^4 + 11 = -87$

17. The student incorrectly applied the exponent law when the bases, (-2) and 2, are not the same. Also, $-9 \div (-3)$ is 3, not -3. Correction:
$(-2)^2 \times 2^3 - 3^2 \div (-3) + (-4)^2$
$= 4 \times 8 - 9 \div (-3) + 16$
$= 32 - (-3) + 16$
$= 35 + 16$
$= 51$

18. a) $5^7 = 78\ 125$ **b)** $(-2)^5 = -32$
    c) $3^6 = 729$ **d)** $-10^4 = -10\ 000$

19. $10^{22} = 10\ 000\ 000\ 000\ 000\ 000\ 000\ 000$

20. a) $7^2 = 49$ **b)** $(-10)^6 = 1\ 000\ 000$
    c) $8^2 = 64$ **d)** $-6^3 = -216$

21. a) No, the laws of exponents cannot be used because the powers have different bases.
     One can only use the exponent laws to simplify power expressions with the same base.

b) Yes, even though these powers have different bases, both bases are powers of 3:
$27^2 \div 9^2 = 3^6 \div 3^4$

22. a) The student divided the exponents instead of subtracting them. $(-3)^6 \div (-3)^2 = (-3)^4 = 81$

b) The student misread the addition sign as a multiplication sign.
$(-4)^2 + (-4)^2 = 16 + 16 = 32$

c) After the first step, the student divided the exponents instead of subtracting them.
$$\frac{(-5)^2 \times (-5)^4}{(-5)^3 \times (-5)^0} = \frac{(-5)^6}{(-5)^3} = (-5)^3 = -125$$

23. a) $3^3 \times 5^3 = 3375$ **b)** $12^5 \div 3^5 = 1024$
    c) $(-4)^4 \times 2^4 = 4096$ **d)** $63^0 \times 44^0 = 1$

e) $\dfrac{3^5}{2^5} = \dfrac{243}{32}$, or 7.593 75

f) $\dfrac{15^2}{2^2} = \dfrac{225}{4}$, or 56.25

24. a) 3^6 **b)** 4^0
    c) $(-2)^9$ **d)** 5^{10}

25. a) i) $(5 \times 3)^3 = 15^3 = 3375$
     ii) $(5 \times 3)^3 = 5^3 \times 3^3 = 3375$

b) i) $(3 \times 3)^4 = 9^4 = 6561$
     ii) $(3 \times 3)^4 = 3^4 \times 3^4 = 6561$

c) i) $(8 \div 2)^5 = 4^5 = 1024$
     ii) $(8 \div 2)^5 = 8^5 \div 2^5 = 1024$

d) i) $\left(\dfrac{9}{3}\right)^2 = 3^2 = 9$ **ii)** $\left(\dfrac{9}{3}\right)^2 = \dfrac{9^2}{3^2} = 9$

e) i) $(2^3)^4 = 8^4 = 4096$ **ii)** $(2^3)^4 = 2^{12} = 4096$

f) i) $(6^2)^0 = 36^0 = 1$ **ii)** $(6^2)^0 = 6^0 = 1$

26. a) $6^7 = 279\ 936$ **b)** $(-11)^2 = 121$
    c) $3^6 = 729$ **d)** $5^0 = 1$
    e) $(-4)^3 = -64$ **f)** $10^1 = 10$

27. a) 33   **b)** $\dfrac{8}{3}$

    c) 186 623   **d)** 199 065.6

Unit 2: Practice Test, page 90

1. a) $3^3 \times 4^3$ **b)** $(-5)^4 \times 2^4$

    c) $\dfrac{1^4}{4^4}$ **d)** $-\dfrac{9^3}{3^3}$

2. a) -2^9 **b)** 6^0
    c) $(-5)^6$ **d)** $-(-3)^8$

3. a) 1296   **b)** $\dfrac{1}{32} = 0.031\ 25$

    c) 1   **d)** 729

4. The value of a power with a negative base is positive when the exponent is an even number, and is negative when the exponent is an odd number.
For example: $(-3)^2 = (-3) \times (-3) = 9$
$(-3)^3 = (-3) \times (-3) \times (-3) = -27$

5. The area of the diamond is: $27 \text{ m} \times 27 \text{ m} = 729 \text{ m}^2$, which is less than 1000 m^2.

6. The brackets are not necessary because the order of operations ensures that the multiplication and division are performed before the subtraction.
$(-3^5 \times 10) - (9 \div 3) = (-243 \times 10) - (9 \div 3) =$
$-2430 - 3 = -2433$

7. a) $(2^3 + 4)^2$ was calculated as $(2^3 + 4) \times 2$.
    b) The answer -1440 is correct.
    c) $(-10)^3$ was evaluated as 1000.
    d) The brackets of $(5 + 5)^2$ were ignored, so $(-10)^3$ was divided by 5 and then 5^2 was added.

8. a) 625; The simplified expression $(-5)^{3 + 2 - 1} = (-5)^4$ has an even exponent, so the value will be positive.

b) 1; A power with an exponent of 0 gives a value of 1, so the answer will be positive.

c) The simplified expression $(-1)^{2 + 4 - 3 - 2} = (-1)^1$ has an odd exponent, so the answer will be negative.

d) 4352; Each power in the simplified expression $(-4)^6 + (-4)^4$ has an even exponent, so the value will be positive.

Unit 3 Rational Numbers, page 92

3.1 What Is a Rational Number?, page 101

5. $\dfrac{-3}{2} = -\dfrac{3}{2} = \dfrac{3}{-2}$; $\dfrac{-2}{3} = -\dfrac{2}{3} = \dfrac{2}{-3}$

6. a) $-\dfrac{7}{9}, \dfrac{-7}{9}$ **b)** $-\dfrac{5}{3}, \dfrac{5}{-3}$

   c) $\dfrac{-6}{11}, \dfrac{6}{-11}$

7. a) 1.2   **b)** −1.2

   c) 2.25   **d)** $-1.8\overline{3}$

8. a) A: −7.9, B: −7.2   **b)** C: −4.4, D: −3.2

   c) J: −0.7, K: −0.2

   d) G: −15.37, H: −15.32

9. a) B: −7.2   **b)** D: −3.2

   c) K: −0.2   **d)** H: −15.32

10. a) E: $-\dfrac{45}{4}$, F: $-\dfrac{43}{4}$ **b)** L: $-\dfrac{41}{8}$, M: $-\dfrac{23}{4}$

   c) N: $-\dfrac{25}{6}$, P: $-\dfrac{11}{3}$ **d)** Q: $-\dfrac{9}{16}$, R: $-\dfrac{3}{16}$

11. a) E: $-\dfrac{45}{4}$ **b)** M: $-\dfrac{23}{4}$

   c) N: $-\dfrac{25}{6}$ **d)** Q: $-\dfrac{9}{16}$

12. Answers will vary. For example:

   a) 3.8, 3.9, 4.1   **b)** −1.2, −1.1, −0.6

   c) −4.4, −4.3, −4.1   **d)** −5.4, −5.1, −4.8

   e) −3.2, −0.1, 4.7   **f)** 4.3, 2.1, −2.9

   g) −5.63, −5.66, −5.68

   h) −2.982, −2.987, −2.989

13. a) *See diagram below.*

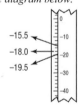

   b) No, the temperature in the freezer may be above −18°C.

14. Answers will vary. For example:

   a) $\dfrac{7}{8}, \dfrac{9}{8}, \dfrac{11}{8}$ **b)** $\dfrac{11}{10}, \dfrac{3}{10}, -\dfrac{13}{10}$

   c) $-\dfrac{179}{48}, -\dfrac{89}{24}, -\dfrac{177}{48}$

   d) $-\dfrac{3}{8}, -\dfrac{1}{4}, -\dfrac{3}{16}$ **e)** $0.25, \dfrac{1}{3}, \dfrac{5}{12}$

f) $-0.27, \dfrac{7}{24}, -0.29$ **g)** $-\dfrac{71}{25}, -\dfrac{72}{25}, -\dfrac{74}{25}$

h) $5\dfrac{16}{25}, 5\dfrac{17}{25}, 5\dfrac{19}{25}$

15.

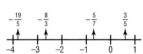

16. a) 2.34   **b)** −2.3

   c) 1.4   **d)** 3.96

   e) −5.6   **f)** $2.8\overline{6}$

17. a) $\dfrac{3}{5}$ **b)** $-1\dfrac{7}{8}$

   c) $-\dfrac{13}{5}$ **d)** $-\dfrac{11}{3}$

18. a) $\dfrac{6}{7}$ **b)** $\dfrac{3}{4}$

   c) $-\dfrac{6}{7}$ **d)** $\dfrac{5}{9}$

19. The statement is true when both numbers are positive.

20. a)

   b) $-\dfrac{17}{3}, -3.6, -\dfrac{11}{8}$ **c)** $-\dfrac{11}{8}, 0.8, 1.4, 4\dfrac{1}{3}$

   d) Answers will vary. For example:

     $-4.5, -2\dfrac{1}{3}, -0.3, 1.1, 3\dfrac{5}{8}$

21. a) $-\dfrac{5}{7} < -\dfrac{4}{7}$ **b)** $-\dfrac{5}{6} < -\dfrac{5}{7}$

   c) $-2.2 = -\dfrac{11}{5}$ **d)** $-4.4\overline{6} < -4.46$

22. a) Hiker A: 26.4 or $\dfrac{132}{5}$ m

     Hiker B: −37.2 or $-\dfrac{186}{5}$ m

     Hiker C: −15.7 or $-\dfrac{157}{10}$ m

   b) *See diagram below.*

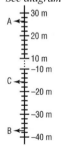

   c) Hiker C   **d)** Hiker B

23. a) $-3.5, -2.5, 0, 1.5, 4, 7.5$

b) $-3.2, -1.7, -0.8, 1, 4.3, 5.9$

c) $-2.01, -1.22, -1.2, 1.2, 1.\overline{2}, 2.1$

d) $-5.44, -5.4, -5.04, 5.04, 5.44, 5.\overline{4}$

24. a) $\dfrac{3}{8}, \dfrac{1}{4}, 0, -\dfrac{1}{2}, -\dfrac{5}{8}, -\dfrac{3}{4}$

b) $\dfrac{17}{3}, \dfrac{7}{2}, \dfrac{10}{9}, -\dfrac{7}{6}, -\dfrac{3}{2}, -\dfrac{5}{3}$

c) $\dfrac{21}{5}, \dfrac{16}{4}, -1\dfrac{1}{2}, -\dfrac{17}{10}, -\dfrac{9}{5}, -\dfrac{11}{4}$

d) $\dfrac{10}{3}, 2\dfrac{1}{4}, \dfrac{7}{12}, -\dfrac{8}{6}, -\dfrac{6}{4}, -\dfrac{11}{2}$

25. a) $-2.3, -1.5 = -\dfrac{3}{2}, \dfrac{3}{8}, \dfrac{5}{3}, 3.8$

b) $-3, -0.\overline{3}, -0.3, 0.3, 0.33, \dfrac{1}{3}$

26. a) $3 = \dfrac{3}{1}$ **b)** $-2 = \dfrac{-2}{1}$

c) $-0.5 = \dfrac{-1}{2}$ **d)** $-7.45 = \dfrac{-149}{20}$

27. a) Rational number   **b)** Irrational number
c) Rational number   **d)** Rational number

Unit 3: Start Where You Are, page 105

1. a) $3\dfrac{1}{6}$ **b)** $2\dfrac{7}{8}$

c) $1\dfrac{1}{2}$ **d)** $5\dfrac{5}{12}$

e) $2\dfrac{7}{10}$ **f)** $\dfrac{1}{2}$

g) $1\dfrac{17}{20}$ **h)** $2\dfrac{5}{6}$

2. a) 4   **b)** -4
c) -10 **d)** 4
e) -1 **f)** -3
g) 18   **h)** -18

3.2 Adding Rational Numbers, page 111

3. a) $0.8 + 1.5 = 2.3$ **b)** $1.5 + (-0.8) = 0.7$
c) $(-0.8) + (-1.5) = -2.3$
d) $(-1.5) + 0.8 = -0.7$

4. a) $\dfrac{1}{2} + \dfrac{5}{4} = \dfrac{7}{4}$ **b)** $\left(-\dfrac{5}{4}\right) + \dfrac{1}{2} = -\dfrac{3}{4}$

c) $\dfrac{5}{4} + \left(-\dfrac{1}{2}\right) = \dfrac{3}{4}$ **d)** $\left(-\dfrac{1}{2}\right) + \left(-\dfrac{5}{4}\right) = -\dfrac{7}{4}$

5. a) i) 5   **ii)** 6.2
b) i) -5 **ii)** -6.2
c) i) -1 **ii)** -1.4
d) i) 1   **ii)** 1.4

6. Parts c and d

7. a) i) 12   **ii)** 6
b) i) -12 **ii)** -6
c) i) -6 **ii)** -3
d) i) 6   **ii)** 3

8. Part c

9. a) -2.4 **b)** 3.44
c) -32.825 **d)** -96.05
e) 182.281   **f)** -17.938

10. Yes, the sum of two negative rational numbers is less than both numbers.

11. a) $-\dfrac{1}{6}$ **b)** $\dfrac{7}{15}$

c) $-3\dfrac{19}{20}$ **d)** $7\dfrac{1}{10}$

e) $-4\dfrac{1}{12}$ **f)** $-1\dfrac{1}{30}$

g) $\dfrac{7}{8}$ **h)** $-3\dfrac{5}{6}$

i) $-5\dfrac{5}{12}$ **j)** $\dfrac{29}{40}$

12. a) The sum is positive. **b)** The sum is negative.
  c) The sum has the same sign as the rational number farther away from 0.

13. a) -36.25 and -25.35
  b) i) $-36.25 + (-25.35) = -61.60$
    ii) $61.60
  c) i) $-61.60 + (14.75) = -46.85$
    ii) $46.85

14. a) -0.38 **b)** 0.38
  c) $\dfrac{16}{15}$ **d)** $\dfrac{11}{20}$

15. a) $-7.7°C$ **b)** $-17.1°C$
  c) *See diagram below.*

16. a) The sum in part ii is greater since the positive number is farther away from 0.
    i) -5.77 **ii)** 5.77
  b) The sum in part ii is greater since the sum in part i is a sum of two negative numbers.
    i) $-1\dfrac{5}{12}$ **ii)** $\dfrac{1}{12}$

17. a) $45.50, 22.25, -15.77, -33.10$
  b) $45.50 + 22.25 + (-15.77) + (-33.10) = 18.88$
  c) $18.88

18. No, Lucille's business lost $266.04 in the first 6 months.
$-545.50 + (-978.44) + 2115.70 + (-888) + 2570.4 + (-2540.2) = -266.04$

19. a) Any number less than or equal to 3.5
  b) Any number greater than or equal to -11.6
  c) Any number greater than or equal to 14.4
  d) Any number less than or equal to 14.4

20. a) $1\dfrac{5}{8}$ **b)** $-1\dfrac{7}{15}$
  c) $5\dfrac{5}{8}$ **d)** $-3\dfrac{7}{12}$

21. Any number less than or equal to 3.3

22. The greatest possible sum less than 0 is $-\dfrac{1}{12}$.
For example: $-\dfrac{1}{3} + \dfrac{1}{4} = -\dfrac{1}{12}$

3.3 Subtracting Rational Numbers, page 119

3. a) i) 2 **ii)** 1.8
  b) i) -8 **ii)** -8.4
  c) i) 2 **ii)** 1.8
  d) i) -2 **ii)** -1.8

4. Part d

5. a) i) 9 **ii)** $\dfrac{9}{5}$
  b) i) -13 **ii)** $-\dfrac{13}{5}$
  c) i) 13 **ii)** $\dfrac{13}{5}$
  d) i) 13 **ii)** $\dfrac{13}{5}$

6. Part c

7. a) 7.3 **b)** -85.77
  c) 64.73 **d)** -31.57
  e) -38.03 **f)** 151.84

8. a) $4.6°C$ or $-4.6°C$
  b) There are two possible answers depending on which temperature is subtracted from the other temperature.

9. a) $-3\dfrac{5}{6}$ **b)** $-4\dfrac{14}{15}$
  c) $-4\dfrac{11}{12}$ **d)** $-4\dfrac{1}{24}$
  e) $3\dfrac{1}{3}$ **f)** $2\dfrac{5}{24}$

10. Yes, it is possible when you subtract a negative number from a positive number. For example:
$1.3 - (-3.5) = 5.8;\ \dfrac{3}{2} - \left(-\dfrac{5}{2}\right) = 4$

11. a) $-417.5, 8844.43$
  b) $8844.43 - (-417.5) = 9261.93$
  The points are 9261.93 m apart.

12. a) Negative; -44.98 **b)** Positive; 7.11
  c) Positive; $2\dfrac{1}{4}$ **d)** Negative; $-6\dfrac{4}{15}$

13. a) $1\dfrac{23}{30}$ **b)** 0.55
  c) $4\dfrac{43}{60}$ **d)** 7.69

14. a) Any number greater than or equal to -4.9
    For example: -4.8
  b) Any number less than or equal to -4.6
    For example: -5.2
  c) Any number greater than or equal to 8.2
    For example: 9.3

d) Any number less than or equal to −3.7
For example: −3.8

15. a) 65.7   **b)** $\dfrac{3}{10}$

c) −2.03   **d)** $4\dfrac{1}{6}$

e) −5   **f)** $-8\dfrac{3}{4}$

16. a) Any 2 numbers with a difference of −3.5
For example: −1.1 and 2.4; 7.2 and 10.7

b) Any 2 numbers with a sum of −13.9
For example: −5.7 and −8.2; −15.7 and 1.8

c) Any 2 numbers with a sum of −6.2
For example: −9.3 and 3.1; 1.3 and −7.5

17. a) Any number greater than or equal to −17.5

b) Any number less than or equal to −3.1

Unit 3: Mid-Unit Review, page 121

1. a)

b) $-\dfrac{9}{3}$, and $-\dfrac{8}{5}$; they are on the left of −1.5 on the number line.

2. $-1\dfrac{3}{8}$, $-\dfrac{6}{5}$, −1.1 , $-\dfrac{1}{4}$, 0.2, 1.2

3. a) >   **b)** <

c) <   **d)** >

4. Answers will vary. For example:

a) 1.3   **b)** 0

c) $\dfrac{7}{20}$ **d)** −1

5. a) The sum of two positive numbers is positive.
The sum of two negative numbers is negative.
The sum of a negative number and a positive
number has the same sign as the number farther
away from 0.

b) **i)** Positive; 5.82   **ii)** Negative; −6.03

iii) Negative; $-1\dfrac{19}{24}$ **iv)** Positive; 1.31

v) Negative; $-2\dfrac{43}{45}$ **vi)** Negative; −0.04

6. a) 8.95   **b)** −57.82

c) −124.7   **d)** $\dfrac{37}{72}$

e) $-3\dfrac{1}{20}$ **f)** $-4\dfrac{20}{21}$

7. a) **i)** 1.4°C   **ii)** An increase

b) 10.9°C

8. a) −22.85   **b)** −97.4

c) $-\dfrac{1}{2}$ **d)** $-8\dfrac{5}{18}$

e) −6.1   **f)** $6\dfrac{3}{8}$

9. 6193.7 − (−86) = 6279.7
The distance between the two points is 6279.7 m.

10. b) **i)** Positive; 8.7   **ii)** Negative; −2.52

iii) Negative; $-\dfrac{49}{60}$ **iv)** Positive; $13\dfrac{1}{6}$

3.4 Multiplying Rational Numbers, page 127

3. Part d

a) −15.6   **b)** −10.4

c) −6.5   **d)** 6.39

4. Parts a, c, and d

a) −2   **b)** $1\dfrac{1}{4}$

c) $-1\dfrac{3}{5}$ **d)** $-\dfrac{7}{16}$

5. a) −0.128   **b)** 2.855

c) 3.304   **d)** 5.95

6. Parts a, b, c, e

7. a) $-\dfrac{2}{15}$ **b)** $-\dfrac{3}{20}$

c) $\dfrac{2}{5}$ **d)** $\dfrac{5}{9}$

8. a) 12.75

b) The product is less than 10.

c) 11

d) The product is less than 10.

e) 12.5

f) The product is less than 10.

9. a) −$96   **b)** −$105

c) $14.95

10. (−10.4)(3.6) = −37.44
The diver's depth is 37.44 m after 3.6 min.

11. a) −3.444   **b)** 28.44

c) 231.04   **d)** 104.52

12. a) −4   **b)** $\dfrac{5}{9}$

c) $-14\dfrac{29}{36}$ **d)** $7\dfrac{1}{3}$

13. a) 104

b) **i)** 1.04   **ii)** −0.104

iii) −10.4   **iv)** 0.104

c) I only need to determine the sign and estimate the decimal point.

d) Answers will vary. For example:
$(260)(0.04) = 10.4$; $(0.026)(4000) = 104$;
$(-2.6)(-4) = 10.4$

14. a) $(-3457.25)(25) = -86\,431.25$
b) $-\$40\,863.38$

15. a) Positive; 3.1   **b)** Negative; $-\dfrac{5}{7}$

16. a) -4.7 **b)** $\dfrac{7}{2}$

c) -0.4 **d)** $1\dfrac{2}{5}$

17. Yes, it is possible when both numbers are between 1 and -1. For example: $(-0.6)(0.4) = -0.24$

18. b) $-\dfrac{2759}{7826}$

3.5 Dividing Rational Numbers, page 134

3. a) -0.5 **b)** -1.4
c) 2.1 **d)** -0.2
e) 2.4 **f)** -0.9

4. a) $-\dfrac{2}{3}$ **b)** $-\dfrac{4}{3}$

c) $\dfrac{7}{16}$ **d)** $\dfrac{3}{44}$

e) $-\dfrac{15}{4}$ **f)** $\dfrac{36}{55}$

5. Parts c, d, e, and f
6. -1.6 m/h
7. a) 0.8 **b)** -1.4625
c) $-0.41\overline{6}$ **d)** 5.1
e) $-12.5\overline{3}$ **f)** 3.5
8. 5 h
9. a) -11.52 **b)** $-23.28\overline{3}$
c) 36.7 **d)** 4.8
e) $-10.217\overline{3}$ **f)** $-0.240\overline{2}$
10. a) 41
b) The quotient will be less than -10.
c) The quotient will be less than -10.
d) -1.2
11. a) 48 weeks
12. a) $-\dfrac{15}{14}$ **b)** $\dfrac{1}{8}$

c) $\dfrac{2}{3}$ **d)** $-6\dfrac{2}{15}$

e) $-1\dfrac{17}{27}$ **f)** $\dfrac{31}{57}$

13. 35 times

14. $-2.8°\text{C/h}$
15. $-\$0.32$
16. Part c; $\left(\dfrac{5}{6}\right) \div \left(-\dfrac{2}{3}\right) = -\dfrac{5}{4} = -1\dfrac{1}{4}$

17. a) -4.5 **b)** $-\dfrac{21}{32}$

c) 2.35 **d)** $-\dfrac{17}{3}$

18. a) -2.6 **b)** -6.9
c) -6.3 **d)** -3.586
19. a) Ellice: 1300 m $\div 7.8$ min $\doteq 166.67$ m/min
Alex: -630 m $\div 4.2$ min $= -150$ m/min
1300 m represents distance in the positive direction and -630 m represents distance in the opposite direction.
b) Ellice runs at the greater average speed.

20. Answers will vary. For example: $-\dfrac{5}{6} \div \dfrac{5}{2} = -\dfrac{1}{3}$

21. Part d

3.6 Order of Operations with Rational Numbers, page 140

3. a) 3.58 **b)** -16.42
c) 73 **d)** -0.192
4. a) $\dfrac{1}{4}$ **b)** $-\dfrac{5}{4}$

c) $\dfrac{15}{8}$ **d)** $\dfrac{263}{60}$

5. a) -9.1
6. a) -52.64 **b)** 98.784
c) -206.99 **d)** -561.834
7. a) $-2\dfrac{7}{12}$ **b)** $\dfrac{8}{9}$

c) $-\dfrac{8}{27}$ **d)** -8

8. a) Correction:
$(-3.7) \times (-2.8 + 1.5) - 4.8 \div (-1.2)$
$= (-3.7) \times (-1.3) - (-4)$
$= 4.81 + 4$
$= 8.81$
b) Correction:
$-\dfrac{3}{8} - \dfrac{4}{5} \times \dfrac{3}{10} \div \left(-\dfrac{4}{5}\right)$
$= -\dfrac{3}{8} - \dfrac{6}{25} \div \left(-\dfrac{4}{5}\right)$
$= -\dfrac{3}{8} - \left(-\dfrac{3}{10}\right)$
$= -\dfrac{3}{40}$

9. $\$192.74$

10. a) 330 cm^2

11. a) i) About −18°C **ii)** −40°C **iii)** About −47°C

b) i) 10°C **ii)** −25°C **iii)** 0°C

12. a) Multiplication, addition; $-6\frac{1}{3}$

b) Multiplication, addition; $6\frac{8}{15}$

c) Division, multiplication, addition; $3\frac{1}{8}$

d) Addition, multiplication, subtraction $1\frac{1}{16}$

13. a) 54.6 **b)** −5.62

c) About 12.82 **d)** About −14.24

14. a) $[-8.1 + (-16.7)] \div 2 = -12.4; -12.4°C$

b) I used brackets to add the two temperatures first before I divided the sum by 2.

15. a) Answers will vary. For example:

$$\frac{-3}{2} + \left(\frac{4}{-5} - \frac{-8}{6}\right) \div \frac{10}{-12} = \frac{-107}{50}$$

b) Answers will vary. For example:

$$\left(\frac{6}{-5} - \frac{-12}{10}\right)\left(\frac{2}{-3} - \frac{4}{-8}\right) = 0$$

16. a) Below 0°C **b)** About −1.01°C

17. Correction:

$$(-8.2)^2 \div (-0.3) - 2.9 \times (-5.7)$$

$$= 67.24 \div (-0.3) - (-16.53)$$

$$= -224.1\overline{3} - (-16.53)$$

$$= -224.1\overline{3} + 16.53$$

$$= -207.60\overline{3}$$

18. a) 1.63

b) The student likely calculated $6.8 \div (-3) \times (-6.7) + 3.5$ instead of calculating the numerator and the denominator and then finding the result of the division.

19. $\frac{5}{9}$ is equivalent to $\frac{1}{1.8}$, or dividing by 1.8.

20. −14.1°C

21. $-3.8 + 9.1 \times (-2.5 - 0.5) = -31.1$

Yes, it is possible to find a positive solution.

For example: $-(3.8 + 9.1) \times (-2.5) - 0.5 = 31.75$

Unit 3: Review, page 144

1. Parts a and c

2. $-\frac{4}{3}$, $-\frac{1}{2}$, −0.4, 0.9, 3.12

3. Answers will vary. For example:

a) −3.475, −3.3, −3.15

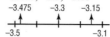

b) $\frac{7}{20}$, $\frac{5}{10}$, $\frac{27}{40}$

c) 0.83, 0.855, 0.8725

d) $-\frac{9}{4}$, −2, $-\frac{7}{4}$

4. −2.00; −0.51; −0.09; 0.54; 0.95

5. a) −1.5 **b)** 78.44

c) −28.17 **d)** 48.053

6. a) −7.9°C

b) *See diagram below.*

7. a) $\frac{13}{8}$ **b)** $1\frac{5}{6}$

c) $-6\frac{1}{4}$ **d)** $-\frac{29}{18}$

8. a) 1.4 **b)** −83.14

c) −9.64 **d)** −16.82

9. $22.35

10. a) $-\frac{1}{2}$ **b)** $\frac{31}{40}$

c) $10\frac{43}{70}$ **d)** $-13\frac{5}{12}$

11. Parts c and d

a) 1.12 **b)** −1.28

c) $-\frac{4}{5}$ **d)** $\frac{5}{9}$

12. −7.1°C

13. Answers will vary. For example:

$$\left(-\frac{7}{9}\right)\left(\frac{4}{5}\right) = \left(-\frac{4}{9}\right)\left(\frac{7}{5}\right)$$

14. a) −1.05 **b)** −9.43

c) $\frac{8}{21}$ **d)** −4

15. The climber will be 22.125 m lower than the base camp.

16. Parts c and d
  a) −5.5   **b)** About −1.15
  c) $-\dfrac{3}{5}$ **d)** $\dfrac{1}{3}$

17. Answers will vary. For example:
$$\left(-\dfrac{3}{8}\right)\div\left(\dfrac{5}{11}\right) = \left(\dfrac{3}{8}\right)\div\left(-\dfrac{5}{11}\right)$$

18. **a)** −3.75   **b)** −8.3
  c) 1.56

19. **a)** −7   **b)** $22.\overline{8}$
  c) $-\dfrac{45}{77}$ **d)** $-\dfrac{10}{21}$

20. **a)** **i)** −4.74   **ii)** −0.54
  b) The orders of operations are different.

21. **a)** $-\dfrac{17}{20}$ **b)** $\dfrac{1}{5}$
  c) $-\dfrac{1}{5}$

22. **a)** 1554.82 cm²

23. **a)** −4.9   **b)** $1\dfrac{13}{36}$
  c) $-1\dfrac{211}{365}$ **d)** $2\dfrac{4}{5}$
  e) $-3\dfrac{6}{7}$ **f)** −5.8
  g) −13.51

Unit 3: Practice Test, page 146

1. **a)** Answers will vary. For example: −0.55

2. **a)**

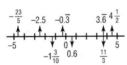

  b) $4\dfrac{1}{2}, \dfrac{11}{3} = 3.\overline{6}, 0.6, -0.\overline{3}, -1\dfrac{3}{10}, -2.5, -\dfrac{23}{5}$

3. **a)** −1.3   **b)** $\dfrac{1}{2}$
  c) 1.6   **d)** $-\dfrac{9}{4}$

4. **a)** It means that she owes $2.34.
  b) −$67.44   **c)** 19 withdrawals

5. **a)** 823.6   **b)** $7\dfrac{2}{3}$
  c) $2\dfrac{17}{30}$ **d)** About −3.75

6. **a)** $3\dfrac{1}{2}$
  b) The student added $\dfrac{1}{2}+\left(-\dfrac{3}{4}\right)$ instead of doing the division first.

7. **a)** −13.75   **b)** 3.54

Cumulative Review Units 1-3, page 148

1. **a)** $\dfrac{1}{5}$ **b)** $\dfrac{15}{13}$
  c) $\dfrac{3}{11}$ **d)** 1.2
  e) 0.4   **f)** 1.8

2. **a)** 8 cm   **b)** 1.1 m
  c) 8.5 mm

3. **a)** 0.49   **b)** 2.56
  c) 0.000 036   **d)** $\dfrac{144}{289}$
  e) $\dfrac{1}{9}$ **f)** $\dfrac{4}{169}$

4. **a)** $\dfrac{7}{63} = \dfrac{1}{9} = \left(\dfrac{1}{3}\right)^2$, so $\dfrac{7}{63}$ is a perfect square.
  b) $\dfrac{12}{27} = \dfrac{4}{9} = \left(\dfrac{2}{3}\right)^2$, so $\dfrac{12}{27}$ is a perfect square.
  c) $\dfrac{4}{18} = \dfrac{2}{9}$, and 2 is not a perfect square, so $\dfrac{4}{18}$ is not a perfect square.
  d) $0.016 = \dfrac{16}{1000}$, and 1000 is not a perfect square, so 0.016 is not a perfect square.
  e) $4.9 = \dfrac{49}{10}$, and 10 is not a perfect square, so 4.9 is not a perfect square.
  f) $0.121 = \dfrac{121}{1000}$, and 1000 is not a perfect square, so 0.121 is not a perfect square.

5. **a)** 2.6 m   **b)** 7.8 m

6. 144.5, 168.9

7. **a)** About $\dfrac{1}{6}$ **b)** About 4
  c) About 0.9   **d)** About $\dfrac{1}{3}$

8. **a)** 17.4 cm   **b)** 6.3 m

9. 24 cm²

10. **a)** 72 cm²   **b)** About 265 cm²

11. a) $4^3 = 64$ **b)** $6^4 = 1296$
c) $(-3)^7 = -2187$ **d)** $-(-2)^7 = 128$
e) $-10^5 = -100\ 000$ **f)** $-1^{12} = -1$
12. a) Negative; -81 **b)** Positive; $15\ 625$
c) Negative; -64 **d)** Positive; 49
e) Negative; -1 **f)** Positive; 1
13. a) 8×10^2 **b)** $5 \times 10^4 + 2 \times 10^3$
c) $1 \times 10^3 + 7 \times 10^2 + 6 \times 10^1$
d) $7 \times 10^6 + 4 \times 10^0$
14. a) 784 **b)** -5
c) -10 **d)** 139
e) 4 **f)** 1
15. a) 6^8 **b)** $(-3)^8$
c) $(-5)^3$ **d)** 2^{14}
16. a) -6 **b)** 12
c) -3250 **d)** 512
17. a) 10^4 m $= 10\ 000$ m **b)** $40\ 000$ m
18. a) $6^8 = 1\ 679\ 616$ **b)** $7^6 + 3^9 = 137\ 332$
c) $(-2)^3 - 1 = -9$ **d)** $6^8 + 3^{10} = 1\ 738\ 665$
e) $(-4)^6 - (-2)^{12} - (-3)^8 = -6561$
f) $3^6 = 729$
19. a) $-3.\overline{3}, -3.3, -2.8, -1.9, 1.2, 4.8$
b) $-\dfrac{13}{4}, -2\dfrac{1}{2}, -\dfrac{13}{10}, -\dfrac{2}{5}, \dfrac{3}{4}, \dfrac{19}{5}$
c) $-1.01, -\dfrac{1}{3}, -0.11, 1.1, \dfrac{4}{3}, 1\dfrac{3}{8}$
d) $-0.2, -\dfrac{1}{6}, -0.\overline{1}, \dfrac{1}{8}, \dfrac{2}{9}, 0.25$
20. a) 1.44 **b)** -10.307
c) 9.17 **d)** -6.43
e) $-\dfrac{1}{12}$ **f)** $-4\dfrac{17}{24}$
g) $-7\dfrac{11}{12}$ **h)** $6\dfrac{1}{2}$
21. 85.648
22. a) -36.5 **b)** 163.84
c) 3.2 **d)** -5.6
e) $11\dfrac{2}{5}$ **f)** $-18\dfrac{2}{3}$
g) $\dfrac{1}{20}$ **h)** $-1\dfrac{1}{5}$
23. a) $-\dfrac{11}{24}$ **b)** -40.55
c) $-6\dfrac{1}{20}$ **d)** $5\dfrac{1}{8}$

Unit 4 Linear Relations, page 150

Unit 4: Start Where You Are, page 153

1. $3n - 2$
2. $3n + 1$

4.1 Writing Equations to Describe Patterns, page 159

4. a) 2 **b)** 3
c) 4 **d)** 5
5. a) 7 **b)** 8
c) 9 **d)** 10
6. Parts a and c
7. $f + 5$
8. $n = 4s + 1$ **9.** $s = 2f + 3$
10. a) The red number 1 represents the red toothpick that is the same in each picture. The number of black toothpicks added is 4 times the number of houses in the picture.
b) $1 + 4n$ **c)** $t = 1 + 4n$
11. a) i) As the term number increases by 1, the term value increases by 11.
ii) $11t$ **iii)** $v = 11t$
b) i) As the term number increases by 1, the term value increases by 3.
ii) $3t + 2$ **iii)** $v = 3t + 2$
c) i) As the term number increases by 1, the term value decreases by 1.
ii) $8 - t$ **iii)** $v = 8 - t$
12. a)

Figure Number, n	Number of Toothpicks, t
1	3
2	5
3	7
4	9

b) $2n + 1$ **c)** 91
d) $t = 2n + 1$ **e)** Figure 8
13. a)

Number of Tables, n	Number of People, p
1	6
2	10
3	14
4	18

b) As the number of tables increases by 1, the number of people who can be seated increases by 4.
d) $p = 4n + 2$ **e)** 10 tables
14. a) $C = 250 + 1.25n$ **b)** $3375
c) 300 brochures
15. a)

Number of Toppings, n	Cost of Pizza, C ($)
1	9.75
2	10.50
3	11.25
4	12.00
5	12.75

b) $C = 9 + 0.75n$ **c)**   8 toppings

16. a) Variables may differ. $C = 12 + 1.5n$

  b) 11 windows

17. The garden size is 73.

18. b) $t = 5 + 4(n - 1)$

19. a)

Figure Number, n	Perimeter, P	Area, A
1	10	4
2	16	7
3	22	10

  b) Variables may differ. $P = 4 + 6n$

  c) $A = 1 + 3n$

  d) Perimeter: 304 cm; area: 151 cm^2

  e) Figure 16   **f)** Figure 33

20. a) $v = 84 - 4t$

21. a)

Number of Cuts	1	2	3	4	5	6	7	8	9	10
Number of Pieces	2	4	8	16	32	64	128	256	512	1024

  b) The number of pieces doubled each time. They are powers of 2.

  c) 32 768 pieces   **d)** $P = 2^n$

  e) 16 cuts

Unit 4 Technology: Tables of Values and Graphing, page 163

1. a) $F = 4.20 + 1.46d$

  b)

Distance, d (km)	Fare, F ($)
1	5.66
2	7.12
3	8.58
4	10.04
5	11.50
6	12.96
7	14.42
8	15.88
9	17.34
10	18.80
11	20.26
12	21.72
13	23.18
14	24.64
15	26.10
16	27.56
17	29.02
18	30.48
19	31.94
20	33.40

c)

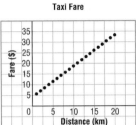

4.2 Linear Relations, page 170

4. Parts a, b, and c

5. a) i) Yes

  ii) When x increases by 1, y increases by 9.

  b) i) Yes

  ii) When x decreases by 1, y increases by 3.

  c) i) No

  iii) When x increases by 1, y does not increase or decrease by a constant value.

  d) i) Yes

  ii) When x decreases by 3, y increases by 2.

6. a) The relation is linear since the points on the graph lie on a straight line.

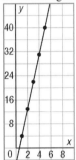

  b) The relation is linear since the points on the graph lie on a straight line.

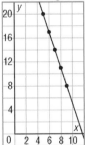

d) The relation is linear since the points on the graph lie on a straight line.

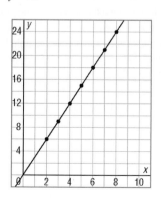

7. a) $y = 2x$

x	y
1	2
2	4
3	6
4	8

b) $y = x + 2$

x	y
1	3
2	4
3	5
4	6

c) $y = -2x$

x	y
2	-4
4	-8
6	-12
8	-16

d) $y = x - 2$

x	y
4	2
5	3
6	4
7	5

8. a)

x	2	3	4	5	6	7	8
y	6	9	12	15	18	21	24

b) When x increases by 1, y increases by 3.

c) $y = 3x$

d)

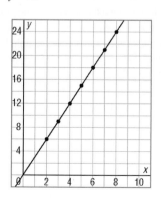

e) $y = -3$

9. a)

x	y
2	11
3	14
4	17
5	20
6	23

b)

x	y
1	7
3	8
5	9
7	10
9	11

c)

x	y
-4	11
-2	7
0	3
2	-1
4	-5

d)

x	y
4	-10
6	-7
8	-4
10	-1
12	2

10. a) $y = 3x$

x	y
-2	-6
-1	-3
0	0
1	3
2	6

b) $y = x + 3$

x	y
-2	1
-1	2
0	3
1	4
2	5

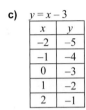

c) $y = x - 3$

x	y
-2	-5
-1	-4
0	-3
1	-2
2	-1

d) $y = 5 - x$

x	y
-2	7
-1	6
0	5
1	4
2	3

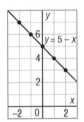

e) $y = 1 - 4x$

x	y
-2	9
-1	5
0	1
1	-3
2	-7

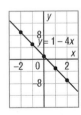

f) $y = -2x - 3$

x	y
-2	1
-1	-1
0	-3
1	-5
2	-7

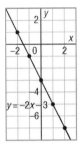

11. a) $d = 4t$

b)

t	d
0	0
1	4
2	8
3	12
4	16
5	20

c) I should join the points since measures of distance and time are not discrete data.

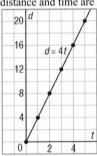

d) The relation is linear.

i) When the time increases by 1, the distance increases by 4.

ii) Points on the graph lie on a straight line.

e) 50.4 km

f) About 1.2 h, or 1 h 11 min

12. a) $T = 0.05p$

b)

p	T
0	0
10	0.50
20	1.00
30	1.50
40	2.00

c) As the purchase price, p, increases by 10, the tax, T, increases by 0.50.

d)

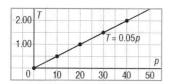

e) I should connect the points with a line because all the values between the points are permitted.

f) To move from one point to the next on the graph, move 10 units right and 0.5 units up.

13. a) Variables may differ: $C = 10 + 2r$

b)

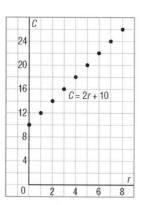

c) $24   **d)** 14 rides

14. b)

n	P
2	12
4	18
6	24
8	30
10	36

c) I would not join the points because the number of pieces of pizza ordered and the number of people attending are whole numbers.

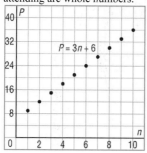

d) The relation is linear.

i) When the number of people increases by 2, the number of pieces increases by 6.

ii) Points on the graph lie on a straight line.

15. a) Variables may differ: $h = 1800 - 150t$

b)

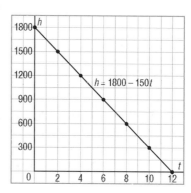

c) 900 m

d) 11 min 20 s after beginning to descend

16. a) $d = 250 - 8t$

b)

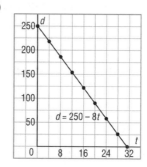

c) 154 km   **d)** 31.25 h or 31 h 15 min

18.

x	−3	−1	2	5	9	14	20
y	29	26.6	23	19.4	14.6	8.6	1.4

4.3 Another Form of the Equation for a Linear Relation, page 178

4. a) $x = -2$ **b)** $y = -2$

5. a) A horizontal line that intersects the y-axis at 7

b) An oblique line

c) A vertical line that intersects the x-axis at −5

d) A vertical line that intersects the x-axis at −9

e) A horizontal line that intersects the y-axis at 2.5

f) An oblique line

6. a) A horizontal line that intersects the y-axis at 5

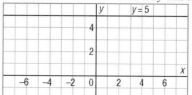

b) A vertical line that intersects the x-axis at -1

A vertical line $x = -1$ through the grid.

c) A vertical line that intersects the x-axis at -5

A vertical line $x = -5$ through the grid.

d) A horizontal line that intersects the y-axis at 7

A horizontal line $y = 7$ through the grid.

7. a) $y = 2$ **b)** $x = 1$

c) $x = -5$

8. $2x + 1 = 0$

9. a)

p	q
-4	19
0	15
2	13
7	8
12	3
15	0

b)

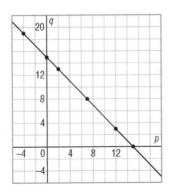

c) $p + q = 15$

10. a) i) $x + y = 6$

x	y
-2	8
0	6
2	4

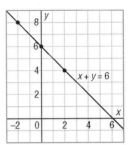

ii) $x - y = 6$

x	y
-2	-8
0	-6
2	-4

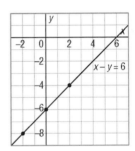

iii) $x + y = -6$

x	y
-2	-4
0	-6
2	-8

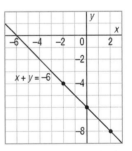

iv) $x - y = -6$

x	y
-2	4
0	6
2	8

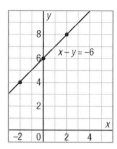

b) The graphs in part a intersect the *x*-axis and the *y*-axis at 6 or –6.

11. a) $y + 3 = -2$ simplifies to $y = -5$.

b) $2x = 7$ simplifies to $x = 3.5$.

c) $3x + 1 = -5$ simplifies to $x = -2$.

d) $2y - 2 = 10$ simplifies to $y = 6$.

12. $x = -1, x = 4, y = -4, y = 3$

13. a) Square

c) Answers may vary. For example:
$x = 0, y = 0, x = 4,$ and $y = -4$

14. a)

Distance Travelled, *t* (km)	Distance to Edmonton, *e* (km)
0	300
50	250
100	200
150	150
200	100
250	50

b) 300

c) I would join the points because distances between Edmonton and Calgary are not discrete data.

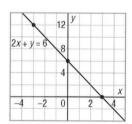

d) $e + t = 300$

15. a) $2x + y = 6$

x	*y*
–3	12
0	6
3	0

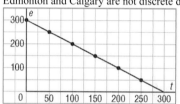

b) $3x - y = 2$

x	*y*
–2	–8
0	–2
2	4

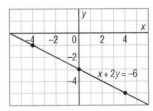

c) $x + 2y = -6$

x	y
-4	-1
0	-3
4	-5

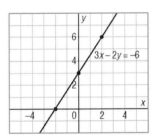

d) $3x - 2y = -6$

x	y
-2	0
0	3
2	6

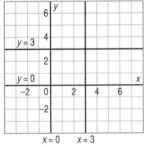

16. a, b) Answers will vary. For example:

c) The other possible sets of equations are:
$x = 0, y = 0, x = 3, y = -3$; $x = 0, y = 0, x = -3$,
$y = 3$; $x = 0, y = 0, x = -3, y = -3$

17. a)

a	b
-2	-8
0	-6
2	-4
4	-2
6	0
8	2

b) I would join the points because all values between the plotted points are permitted.

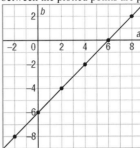

c) $a - b = 6$

18. a)

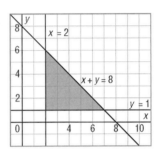

b) Right triangle; the lines $x = 2$ and $y = 1$ are perpendicular.

19. a) Let x and y represent 2 rational numbers with a sum of $2\frac{1}{2}$.

x	y
$3\frac{1}{2}$	-1
$2\frac{1}{2}$	0
$1\frac{1}{2}$	1
0	$2\frac{1}{2}$
-1	$3\frac{1}{2}$

b) The graph is an oblique line that intersects both axes at 2.5.

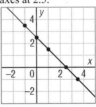

c) $x + y = 2\frac{1}{2}$

20. a) Variables may differ.

s	u
7	14.5
3.5	11
0	7.5
−3.5	4
−7.5	0

b) The graph is an oblique line that intersects the s-axis at −7.5 and the u-axis at 7.5.

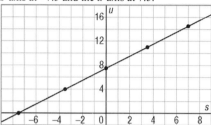

c) $s - u = -7.5$

21. a) $\dfrac{1}{2}x + y = 4$

x	y
−4	6
0	4
8	0

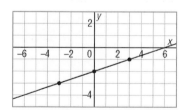

b) $\dfrac{1}{3}x - y = 2$

x	y
−3	−3
0	−2
3	−1

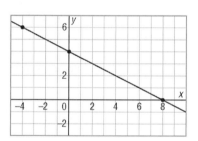

c) $\dfrac{1}{2}x + \dfrac{1}{3}y = 6$

x	y
0	18
4	12
12	0

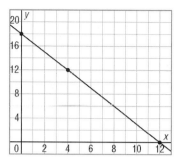

d) $\dfrac{1}{3}x - \dfrac{1}{2}y = -1$

x	y
−3	0
0	2
3	4

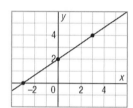

e) $\dfrac{1}{3}x + \dfrac{1}{2}y = -3$

x	y
−9	0
−3	−4
0	−6

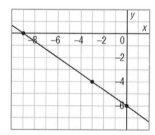

f) $\dfrac{1}{4}x - \dfrac{1}{2}y = 1$

x	y
−4	−4
2	−1
6	1

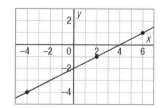

1. a)

Figure Number, n	Perimeter, P
1	4
2	10
3	16
4	22

b) $6n - 2$ **c)** 238 units

d) $P = 6n - 2$ **e)** Figure 23

2. a) $C = 10 + 0.25t$ **b)** $23.75

c) 50 min

3. a) $y = -3x$

x	y
−3	9
−1	3
1	−3
3	−9

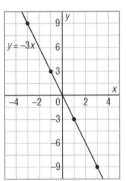

b) $y = 2x$

x	y
−3	−6
−1	−2
1	2
3	6

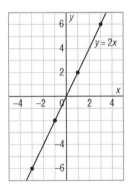

c) $y = 2 - 4x$

x	y
−3	14
−1	6
1	−2
3	−10

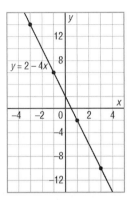

d) $y = -2x + 4$

x	y
−3	10
−1	6
1	2
3	−2

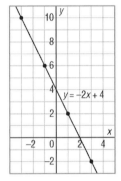

e) $y = -3 + x$

x	y
−3	−6
−1	−4
1	−2
3	0

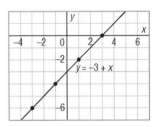

f) $y = -x + 3$

x	y
−3	6
−1	4
1	2
3	0

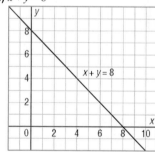

The graph shows $y = -x + 3$ plotted with points, x-axis from -4 to 4, y-axis from 0 to 6.

4. a)

Number of Weeks, n	Total Paid, P ($)
1	45
2	60
3	75
4	90
5	105

b) I should not join the points because Alicia pays once a week, so the data are discrete.

The graph shows points with $P = 15n + 30$, P-axis from 0 to 100, n-axis from 0 to 5.

c) In the table, P increases by $15 each week. On the graph, to get from one point to the next, move 1 unit right and 15 units up.

5. a)

x	y
1	10
2	14
3	18
4	22
5	26

b)

x	y
1	−6
3	−10
5	−14
7	−18
9	−22

c)

x	y
−2	−15
−1	−9
0	−3
1	3
2	9

d)

x	y
2	1
4	−2
6	−5
8	−8
10	−11

6. a) i) $y = 1$

The graph shows horizontal line $y = 1$.

ii) $x = -4$

The graph shows vertical line $x = -4$.

iii) $x + y = 8$

The graph shows line $x + y = 8$.

iv) $2x - y = 12$

The graph shows line $2x - y = 12$.

7. a)

g	n
5	4
2	1
−1	−2
−4	−5

b) I would join the points because all values between the plotted points are permitted.

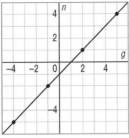

c) $g - n = 1$

4.4 Matching Equations and Graphs, page 188

3. a) iii   b) i
   c) ii
4. a) C   b) B
   c) A
5. a) ii   b) iii
   c) i
6. a) i   b) iii
   c) ii
7. a) B   b) A
   c) C
8. Graph B
9. a) $y = -x + 2$ b) $3x - y = -3$
11. c) i) C   ii) A
    iii) D   iv) B
12. a) $2y - x = 6$ b) $y = 1$
    c) $2x + y = 8$
13. a) $x - 2y = -8$ b) $y = -2x - 8$
    c) $y = -2x + 5$ d) $y = \frac{1}{2}x - \frac{1}{2}$

4.5 Using Graphs to Estimate Values, page 196

4. a) i) 6   ii) 0
   iii) −1
   b) i) −5   ii) 1
   iii) 4
5. a) i) −3   ii) 1
   iii) 7
   b) i) 3   ii) 0
   iii) $-1\frac{1}{2}$
6. a) i) −10   ii) 10
   iii) 18
   b) i) 4   ii) −2
   iii) $-3\frac{1}{2}$
7. a) i) 2.5   ii) −2.5
   iii) −4

b) i) −9   ii) 7
   iii) 11
8. a) About \$550   b) 10 months
   c) About \$480
9. a) About 300 Calories   b) About 24 min
   c) About 100 Calories
10. a) About 0.5   b) About 1.25
    c) About 1.5
11. a) i) About 20 m/s   ii) About 30 m/s
    b) i) About 220 km/h   ii) About 30 km/h
    c) i) I used interpolation for part a, i and ii and part b, ii.
       ii) I used extrapolation for part b, i.
12. i) About −2.5   ii) About 0.5
    iii) About 3.5
13. a) About \$300
    b) About 11 weeks, assuming her rate of pay stays the same.
    c) If the rate of pay changed, the graph would no longer be valid.
14. a) i) About $-\frac{17}{3}$ ii) About $-\frac{25}{3}$
    iii) About $\frac{35}{3}$
    b) i) About −2.5   ii) About 7.25
    iii) About 8.75
15. a)

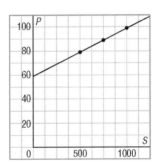

b) About \$1.15   c) About 150 mL

Unit 4 Technology: Interpolating and Extrapolating, page 199

1. a) i) \$8.50   ii) About \$42.50
   b) i) About 76 L   ii) About 14 L

Unit 4: Review, page 201

1. a) Figure 1: 10 units   Figure 2: 14 units
      Figure 3: 18 units   Figure 4: 22 units

b)

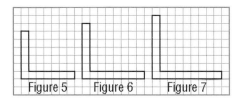

Figure 5   Figure 6   Figure 7

c)

Figure Number, n	Perimeter, P
1	10
2	14
3	18
4	22
5	26
6	30
7	34

d) $6 + 4n$ **e)** $P = 6 + 4n$

f) 126 units   **g)** Figure 21

2. a) As n increases by 1, v increases by 3.

b) $3n - 8$ **c)** $v = 3n - 8$

e) 55   **f)** 38

3. a)

Term Number, n	Term Value, v
1	75
2	71
3	67
4	63
5	59
6	55
7	51

b) $79 - 4n$

4. a)

Time, t (months)	Account Balance, A ($)
0	140
1	160
2	180
3	200
4	220
5	240
6	260
7	280

b) I will not join the points because Norman deposits money once a month, making the data discrete.

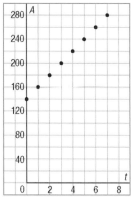

c) The relation is linear because the points lie on a straight line.

d) In the table, as t increases by 1, A increases by $20. On the graph, to get from one point to the next, move 1 unit right and 20 units up.

e) $A = 140 + 20t$

5. a) $y = 4x$

x	y
1	4
2	8
3	12

b) $y = 10 - 2x$

x	y
0	10
1	8
2	6

c) $y = 3x + 4$

x	y
−3	−5
−2	−2
−1	1

6. a) In the table, as x increases by 1, y increases by 4. On the graph, to get from one point to the next, move 1 unit right and 4 units up.

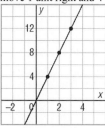

b) In the table, as x increases by 1, y decreases by 2. On the graph, to get from one point to the next, move 1 unit right and 2 units down.

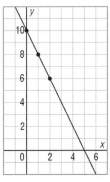

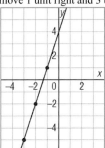

c) In the table, as x increases by 1, y increases by 3. On the graph, to get from one point to the next, move 1 unit right and 3 units up.

7. a) Let l and m represent the two lengths of string.

l	m
20	5
15	10
10	15
5	20

b) **i)** The relation is linear because the points lie on a straight line.

ii) I should join the points because the string can be cut anywhere, so values between points are permitted.

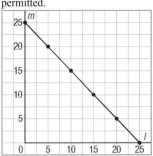

c) **i)** Variables may differ: $l + m = 25$

8. I do not need to make a table of values since the graphs are vertical lines and horizontal lines.

a) $x = -2$

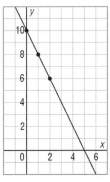

b) $y = 3$

c) $x = 5$

d) $y = -1$

9. a) $3x + y = 9$

x	y
-3	18
0	9
3	0

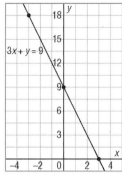

b) $2x - y = 4$

x	y
-2	-8
0	-4
2	0

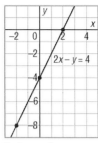

c) $2x + y = -6$

x	y
-4	2
0	-6
4	-14

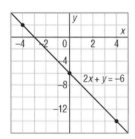

d) $x - 2y = -6$

x	y
-2	2
0	3
2	4

10. a) Vertical   **b)** Oblique
c) Horizontal   **d)** Vertical
11. $y = -3x - 2$
12. Graph B
13. a) iii   **b)** i
c) iv   **d)** ii
14. a) About 2.6 m^3
b) About 1950 kg
15. a) About 1035 km
b) About 590 km
16. a) About 130 L   **b)** About 400 km
17. a) i) $9\dfrac{1}{3}$ **ii)** $1\dfrac{1}{3}$
iii) $-2\dfrac{2}{3}$
b) i) $-2\dfrac{1}{4}$ **ii)** $1\dfrac{1}{2}$
iii) $5\dfrac{1}{4}$

1. a)

Figure Number, f	Number of Square Tiles, s
1	5
2	10
3	15
4	20

b) $5f$ **c)** $s = 5f$
e) Figure 45

2. a) Tables may vary. For example:

x	y
-2	11
0	7
1	5
3	1
5	-3

b)

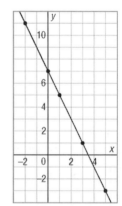

c) In the table, as the x increases by 2, y decreases by 4. On the graph, to go from one point to the next, move 2 units right and 4 units down.
3. a) Vertical   **b)** Horizontal
c) Vertical
4. a) i   **b)** ii
c) iv   **d)** iii
5. a) About 8 days   **b)** About 450 L
c) About 350 L
d) The rate of water usage remains constant and no water was added to the cistern.

Unit 5 Polynomials, page 208

5.1 Modelling Polynomials, page 214

4. Parts a, c, d, and f; the terms in the polynomial are of degree 1, 2, or a constant.
5. a) Trinomial; it has three terms of different degrees.
b) Binomial; it has two terms of different degrees.
c) Monomial: it has only one term of degree 1.
d) Monomial: it has only one term of degree 0.
6. a) Coefficient: -7; variable: x; degree: 1

b) Coefficient: 14; variable: a; degree: 2

c) Coefficient: 1; variable: m; degree: 1

d) No coefficient; no variable; degree: 0

7. a) 2   **b)** 1

    c) 2   **d)** 0

8. Parts a and d can be modelled by the same set of algebra tiles. Parts b and f can be modelled by the same set of algebra tiles.

9. a) Coefficients: 5, −6; variable: x; degree: 2; constant term: 2

    b) Coefficient: 7; variable: b; degree: 1; constant term: −8

    c) Coefficient: 12; variable: c; degree: 2; constant term: 2

    d) Coefficient: 12; variable: m; degree: 1

    e) No coefficients; no variable; degree: 0; constant term: 18

    f) Coefficients: 5, −8; variable: x; degree: 2; constant term: 3

10. Both students are correct. A monomial is a polynomial with one term.

11. a)

    b)

    c)

    d)

    e)

    f)

12. a) B   **b)** D

    c) E   **d)** A

    e) C

13. a) −16; monomial   **b)** $x − 8$; binomial

    c) $4x$; monomial   **d)** $2x^2 − 8x + 3$; trinomial

    e) $−5t + 5$; binomial   **f)** $5x^2$; monomial

    g) $−2x^2 + 2x − 3$; trinomial

    h) $−3x^2 + 8$; binomial

14. Answers will vary. For example:

    a) $3x − 2$ **b)** 5

c) $−2x^2$

d) $x^2 + 3x + 5$

15. Parts a and f; b, d, and h; c and e; g and i are equivalent.

16. Parts b and e are equivalent because they can be represented by the same algebra tiles. Parts c and d are equivalent because they can be represented by the same algebra tiles.

17. Answers will vary. For example: 4^x

18. a) i) Variable: x; degree: 2; number of terms: 3; coefficients: −3, −2

    ii) Variable: m; degree: 2; number of terms: 2; coefficients: 1, 1

    b) Answers will vary. For example: $c^2 − 5$

    c) $−5 + c^2$; they can be represented by the same algebra tiles.

19. a) $−8d^2 − 4 − 3d$; $−3d − 8d^2 − 4$; $−3d − 4 − 8d^2$; $−4 − 3d − 8d^2$; $−4 − 8d^2 − 3d$

    b) $−8d^2 − 3d − 4$; for 3 terms, the maximum number of arrangements is 6.

20. a) i) 22.5 m

    ii) 70 m

    iii) 240 m

    b) No, doubling the speed more than doubles the stopping distance.

5.2 Like Terms and Unlike Terms, page 222

4. a) $3d$

    $−5d$

    b) $3d$ and $−5d$ are like terms because both can be modelled by algebra tiles of the same shape and size. They have the same variable raised to the same exponent.

5. a) $4p$

    $2p^2$

b) $4p$ and $2p^2$ are unlike terms because they cannot be modelled by algebra tiles of the same shape and size. They have the same variable, but raised to different exponents.

6. $-3x, 3x, 7x$; they have the same variable raised to the same exponent.

7. $-n^2, 2n^2, 5n^2$; they have the same variable raised to the same exponent.

8.
a) $x + 4$
b) $x - 2$
c) $2x^2 + x + 1$
d) $5x^2 - 3x + 1$
e) $-2x + 4$
f) $-x^2 - 2x - 1$

9. Parts a and e are equivalent; both simplify to $2x^2 + 1$. Parts b and f are equivalent; both simplify to $-x - 3$. Parts c and d are equivalent; both simplify to $-x^2 + 2x$.

10. $2x + 3x = 5x$; $4 + 3x$ cannot be simplified.

11.
a) $5c + 4$

b) $2x^2 - 2x$

c) $-3f^2 + 1$

d) $7b^2 + 3b + 1$

e) $4t^2 + 5t - 1$

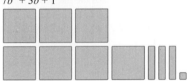

f) $a^2 + 7a - 4$

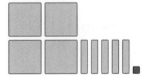

12.
a) $-m - 4$
b) $x + 2$
c) $g + 3$
d) $-3h - 4$
e) $-11n - 11$
f) $-s - 11$

13.
a) $x^2 - 4x + 15$
b) $-3m^2 + 10m$
c) $8x - 7$
d) $4p^2 - 2p + 7$
e) 0
f) $-9x^2 + 5x + 4$

14.
a) $x^2 + 4y - 1$
b) $-p^2 + 3p - 4pq - 1$
c) $4x^2 - 7x + 7xy - 2y$
d) $4r^2 - 3rs + s$
e) $-2g^2 + 6g + gh - 4$
f) $-6s^2 + 5s - 11st$

15. Parts a and f are equivalent; both simplify to $5x + 1$. Parts b and e are equivalent; part b simplifies to $2x^2 - 3x + 5$. Parts c and d are equivalent; part c simplifies to $-3x^2 - 5x + 4$.

16. Answers will vary. For example:
$5a^2 - 7a^2 + 6a - 2a - 8$

17. Answers will vary. For example:
$x^2 + 3 + 2x - 2x + 7$

18.
a) $x + x = 2x$

$x + x = 2x$

b)
i) $2r + 1$
ii) $6t^2 - 9t$
iii) $4c^2 + 6c + 3$
iv) $6x^2 - 2xy - 3y$

c) Answers will vary. For example: $-8d^2 - 3d - 4$

19.
a) $5x + x + 5x + x = 12x$
b) $2x + 2 + 2x + 2 = 4x + 4$
c) $3x + 2x + 3x + 2x = 10x$
d) $4x + 3 + 4x + 3 = 8x + 6$

20.
a) 5 rectangles; for example:

b) 1 rectangle

c) 4 rectangles; for example:

d) 3 rectangles; for example:

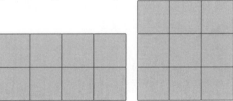

e) 1 rectangle

f) 8 rectangles; for example:

21. An xy tile would be a rectangle with dimensions equal to the lengths of the x-tile and the y-tile.

22. $x + y + 2x + 2y + 3x + 3y = 6x + 6y$

5.3 Adding Polynomials, page 228

3. a) $(3x + 5) + (-2x + 2)$

   b) $(-2x^2 + 4x - 2) + (2x^2 + 4x + 8)$

   c) $(3x^2 - 6x + 4) + (-x^2 - 4x + 2)$

4. $4x^2 + 1$

5. a) $7g + 7$ **b)** -1

   c) $6p - 5$ **d)** $-m + 11$

6. a) $5x - 1$ **b)** $x^2 - 3x$

   c) $-5x^2 + 2x + 12$

8. a) $9x + 7$ **b)** $7b + 5$

   c) $-5y + 3$ **d)** $2n + 5$

   e) $-7s + 1$ **f)** $-14h$

   g) $11m - 5$ **h)** $-11m + 5$

9. a) $6m^2 + 2m - 4$ **b)** $-6k + 4$

   c) $p^2 - 7p + 2$ **d)** $3t^2 + 9$

   e) $5x^2 - 2x + 7$ **f)** $-3x^2 - x + 13$

   g) $-5x^2 - x + 16$ **h)** $-2r^2 + r + 6$

10. a) i) $(2n + 1) + (n + 5) + (2n + 5) = 5n + 11$

   ii) $(7r + 2) + (7r + 2) + (7r + 2) + (7r + 2) =$
   $28r + 8$

   iii) $(6t + 5) + (2t + 1) + (6t + 5) + (2t + 1) =$
   $16t + 12$

   iv) $(f + 2) + (3f + 1) + (f + 2) + (3f + 1) = 8f + 6$

11. Answers will vary. For example:

   a)
   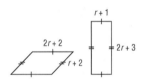

   b)
   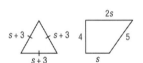

   c)
   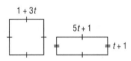

   d)
   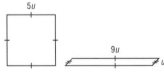

   e)
   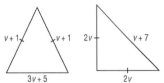

f)
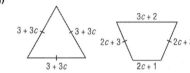

g)
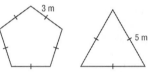

h)
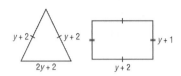

12. No, the student made errors in simplifying.
   $-7x - 5x = -12x$, not $-2x$, and $3 + 9 = 12$, not 1.
   The correct answer is: $3x^2 - 12x + 12$

13. a) Answers will vary. For example:
   $-2x^2 + 2x + 1 = (-x^2 + x + 1) + (-x^2 - x)$

   b) There are many possibilities.

14. $8m^2 + 8m - 4$

15. a) $2x^2 + 3x - 1$ **b)** $-x^2 - 2x + 6$

   c) $x^2 - 4x - 2$ **d)** $-4x^2 - 6x - 3$

   e) $-3x^2 - 5x + 1$ **f)** $-3x^2 - 7x + 2$

16. a) $-5x^2 - 3x + 1$

   b) The coefficients of the like terms are opposites.

17. a) $-4y^2 - xy$ **b)** $p^2 - 5q^2 + 7p - q + pq$

   c) $m^2 + 4n^2 + 5m - 8n + 3mn + 10$

   d) $-f^2 + 2g^2 - 11f + 9g - 2$

18. a) $3x + 2y + 2$

19. There are many possibilities.
   For example: $(x + y + 1)$, $(x + y + 1)$, $(x + 3y + 5)$

5.4 Subtracting Polynomials, page 234

4. a) $(-2x^2 + 4x - 2) - (-x^2 + 3x - 1) = -x^2 + x - 1$

   b) $(x^2 - 5x - 4) - (x^2 - 4x - 2) = -x - 2$

5. a) $(5r) - (3r) = 2r$

   b) $(5r) - (-3r) = 8r$

   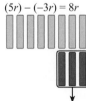

c) $(-5r) - (3r) = -8r$

d) $(-5r) - (-3r) = -2r$

e) $(3r) - (5r) = -2r$

f) $(-3r) - (5r) = -8r$

g) $(3r) - (-5r) = 8r$

h) $(-3r) - (-5r) = 2r$

6. a) $2x + 1$ **b)** $2x + 5$
   c) $8x + 1$ **d)** $8x + 5$

7. a) $s^2 + s + 3$ **b)** $s^2 - s + 3$
   c) $5s^2 - 3s - 3$ **d)** $-5s^2 + 3s - 3$

8. a) $5x + 9$ **b)** $4b^2 - 3b$
   c) $-7x + 2$ **d)** $2p + 1$
   e) $2x^2 + 4x + 8$ **f)** $4m^2 - 7m + 10$
   g) $-5x^2 + x + 4$ **h)** $4r^2 - 7r - 4$

9. a) $(4n + 2500) - (2n + 2100)$
   b) $6400 more

10. a) Answers may vary. For example:
Substitute $x = 4$.

$$[2(4)^2 + 5(4) + 10] - [(4)^2 - 3]$$
$$= 2(16) + 20 + 10 - (16 - 3)$$
$$= 32 + 20 + 10 - 13$$
$$= 49$$
$$(4)^2 + 8(4) + 10$$
$$= (16) + 32 + 10$$
$$= 58$$
$49 \neq 58$, so the answer is incorrect.

b) Correction:
$$(2x^2 + 5x + 10) - (x^2 - 3)$$
$$= 2x^2 + 5x + 10 - x^2 + 3$$
$$= 2x^2 - x^2 + 5x + 10 + 3$$
$$= x^2 + 5x + 13$$

12. a) The student did not change the signs of $+5y$ and
-2 inside the second pair of brackets.

b) Correction:
$$(2y^2 - 3y + 5) - (y^2 + 5y - 2)$$
$$= 2y^2 - 3y + 5 - y^2 - 5y + 2$$
$$= y^2 - 8y + 7$$

13. a) $w + 4$ **b)** $s + 3$
   c) $4p + 1$

14. c) The sum of the two polynomials is 0.
The coefficients of the like terms in each
polynomial are opposites.

15. a) $3r^2 + 10s^2$ **b)** $-8m^2 - 3mn - 3n^2$
   c) $12c^2 - 10d^2 - cd$ **d)** $-e^2 + 15e + 6f + 5f^2$
   e) $-2j^2 - 10j + 5jk - 2k + k^2$

16. a) $-5x^2 + 9x - 11$ or $-11x^2 + x + 3$
   b) $(-5x^2 + 9x - 11) - (-8x^2 + 5x - 4) = 3x^2 + 4x - 7$
$(-8x^2 + 5x - 4) - (-11x^2 + x + 3) = 3x^2 + 4x - 7$

17. $6x - 8$

18. There are many possibilities.
For example: $(-4x^2 - 2x) - (-4x + 5) = -4x^2 + 2x - 5$

Unit 5: Mid-Unit Review, page 237

1. a) Variable: m; number of terms: 2; coefficient: 3;
constant term: -5; degree: 1

b) Variable: r; number of terms: 1; coefficient: 4;
constant term: none; degree: 1

c) Variable: x; number of terms: 3; coefficients: 1,
4; constant term: 1; degree: 2

2. Answers will vary, for example: $3m^2 - 4m - 5$

3. a) $-x^2 + 12$; binomial
   b) $-2x^2 - 4x + 8$; trinomial   **c)** $-4x$; monomial

4. a)

b)

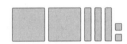

c)

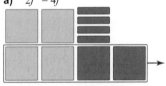

5. a) $2x$ and $-5x$ are like terms because they have the same variable raised to the same exponent.

b) 3 and $4g$ are unlike terms because one is a constant and the other has a variable.

c) 10 and 2 are like terms because they are both constants.

d) $2q^2$ and $-7q^2$ are like terms because they have the same variable raised to the same exponent.

e) $8x^2$ and $3x$ are unlike terms because they have variables raised to different exponents.

f) $-5x^2$ and $-5x$ are unlike terms because they have variables raised to different exponents.

6. $-2x^2 - 3x + 1$

7. No, both answers are correct. The polynomials have their terms ordered differently.

8. No, Cooper is incorrect. $5x$ and -2 are unlike terms that cannot be simplified.

9. Parts a and h, b and e, d and f are equivalent.

10. a) $2f^2 - 4f$

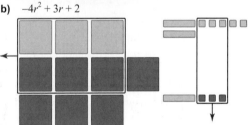

b) $-4r^2 + 3r + 2$

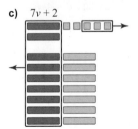

c) $7v + 2$

d) $4g^2 - 4g - 11$

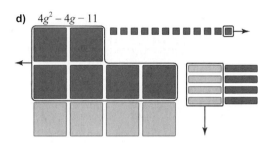

11. a) $15w^2 + 14w$ **b)** $6m^2$

c) $6h - 6$ **d)** $-a^2 + 6a + 9$

e) $y^2 + 13y - 6$ **f)** $10p^2 + 7p - 24$

12. a) $2x^2 + 2x + 3$ **b)** $-2x^2 - 2x - 3$

5.5 Multiplying and Dividing a Polynomial by a Constant, page 246

3. a) $(4)(5) = 20$ **b)** $(3)(x) = 3x$

c) $2(x + 2) = 2x + 4$ **d)** $3(3x + 2) = 9x + 6$

4. a) $20 \div 4 = 5$ **b)** $3x \div 3 = x$

c) $(2x + 4) \div 2 = x + 2$ **d)** $(9x + 6) \div 3 = 3x + 2$

5. a) ii

6. Part c

7. a) i) $15r$ **ii)** $-15r$

iii) $15r$ **iv)** $-15r$

v) $15r$ **vi)** $-15r$

b) The product of two negative numbers or two positive numbers is positive. The product of a negative number and a positive number is negative.

c) i)

ii)

iii)

iv)

v)

vi)

8. a) i) $3k$ **ii)** $-3k$
iii) $-3k$ **iv)** $3k$

b) Dividing two numbers with the same sign gives a positive quotient. Dividing two numbers with opposite signs gives a negative quotient.

c) i)

ii)

9. a) $(2)(3v^2 + 2v + 4) = 6v^2 + 4v + 8$
b) $5(m^2 + 3) = 5m^2 + 15$

10. a) $\dfrac{6v^2 + 4v + 8}{2} = 3v^2 + 2v + 4$

b) $\dfrac{5m^2 + 15}{5} = m^2 + 3$

11. a) $7(3s + 1) = 21s + 7$

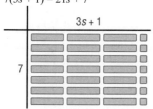

b) $-2(-7h + 4) = 14h - 8$

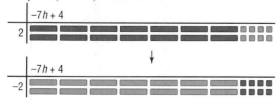

c) $2(-3p^2 - 2p + 1) = -6p^2 - 4p + 2$

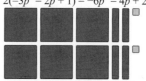

d) $-6(2v^2 - v + 5) = -12v^2 + 6v - 30$

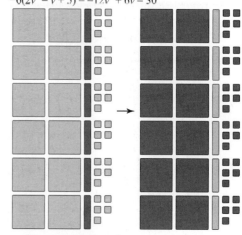

e) $(-w^2 + 3w - 5)(3) = -3w^2 + 9w - 15$

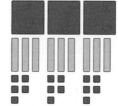

f) $(x^2 + x)(-5) = -5x^2 - 5x$

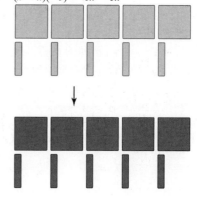

12. The errors are: $-2(-r) = 2r$, not $-2r$, and $-2(7) = -14$, not -16.
Correction:
$$-2(4r^2 - r + 7)$$
$$= (-2)(4r^2) + (-2)(-r) + (-2)(7)$$
$$= -8r^2 + 2r - 14$$

13. a) $\dfrac{12p-18}{6} = 2p-3$

b) $\dfrac{-6q^2-10}{2} = -3q^2-5$

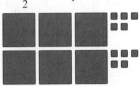

c) $\dfrac{5h^2-20h}{5} = h^2-4h$

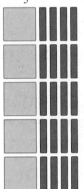

d) $\dfrac{4r^2-16r+6}{2} = 2r^2-8r+3$

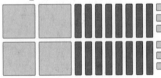

e) $\dfrac{-8a^2+4a-12}{4} = -2a^2+a-3$

f) $\dfrac{6x^2+3x+9}{3} = 2x^2+x+3$

14. Errors are: The negative sign should apply to all the denominators. $\dfrac{-7}{7}$ simplifies to -1, not 0.

$2m^2 - 4m$ cannot be simplified to $-2m$.

Correction:

$(-14m^2 - 28m + 7) \div (-7)$

$= \dfrac{-14m^2}{-7} + \dfrac{-28m}{-7} + \dfrac{7}{-7}$

$= 2m^2 + 4m - 1$

15. a) $12u^2 - 48u - 24$ **b)** $24m^2 - 36m$
   c) $-20t^2 - 8t$ **d)** $30s^2 + 25s + 35$
   e) $-28y^2 + 12y - 36$ **f)** $80n^2 - 10n - 60$

16. a) $2d^2 - 1$ **b)** $2x + 1$
   c) $5 - 2m^2$ **d)** $-5 + n$
   e) $-2k^2 + 4k - 7$ **f)** $6d^2 - 3d - 5$
   g) $2c^2 - 3c + 1$

17. Parts c and f; the expressions in each pair are equivalent because of the distributive property.

18. a) i) $12p$ **ii)** $-7x$
   iii) $-12m^2 + 28$ **iv)** $-f^2 + 7f - 4$
   v) $-y^2 + 6y$ **vi)** $-24n + 6 - 9n^2$

b) The products and quotients in parts i, ii, iii, iv, and vi can be modelled with algebra tiles.

19. a) i) $4x + 2; 6x + 3; 8x + 4; 10x + 5$
   ii) $2 - 4x; 3 - 6x; 4 - 8x; 5 - 10x$

b) i) Each time, the coefficient of the x-term increases by 2 while the constant term increases by 1.

   ii) Each time, the coefficient of the x-term decreases by 2 while the constant term increases by 1.

c) i) $12x + 6; 14x + 7; 16x + 8$
   ii) $6 - 12x; 7 - 14x; 8 - 16x$

d) i) $2x + 1; 0; -2x - 1$
   ii) $1 - 2x; 0; -1 + 2x$

20. a) $5a^2 + 7a + 2$ **b)** 110 cm

21. a) Perimeter of square A: $4(4s + 1) = 16s + 4$
   Perimeter of square B: $3(16s + 4) = 48s + 12$

b) $32s + 8$

22. a) $4x^2 - 6xy + 14y^2$ **b)** $-4pq - 12p^2 - 12q^2$
   c) $-6gh + 18h^2 - 9g^2 - 27g$

d) $-5r^2 + 40rs - 15s^2 - 25s + 20r$

e) $-8t^2 + 6v^2 - 38tv + 12v + 2t$

23. a) $n^2 - 4mn + 2m^2$ **b)** $3rs + 8r + 2s$

    c) $2gh - 6g^2 - 3h$ **d)** $-2t^2 + 4ut + 8t$

24. $\pi(3x)^2 - \pi x^2 = 8\pi x^2$

5.6 Multiplying and Dividing a Polynomial by a Monomial, page 255

4. a) $(3c)(3c) = 9c^2$ **b)** $m(m + 3) = m^2 + 3m$

    c) $2r(r + 2) = 2r^2 + 4r$

5. a) $\dfrac{9c^2}{3c} = 3c$

    b) For example: $\dfrac{m^2 + 3m}{m} = m + 3$

    c) For example: $\dfrac{2r^2 + 4r}{2r} = r + 2$

6. Part c

7. a) $3x(2x + 1) = 6x^2 + 3x$

    b) $4x(2x + 7) = 8x^2 + 28x$

8. a) For example: $\dfrac{6x^2 + 3x}{3x} = 2x + 1$

    b) For example: $\dfrac{8x^2 + 28x}{4x} = 2x + 7$

9. a)   **i)** $12m^2$ **ii)** $-12m^2$

     iii) $-12m^2$ **iv)** $12m^2$

     v) $12m^2$ **vi)** $-12m^2$

    b) The products have the same two factors, $3m$ and $4m$, that only differ by the sign of the coefficient.

    c) Each of the problems can be modelled by algebra tiles.

     i)

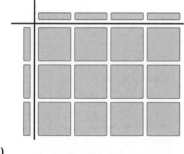

     ii)

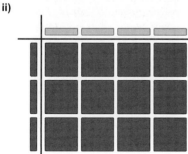

     iii)

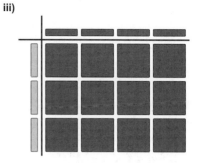

     iv)

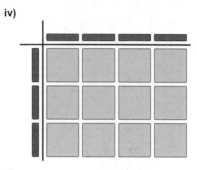

     v)

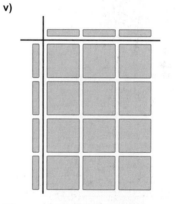

     vi)

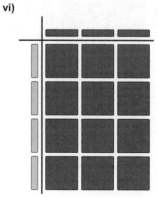

10. a)   **i)** 6 **ii)** -6

     iii) -6 **iv)** 6

     v) $6x$ **vi)** 6

     vii) -6 **viii)** -6

b) Some quotients are the same because they have the same numerators and denominators that only differ by the signs of the coefficients.

c) **i)**

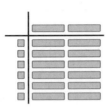

ii)

iii)

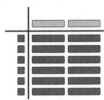

iv)

v)

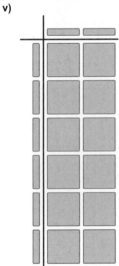

11. a) $-12r^2$ **b)** $2n$
c) $-35g^2$ **d)** -4
e) $27h^2$ **f)** $4p$

g) -6 **h)** 3
12. a) $2x^2 + 12x$ **b)** $15t^2 + 6t$
c) $-6w^2 + 10w$ **d)** $-2x - 8x^2$
e) $-15g - 3g^2$ **f)** $8y + 6y^2$
g) $7sy + y$ **h)** $-6r + 12r^2$
13. $2x(x + 1) = 2x(x) + 2x(1) = 2x^2 + 2x$
14. The student calculated $(-2d)(-3d)$ as $-6d^2$ instead of $6d^2$ and wrote $- (9)(-3d)$ instead of $+ (9)(-3d)$ in the second line.
Correction:
$(-2d + 9)(-3d)$
$= (-2d)(-3d) + (9)(-3d)$
$= 6d^2 - 27d$
15. Think multiplication: $3r(r - 4) = 3r^2 - 12r$

$$\frac{3r^2 - 12r}{3r} = r - 4$$

Or, write the quotient expression as the sum of two fractions:

$$\frac{3r^2 - 12r}{3r}$$

$$= \frac{3r^2}{3r} + \frac{-12r}{3r}$$

$$= r - 4$$

16. a) $5x + 2$ **b)** $6x + 4$
c) $2 + y$ **d)** $5x - 2$
e) $3 - 2g$ **f)** $-4 - 8k$
g) $-6h - 9$ **h)** $4m - 9$
17. a) i) $3n + 1$ **ii)** $-12r + 21r^2$
iii) $8s - 2$ **iv)** $4t^2 - 36t$
18. a) $6x + 6$

19. a) Larger rectangle: $(2s)(3s + 2) = 6s^2 + 4s$
Smaller rectangle: $(2s)(s + 1) = 2s^2 + 2s$
b) $(6s^2 + 4s) - (2s^2 + 2s) = 4s^2 + 2s$
c) 30 cm^2
20. a) $6mn + 12m$ **b)** $10g - 6fg$
c) $-42mp + 49m^2$ **d)** $-32hk - 12k^2$
e) $-8t^2 + 12rt$ **f)** $-8gh + 5g^2$
21. a) $4x + 2y$ **b)** $6h + 3$
c) $-3p + 4q$ **d)** $- 8s + 7$
e) $-2n - 6p$
22. Divide the shape into two rectangles.
$(7x)(5x) + (4x)(7x) = 63x^2$
23. a) $\dfrac{54s^2}{6} = 9s^2$ **b)** $3s$

24. a) $2\pi r(r+h) = 2\pi r^2 + 2\pi rh$

b) $2\pi(5)(5+3) = 251$ cm^2

$2\pi (5)^2 + 2\pi(5)(3) = 251$ cm^2

25. $\dfrac{13}{2}x - 6 - \dfrac{9}{4}y + \dfrac{5}{4x}$

Unit 5: Review, page 259

1. a)

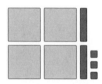

b)

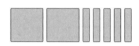

2. a) Variable: w; coefficient: 4; constant: -3

b) Variable: v; coefficient: 5; constant: 3

c) Variable: y; coefficients: -1, 5; constant: -6

3. a) i) Binomial **ii)** 1st degree

b) i) Monomial **ii)** 2nd degree

c) i) Trinomial **ii)** 2nd degree

4. a) $-y^2 - 3y + 4$

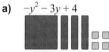

b) $-3x + 4$

5. Parts a and h; b and g; d and e are equivalent.

6. a) $4x + 3$; 1st degree

b) $2x^2 - 2x + 6$; 2nd degree

c) $-x^2 - 9$; 2nd degree

7. $2k = k + k$; $k^2 = k \times k$

$2k \qquad k^2$

8. a) $-2h - 1$ **b)** $2j^2 + 3j - 4$

c) $p^2 - 5p$

9. a) $5x^2$ and $-2x^2$ are like terms.

b) $-8x$, $5x$, and $-x$; 8, -2, and 11 are like terms.

10. a) B **b)** C

c) E **d)** A

e) D

11. Answers will vary. For example:

$-x^2 + 3x - 2x + 3 + 5$

12. a) $4x - 7$ **b)** $-7y^2 + y$

c) $3a + 3$ **d)** $2a$

13.

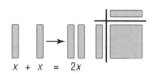

$x \ + \ x \ = \ 2x$

14. a) $(-2x^2 + 3x - 4) + (-4x^2 + x - 3) = -6x^2 + 4x - 7$

b) $(3x^2 - 6x + 7) - (2x^2 - 2x + 3) = x^2 - 4x + 4$

15. a) $4p^2 + 4p + 6$ **b)** $q^2 + 2q + 5$

c) $4r^2 - 7r - 3$ **d)** $-3s^2 + 8s + 8$

e) $-2t^2 + 2t + 10$ **f)** $-6u^2 + 4$

g) $-4a^2 - 5ab - 4b^2$

h) $4x^2 + 2x + 9xy - 5y - 3y^2$

16. $12c + 13$

17. A – Q; B – S; C – P; D – R; E – T

18. $-5d^2 - 12d + 5$ or $-11d^2 + 2d - 3$

19. a) $10a + 10$; 40 cm **b)** $15a + 21$; 66 cm

20. a) $(4)(-x) = -4x$ **b)** $2(2x + 3) = 4x + 6$

21. a) For example: $\dfrac{-4x}{4} = -x$

b) For example: $\dfrac{4x + 6}{2} = 2x + 3$

22. a) $5k$ **b)** $-20x^2$

c) $-6m + 8$ **d)** $-2n^2$

e) $-12s + 3$ **f)** $3 - 4m$

g) $-35 + 10x$ **h)** $-2 + 4n - 6n^2$

i) $2x + 6x^2$ **j)** $3p^2 + 3p - 2$

k) $-5 + 7q - 2q^2$ **l)** $-12 - 30n + 42n^2$

23. a) $2x^2 - 2xy - 2y^2$ **b)** $-6m^2 + 3n - 4m$

c) $-6pq + p^2 - 3q$ **d)** $8r^2 - 12r + 16s - 20s^2$

24. a) $(3x)(2x + 3) = 6x^2 + 9x$

b) $(5a)(8a + 3) = 40a^2 + 15a$

25. a) For example: $\dfrac{6x^2 + 9x}{3x} = 2x + 3$

b) For example: $\dfrac{40a^2 + 15a}{5a} = 8a + 3$

26. a) $14s^2$ **b)** $15g^2$

c) $3m^2 + 2m$ **d)** $-5t^2 + 15t$

e) $-28z^2 - 7z$ **f)** $6f^2 + 10f$

g) $-15k + 5k^2$ **h)** $y - y^2$

27. a) Inside rectangle: $8x^2$; outside rectangle: $18x^2$

b) $18x^2 - 8x^2 = 10x^2$

28. a) -4 **b)** 8

c) $4x$ **d)** $-2a - 3$

e) $-2 + c$ **f)** $-2y + 3$

29. a) $(2d + 5)$ metres

b) The deck is 16 m by 13 m with an area of 208 m^2.

1. a) $2t^2 - 6t + 4$

b) Degree: 2; number of terms: 3

c) Constant: 4; coefficient of t^2: 2

2. a) $d + 2 + (d + 3) + 6 + (d + d + 3) + 4 = 4d + 18$

b) 38 m

3. a)

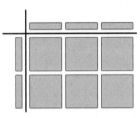

b)

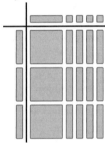

4. The student's answer is incorrect.

$3r(r + 4) = 3r^2 + 12r$

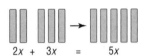

5. a) $-18d + 18$　　**b)** $3h^2 + 9h - 6$

c) $-5y^2 + 7y - 12$　　**d)** $8y^2 - 2y$

6. a) $75m^2 - 50m$　　**b)** $-15v^2 + 10v + 5$

c) $4x - 2$　　**d)** $2 - g^2 + 5g$

7. Answers will vary. For example:

a) $(x^2 + x + 1) + (2x^2 - 5x - 3) = 3x^2 - 4x - 2$

b) $(5x^2 + 2x + 2) - (2x^2 + 6x + 4) = 3x^2 - 4x - 2$

8. a)

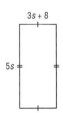

b) $15s^2 + 40s$　　**c)** $16s + 16$

6.1 Solving Equations by Using Inverse Operations, page 271

5. a) $s = 3$

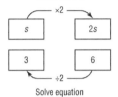

b) $b = 15$

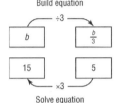

c) $e = -7$

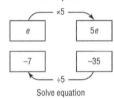

d) $x = -14$

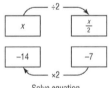

e) $w = -0.3$

f) $c = -6$

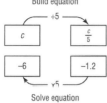

Build equation

Solve equation

6. a) $x = 2$

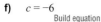

Build equation

Solve equation

b) $a = -2.6$

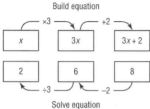

Build equation

Solve equation

c) $m = 14$

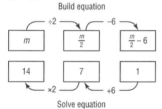

Build equation

Solve equation

d) $r = -28$

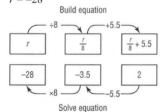

Build equation

Solve equation

7. The student should divide each side by −5 instead of adding 5 to undo multiplying m by −5.
Correction:
$$-5m = 15$$
$$m = \frac{15}{-5}$$
$$m = -3$$

8. a) $x = 2.4$ **b)** $b = 7.5$
c) $x = 40$ **d)** $x = 4.3$
e) $n = 120$ **f)** $c = -4$

9. a) $2x = -10; x = -5$

b) $3x + 6.4 = 13.9; x = 2.5$
c) $4x = -8.8; x = -2.2$ **d)** $2x + 3.6 = 10; x = 3.2$

10. a) $c = 45$ **b)** $m = -33$
c) $n = -6$ **d)** $q = -20$
e) $c = 3$ **f)** $a = -5.85$

11. a) $\frac{x}{4} = -7 ; x = -28$ **b)** $3 + \frac{x}{5} = 6 ; x = 15$

c) $\frac{x}{2} = 2.5 ; x = 5$ **d)** $\frac{x}{3} - 4 = 2 ; x = 18$

12. No, Jenna's partner should undo the operations in the reverse order: subtract 4 then divide by −2.

13. a) $\frac{b}{3} - 13.5 = 2.8$ **b)** $b = 48.9$

14. a) $2(1.2 + l) = 6.6$ **b)** $l = 2.1$

15. a) $0.12x = 39.48; x = 329$
b) $0.12(329) = 39.48$

16. a) $3500

17. a) Let s represent Steve's sales, in dollars.
$1925 + 0.1s = 2725$
b) $8000

18. a) $x = 4$ **b)** $m = 1.5$
c) $t = 2.1$ **d)** $y = 0.8$
e) $a = -3.8$

19. a) Let w represent the volume of 1 bottle of water, in litres. $4w + 6(0.5) = 4.42$
b) 0.355 L

20. a) The student should not multiply 4.2 by 3 in line 2.
Correction:
$$3(x - 2.4) = 4.2$$
$$3x - 3(2.4) = 4.2$$
$$3x - 7.2 = 4.2$$
$$3x = 4.2 + 7.2$$
$$3x = 11.4$$
$$x = \frac{11.4}{3}$$
$$x = 3.8$$

b) The student forgot the negative sign for $\frac{1}{2}x$ in line 3, and should multiply −2 by −2 instead of dividing it by 2 in line 4.
Correction:
$$5 - \frac{1}{2}x = 3$$
$$5 - \frac{1}{2}x - 5 = 3 - 5$$
$$-\frac{1}{2}x = -2$$
$$x = 4$$

21. a) Let t represent the number of extra toppings.
$16.50 = 7.50 + 1.50t$

b) The customer ordered 6 toppings.

22. a) Let c dollars represent the original price.
$0.09c = 4.95$

b) The item cost \$55.00.
$$0.09c = 4.95$$
$$c = \frac{4.95}{0.09}$$
$$c = 55$$

23. a) $180(n-2) = 1080$

b) Kyler's solution:
$$180(n-2) = 1080$$
$$180n - 360 = 1080$$
$$180n - 360 + 360 = 1080 + 360$$
$$180n = 1440$$
$$n = \frac{1440}{180}$$
$$n = 8$$

c) Esta's solution:
$$180(n-2) = 1080$$
$$n - 2 = \frac{1080}{180}$$
$$n - 2 = 6$$
$$n = 6 + 2$$
$$n = 8$$

d) Answers may vary. Esta's method of undoing the operations is simpler.

24. a) $x = -6.1$ **b)** $m = 3.25$

c) $p = -2\frac{1}{12}$ **d)** $g = 0.965$

6.2 Solving Equations by Using Balance Strategies, page 280

4. a) $3t + 2 = t + 8; t = 3$ **b)** $5s + 3 = 2s + 9; s = 2$

5. a) Step 1: Subtract f from each side.
Step 2: Add 2 to each side.
Step 3: Divide each side by 2.

b) Algebraic solution:
$$3f - 2 = f + 4$$
$$3f - 2 - f = f + 4 - f$$
$$2f - 2 = 4$$
$$2f - 2 + 2 = 4 + 2$$
$$2f = 6$$
$$\frac{2f}{2} = \frac{6}{2}$$
$$f = 3$$

6. a) $g = 1$ **b)** $k = -2$
c) $a = -2$ **d)** $h = 2$

7. a) i) $h = 3$ **ii)** $h = -3$
iii) $h = -3$ **iv)** $h = -3$
v) $h = 3$ **vi)** $h = 3$

b) There are only 2 solutions because the equations only differ by their signs.

8. a) $s = 2$ **b)** $t = -3$
c) $w = 0.2$

9. $\frac{10}{x} = -3 ; x = -3\frac{1}{3}$

10. a) $a = 5$ **b)** $y = -3.2$
c) $z = 5.4$ **d)** $u = 6.3$
e) $b = 4.1$ **f)** $p = -2.5$

11. a) $n = -1$ **b)** $q = 9$
c) $a = 3.6$ **d)** $v = -2.8$
e) $x = 2.5$ **f)** $b = -3.5$

12. a) Let n represent the number of people.
$50n = 2000 + 40n$

b) The two halls will cost the same with 200 people.

13. $5 - 3n = 3.5n - 8; n = 2$

14. a) $1500 + 0.04s$ **b)** $1700 + 0.02s$
c) $1500 + 0.04s = 1700 + 0.02s$
d) $s = 10\,000$; \$10 000 of sales would result in the same total earnings from both plans.

15. a) Student A forgot to write the negative sign for -5 in the last line.
Correction:
$$2.2x = 7.6x + 27$$
$$2.2x - 7.6x = 7.6x - 7.6x + 27$$
$$-5.4x = 27$$
$$x = -5$$

b) Student B should subtract $2.2x$ instead of adding $2.2x$ on each side in line 2.
Correction:
$$-2.3x - 2.7 = 2.2x + 11.7$$
$$-2.3x - 2.2x - 2.7 = 2.2x - 2.2x + 11.7$$
$$-4.5x - 2.7 = 11.7$$
$$-4.5x - 2.7 + 2.7 = 11.7 + 2.7$$
$$-4.5x = 14.4$$
$$x = \frac{14.4}{-4.5}$$
$$x = -3.2$$

16. a) i) $x = 81; x = 9$ **ii)** $a = 432; a = 3$
b) An additional step of multiplying each side by the variable is required to solve a variable in the denominator. After this step, solving for the variable is the same as solving for a variable in the numerator.

17. a) $g = 35$ **b)** $j = -17.5$
c) $h = 2.54$ **d)** $s = 10$

18. a) Let k represent the number of kilometres driven.
$199 + 0.2k = 149 + 0.25k$

b) Hendrik must drive a distance of 1000 km for the two rental costs to be the same.

19. a) $m = 8$ **b)** $t = \dfrac{20}{11}$

c) $r = -\dfrac{1}{39}$ **d)** $x = \dfrac{67}{90}$

20. a) Dembe's method:
$$\frac{x}{3} + \frac{x}{4} = x - \frac{1}{6}$$
$$12\left(\frac{x}{3} + \frac{x}{4}\right) = 12\left(x - \frac{1}{6}\right)$$
$$4x + 3x = 12x - 2$$
$$7x = 12x - 2$$
$$7x - 12x = 12x - 12x - 2$$
$$-5x = -2$$
$$\frac{-5x}{-5} = \frac{-2}{-5}$$
$$x = \frac{2}{5}$$

Bianca's method:
$$\frac{x}{3} + \frac{x}{4} = x - \frac{1}{6}$$
$$24\left(\frac{x}{3} + \frac{x}{4}\right) = 24\left(x - \frac{1}{6}\right)$$
$$8x + 6x = 24x - 4$$
$$14x = 24x - 4$$
$$14x - 24x = 24x - 24x - 4$$
$$-10x = -4$$
$$\frac{-10x}{-10} = \frac{-4}{-10}$$
$$x = \frac{4}{10}$$
$$x = \frac{2}{5}$$

b) Using the least common denominator saves the step of simplifying the final answer.

21. a) $x = -3\dfrac{2}{3}$ **b)** $x = 20$

c) $x = 4$ **d)** $x = 5$

22. Marlene made 10 assisted blocks.

23. a) Let m represent the number of minutes.
$28 + 0.45(m - 30) = 40 + 0.25m$

b) The monthly costs for both plans are the same at 127.5 min.

Unit 6: Start Where You Are, page 285

1. The price before the increase was $1.28/L.

Unit 6 Mid-Unit Review, page 286

1. a) Divide by -3. **b)** Add 2.
c) Divide by 2. **d)** Subtract 9.

2. a)

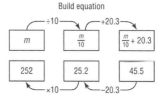

b)
$$\frac{m}{10} + 20.3 = 45.5$$
$$\frac{m}{10} + 20.3 - 20.3 = 45.5 - 20.3$$
$$\frac{m}{10} = 25.2$$
$$\frac{m}{10} \times 10 = 25.2 \times 10$$
$$m = 252$$

3. a) $2.5 + 1.2k = 27.7;\ k = 21$
Sheila travelled 21 km.

4. a) Let s represent the length of the third side in centimetres: $2(2.7) + s = 7.3$, or $5.4 + s = 7.3$

b) $s = 1.9$

5. a) $k = -4.5$ **b)** $b = 7\dfrac{2}{3}$

c) $x = 10.1$ **d)** $b = 7$

e) $n = 2.4$ **f)** $h = -23.2$

6. $6k + 1 = 2k + 9;\ k = 2$

7. a) $a = -16$ **b)** $w = 6.4$

c) $z = 8.4$ **d)** $x = 6$

e) $r = 7$ **f)** $y = -3$

g) $m = -1$

8. a) Let t represent the time in hours. $15 + 3t = 12 + 4t$

b) $t = 3$

6.3 Introduction to Linear Inequalities, page 292

3. a) True **b)** False

c) False **d)** False

e) True **f)** True

g) True **h)** False

4. a) $x < -2$ **b)** $p \geq 6$

c) $y < 0$ **d)** $m > 0$

5. a) No, $0 > -2$ **b)** Yes, $-6.9 < -2$

c) Yes, $-2.001 < -2$ **d)** Yes, $-3 < -2$

e) No, $-2 = -2$ **f)** No, $-\dfrac{1}{2} > -2$

6. Answers will vary. For example:

a) 5.01, 8, 10, 35 **b)** 6.9, 6, 0, −7

c) −1.5, 0, 2, 2.01 **d)** −20, −15, −13, −12.25

7. a) No **b)** Yes

c) No **d)** Yes

8. a) Let c represent the number of cups of water a coffee maker can hold. $c \leq 12$

b) Let a years represent the age to obtain a learner's permit to drive in Nunavut. $a \geq 15$

c) Let m represent the maximum seating capacity of a school bus. $m \leq 48$

d) Let n represent the number of people participating in the charity bike-a-thon each year. $n > 2500$

e) Let s represent the size of shoes in a shoe store. $s \leq 13$

9. a) Graph v   **b)** Graph iii
c) Graph iv   **d)** Graph ii
e) Graph i   **f)** Graph v
g) Graph iv   **h)** Graph i

10. Both are correct. They wrote the same inequality using a different variable.

11. a) i) Let k represent the mass in kilograms of a child who must ride in a car seat in Canada. $k < 23$

ii) Let t represent the temperature in degrees Celsius that a silicone oven mitt can resist. $t \leq 485$

iii) Let w dollars represent the minimum hourly wage in dollars in Alberta. $w \geq 8.40$

b) i)
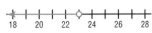

ii)

iii)

12. a) $x > 1$; neither 1 nor -3 is part of the solution.
b) $x \leq 2$; both 1 and -3 are part of the solution.
c) $x < -10$; neither 1 nor -3 is part of the solution.

13. a)

b)
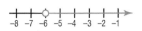

c)

d)

e)
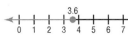

f)

g)

h)

14. Let t represent the possible show time in minutes. $t \leq 48$ and $t \geq 40$

15. a) Over is $>$; under is $<$; maximum is $\leq$; minimum is $\geq$; at least is $\geq$; no more than is $\leq$.

16. $y \geq 0$

6.4 Solving Inequality by Using Addition and Subtraction, page 298

4. a) Subtract 4.   **b)** Add $\frac{2}{3}$.
c) Add 4.   **d)** Add 4.5.
e) Subtract $\frac{3}{10}$.
f) Subtract 4.9.

5. a) Add 2.   **b)** Subtract 4.2.
c) Add $\frac{1}{2}$.

6. Answers will vary. For example:
a) $5, 6.5, \frac{15}{2}$ **b)** $10, 9.5, \frac{3}{2}$
c) $-5, -7.1, -8\frac{1}{4}$ **d)** $11, 11.2, \frac{23}{2}$

7. a) $c > 4$ corresponds to graph iii; 3 is not a solution.
b) $w \leq 13$ corresponds to graph ii; 3 is a possible solution.
c) $r < -7$ corresponds to graph i; 3 is not a solution.
d) $m \leq -9$ corresponds to graph iv; 3 is not a solution.

8. a) $x > -3$ **b)** $y \leq -6$
c) $a \leq 4$ **d)** $x < -5$
e) $k < -21$ **f)** $q < 6.4$

9. a) $t < 43$ **b)** $x < -11$
c) $x < 11$ **d)** $a \leq -7$
e) $p \geq -10.4$ **f)** $y \geq -37.4$

10. No, -9 is only one of the possible solutions. The solution of $-7 \geq b + 2$ is $-9 \geq b$.

11. a) $p = -10.2$ **b)** $p \geq -10.2$
c) The processes are the same.

d) The solution of an inequality is a range of numbers, whereas the solution of the related equation is one number.

12. a) Let v dollars represent the money that Joel can deposit in his account. $212.35 + v \geq 750$

b) $v \geq 537.65$; Joel can deposit $537.65 or more in his account to avoid paying a monthly fee.

c)

537.65

+—+—+—+—+●—+—+—+—+—+→
500 520 540 560 580

13. a) Let b dollars represent the money that Teagan should have in her savings before adding $20. $b + 20 \geq 135.99$

b) $b \geq 115.99$; Teagan should have $115.99 or more in her savings before adding $20.

c)

115.99

+—●—+—+—+—+—+—+—+—+—+—+→
0 100 200 300 400 500 600

14. a) Let m dollars represent the money that Marie can spend on a muffin. $3.45 + m \leq 4.85$

b) $m \leq 1.40$; Marie cannot spend more than $1.40 on a muffin.

c)

1.40

○—+—+—●—+—+—+—+—+—+—+→
0 1.00 2.00 3.00 4.00 5.00

d) Since $1.40 is less than $1.45, Marie cannot afford to buy the deluxe muffin.

15. a) i) $a \leq -7$

←—+—+—+—+—◆—+—+—+—+—+→
−11 −10 −9 −8 −7 −6 −5 −4 −3

ii) $p \geq -10.4$

−10.4

+—+—+—+—●—+—+—+—+→
−14 −13 −12 −11 −10 −9 −8 −7

c) The graphs and solutions of part a are the same as those of questions 9d and 9e.

16. a) i) The value of x is less than −2.57.

−2.57

←—+—+—+—○—+—+—+—+→
−2.8 −2.6 −2.4 −2.2

ii) The value of b is greater than or equal to −10.25.

−10.25

+—+—+—+—●—+—+—+→
−12   −11   −10   −9

iii) The value of p is less than or equal to 1.005.

←—+—+—+—◆—+—+—+→
0.985 0.995 1.005 1.015 1.025

b) It is more difficult to accurately place the values of the solutions in these graphs.

c) Using an inequality is more accurate.

6.5 Solving Inequality by Using Multiplication and Division, page 305

3. a) No, the sign will not change.
$$-9 < -2$$
$$(4)(-9) < (4)(-2)$$
$$-36 < -8$$

b) Yes, the sign will change.
$$14.5 > 11.5$$
$$(14.5)(-3) < (11.5)(-3)$$
$$-43.5 < -34.5$$

c) Yes, the sign will change.
$$6 > -12$$
$$6 \div (-4) < (-12) \div (-4)$$
$$-1.5 < 3$$

d) No, the sign will not change.
$$-4 < 10$$
$$(-4) \div 4 < 10 \div 4$$
$$-1 < 2.5$$

4. a) $-2, 0$ **b)** -5

5. a) i) I would reverse the inequality symbol; $y \geq 6$
ii) I would not reverse the inequality symbol; $c > -4$
iii) I would reverse the inequality symbol; $x > -5$
iv) I would reverse the inequality symbol; $m > -6$

b) Answers will vary. For example:
i) $6, \dfrac{13}{2}, 6.1$ **ii)** $-2, -\dfrac{1}{4}, -3.5$
iii) $-4, -\dfrac{14}{3}, -4.5$ **iv)** $-5, \dfrac{3}{2}, -3.5$

6. No, the student is incorrect. The inequality symbol will change when multiplying each side of an inequality by −3.

7. a) $t > -\dfrac{3}{2}$ **b)** $x < -\dfrac{22}{5}$
c) $m \leq -5$ **d)** $x < -3$

8. Let c represent the number of cars washed.
$$5c \geq 300$$
$$5c \div 5 \geq 300 \div 5$$
$$c \geq 60$$
At least 60 cars would have to be washed.

9. a) $k \geq -\dfrac{3}{2}$

$-\frac{3}{2}$

+—+—+—●—+—+—+—+→
−4 −3 −2 −1 0 1 2 3

b) $g < -\dfrac{7}{2}$

$-\frac{7}{2}$

←—+—+—+—○—+—+—+→
−8 −7 −6 −5 −4 −3 −2 −1 0

c) $a < -0.6$

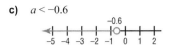

d) $b \geq \dfrac{10}{3}$

e) $s \leq 4.5$

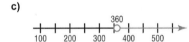

f) $v \geq -2.4$

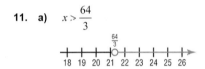

10. a) $7.5s - 1200 > 1500$, where s is the whole number representing the number of tickets sold.

b) $s > 360$; more than 360 tickets need to be sold.

c)

11. a) $x > \dfrac{64}{3}$

b) $c \geq 16$

c) $d \leq 6$

d) $f > -\dfrac{25}{4}$

12. a) $a \geq 2\dfrac{1}{3}$ **b)** $t \geq 2$

c) $z \geq 2$ **d)** $b \geq -9$

13. a) Let k represent the number of kilometres driven.
$2.5 + 1.2k \leq 12$

b) $k \leq 7.91\overline{6}$ or $k \leq 7\dfrac{11}{12}$

Jake can travel up to $7.91\overline{6}$ km for \$12.

d)

14. a) $w = \dfrac{2}{5}$ **b)** $w \leq \dfrac{2}{5}$

c) The processes are the same, except when multiplying each side by a negative fraction. The equality symbol stays the same but the inequality symbol reverses.

d) Both solutions involve the same fraction. The solution of an inequality is a range of numbers, whereas the solution of the related equation is one number.

15. a) Let h represent the number of hours.
$0.55 + 0.004\,20h > 5 + 0.001\,05h$

b), c) $h > 1412.7$; Since the minimum cost of electricity, \$0.01, is for about 2 h use of the regular light bulb or for about 10 h use of the energy saver light bulb, we need to check the time of use near 1413 h for a more accurate solution. For 1413 h, electricity cost of regular light bulb: $\$0.55 + \$0.004\,20(1413) = \$6.48$
For 1413 h, electricity cost of energy saver light bulb: $\$5.00 + \$0.001\,05(1413) = \$6.48$
For 1414 h, electricity cost of regular light bulb: $\$0.55 + \$0.004\,20(1414) = \$6.49$
For 1414 h, electricity cost of energy saver light bulb: $\$5.00 + \$0.001\,05(1414) = \$6.48$
So, for 1414 h or more, it is cheaper to use an energy saver light bulb.

d)

16. a) $h > 32.5$

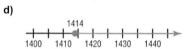

b) $n \leq 2$

c) $v \leq 1$

d) $z > -\dfrac{13}{17}$

17. a) $a > \dfrac{3}{2}$

b) $m < 20.925$

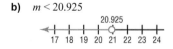

ANSWERS

18. a) 5000 brochures   **b)** 0 to 4999 brochures

c) More than 5000 brochures

Unit 6: Review, page 308

1. a) **i)** $h = 0.9$

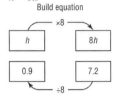

ii) $t = -35$

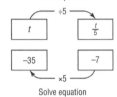

iii) $c = 0.68$

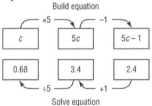

b) i)

$$8h = 7.2$$
$$\frac{8h}{8} = \frac{7.2}{8}$$
$$h = 0.9$$

ii)

$$\frac{t}{5} = -7$$
$$5\left(\frac{t}{5}\right) = 5(-7)$$
$$t = -35$$

iii)

$$5c - 1 = 2.4$$
$$5c - 1 + 1 = 2.4 + 1$$
$$5c = 3.4$$
$$\frac{5c}{5} = \frac{3.4}{5}$$
$$c = 0.68$$

2. a) Milan's steps:

$$4(3.2s + 5.7) = -6$$
$$\frac{4(3.2s + 5.7)}{4} = \frac{-6}{4}$$
$$3.2s + 5.7 = -1.5$$
$$3.2s + 5.7 - 5.7 = -1.5 - 5.7$$
$$3.2s = -7.2$$
$$\frac{3.2s}{3.2} = \frac{-7.2}{3.2}$$
$$s = -2.25$$

b) Daria's steps:

$$4(3.2s + 5.7) = -6$$
$$4(3.2s) + 4(5.7) = -6$$
$$12.8s + 22.8 = -6$$
$$12.8s + 22.8 - 22.8 = -6 - 22.8$$
$$12.8s = -28.8$$
$$\frac{12.8s}{12.8} = \frac{-28.8}{12.8}$$
$$s = -2.25$$

3. a) $b = -12.4$ **b)** $t = -10.2$

c) $w = 29.6$ **d)** $x = -2.5$

4. a) Let l represent the length of the shorter side in centimetres. $2(3.1 + l) = 8.4$

b) $l = 1.1$; the length of the shorter side is 1.1 cm.

5. Algebraic solution:

$$3r + 3 = r + 7$$
$$3r + 3 - r = r + 7 - r$$
$$2r + 3 = 7$$
$$2r + 3 - 3 = 7 - 3$$
$$2r = 4$$
$$\frac{2r}{2} = \frac{4}{2}$$
$$r = 2$$

6. Algebraic solution:

$$2x - 3 = 6 - x$$
$$2x - 3 + x = 6 - x + x$$
$$3x - 3 = 6$$
$$3x - 3 + 3 = 6 + 3$$
$$3x = 9$$
$$\frac{3x}{3} = \frac{9}{3}$$
$$x = 3$$

7. a) $a = 16$ **b)** $m = \frac{1}{15}$

c) $x = \frac{880}{63}$ **d)** $g = -5.5$

e) $x = \frac{4}{3}$ **f)** $p = 3.4$

8. a) Let k represent the distance driven in kilometres.
$200 = 25 + 0.35k$

b) $k = 500$; for a distance of 500 km, the cost will be the same for the two companies.

9. The student forgot to multiply 5.4 by 3.5 and multiply 1.2 by 2.5 in line 2. The result of $7v - 7.5v$ should be $-0.5v$ instead of $0.5v$ in line 4.

Correction:
$$3.5(2v - 5.4) = 2.5(3v - 1.2)$$
$$7v - 18.9 = 7.5v - 3$$
$$7v - 7v - 18.9 = 7.5v - 7v - 3$$
$$-18.9 + 3 = 0.5v - 3 + 3$$
$$0.5v = -15.8$$
$$\frac{0.5v}{0.5} = \frac{-15.8}{0.5}$$
$$v = -31.8$$

10. a) Let a years represent the age of a person being admitted. $a \geq 18$

b) Let h represent the height of a person in centimetres admitted to the ride. $h \geq 90$

c) Let c represent the amount that Horton can spend in dollars. $c \leq 50$

d) Let y years represent the age of a player for the game. $y \geq 5$

11. a) $x \leq -5$ **b)** $x < 1$

c) $x > 3.5$ **d)** $x \geq 1\frac{2}{3}$

12. a) i)

ii)

iii)

iv)

b) i) Neither -3 nor 5 are possible solutions.
ii) Both 5 and -3 are possible solutions.
iii) 5 is a possible solution.
iv) Neither 5 nor -3 are possible solutions.

13. Answers will vary. For example:

a) $h < -3; -10, -\frac{9}{2}, -7.5$

b) $k > -3; 0, \frac{12}{5}, -1.5$ **c)** $y < 5; 4, \frac{1}{2}, 3.5$

14. a) No **b)** No
c) No **d)** Yes

15. a) Let p represent the number of students that can attend the prom. $400 + 30p \leq 10\,000$

b) $p \leq 320$

16. a) $y < 18$

b) $y > -2$

c) $x > -10$
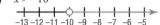

d) $y > 10.7$
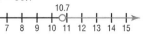

e) $y \leq 2.5$

f) $a \geq 7.5$

Unit 6: Practice Test, page 310

1. Algebraic solution:
$$15 + 2d = 5d + 6$$
$$15 + 2d - 2d = 5d + 6 - 2d$$
$$15 = 3d + 6$$
$$15 - 6 = 3d + 6 - 6$$
$$3d = 9$$
$$\frac{3d}{3} = \frac{9}{3}$$
$$d = 3$$

2. a) $x = 2.1$ **b)** $x = \frac{52}{7}$ or $7\frac{3}{7}$

c) $r = -25.8$ **d)** $w = 18.6$
e) $c = -17$ **f)** $m = -1.2$

3. a) Let n represent the number of meals.
$100 + 15n = 25 + 20n$

b) $n = 15$

4. a) $t < 2$

b) $t \geq \frac{5}{8}$

c) $m \leq -3.6$

5. a) Let k represent the distance the business person can travel, in kilometres. $24.95 + 0.35k \leq 50$

b) $k \leq 71.57$

6. a) The student forgot to multiply 2 by 4 in line 2. Correction:

$$\frac{1}{4}c - 2 = 3$$

$$\frac{1}{4}c - 2 + 2 = 3 + 2$$

$$\frac{1}{4}c = 5$$

$$4 \times \frac{1}{4}c = 4 \times 5$$

$$c = 20$$

b) The student should not change the inequality symbol when subtracting 4 in line 2. The negative sign for -12 should stay in line 5. Correction:

$$x + 4 < -8 - 2x$$

$$x + 4 - 4 < -8 - 2x - 4$$

$$x < -2x - 12$$

$$x + 2x < -2x - 12 + 2x$$

$$3x < -12$$

$$3x \div 3 < -12 \div 3$$

$$x < -4$$

Cumulative Review Units 1-6, page 312

1. a) About 1.9   **b)** 0.9

c) $\frac{4}{5}$ **d)** 0.02

e) About 5   **f)** 2.1

g) 1.6   **h)** About 0.5

2. a) -8

b) 1

c) $-33\ 497$

d) -304

e) 18

3. a) $-2\frac{13}{24}$ **b)** $-11\frac{3}{20}$

c) -4.42 **d)** $\frac{7}{18}$

e) -34.43 **f)** $-\frac{1}{8}$

g) 3

4. a) When the term number increases by 1, the term value increases by 2.

b) $v = 2n + 3$ **d)** 51

e) Term number 115

5. a)

x	y
1	1
2	4
3	7
4	10

b) As x increases by 1, y increases by 3.

6. a) **i)** Vertical   **ii)** Horizontal

iii) Oblique

7. a) Graph B   **b)** Graph C

c) Graph A

8. a) About 5.5 days   **b)** About 1600 km

9. a) Coefficient: 3; variable: x; degree: 1; constant: -6

b) Coefficients: 4, -2; variable: n; degree: 2; constant: 5

c) Coefficients: none; variable: none; degree: 0; constant: 19

d) Coefficients: -1, -21; variable: a; degree: 2; constant: 7

10. a) $-7a + 1$ **b)** $y^2 + 2y - 4$

c) $2c - 10cd + d + 4$ **d)** $6m^2 - 2n^2 + 2m - 3n$

11. a) $10s^2 - 6s + 3$ **b)** $3x^2 - 8x + 6$

c) $-t^2 + 14t + 2$ **d)** $n^2 + n - 6$

e) $x^2 + 4y^2 + 9xy - 7$

f) $-3a^2 - 4b^2 + 5ab - 15b + 8a + 6$

12. a) $27s^2 - 63s + 36$ **b)** $7w^2 + 8w - 5$

c) $21m^2 - 63m$ **d)** $2d - 3$

13. a) $x = 0.8$ **b)** $a = -10.8$

c) $s = -4.2$ **d)** $c = 24$

e) $n = 5.1$ **f)** $c = -\frac{7}{8}$

g) $d = 6$ **h)** $v = -44.6$

i) $t = 10$ **j)** $r = 6$

14. b) **i)** Both   **ii)** Both

iii) -4 only   **iv)** Neither

15. a) $x < -4$ **b)** $x < -2$

c) $b \geq 3.3$ **d)** $n \geq 72$

e) $m \leq -38$ **f)** $t < -7.5$

g) $s \geq 11$

16. a) $140 + 15n \leq 210$, n is an integer

b) $n \leq 4.\overline{6}$, n is an integer

Unit 7 Similarity and Transformations, page 314

Unit 7: Start Where You Are, page 317

1. a) $\angle ACB = 76°$

b) $\angle GEF = 36°$; $\angle GFE = 108°$

c) $\angle HJK = \angle KHJ = 72°$

7.1 Scale Diagrams and Enlargements, page 323

4. a) 4   **b)** 1.5

5. a) 36 cm   **b)** 205 mm

    c) 6.51 cm   **d)** 171 mm

    e) 10 cm

6. a) 210 cm by 150 cm   **b)** 350 cm by 250 cm

    c) 61 cm by 44 cm   **d)** 74 cm by 53 cm

7. About 1.6

8. About 7.5

9.

2.5 cm

11. a) Diagram C

    i) The scale factor is 2.

    ii) Each side is 2 times the length of the corresponding side on the original diagram.

    b) Diagrams C and D

    i) The scale factor for both diagrams is 1.5.

    ii) Each side is 1.5 times the length of the corresponding side on the original diagram.

12. a) 320   **b)** 11.2 m

14. Dimensions of enlargement are marked on diagram:

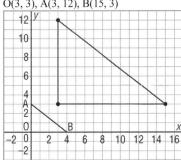

10 cm

7.5 cm

15. There are 3 possible enlargements of △ABC.

a) O(3, 3), A(3, 12), B(15, 3)

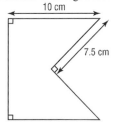

b) O(3, −6), A(3, 3), B(15, −6)

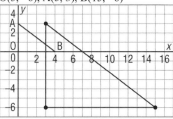

O(−9, 3), A(−9, 12), B(3, 3)

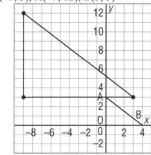

16. a) 80 000 microns, or 0.08 m, or 8 cm, or 80 mm

    b) 12 500

7.2 Scale Diagrams and Reductions, page 329

4. a) 0.025   **b)** 0.04

    c) 0.002   **d)** $0.01\overline{6}$

5. a) $\dfrac{1}{5}$ **b)** $\dfrac{3}{4}$

6. a) $\dfrac{3}{5}$ **b)** $\dfrac{2}{3}$

    c) $\dfrac{17}{63}$ **d)** $\dfrac{1}{250}$

    e) $\dfrac{3}{40}$

7. $\dfrac{1}{2}$; 0.5

8. Rectangle C; each side of rectangle C is $\dfrac{1}{4}$ the corresponding length on the larger rectangle.

9. Triangle B is a reduction of triangle A; the scale factor for the reduction is $\dfrac{1}{3}$.

10. Polygon C is a reduction of polygon B; the scale factor for the reduction is $\dfrac{2}{3}$.

11. a) 25 cm   **b)** 3.6 cm

c) 10 cm   **d)** 0.16 m, or 16 cm

e) 48 cm

12. a)

b)

13. a) 4.55 mm   **b)** 16 m

14. Length: $\dfrac{1}{200} \times 18$ m $= 0.09$ m, or 9 cm

Width: $\dfrac{1}{200} \times 9$ m $= 0.045$ m, or 4.5 cm

15. Length: 0.002×99 m $= 0.198$ m, or 19.8 cm
Width: 0.002×54 m $= 0.108$ m, or 10.8 cm

19. a) 1:50, or $\dfrac{1}{50}$, or 0.02

b) i) Length: 2.75 m; width: 1.5 m

ii) Length: 2.5 m; width: 1.25 m

c) 1.5 m

d) $4.99/m $\times$ 27 m $= $134.73

20. a) 0.004   **b)** 60 m

c) 19 m

7.3 Similar Polygons, page 341

4. a) AB = 12   **b)** BC = 20

c) CD = 9   **d)** DE = 5.6

5. a) $x = 12.5$ **b)** $y = 32.1$

c) $z = 8.\overline{3}$ **d)** $a = 0.0525$

6. Square IJKL ~ square QRST:

$\dfrac{IJ}{QR} = \dfrac{JK}{RS} = \dfrac{KL}{ST} = \dfrac{LI}{TQ} = 2$; $\angle I = \angle Q$, $\angle J = \angle R$,

$\angle K = \angle S$, $\angle L = \angle T$

Quadrilateral ABCD ~ quadrilateral QPMN:

$\dfrac{AB}{QP} = \dfrac{BC}{PM} = \dfrac{CD}{MN} = \dfrac{DA}{NQ} = \dfrac{1}{2}$; $\angle A = \angle Q$, $\angle B = \angle P$,

$\angle C = \angle M$, $\angle D = \angle N$

7.

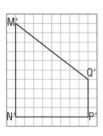

8.

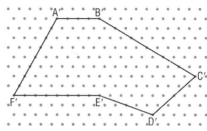

9. Rectangle EFGH ~ rectangle IJKM since the corresponding sides are proportional.

$\dfrac{EF}{IJ} = \dfrac{FG}{JK} = 1.5625$

10. a) i)

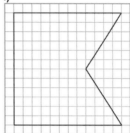

ii)

b) i)

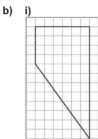

ii)

11. a) No; some corresponding angles are not equal.

b) Yes; the corresponding sides are proportional and the corresponding angles are equal.

12.

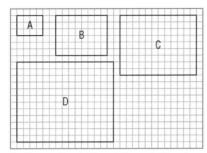

a) **i)** Rectangles A, B, and C are similar, the corresponding sides are proportional and all the angles are right angles.

Rectangle D is not similar to any other rectangle since the corresponding sides are not proportional:

$$\frac{\text{Length of D}}{\text{Length of C}} \neq \frac{\text{Width of D}}{\text{Width of C}}$$

ii) For example:

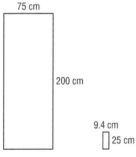

b) The diagonal of rectangle B is 10 units and the diagonal of rectangle C is 15 units.

13. a)

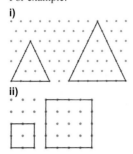

b) The width of the doll's house door is about 9.4 cm.

14. No; the corresponding angles are not equal.

15. a) For example:

i)

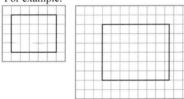

ii)

iii)

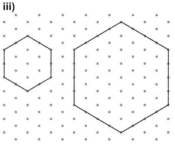

b) Yes; all regular polygons of the same type are similar. Their corresponding sides are proportional and their corresponding angles are equal.

16. Yes, all circles are similar since they have the same shape.

17. a) Answers will vary. For example:

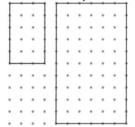

The ratio of the corresponding sides is 2:1.

b) The ratio of the areas is 4:1.

c) The ratio of the areas is the square of the ratio of the corresponding sides.

d) Yes; this relationship is true for all similar shapes.

7.4 Similar Triangles, page 349

4. a) Yes; the corresponding angles are equal:
$\angle P = \angle N$, $\angle Q = \angle M$, $\angle R = \angle H$

b) Yes; $\dfrac{ST}{JH} = \dfrac{TU}{HG} = \dfrac{US}{GJ} = \dfrac{1}{2}$

c) Yes; the corresponding angles are equal:
$\angle C = \angle R$, $\angle E = \angle Q$, $\angle D = \angle P = 50°$

d) No; $\dfrac{DE}{TS} = \dfrac{FD}{VT} = \dfrac{1}{2}$ but $\dfrac{EF}{SV} = \dfrac{5}{9}$

5. a) $\triangle HGF \sim \triangle HJK$; the corresponding angles are equal: $\angle H = \angle H$, $\angle G = \angle J$, $\angle F = \angle K$

b) $\triangle CED \sim \triangle CAB$; the corresponding sides are proportional: $\dfrac{CE}{CA} = \dfrac{ED}{AB} = \dfrac{DC}{BC} = \dfrac{1}{2}$.

c) $\triangle QMN \sim \triangle QRP$; corresponding angles are equal: $\angle Q = \angle Q$, $\angle M = \angle R$, $\angle N = \angle P$

6. a) 6   **b)** 16

   c) 8.0

7. The flagpole is 12.8 m tall.

9. a) 7.65 m   **b)** 27.2 m

10. a)

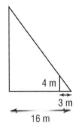

b) The building is about 21.3 m tall.

11. Using similar triangles, the length of the lake is 105 m.

12. The distance across the river is 82.5 m.

13. Equate the ratios of the corresponding sides.
The height of the tree is 5.3 m.

14. Equate the ratios of the corresponding sides for similar triangles. The ladder reaches 7 m up the wall.

15. $x \doteq 4.3$ m; $y = 9.6$ m

Unit 7: Mid-Unit Review, page 352

1. 21 cm by 14 cm

2. a) The diagram is an enlargement with a scale factor of 3.

b) The scale diagram is a 12-cm by 6.4-cm rectangle.

3. a) **b)**

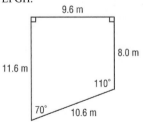

4. $\dfrac{1}{2000}$

5. a) Quadrilateral ABCD ~ quadrilateral MKJN; the corresponding sides are proportional:

$$\frac{AB}{MK} = \frac{BC}{KJ} = \frac{CD}{JN} = \frac{DA}{NM} = \frac{2}{3}$$

b) Answers will vary. For example:
This quadrilateral is similar to quadrilateral EFGH.

6. The length of each side of this hexagon is 2 times the length of the corresponding side in the original hexagon and the corresponding angles are all equal.

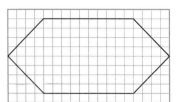

7. a)

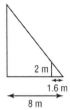

b) The height of the tree is 10 m.

7.5 Reflections and Line Symmetry, page 357

3. a) 1 **b)** 0
c) 1 **d)** 1
e) 3 **f)** 0

4. a) The 3 lines through the centre of the diagram are lines of symmetry.

b) The 3 lines through the centre of the diagram are lines of symmetry:

5. a)

b)

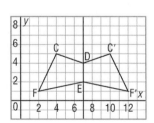

c)

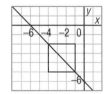

6. a) The vertical line through the centre of the tessellation is a line of symmetry.

b) The vertical line through the centre of the blanket is a line of symmetry.

7. a) Answers will vary. For example:

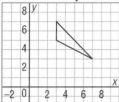

b) i) and ii)

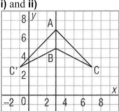

iii) A(3, 7), B(3, 5), C(7, 3), C'(−1, 3)

iv) The line of symmetry is the vertical line through 3 on the x-axis.

c) For one side:

i) and ii)

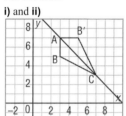

iii) B'(5, 7)

iv) The line of symmetry is the line through AC.

For the other side:

i) and ii)

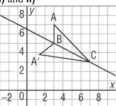

iii) A'(1.4, 3.8)

iv) The line of symmetry is the line through BC.

d), e) A scalene triangle always produces a shape that is a quadrilateral with line symmetry. Right triangles or isosceles triangles may reflect to produce another triangle instead of a quadrilateral. A right triangle, when reflected in one of its legs, produces another triangle.

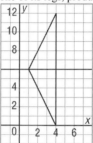

An isosceles triangle, when reflected in its height, produces the same triangle.

8. a)

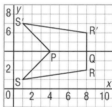

The larger shape has coordinates: R(8, 2), S(1, 1), P(4, 4), S'(1, 7), R'(8, 6).
It is a pentagon with a line of symmetry through PQ.

b)

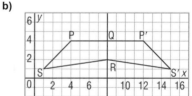

The larger shape has coordinates: R(8, 2), S(1, 1), P(4, 4), P'(12, 4), S'(15, 1)
It is a pentagon with a line of symmetry through QR.

c) The larger shape has coordinates: P(4, 4), Q(8, 4), R(8, 2), S(1, 1), R'(2, 8), Q'(4, 8)
It is a hexagon with a line of symmetry through PS.

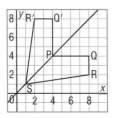

9. **a)**

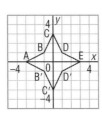

b)

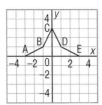

c) A(−3, 0), B(−1, 1), C(0, 3), D(1, 1), E(3, 0),
D′(1, −1), C′(0, −3), B′(−1, −1)

d) The shape has 4 lines of symmetry: *x*-axis, *y*-axis,
the line through points B′ and D, the line through
points B and D′

10. Pentagon A is the reflection image in the horizontal
line through 7 on the *y*-axis.
The line of symmetry is the horizontal line through 7
on the *y*-axis.
Pentagon C is the reflection image in the vertical line
through 5 on the *x*-axis.
The line of symmetry is the vertical line through 5 on
the *x*-axis.
Pentagon D is the reflection image in the horizontal
line through 3 on the *y*-axis.
The line of symmetry is the horizontal line through 3
on the *y*-axis.

11. **a)**

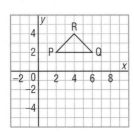

b)

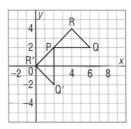

c)

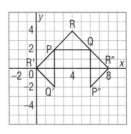

d)

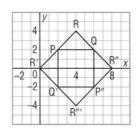

e) The final shape has 4 lines of symmetry: *x*-axis,
the vertical line through 4 on the *x*-axis, the line
through the points (2, 2) and (6, −2) and the line
through the points (6, 2) and (2, −2).

7.6 Rotations and Rotational Symmetry, page 365

4. **a)** 120°   **b)** 72°
    c) 40°   **d)** 30°
5. **a)** 6   **b)** 18
    c) 8   **d)** 10
6. **a)** 3; 120°   **b)** 5; 72°
    c) 4; 90°   **d)** 8; 45°
7. **a)** Yes; the snowflake has rotational symmetry of
        order 6 and the angle of rotation symmetry is 60°.
    b) No; the picture does not have rotational
        symmetry.
8. **a)** Yes; the shape has rotational symmetry of order 4
        and the angle of rotation symmetry is 90°.
    b) Yes; the shape has rotational symmetry of order 6
        and the angle of rotation symmetry is 60°.

9. a)

b)

c)

10. a)

b)

11. a) The tessellation has rotational symmetry of order 4 about a point where the heads of 4 lizards meet.

b) Rotational symmetry of order 15 about the centre

12. a)

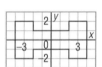

b) The shape formed is a dodecagon that has rotational symmetry of order 2.

13. a) i)

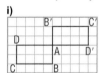

ii)

b) i)

ii)

c) i)

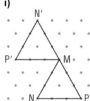

ii)

d) In parts a, b, and c, the image is the same in part ii. It is because each shape is rotated about the centre of the shape through the angle of rotation symmetry.

14. a) i)

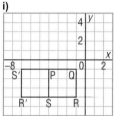

ii)

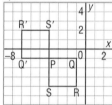

iii)

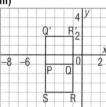

b) The shape formed has rotational symmetry of order 2 about P.

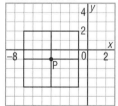

15. a) i)

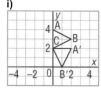

ii)

iii)

b) The shape formed has rotational symmetry of order 4 about C.

7.7 Identifying Types of Symmetry on the Cartesian Plane, page 373

3. a) Rotational symmetry of order 2
b) Rotational symmetry of order 2
c) Line symmetry: the horizontal line through the centre is a line of reflection.
d) Line symmetry: the horizontal line through the centre is a line of reflection.

4. a) 8 lines of symmetry through the centre; rotational symmetry of order 8 about the centre
b) 5 lines of symmetry through the centre; rotational symmetry of order 5 about the centre
c) No line symmetry; no rotational symmetry
d) No lines of symmetry; rotational symmetry of order 5 about the centre

5. This face has 4 lines of symmetry and rotational symmetry of order 4:

This face has 2 lines of symmetry and rotational symmetry of order 2.

This face has 2 lines of symmetry and rotational symmetry of order 2.

This face has 4 lines of symmetry and rotational symmetry of order 4.

This face has 4 lines of symmetry and rotational symmetry of order 4.

This face has 2 lines of symmetry and rotational symmetry of order 2.

6. a) Square D is a rotation of 180°; Square A is a rotation of 90° counterclockwise.
b) Square B is a reflection in the vertical line through 5 on the x-axis; Square C is a reflection in the x-axis.

7. a) By reflection in the y-axis
b) By reflection in the line through $(1, -1)$ and $(-1, 1)$ and by a 180° rotation about the origin
c) By reflection in the x-axis
d) By reflection in the line through $(-1, -1)$ and $(1, 1)$ and by a 180° rotation about the origin

8. a) By reflection in the x-axis, and by a 180° rotation about the point $(-2.5, 0)$
b) By 90° clockwise rotation about the point $(2, 3)$

9. The diagram formed by $\triangle FGH$ and $\triangle F'G'H'$ has rotational symmetry of order 2.

10. a) The diagram has 1 line of symmetry, which is the vertical line through the centre of the diagram.

b) The diagram has rotational symmetry of order 2 about the centre of the diagram.

11. a) A(–2, 5), B(–2, 1), C(–4, 4), A′(–2, 11), B′(–2, 7), C′(–4, 10). There is no symmetry.

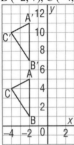

b) Vertices are: D(2, –1), E(2, –3), F(6, –3) = E′, G (6, –1) = D′, G′(10, –1), F′(10, –3)

The diagram has line symmetry and rotational symmetry. The line of symmetry is the vertical line through 6 on the *x*-axis and the 2 rectangles are related by rotational symmetry of order 2 about (6, –2).

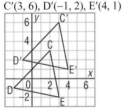

12. a)-c) Vertices are: C(2, 3), D(–2, –1), E(3, –2), C′(3, 6), D′(–1, 2), E′(4, 1)

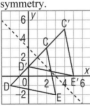

d) The translation does not result in any symmetry because there is no axis of symmetry and there is no line of symmetry.

e) The translation R2, U2 results in a line of symmetry.

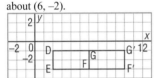

13. a), b) i) The diagram has rotational symmetry of order 4 about (4, 2).

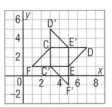

ii) The diagram has a line of symmetry, which is the horizontal line through 1 on the *y*-axis.

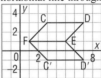

iii) The diagram does not have line or rotational symmetry.

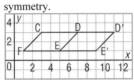

14. a)

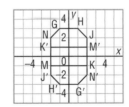

Digits 1 and 3 have a horizontal line of symmetry.
Digits 1, 2, and 5 have rotational symmetry of order 2.
Digits 4, 6, 7, and 9 have no line or rotational symmetry.
Digits 8 and 0 have both horizontal and vertical lines of symmetry and rotational symmetry of order 2.

b) Digits 1, 3, 8, and 0 can be completed by reflecting these halves of the digits in the dotted line in this diagram.

c) Digits 1, 2, 5, 8, and 0 can be completed by rotating part of the digit about each dot shown.

15. a)

b) G(–1, 3), H(1, 3), J(2, 2), N′(2, –2), G′(1, –3), H′(–1, –3), J′(–2, –2), N(–2, 2)

c) The larger shape has line symmetry about the
x-axis and the y-axis, and rotational symmetry of
order 2 about the origin.

Unit 7: Review, page 377

1. a) 9 cm by 15 cm **b)** 7.5 cm by 12.5 cm
c) 4.5 cm by 7.5 cm **d)** 12.6 cm by 21 cm

2.

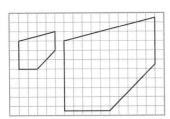

3. a) $\dfrac{2}{3}$ **b)** 96 cm

4. About 10.4 m

5. About 2.4 m and about 3.1 m

6. Pentagon Z is similar to the red pentagon. The ratios
of the corresponding sides are all equal to $\dfrac{10}{9}$.

7. a) 6 m **b)** 4 m
c) About 5.3 m

8. a) 2 cm **b)** 2.8 cm

9. 46.4 m

10. About 35.6 m

11. In similar triangles, the ratios of the corresponding
sides are proportional.

$$\dfrac{25}{25+12.5}=\dfrac{x}{22.5}$$

$x = 15$ m

12. a) 1 **b)** 0
c) 2 **d)** 3

13. a) i)

ii)

iii)

b)

c) i) A(−1, 2), B(0, 2), C(0, 1), D(1, 1), E(1, 0),
F(−1, 0), A′(1, 2), D′(−1, 1)
ii) A(−1, 2), B(0, 2), C(0, 1), D(1, 1), E(1, 0),
F(−1, 0), A′(−1, −2), B′(0, −2), C′(0, −1),
D′(1, −1)
iii) A(−1, 2), B(0, 2), C(0, 1), D(1, 1), E(1, 0),
F(−1, 0)

d) i) 4 lines of symmetry
ii) 1 line of symmetry
iii) 1 line of symmetry
b) 0 lines of symmetry

14. a) 3 **b)** 2
c) 6 **d)** 8

15. a) i)

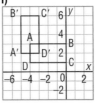

ii)

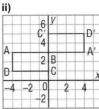

iii)

b) i) The diagram has no rotational symmetry.
ii) The diagram has rotational symmetry of order
2 about B(0, 3).

iii) The diagram has rotational symmetry of order 4 about (−2, 2).

16. i) 1 line of symmetry: the line through the points (−6, 0) and (0, 6)

ii) No line symmetry

iii) 4 lines of symmetry: the vertical line through −2 on the x-axis, the horizontal line through 2 on the y-axis, the line through the points (−3, 1) and (−1, 3), the line through the points (−3, 3) and (−1, 1)

17. a) 1 line of symmetry: the line through the points (−2, 2) and (2, −2); rotational symmetry of order 2 about the origin

b) 1 line of symmetry: the vertical line through 0.5 on the x-axis

18. a) Rotational symmetry of order 3 about the centre; 3 lines of symmetry

b) 1 line of symmetry: the vertical line through the centre

19. a) i)

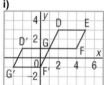

ii)

b) i) Yes; rotational symmetry of order 2 about G(1, 1).

ii) Yes; rotational symmetry of order 2 about (3.5, 3).

Unit 7: Practice Test, page 380

1. a) 8.1 m   **b)** 5.2 m

c)

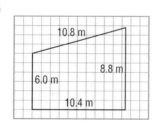

d)

2. a)

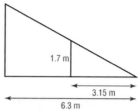

b) The corresponding angles in the triangles are equal.

c) The height of the tree is 3.4 m.

3. a)

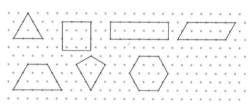

b) i)

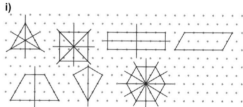

ii) Equilateral triangle: rotational symmetry of order 3; angle of rotation symmetry 120°
Square: rotational symmetry of order 4; angle of rotation symmetry 90°
Rectangle: rotational symmetry of order 2; angle of rotation symmetry 180°
Parallelogram: rotational symmetry of order 2; angle of rotation symmetry 180°
Regular hexagon: rotational symmetry of order 6; angle of rotation symmetry 60°

c) Answers will vary. For example:

d) Answers will vary. For example:

4. a) i)

ii) A′(0, 3), B′(1, 4), C′(3, 4), D′(4, 3), E′(3, 2), F′(1, 2)

iii) 4 lines of symmetry: the vertical line through 2 on the *x*-axis, the horizontal line through 3 on the *y*-axis, the line through the points (0, 1) and (4, 5), the line through the points (0, 5) and (5, 0); and rotational symmetry of order 4 about (2, 3)

b) i)

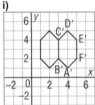

ii) A′(4, 1), B′(3, 2), C′(3, 4), D′(4, 5), E′(5, 4), F′(5, 2)

iii) 2 lines of symmetry: the vertical line through 3 on the *x*-axis, the horizontal line through 3 on the *y*-axis; and rotational symmetry of order 2 about (3, 3)

c) i)

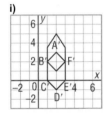

ii) A′(2, 3), B′(1, 2), C′(1, 0), D′(2, −1), E′(3, 0), F′(3, 2)

iii) 2 lines of symmetry: the vertical line through 2 on the *x*-axis, the horizontal line through 2 on the *y*-axis; and rotational symmetry of order 2 about (2, 2)

Unit 8 Circle Geometry, page 382

8.1 Properties of Tangents to a Circle, page 388

3. a) QR   **b)** CE
4. a) 90°   **b)** 90°
5. a) 90°   **b)** 67°
    c) 43°

6. a) 5   **b)** 12
    c) 20
7. a) $d° = 62°, e° = 55°$ **b)** $d° = 57°, e° = 21°$
8. a) $a \doteq 8.5$ **b)** $a \doteq 7.9$
9. $a \doteq 11.5, b \doteq 5.3$
11. Answers may vary. For example: Both the line perpendicular to AB at P and the line perpendicular to CD at Q pass through the centre of the circle. The intersection of these two lines is the centre of the circle.
12. About 139 km
13. About 196 km
14. $x \doteq 10.8; y \doteq 10.4; z° = 60°$
15. a) Two tangents
    b) All other lines from this point would intersect the circle twice or not at all.

    c) Each of the lines intersects the circle at exactly one point.
16. a) The distances from N to the two points of tangency are equal.

    b) The lengths of the two tangents are equal.
    c) $x = y \doteq 19.4$
17. 5 cm
18. 2835 km
19. About 61.7 cm
20. About 8.5 cm
21. 50 cm
22. a) About 6 m
    b) The actual strap should be slightly longer to be able to join the ends of the strap.

8.2 Properties of Chords in a Circle, page 397

3. a) $d° = 90°$ **b)** $e = 5$
    c) $f = 7$
4. a) $x° = 50°, y° = 90°$ **b)** $x° = 22°, y° = 136°$
    c) $x° = y° = 35°$
5. a) $a = b \doteq 9.5$ **b)** $a \doteq 5.7, b \doteq 11.5$
6. $b \doteq 7.5$
7. a) $r \doteq 2.2$ **b)** $r = 6$

8. The distances between the centre and all chords of the same length are equal.

9. Draw two chords and their perpendicular bisectors. The intersection point of the perpendicular bisectors is the centre of the circle.

10. a) $s \doteq 3.8$ **b)** $s \doteq 7.3$

11. 9.6 cm

12. a) Parts i, ii, and iii
    b) **i)** About 6.5 cm   **ii)** About 5.4 cm
    iii) 0 cm

13.

14. About 15.3 cm

15. a) About 5.1 cm
    b) The congruent chords are equidistant from the centre of the circle.

17. About 39.0 km

18. About 3.0 m

19. a) About 21.3 cm; about 4.7 cm
    b) Two answers; the water level could be below or above the centre of the bowl

Unit 8: Mid-Unit Review, page 403

1. a) $x° = 22°, y° = 90°$ **b)** $x° = 46°, y = 33°$

2. About 10.4

3. About 35.4 cm

4. $m° = 19°$

5. a) About 19.6   **b)** About 6.2

6. a)   **b)** About 29.7 cm

7. About 26.2 cm

8.3 Properties of Angles in a Circle, page 410

3. a) Inscribed angle: $\angle DFE$; central angle: $\angle DOE$
    b) Inscribed angle: $\angle PRQ$; central angle: $\angle POQ$
    c) Inscribed angles: $\angle NJM$ and $\angle NKM$; central angle: $\angle NOM$

4. a) $x° = 65°$ **b)** $x° = 90°$
   c) $x° = 40°$ **d)** $x° = 58°$

5. a) $y° = 140°, z° = 70°$ **b)** $y° = 25°, z° = 130°$
   c) $y° = 27°, z° = 42°$

6. a) $x° = 80°, y° = 50°$ **b)** $x° = 25°, y° = 65°$

7. a) A rectangle   **b)** A square

8. a)   **b)**

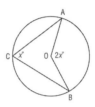

9. a)

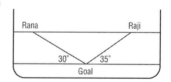

    b) About 7.2 cm

11. a) $x° = 40°, y = 40°$
    b) $x° = 45°, y° = 40°$
    c) $x° = 58°, y° = 116°$

12. Yes

13. a)

    b) Raji

14. $45°$

15. a) $\angle QRS = \angle QPR$ and $\angle PRT = \angle PQR$
    b) For example:

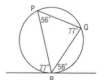

Unit 8: Review, page 418

1. **a)** $x° = 90°$, $y = 65°$
   b) $a \doteq 9.7$, $y° = 36°$
   c) $a = b \doteq 17.9$
2. Since $7^2 + 13^2 \neq 16^2$, $\angle HPO \neq 90°$. So, the wire HP is not a tangent.
3. Draw a line perpendicular to the radius OP at the point P. This line is a tangent using the Tangent-Radius Property.
4. About 14.1 cm
5. **a)** $x \doteq 6.2$
   b) $x \doteq 3.9$
6. **a)**

   b) The chord is about 6.3 cm from the centre of the circle.
7. **a)** $x° = 35°$, $y° = 110°$
   b) $x° = y° = 45°$
8. About 3.5 cm
9. **a)** $x° = y° = 90°$
   b) $x° = y° = 60°$
   c) $x° = 15°$, $y° = 75°$
10. About 34.6 cm

Unit 8: Practice Test, page 420

1. $x \doteq 6.6$ cm, $y = 34°$
2. $x° = 61°$, $y° = 90°$, $z° = 30.5°$
3. **a)**

   b) About 4.5 cm
   c) CD is shorter than AB.
4. The central angle of a semicircle is 180°. The inscribed angle is one-half of the central angle, which is 90°.
5. The longest chord is the diameter. The farther away a chord is from the centre of the circle, the shorter the chord.

6. **a)** Parts i and ii
   b) **i)** About 13.9 cm   **ii)** About 10.6 cm
7. **a) to c)**

   d) $\angle PRQ$ and $\angle PSQ$ have a sum of 180°.

Unit 9 Probability and Statistics, page 422

9.1 Probability in Society, page 427

3. **a)** Experimental probability; decision is based on Andrei's past experience.
   b) Theoretical probability; the more tickets you buy, the greater your chance of winning.
   c) Experimental probability; decision is based on Anita's past experience.
   d) Subjective judgment; decision is based on Doug's feelings.
4. **a)** Claudia will continue to perform at the same level and the next math quiz will have the same difficulty.
   b) Omar will leave work at the same time and the traffic patterns will be the same every day.
5. If Winona doesn't go canoeing, her decision will be based on probability (it is likely that it will rain). If she does go, her decision will be based on subjective judgment (the feeling that it will not rain).
6. Theoretical probability and subjective judgment
7. **a)** More money should be spent to increase the probability of recovering a stolen vehicle.
   b) Because the probability of recovering a stolen vehicle is so low, there are better ways of spending money than on solving this problem.
8. **a)** Vanessa made the assumption that the same types of birds visit her birdfeeder at different times of the day, every day.
   b) The percent of birds that are cardinals would change.
9. **a)** Kathryn assumes that the next 10 people she meets are a fair representation of the community.

b) The next 10 people may favour one candidate very strongly over the other, making the number of those who support Choo greater than or less than 7.

10. Since there is such a small chance the blood was not the suspect's, it is very likely the suspect committed the crime. There is a chance the blood belongs to someone else, so the jury should not convict a possibly innocent man.

11. a) The experimental probability may convince the teenager to try the treatment. He may also use subjective judgment about whether to try the treatment, depending on his personal beliefs of the effectiveness of acne treatment.

b) He would be assuming that he will respond to the treatment in a way that is similar to the response of other people who tried the treatment. His response to the treatment may differ from most people's.

14. The student is assuming that it is equally likely for Shaquille to miss as to make the shot, which ignores Shaquille's skill level in free throws. His skill makes it more likely that he will make free throws.

16. The Farmer's Almanac makes the assumption that long range weather patterns can be predicted from previous years' weather patterns.

17. a) This gives the impression that it is much more dangerous to travel by car than by plane. This information could be misleading because there are more people travelling by road than by air.

b) We need to know how many people travelled by plane and by car in 2004.

9.2 Potential Problems with Collecting Data, page 435

3. a) Privacy **b)** Use of language
c) Cultural sensitivity **d)** Time

4. a) Part a: Since the survey is not anonymous, the students may hesitate to respond negatively (to the principal) or positively (to avoid seeming to flatter the principal in front of their friends).
Part b: The principal should give students a written survey and ask them to return it anonymously to his/her office. The question should ask: "Are you enjoying school?"

b) Part a: The statement presents the most ethical option and no reasons for choosing another option, which may affect the results in favour of turning the wallet in.
Part b: The statement could be made into a question: "If you find a $20-bill, do you keep it or turn it in?"

c) Part a: Some people would not be aware of the cultural importance of head covering.
Part b: Brenda should ask if students are aware of the cultural significance of someone covering her or his head, and then ask the question.

d) Part a: Carlos will probably run out of time before he asks every student.
Part b: Carlos should choose a representative sample of the students to survey.

5. a) Students will think Parinder's question asks about how much time they spend on the computer at school and at home.

b) "How much time do you spend on the school computers?"

c) The school administration could be interested in the results to plan the school's budget for new computers.

6. a) No; many students who are bullied are afraid to tell people, especially in a non-anonymous environment.

b) An anonymous survey

7. a) On a warm August evening, the fans may not immediately see the point of building an indoor stadium, so many may respond negatively.

b) On a very cold November evening, Trinity may receive many more responses in favour of an indoor stadium.

8. a) i) The use of the words "violent criminal"; bias toward using DNA tests
ii) The use of the words "gas guzzling"; negative description of SUVs
iii) The question emphasizes the positive aspect of spell checks.

b) i) Do you think that DNA evidence should be allowed in courts?
ii) Are you in favour of banning SUVs?
iii) Do you think students should be allowed to use spell check?

9. a) No

b) Rebecca should have asked if her friends had any problems with their service provider, what service providers they had in the past, and whether they are satisfied with their current service providers.

10. a) Ethics: The survey designers didn't tell Sasha that promotional emails might be sent to the email address he provided. This reflects poorly on the brands advertised on the website.

b) Tell people their email addresses may be used for future correspondence and allow people then to indicate whether they wish to receive such emails.

11. Finding the favourite ice cream flavour of Canadian teens by surveying each teen would be expensive and time-consuming.

13. a) Privacy: People may not want to admit how much or how little they spend on clothes. Timing: Depending on the month in which Bridget interviews people, there may be clothing sales because a new season begins or for a holiday season shopping. Ethics: People may want to know *why* Bridget is asking them.

b) Privacy: Bridget could ask people to write a number on a slip of paper and leave it on her desk later. Timing: Bridget could ask at different months in the year. Ethics: Bridget could tell people why she is doing this survey.

15. Personal interviews: time-consuming, costly, and do not allow for anonymity; phone interviews: seen as invasive, so low response rate; email surveys: often returned by those with strong opinions about the issues

16. a) Some people may not understand the religious significance of the holiday.

9.3 Using Samples and Populations to Collect Data, page 440

3. a) Residents of Comox aged 13 to 25 years
b) All 1-L juice cartons
c) All schools managed by the board
d) All First Nations people in Nunavut
4. a) Census   **b)** Sample
5. a) People who ride buses
b) All residents of Canada over the age of 18
c) Parents or guardians
d) People who have had relatives or friends in the emergency room
6. a) James; Courtney only surveyed a small sample.
b) Courtney's friends may not be representative of the grade 9 students.
7. a) It would be very time-consuming to test every AAA battery and there would be none left to sell.
b) It would be difficult to find every single First Nations child in Canada, requiring a lot of time and people.
8. a) Sample   **b)** Sample
c) Sample   **d)** Census
9. a) Invalid   **b)** Invalid
10. a) All students in the high school

b) Sample
c) Ask a sample that is representative of the students in the high school. Include students of different grades, gender, ethnicity, and so on.

11. a) The topping your family wants on a pizza
b) Typical prices for a skateboard

Unit 9: Mid-Unit Review, page 444

1. a) 90% of a person's lies will be detected, not 1 out of 10 people will be able to lie undetected.
b) His reaction to the test will be different from most other people's.

2. 1 in 20 is a fairly small chance, so we probably don't need to worry about the WAIS collapsing. However, 1 in 20 is far from impossible, and considering the gravity of the situation if WAIS were to collapse, we should do everything possible to avoid it.

3. a) i) Do you find listening to music helps you relax while studying?
     ii) Do you find listening to music distracting when you're trying to study?
b) Do you support listening to music while studying?

4. a) Privacy: The survey is not anonymous.
b) Many student smokers would lie and claim that they do not smoke, thus skewing the results toward a low number of student smokers.

5. a) i) People may refuse to disclose how much they earn.
     ii) Well-educated parents who choose to stay home with children may resent the question.
     iii) Change "years of post-secondary education" to levels of education, or number of courses at each level.
     iv) Surveying a very large sample would take a lot of time and would be costly.
b) i) People may lie about the amount of money they make.
     ii) People may be reluctant to answer or may answer dishonestly.
     iii) People's answers may not reflect their true situations if the questions are unclear.
     iv) Ahmed may not get as many results as he hopes for.

6. Asking students on a Monday morning if they enjoy going to school

7. a) Students who regularly eat at the cafeteria
b) Students who are enrolled in phys-ed classes
c) Students who drive to school

d) Students who go to or participate in football games

8. a) Too time-consuming

b) Too many DVD players to conduct a census; moreover, DVD player prices change often.

c) It is probably impossible to catch all the northern pike in Misaw Lake, and doing so could devastate the local ecosystem.

9. a) Census   **b)** Sample

9.4 Selecting a Sample, page 448

3. a) Not a representative sample: People who do not enjoy shopping are not likely to be in a mall.

b) Not a representative sample: The majority of the cafeteria's customers are likely to be students, not teachers.

c) Not a representative sample: The neighbourhood sampled has a high crime rate, and probably has a different police presence than neighbourhoods with lower crime rates.

d) Not a representative sample: The survey targets those people (not necessarily teenagers) already interested in fitness and willing to take the time to participate.

4. a) Not appropriate   **b)** Not appropriate

c) Appropriate   **d)** Appropriate

e) Not appropriate

5. a) i) No   **ii)** Yes

iii) Yes

b) i) The arena should survey residents of the surrounding community who skate or want to learn to skate.

6. a) Stratified random sampling: Survey 100 Canadian citizens from each of the income tax brackets.

b) Simple random sampling: Have a computer randomly select 300 student IDs and poll those students.

7. No

8. a) Surveying 300 15-year-olds

b) Survey 300 randomly selected members of the population

9. a) People who work for companies that make fur coats

b) A group of people from homes where people always recycle

10. a) No, the number of people in the sample is probably too small to represent the Canadian population.

b) The survey may have been conducted at a climate change rally.

c) Survey Canadian citizens using simple random sampling.

11. Self-selected sampling and convenience sampling

12. a) i) Randomly select student ID numbers.

ii) Inspect every 10th phone in the assembly line.

iii) Randomly select a high school and then a grade within that high school and survey every student in that grade.

iv) Divide the orchard into 8 equal plots of land and survey 5 apple trees from each plot.

b) Answers will vary. For example:

i) Course offerings

ii) Making sure there are no defects in the cell phones

iii) The most popular music artist among teenagers

iv) The average number of apples produced per season

Unit 9: Start Where You Are, page 453

1. Left box: has many spelling or grammatical errors; right box: ideas are mostly in an order that makes sense

Unit 9: Review, page 458

1. a) Mustafa Abaz

b) Assumptions: The sample surveyed is representative of the voting population. Nothing would happen before the election to change the popularity of the candidates.

2. Experimental probability: The players' past results indicate that they have a very good team with a very high probability of winning. Subjective judgment: Darrell strongly believes that the winning streak cannot last.

3. a) The chance of winning (1 in 3) is relatively high for a lottery, so there is a good chance of winning.

b) The chance of winning is still less than 50%, so it's better to not risk money on what will likely be a loss.

5. a) i) Use of language: The question is biased toward increasing the minimum wage.

ii) Ethics: The student used the results of the survey for something other than what she had claimed.

iii) Bias: It is not clear how the 1000 cars are tested.

iv) Timing: During November, not many people in the northern hemisphere think about outdoor pools.

b) i) More people surveyed will be in favour of increasing the minimum wage.

ii) It may not affect the data collection, but participants may feel frustrated or angry.

iii) There could be a defect later on in the assembly that might not be discovered.

iv) There would be fewer people who are in favour of building a new outdoor pool.

6. a) The best quality camera for its price. "What do you think is the best digital camera for its price?"

b) The question avoids bias by not leading the reader to answer one way or another.

7. a) Pregnant teens may not want to admit that they are pregnant.

b) There could be different cultural opinions regarding teen pregnancy that should be taken into account.

c) Raheem must word the question in a way that does not support or condemn teen pregnancy.

8. a) "What is your favourite fruit: apple, orange, or banana?"

b) "What is your favourite fruit?"

10. Census; if even one parachute is no longer working, a person could die.

11. a) Testing every brand of battery would be very time-consuming and would use up the batteries.

b) A sample of randomly selected brands would most likely represent the population.

12. a) i) Too time-consuming

ii) Time-consuming and difficult if people do not wish to share that information

b) Determining brands of calculators used by students in your math class

13. No; people who do not watch the TV show are excluded and only those who feel strongly about the competition would be likely to pay to vote.

14. a) Yes

b) Depends on the size of the school.

c) No

15. a) Simple random sampling of the entire country's voting population

b) Convenience sampling near several local tennis courts

16. a) Which brand of chewing gum do you recommend most?

b) Get the membership list of the province's dental association and call every 10th dentist.

c) Phone interviews; bar graph

d) The total number of dentists who selected a particular brand, divided by the total number of dentists surveyed

Unit 9: Practice Test, page 460

1. Shawnie: experimental probability; Owen: subjective judgment; Jovana: theoretical probability

2. a) Assumptions: The next team she plays is as skilled as the previous teams; her own team's skill level will not change.

b) If Hannah's team plays a team that is better than previous teams, or if Hannah's team loses a player, the chance of winning will be lower (a probability less than 0.875). If Hannah's team plays a team that is worse than previous teams, or if Hannah's team improves, the chance of winning will be higher (greater than 0.875).

3. a) If Manroop surveys people on a Monday morning at work, she would probably get a larger number of depressed people than if she surveyed people on a Saturday night. Also, time of the year may change responses since many people are depressed in the winter when there is less light.

b) People may not want to give such personal information to a stranger. Manroop should conduct an anonymous survey.

c) Use of language: "Satisfaction with life" does not necessarily mean happiness. The data might not reflect how happy or depressed Canadians are, but how much satisfaction they feel.

4. a) The cost of a new snowboard

b) Asking students in a grade 9 drama class to determine the most popular movie in a high school

5. a) Collect vials of water from 3 water fountains and 3 taps that are randomly selected from around the school. This sample would be representative of the school's entire water supply, assuming that any contamination in the water supply would affect all water fountains and taps.

b) Have the computer randomly select 50 student ID numbers and survey those students.

c) Randomly select 10 students from each grade and weigh their backpacks.

6. Emile could have problems with language if he asks questions in a way that would lead toward a certain answer. He could also have cultural sensitivity problems if he asks groups that have religious objections to shopping on Sundays.

1. a) 0.8   **b)** $\dfrac{6}{5}$

c) 8.9   **d)** 2.1

e) $\dfrac{10}{3}$ **f)** 1

g) 5.5   **h)** 2.1

2. 978 m^2

3. No; −43

4. $6^6 = 46\ 656$

5. a) 225, 89.25, −223.94, 3 × (−22.39)

b) 225 + 89.25 + (−223.94) + 3 × (−22.39)

c) $23.14

6. −0.63

7. a)

t	0	1	2	3	4
d	0	3	6	9	12

b) Yes, because time and distance are not discrete.

c) The relation is linear; the graph is a straight line.

d) $d = 3t$

e) 45 m

f) About 5.6 min

8. a) About $140   **b)** About 15 weeks

c) For example, Colton may change the number of hours he works per week

9. a) $-2n^2 - 9n + 13$ or $-10n^2 - 5n + 3$

10. a) $6x^2 + 7x$ **b)** 24 cm^2

11. b) $t = 5$

12. b) Jerry can ride the pedicab for about 15 min.

13. a) 9.4 cm by 8 cm

b) 8.225 cm by 7 cm

c) 16.45 cm by 14 cm

14. a) $\dfrac{1}{40}$ **b)** 0.045 m by 0.03 m

15. About 8.2 m

16. a) Line symmetry about the horizontal line through 5 on the y-axis

b) Line symmetry about the vertical line through 4 on the x-axis

c) Line symmetry about the line through AD; line symmetry about the line through (0, 1) and (4, 5); rotational symmetry of order 2 about the midpoint of AD

17. a) Yes, rotational symmetry of order 2 with an angle of 180°.

b) ii) 90° clockwise about (−2, −3): (−1, 1), (−1, −3), (−2, −3), (−2, −4), (−6, −4), (−6, −2), (−3, −2), (−3, 1)
180° about Q: (−2, −2), (−2, −4), (−6, −4), (−6, −6), (−10, −6), (−10, −4), (−6, −2); rotational symmetry of order 2 around Q

270° clockwise about (−4, −4): (−2, −2), (−2, −4), (−4, −4), (−4, −6), (−6, −6), (−6, −2)

18. About 15.0 cm

19. About 10.1 cm

20. $x° = 250°, y° = 110°, z° = 55°$

21. About 18.5 cm

22. About 125 cm

23. $x° = 65°, y° = 50°, z° = 130°$

24. a) The other team will be the same skill level as the previous teams.

b) If the other team is better than previous teams, Bao's team is more likely to lose; if the other team is worse, Bao's team is more likely to win.

26. a) On-line survey

b) Not valid, because readers of a fashion magazine would be more likely to spend money on clothing than the average person.

27. a) Too time-consuming

b) Too time-consuming

28. a) Sample   **b)** Census

Illustrated Glossary

acute angle: an angle measuring less than 90°

acute triangle: a triangle with three acute angles

algebraic expression: a mathematical expression containing a variable: for example, $6x - 4$ is an algebraic expression

angle bisector: the line that divides an angle into two equal angles

angle of rotation symmetry: the minimum angle required for a shape to rotate and coincide with itself

approximate: a number close to the exact value of an expression; the symbol $\doteq$ means "is approximately equal to"

arc: a segment of the circumference of a circle

Arc of a circle

area: the number of square units needed to cover a region

average: a single number that represents a set of numbers (see *mean*, *median*, and *mode*)

bar graph: a graph that displays data by using horizontal or vertical bars

bar notation: the use of a horizontal bar over a decimal digit to indicate that it repeats; for example, $1.\overline{3}$ means 1.333 333 …

base: the side of a polygon or the face of an object from which the height is measured

base of a power: see *power*

bias: a prejudice that is in favour of or against a topic

binomial: a polynomial with two terms; for example, $3x - 8$

bisector: a line that divides a line segment or an angle into two equal parts

capacity: the amount a container can hold

Cartesian Plane: another name for a coordinate grid (see *coordinate grid*)

census: a data collection method using each member of the population

central angle: an angle whose arms are radii of a circle

certain event: an event with probability 1, or 100%

chance: probability expressed as a percent

chord: a line segment that joins two points on a circle

circle graph: a diagram that uses sectors of a circle to display data

circumference: the distance around a circle, also the perimeter of the circle

coefficient: the numerical factor of a term; for example, in the terms $3x$ and $3x^2$, the coefficient is 3

common denominator: a number that is a multiple of each of the given denominators; for example, 12 is a common denominator for the fractions $\frac{1}{3}, \frac{5}{4}, \frac{7}{12}$

common factor: a number that is a factor of each of the given numbers; for example, 3 is a common factor of 15, 9, and 21

commutative property: the property of addition and multiplication that states that numbers can be added or multiplied in any order; for example,

$3 + 5 = 5 + 3; 3 \times 5 = 5 \times 3$

composite number: a number with three or more factors; for example, 8 is a composite number because its factors are 1, 2, 4, and 8

composite object: the result of combining one or more objects to make a new object

composite shape: the result of combining one or more shapes to make a new shape

concave polygon: has at least one angle greater than 180°

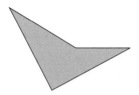

congruent: shapes that match exactly, but do not necessarily have the same orientation

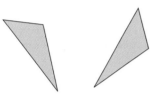

consecutive numbers: integers that come one after the other without any integers missing; for example, 34, 35, 36 are consecutive numbers, so are −2, −1, 0, and 1

constant term: the number in an expression or equation that does not change; for example, in the expression $4x + 3$, 3 is the constant term

convex polygon: has all angles less than 180°

coordinate axes: the horizontal and vertical axes on a grid

coordinate grid: a two-dimensional surface on which a coordinate system has been set up

coordinates: the numbers in an ordered pair that locate a point on a coordinate grid (see *ordered pair*)

corresponding angles: matching angles in similar polygons

corresponding lengths: matching lengths on an original diagram and its scale diagram

corresponding sides: matching sides of similar polygons

cube: an object with six congruent square faces

cube number: a number that can be written as a power with an integer base and exponent 3; for example, $8 = 2^3$

cubic units: units that measure volume

data: facts or information

database: an organized collection of facts or information, often stored on a computer

degree of a polynomial: the value of the greatest exponent of a term in a polynomial

degree of a term: the value of the exponent of the term

denominator: the term below the line in a fraction

dependent variable: a variable whose value is determined by the value of another (the independent) variable

diagonal: a line segment that joins two vertices of a shape, but is not a side

diameter: the distance across a circle, measured through its centre; or the line segment that joins two points on the circle and passes through its centre

digit: any of the symbols used to write numerals; for example, 0, 1, 2, 3, 4, 5, 6, 7, 8, and 9

dimensions: measurements, such as length, width, and height

discrete data: data that can be counted

distributive property: the property stating that a product can be written as a sum or difference of two products; for example, $a(b + c) = ab + ac$, $a(b - c) = ab - ac$

dividend: the number that is divided

divisor: the number that divides into another number

double bar graph: a bar graph that shows two sets of data

equation: a mathematical statement that two expressions are equal

equilateral triangle: a triangle with three equal sides

equivalent: having the same value; for example, $\frac{2}{3}$ and $\frac{6}{9}$; 3:4 and 9:12

estimate: a reasoned guess that is close to the actual value, without calculating it exactly

evaluate: to determine the value of a numerical expression

even number: a number that has 2 as a factor; for example, 2, 4, 6

event: any set of outcomes of an experiment

experimental probability: the probability of an event calculated from experimental results

exponent: see *power*

expression: a mathematical statement made up of numbers and/or variables connected by operations

extrapolate: to estimate a value that lies beyond data points on a graph

factor: to factor means to write as a product; for example, $20 = 2 \times 2 \times 5$

formula: a rule that is expressed as an equation

fraction: an indicated quotient of two quantities

frequency: the number of times a particular number occurs in a set of data

greatest common factor (GCF): the greatest number that divides into each number in a set; for example, 5 is the greatest common factor of 10 and 15

height: the perpendicular distance from the base of a shape to the opposite side or vertex; the perpendicular distance from the base of an object to the opposite face or vertex

hexagon: a six-sided polygon

horizontal axis: the horizontal number line on a coordinate grid

hypotenuse: the side opposite the right angle in a right triangle

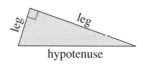
hypotenuse

image: the shape that results from a transformation

impossible event: an event that will never occur; an event with probability 0, or 0%

improper fraction: a fraction with the numerator greater than the denominator; for example, both $\frac{6}{5}$ and $\frac{5}{3}$ are improper fractions

independent events: two events in which the result of one event does not depend on the result of the other event

independent variable: a variable whose value is not determined by the value of another variable, and whose value determines the value of another (the dependent) variable

inequality: a statement that one quantity is greater than (or less than) another quantity; or a statement that one quantity is greater than or equal to (or less than or equal to) another quantity

inscribed angle: an angle in a circle with its vertex and the endpoints of its arms on the circle

Inscribed ∠PQR

inscribed polygon: a polygon whose vertices lie on a circle

inspection: solving an equation by finding the value of the variable by using addition, subtraction, multiplication, and division facts

integers: the set of numbers $\ldots -3, -2, -1, 0, +1, +2, +3, \ldots$

interpolate: to estimate a value that lies between 2 data points on a graph

inverse operation: an operation that reverses the result of another operation; for example, subtraction is the inverse of addition, and division is the inverse of multiplication

irrational number: a number that *cannot* be written in the form $\frac{m}{n}$, $n \neq 0$, where m and n are integers

irregular polygon: a polygon that does not have all sides equal or all angles equal

isometric: equal measure; on isometric dot paper, the line segments joining 2 adjacent dots in any direction are equal

isometric drawing: a representation of an object as it would appear in three dimensions

isosceles triangle: a triangle with two equal sides

legend: part of a circle graph that shows what category each sector represents

legs: the sides of a right triangle that form the right angle (see *hypotenuse*)

like terms: terms that have the same variables; for example, $4x$ and $-3x$ are like terms

line graph: a graph that displays data by using points joined by line segments

line of best fit: a line that passes as close as possible to a set of plotted points

line segment: the part of a line between two points on the line

line symmetry: a shape that can be divided into 2 congruent parts, so that the parts coincide when the shape is folded along a line of symmetry

linear relation: a relation that has a straight-line graph

lowest common multiple (LCM): the lowest multiple that is the same for two numbers; for example, the lowest common multiple of 12 and 21 is 84

major arc: the longer of the two arcs between two points on a circle

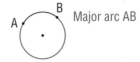

mass: the amount of matter in an object

mean: the sum of a set of numbers divided by the number of numbers in the set

measure of central tendency: a single number that represents a set of numbers (see *mean*, *median*, and *mode*)

median: the middle number when data are arranged in numerical order; if there is an even number of data, the median is the mean of the two middle numbers

midpoint: the point that divides a line segment into two equal parts

minor arc: the shorter of the two arcs between two points on a circle

mixed number: a number consisting of a whole number and a fraction; for example, $1\frac{1}{18}$ is a mixed number

mode: the number that occurs most often in a set of numbers

monomial: a polynomial with one term; for example, 14 and $5x^2$ are monomials

multiple: the product of a given number and a natural number; for example, some multiples of 8 are 8, 16, 24, ...

natural numbers: the set of numbers 1, 2, 3, 4, 5, ...

negative number: a number less than 0

net: a pattern that can be folded to make an object

non-perfect square: a fraction or a decimal that is not a perfect square

numerator: the term above the line in a fraction

numerical coefficient: the number by which a variable is multiplied; for example, in the expression $4x + 3$, 4 is the numerical coefficient

obtuse angle: an angle whose measure is greater than 90° and less than 180°

obtuse triangle: a triangle with one angle greater than 90°

octagon: an eight-sided polygon

odd number: a number that does not have 2 as a factor; for example, 1, 3, 7

operation: a mathematical process or action such as addition, subtraction, multiplication, division, or raising to a power

opposite numbers: two numbers with a sum of 0; for example, 2.4 and -2.4 are opposite numbers

order of operations: the rules that are followed when simplifying or evaluating an expression

order of rotational symmetry: the number of times a shape coincides with itself during a rotation of 360°

ordered pair: two numbers in order, for example, (2, 4); on a coordinate grid, the first number is the horizontal coordinate of a point, and the second number is the vertical coordinate of the point

origin: the point where the *x*-axis and the *y*-axis intersect

outcome: a possible result of an experiment or a possible answer to a survey question

parallel lines: lines on the same flat surface that do not intersect

parallelogram: a quadrilateral with both pairs of opposite sides parallel

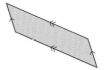

part-to-part ratio: a ratio that compares a part of the whole to another part of the whole

part-to-whole ratio: a ratio that compares a part of the whole to the whole

pentagon: a five-sided polygon

percent: the number of parts per 100; the numerator of a fraction with denominator 100

perfect square: a number that is the square of a number; for example, 16 is a perfect square because $16 = 4^2$

perimeter: the distance around a closed shape

perpendicular: lines or line segments that intersect at right angles

perpendicular bisector: the line that is perpendicular to a line segment and divides it into two equal parts

The broken line is the perpendicular bisector of AB.

pi (π): the ratio of the circumference of a circle to its diameter; $\pi = \frac{\text{circumference}}{\text{diameter}}$

plane: a flat surface with the property that a line segment joining any two points lies completely on its surface

point of tangency: the point where a tangent intersects a circle (see *tangent*)

polygon: a closed shape that consists of line segments; for example, triangles and quadrilaterals are polygons

polyhedron (*plural,* polyhedra): an object with faces that are polygons

polynomial: one term or the sum of terms whose variables have whole-number exponents; for example, $x^2 + 3xy - 2y^2 + 5x$

population: the set of all things or people being considered

power: an expression of the form a^n, where a is the base and n is the exponent; it represents a product of equal factors; for example, $4 \times 4 \times 4$ can be written as 4^3

power of a power: a power that is raised to a power; for example, $(3^2)^4$

power of a product: a product that is raised to a power; for example, $(3 \times 4)^5$

power of a quotient: a quotient that is raised to a power; for example, $\left(\dfrac{5}{6}\right)^3$

prediction: a statement of what you think will happen

prime number: a whole number with exactly two factors, itself and 1; for example, 2, 3, 5, 7, 11, 29, 31, and 43

probability: the likelihood of a particular outcome; the number of times a particular outcome occurs, written as a fraction of the total number of outcomes

product: the result when two or more numbers are multiplied; or the expression of one number multiplied by another

proper fraction: a fraction with the numerator less than the denominator; for example, $\dfrac{5}{6}$

proportion: a statement that two ratios are equal; for example, $r:24 = 3:4$

Pythagorean Theorem: the rule that states that, for any right triangle, the area of the square on the hypotenuse is equal to the sum of the areas of the squares on the legs

Pythagorean triple: three whole-number side lengths of a right triangle

quadrant: one of four regions into which coordinate axes divide a plane

quadrilateral: a four-sided polygon

quotient: the result when one number is divided by another; or the expression of one number divided by another

radius (*plural,* **radii**)**:** the distance or line segment from the centre of a circle to any point on the circle

random sample: a sampling in which all members of the population have an equal chance of being selected

range: the difference between the greatest and least numbers in a set of data

rate: a comparison of two quantities measured in different units

ratio: a comparison of two or more quantities with the same unit

rational number: any number that can be written in the form $\dfrac{m}{n}$, $n \neq 0$, where m and n are integers

reciprocals: two numbers whose product is 1; for example, $\dfrac{2}{3}$ and $\dfrac{3}{2}$

rectangle: a quadrilateral that has four right angles

reflection: a transformation that is illustrated by a shape and its image in a line of reflection

line of reflection

reflex angle: an angle between 180° and 360°

regular polygon: a polygon that has all sides equal and all angles equal

regular prism: a prism with regular polygons as bases; for example, a cube

regular pyramid: a pyramid with a regular polygon as its base; for example, a tetrahedron

regular tetrahedron: an object with four congruent triangular faces; a regular triangular pyramid

relation: a rule that relates two quantities

repeating decimal: a decimal with a repeating pattern in the digits to the right of the decimal point; it is written with a bar above the repeating digits; for example, $\frac{1}{15} = 0.0\overline{6}$

rhombus: a parallelogram with four equal sides

right angle: a 90° angle

right cylinder: an object with two parallel, congruent, circular bases

right prism: an object that has two congruent and parallel faces (the *bases*), and other faces that are rectangles

right pyramid: an object that has one face that is a polygon (the *base*), and other faces that are triangles with a common vertex

right rectangular prism: a prism that has rectangular faces

right rectangular pyramid: a pyramid with a rectangular base

right triangle: a triangle that has one right angle

rotation: a transformation in which a shape is turned about a fixed point

rotational symmetry: the property of a shape that it coincides with itself after a rotation of less than 360° about its centre

sample: a portion of the population

scale: the numbers on the axes of a graph

scale diagram: a diagram that is an enlargement or a reduction of another diagram

scale factor: the ratio of corresponding lengths of two similar shapes

scalene triangle: a triangle with all sides different

sector: part of a circle between two radii and the included arc

semicircle: half a circle

similar polygons: polygons with the same shape; one polygon is an enlargement or a reduction of the other polygon

simplest form: a ratio with terms that have no common factors, other than 1; a fraction with numerator and denominator that have no common factors, other than 1

spreadsheet: a computer-generated arrangement of data in rows and columns, where a change in one value results in appropriate calculated changes in the other values

square: a rectangle with four equal sides

square number: a number that can be written as a power with an integer base and exponent 2; for example, $49 = 7^2$

square root: a number which, when multiplied by itself, results in a given number; for example, 5 is a square root of 25

statistics: the branch of mathematics that deals with the collection, organization, and interpretation of data

straight angle: an angle measuring 180°

supplementary angles: two angles whose sum is 180°

surface area: the total area of the surface of an object

symmetrical: having symmetry (see *line symmetry*)

tangent: a line that intersects a circle at only one point

Tangent BD has point of tangency at C.

term: a number, a variable, or the product of numbers and variables; for example, -5, y, $7a^2$

terminating decimal: a decimal with a certain number of digits after the decimal point; for example, $\frac{1}{8} = 0.125$

tessellate: to use congruent copies of a shape to cover a plane with no overlaps or gaps

theoretical probability: the number of favourable outcomes written as a fraction of the total number of possible outcomes

three-dimensional: having length, width, and depth or height

transformation: a translation, rotation, or reflection

translation: a transformation that moves a point or a shape in a straight line to another position on the same flat surface

trapezoid: a quadrilateral that has exactly one pair of parallel sides

triangle: a three-sided polygon

trinomial: a polynomial with three terms; for example, $3x^2 - 5x + 8$

two-dimensional: having length and width, but no thickness, height, or depth

two-term ratio: a comparison of two quantities with the same unit

unit fraction: a fraction that has a numerator of 1

unit price: the price of one item, or the price of a particular mass or volume of an item

unit rate: a quantity associated with a single unit of another quantity; for example, 6 m in 1 s is a unit rate; it is written as 6 m/s

valid conclusions: results of data collection that represent what is typical of the population

variable: a letter or symbol representing a quantity that can vary

vertex (*plural,*** vertices):** the point where 2 sides of a shape meet, or the point where 3 or more edges of an object meet

vertical axis: the vertical number line on a coordinate grid

volume: the amount of space occupied by an object

whole numbers: the set of numbers 0, 1, 2, 3, …

***x*-axis:** the horizontal number line on a coordinate grid

***y*-axis:** the vertical number line on a coordinate grid

zero pair: two opposite numbers whose sum is equal to zero; for example, -4.1 and 4.1

zero property: the property of addition that states that adding 0 to a number does not change the number; for example, $3 + 0 = 3$; for multiplication, multiplying a number by 0 results in the product 0; for example, $3 \times 0 = 0$

Index

linear equations, 174–177

linear inequality (*see* inequalities)

linear relations, 164–169, 200
  estimating values from graphs of, 191–195
  graphing from an equation, 167, 168
  graphing from a table of values, 167
  matching graphs to equations, 183–187

M

Math Links:
  History, 13, 129
  Literacy, 391
  Science, 173, 269, 283
  Your World, 62, 144, 216, 224, 236, 344, 429, 456

major arc, 405

minor arc, 405

mixed numbers, 96, 100
  adding, 108, 109
  dividing, 131, 132
  multiplying, 124, 125
  representing stocks with, 129
  subtracting, 115–117

monomial, 211, 231, 258
  dividing by a constant, 244
  dividing by a monomial, 254
  multiplying and dividing polynomials by, 249–254
  multiplying by a constant, 242

N

natural numbers, 206

negative integers, 54, 55, 95

non-perfect squares,
  square roots of, 14–18, 44

number line,
  ordering decimals on, 99, 100, 117, 118
  ordering fractions on, 99, 100, 107, 108, 115, 143
  recording solutions of an inequality on, 290, 291
  showing negative integers on, 95–100, 143

O

Ohm's Law, 283

order of operations,
  and exponent laws, 76, 82, 83
  with decimals, 138
  with fractions, 139
  with rational numbers, 137–139, 143

order of rotation, 362–365

overlapping objects, 26

P

patterns,
  describing with equations, 154–158

pentagon,
  rotation image of, 364

perfect squares,
  square roots of, 6–10, 15, 16, 44

perpendicular bisector, 393–396, 417

point of tangency, 385–387, 417

polygon,
  inscribed, 408, 409

polynomials, 224, 236, 258
  adding, 225–228, 258
  adding symbolically, 227
  adding with two variables, 228
  determining the perimeter of a rectangle, 227, 228
  modelling projectile motion, 216
  modelling with algebra tiles, 211–213
  multiplying and dividing by a constant, 241–245, 258
  multiplying and dividing by a monomial, 249–254
  recording symbolically, 226
  simplified form of, 218–221
  simplifying symbolically, 220
  simplifying with two variables, 221
  subtracting, 231–234, 258

populations in data collection, 438–440, 457

positive integers, 53–55, 95–100

power of a power, 79–83

power of a product, 79–83

power of a quotient, 81, 82

powers, 53–55, 86
  adding and subtracting, 64
  exponent laws for, 74–76, 80–83
  multiplying and dividing, 64, 65
  order of operations with, 63–65, 86

powers of 10, 58–60

prime number, 240

privacy in data collection, 438, 457

probability, 425–427, 457
  applied in risk assessments, 429
  applied to support opposing views, 426, 427
  effect of assumptions, 426
  effect on decisions, 425
  experimental, 425, 426
  theoretical, 425, 426

proportion, 319, 326, 339, 340, 346

Pythagoras, 13

Pythagorean Theorem, 316
  applied to circles, 386, 395
  estimating non-perfect square roots with, 17, 18
  in surface area calculations, 38

R

radius, 385–387, 417

ratio,
  as a scale, 327, 328

rational coefficients,
  equations with, 278, 279

rational numbers, 95–100, 143
  adding, 106–110, 143
  dividing, 130–134, 143
  multiplying, 123–127, 143
  order of operations with, 137–139, 143
  ordering, 98–100
  subtracting, 114–118, 143
  writing between two given numbers, 97, 98

real numbers, 206

rectangle,
  determining a polynomial for the perimeter, 227, 228

Acknowledgments

The publisher would like to thank the following people and institutions for permission to use their © materials. Every reasonable effort has been made to find copyright holders of the material in this text. The publisher would be pleased to know of any errors or omissions.

Photography

Cover: Martin Vrlik/Shutterstock

p. 3 Ian Crysler; pp. 4–5 (clockwise) Ian M. Butterfield/Alamy, Photos.com/Jupiter Images Unlimited, The Image Bank/Getty Images, PhotoObjects.net/Jupiter Images Unlimited, tbkmedia.de/Alamy, Mark Winfrey/Shutterstock, Pat Behnke/Alamy; p. 6 Lynne Furrer/Shutterstock; p. 8 Ian Crysler; p. 12 Pixonnet.com/Alamy; p. 13 (top to bottom) Ian Crysler, terry harris just Greece photolibrary/Alamy; pp. 22, 24 Ian Crysler; p. 25 Hugo Nienhuis/Alamy; p. 26 Ian Crysler; p. 27 Ian Crysler; pp. 30–31 Ian Crysler; p. 32 Aurora/Getty Images; p. 33 Photographer's Choice/Getty Images; p. 43 Brian & Cherry Alexander Photography/Alamy; p. 46 Ian Crysler; p. 47 B&C Alexander/Firstlight; p. 49 Corbis Premium RF/Alamy; pp. 50–51 Shutterstock; p. 52 (left to right) Ian Crysler, Andy Crawford/Dorling Kindersley; p. 56 Library and Archives Canada. Reproduced with the permission of Canada Post; p. 57 C Squared Studios/Photodisc/Getty Images; p. 58 Stephen Coburn/Shutterstock; p. 60 Courtesy Head-Smashed-In-Buffalo Jump; p. 62 (top to bottom) CP Photo/Ted S. Warren, Shutterstock; p. 63 Ray Boudreau; p. 65 Jupiter Images/Creatas/Alamy; p. 67 jonphoto/Shutterstock; p. 70 Ian Crysler; p. 71 (top to bottom) Dave Starrett, Ray Boudreau; p. 72 Paul B. Moore/Shutterstock; p. 73 Photos.com/Jupiter Images Unlimited; p. 77 Mary E. Cioffi/Shutterstock; p. 78 Ian Crysler; p. 87 Ian Crysler/Pearson Education Canada; p. 88 James P. Blair/National Geographic/Getty Images; Comstock Images/Jupiter Images Unlimited; p. 90 Comstock Images/Jupiter Images Unlimited; pp. 92–93 Tessa Macintosh Photography; p. 94 Stock Food/MaXx Images; p.102 WireImage Stock/Masterfile; p. 103 Brad Wrobleski/Alamy; p. 105 Ian Crysler; p. 106 (left to right) Judith Collins/Alamy, Blend Images/Alamy; p. 110 Flashon Studio/Shutterstock; p. 112 All Canada Photos/Alamy, p. 114 Andre Jenny/Alamy; p. 116 Gabe Palmer/Alamy; p. 118 All Canada Photos/Alamy; p. 119 Wolfgang Kaehler/Alamy; p. 120 Robert Harding Picture Library Ltd. Alamy; p. 122 Ian Crysler; p. 123 Ian Crysler; p. 125 Ian Shaw/Alamy; p. 128 (left to right) cb pix/Shutterstock, Samuel Acosta/Shutterstock; p. 129 Classic Stock/Alamy; p. 130 Ian Crysler; p. 135 (left to right) Design Pics Inc./Alamy, Shutterstock; p. 136 Peter Griffith/Masterfile; p. 138 George Simhoni/Masterfile; p. 141 (left to right) Jupiter Images/Brand X Alamy, National Geographic/Getty Images; p. 147 (top to bottom) Wendy Nero/Shutterstock; LOOK Die Bildagentur der Fotografen GmbH/Alamy; p. 148 Ian Crysler; pp. 150–151 (clockwise) Dash Shutterstock, Digital Vision/Alamy, Pablo Eder/Shutterstock, Thinkstock Images/Jupiter Images Unlimited, PhotosIndia.com/LLC/Alamy, Morgan Lane Photography/Shutterstock; pp. 152–153 Ian Crysler; p. 156 CP Photo/Larry MacDougall; p. 161 (left to right) John McKenna/Alamy, Photodisc/Getty Images; p. 162 Ian Crysler; p. 164 Dennis Sabo/Shutterstock; p. 172 (left to right) BananaStock/Jupiter Images Unlimited, Harris Shiffman/Shutterstock; p. 173 (top to bottom) Lori Adamski Peek/Stone/Getty Images, Perry Harmon/Shutterstock; p. 174 Ian Crysler; p. 179 Jeff Whyte/Shutterstock; p. 183 Carlos Osono/Toronto Star; p. 191 Larry Lee Photography/Corbis; p. 192 Jeremy Maudde/Masterfile; p. 193 Jeff Greenberg/Alamy; p. 194 liquidlibrary/Jupiter Images Unlimited; p. 205 Rolf Bruderer/Corbis; p. 207 Ian Crysler; pp. 208–209 (clockwise) Chris Cooper-Smith/Alamy, Oleg Kozlova/Sophy Kozlova/Shutterstock, Pelham James Mitchinson/Shutterstock, iwka/Shutterstock, maigi/Shutterstock, david sanger photographer/Alamy; p. 210 Ian Crysler; p. 216 (top to bottom) Dennis Hallinan/Alamy, WireImage/Getty Images; p. 217 Ian Crysler; p. 224 AFP/Getty Images; p. 225 Ian Crysler; p. 231 Ian Crysler; p. 236 J.A. Kraulis/Masterfile; pp. 238–239, 249, 253 Ian Crysler; p. 261 David Papazian/Beateworks/Corbis; pp. 264–265 (clockwise) Kevin Cooley/Taxi/Getty Images, Comstock/Jupiter Images Unlimited, Blend Images/MaXx Images/Getty Images, Tim Pannell/Corbis, agefotostock/MaXx Images; p. 266 Sergiy Zavgorodny/Shutterstock, p. 269 Mike Perry/Alamy, p. 281 LOOK Die Bildagentur der Fotografen GmbH/Alamy; p. 282 Jon Riley/Stone/Getty; p. 283 Stockbyte/Getty Images; p. 285 Photodisc/Alamy; p. 287 Ian Crysler; p. 288 (top) PhotoObjects.net/Jupiter Images Unlimited, (bottom left to right) Elisabeth Reisinger/Shutterstock, Reproduced with permission from the Motion Picture Classification Corporation of Canada; p. 293 Carslen Reisinger/Shutterstock; p. 294 Ian Crysler; p. 297 Jeff Greenberg/Alamy, p. 299 Sasha Burkard/Shutterstock; p. 304 Kelly-Mooney Photography/Corbis; p. 306 terekhov igor/Getty Images; p. 311 (top to bottom) Corbis Premium RF/Alamy, Cindy Charles/PhotoEdit; pp. 314–315 (clockwise) Comstock Images/Jupiter Images Unlimited, Jupiter Images/Polka Dot/Alamy, CP Photo/Jonathan Hayward, Terrance Klassen/Alamy, Kris Butler/Shutterstock, Corbis Premium RF/Alamy, Edwin Verin/Shutterstock; p. 318

Chris Cheadle/Alamy, p. 320 Gunter Marx Photography/Corbis, p. 323 (top to bottom) Visuals Unlimited/Corbis, YYS/Shutterstock; p. 330 Chris Rabiar/Alamy; p. 331 (top to bottom) JRTT Transport/Alamy, Denis Scott/Corbis; p. 332 agefotostock/MaXx Images; p. 333 Michael Newman/PhotoEdit; p. 343 All Canada Photos/Alamy; p. 344 Courtesy of NASA Goddard Space Flight Center and U.S. Geological Survey; p. 347 Minden Pictures/Getty Images; p. 353 Photos.com/Jupiter Images Unlimited; p. 357 Reproduced with the permission of the Minister of Public Works and Government Services Canada, 2008; p. 358 (top to bottom) The M.C. Escher Company, Haida Button Blanket. Photo © Canadian Museum of Civilization, artifact VII-B-1525, Image D2004-26626; p. 360 (top to bottom) Ruslana Stovner/Shutterstock, Ian Crysler; p. 361 (clockwise) Thinkstock Images/Jupiter Images Unlimited, Henrik Lehnerer/Shutterstock, R/Shutterstock; p. 365 Dariusz Sas/Shutterstock; p. 366 (top to bottom) The M.C. Escher Company, Big Stock Photo; p. 368 (clockwise) Photodisc/Getty Images, Photodisc/Alamy, B.A.E. Inc/Alamy, blickwinkel/Alamy, agefotostock/MaXx Images, Photodisc/Getty Images; p. 373 (top left to right) Sivolob Igor/Shutterstock, Photodisc/Getty Images (bottom left to right) Westend 61/Alamy, Wolfgang Deuter/zefa/Corbis; p. 374 Blaine Billman; p. 375 Denis Dryashkin/Shutterstock; p. 377 Sol Neelman/Corbis; p. 378 (clockwise) Image Farm Inc./Alamy, Christophe Testil/Shutterstock, PhotoObjects.net/Jupiter Images Unlimited, PhotoObjects.net/Jupiter Images Unlimited; p. 379 (top to bottom) Jane McIlroy/Shutterstock, Feathered Rainbow. Kenojuak Ashevak. Lithograph, 2002. Reproduced with permission of Dorset Fine Arts; p. 381 Martine Oger/Shutterstock; pp. 382–383 (clockwise) Alan Sirulnikoff/firstlight, nialat/Shutterstock, The National Trust Photolibrary/Alamy, R/Shutterstock, George H.H. Huey/Corbis, Shubochkin Vasily A./Shutterstock, CP Photo Jeff McIntosh; p. 384 (clockwise) Mandy Godbehear/Shutterstock, Mark Yuill/Shutterstock, Image Source Pink/Alamy, D. Hurst/Alamy, Thinkstock Images/Jupiter Images Unlimited; p. 385 Ian Crysler; p. 387 Oote Boel Photography/Alamy; p. 391 Tony Pleavin/Alamy; p. 392 (top left to right) James RT Bossert/Shutterstock, Anastasiya Igolkina/Shutterstock, Bob Gibbons/Alamy (left top to bottom) Ian Crysler; p. 402 Ian Crysler; p. 404 Riser/Getty Images; p. 409 Ace Stock Limited/Alamy; p. 412 David Stoecklein/Corbis; p. 413 Royalty-Free/Masterfile; p. 421 Ian Crysler; pp. 422–423 (clockwise) Jupiter Images/Brand X/Alamy, Picture Partners/Alamy, Blend Images/Alamy; p. 424 GPI Stock/Alamy; p. 425 Yvette Cardozo/Alamy; p. 426 (top to bottom) Images-USA/Alamy, Stock Foundry Images/Shutterstock; p. 428 John Van Decker/Alamy; p. 429 Transtock Inc./Alamy; p. 431 The Canadian Press/Brandon Sun-Tim Smith; p. 433 tbkmedia.de/Alamy; p. 435 CP Photo/Winnipeg Free Press/Boris Minkevich; p. 436 Anetta/Shutterstock; p. 437 Visual & Written SL/Alamy; p. 438 photobank.ch/Shutterstock; p. 439 cardiae/Shutterstock; p. 440 Blend Images/Alamy; p. 441 Megapress/Alamy; p. 444 Stock Connection Distribution/Alamy; p. 445 (top to bottom) Rachel Epstein/PhotoEdit, Michael Newman/PhotoEdit; p. 446 (left to right) Design Pics Inc./Alamy; Brian Goodman/Shutterstock; p. 449 (left to right) digital vision/Firstlight, Vick Fisher/Alamy; p. 452 Michael Newman/PhotoEdit; p. 454 Photoresearchers/Firstlight; p. 457 CP Photo/Geoff Howe; p. 459 (left to right) Real World People/Alamy, Nonstock/Firstlight; p. 461 Ian Crysler; p. 462 Stephen L. Alvarez/National Geographic/Getty Images; p. 463 SuperStock/MaXx Images; p. 465 Carlos E. Santa Maria/Shutterstock

Illustrations

ArtPlus Limited, Brian Hughes, Stephen MacEachern/Quack, Allan Moon, Neil Stewart/NSV Productions

p. 325 Map of Victoria Island reproduced with the permission of Natural Resources Canada 2008, courtesy of the Atlas of Canada.

p. 442 Screen Capture: "*Census at School*" homepage Source: Statistics Canada, Census at School, from the Statistics Canada Website

p. 443 Screen Captures: "*Canadian summary results*" and "*Canadian summary results for 2007/2008*" Source: Statistics Canada, Census at School, from the Statistics Canada Website

p. 444 Screen Capture: *Results and Data*, Courtesy of CensusAtSchool, from the International CensusAtSchool Project Website

p. 450 Screen Capture: *Which method do you use most often to communicate with friends?* Source: Statistics Canada, Census at School, from the Statistics Canada Website

p. 451 Screen Capture: *How long does it usually take you to travel to school?* Source: Statistics Canada, Census at School, from the Statistics Canada Website

Statistics Canada information is used with the permission of Statistics Canada. Users are forbidden to copy this material and/or redisseminate the data in an original or modified form, for commercial purposes, without the express permission of Statistics Canada. Information on the availability of the wide range of data from Statistics Canada can be obtained from Statistics Canada's Regional Offices or the Statistics Canada Website.